Chemical Induction of Cancer

**Structural Bases
and Biological Mechanisms**

VOLUME I

CHEMICAL INDUCTION OF CANCER

Structural Bases and Biological Mechanisms

JOSEPH C. ARCOS
TULANE UNIVERSITY SCHOOL OF MEDICINE
NEW ORLEANS, LOUISIANA

MARY F. ARGUS
TULANE UNIVERSITY SCHOOL OF MEDICINE
NEW ORLEANS, LOUISIANA

GEORGE WOLF
DEPARTMENT OF NUTRITION AND FOOD SCIENCE
MASSACHUSETTS INSTITUTE OF TECHNOLOGY
CAMBRIDGE, MASSACHUSETTS

VOLUME I

 ACADEMIC PRESS   New York and London   1968

The first edition of "Chemical Induction of Cancer,"
by George Wolf, was published in 1952 by
Harvard University Press, Cambridge, Massachusetts,
and Cassell and Company Ltd., London.

ACADEMIC PRESS INC.
111 Fifth Avenue, New York, New York 10003

United Kingdom Edition published by
ACADEMIC PRESS INC. (LONDON) LTD.
Berkeley Square House, London W.1

LIBRARY OF CONGRESS CATALOG CARD NUMBER: 66–30118

PRINTED IN THE UNITED STATES OF AMERICA

Dedicated to those whose teaching
and inspiration made a lasting mark:

GEORGE BÁRSONY
SAMUEL BORBÉLY
NGUYEN PH. BUU-HOI
AUGUSTE CHAGNON
LÉON DENIVELLE
EMERICH EGRI
ANDRÉ ETIENNE
SR. MARY FINBAR, O.S.F.
CHARLES HEIDELBERGER
ANTOINE LACASSAGNE
ELIZABETH C. MILLER
JAMES A. MILLER
SIR KARL POPPER
FRANCIS E. RAY
SIR ROBERT ROBINSON
SR. IGNATIUS SANCHE, S.C.
LADISLAU VON VARGHA

General Plan

Volume I

Volume II

Volume III

Foreword

The years since the first edition of this book have seen many remarkable advances in biology. Studies on the chemical basis for gene action, the synthesis of important cellular macromolecules such as proteins and nucleic acids, and the ultrastructure of cell organelles together with relatively simple methods for cell culture are providing a new foundation for our understanding of cell behavior. As anticipated, these concepts and tools are leading to rapid progress in the nature and mechanism of interaction of chemical carcinogens and cell components.

Coincident with these developments has been a new awareness of the possible importance of chemicals as carcinogens in man's environment. It is becoming increasingly evident that not only our external physical environment but also foods and food contaminants contain potent compounds which may play an important role in the genesis of cancer in man.

These considerations make a second edition of this book both timely and significant. By presenting an up-to-date survey of the role of *chemicals in the genesis of cancer*, the authors offer an opportunity for all who are interested in cancer to familiarize themselves with the latest advances in this important area of cancer research and environmental medicine. However, the authors have made an additional important contribution in presenting and stressing the multifaceted nature of the problem at hand. Although it is commonplace to hear expressed the need in cancer research for a multidisciplinary approach, too much of the research being done today is still highly oriented along classical disciplines, without much interdisciplinary interaction. In fact, one of the impediments to progress in several phases of the study of cancer is the restricted nature of the outlook and background of the investigator. By virtue of their own varied experiences and interests, the authors have been able to encompass in this edition many of the major scientific fields which are relevant to the problem. The presentation of morphologic, chemical, and metabolic aspects of chemical carcinogenesis in a single work is both refreshing and encouraging.

The majority of changes in the cell's environment leading to disease, including the presence of carcinogenic chemicals, evoke many cellular chemical responses. Some of these are no doubt the consequence of specific chemical interactions with cell components. Since these reactions frequently involve more than one class of cellular macromolecules, some selection for relevance to the neoplastic process will have to be made. The discrimination between the significant and the insignificant reactions will be dependent upon the use of ingenious biological approaches in close association with the chemical. The reader is offered in this edition the opportunity to acquire some of the conceptual framework upon which the intelligent selection of the relevant from the irrelevant may be made. This contribution alone makes this work recommended reading for those interested in understanding the nature and causation of cancer.

March, 1968   EMMANUEL FARBER
Department of Pathology
University of Pittsburgh School of Medicine
Pittsburgh, Pennsylvania

Foreword
to the First Edition

All who are actively engaged upon the experimental study of cancer, and especially upon the elucidation of its chemical causation, are well aware of a strong demand for some comprehensive, authoritative, yet not over-elaborate description of developments in this field, which would be of value at once to the general medical and scientific reader and to the interested layman. It is a matter for regret that the very pace of discovery has hindered the satisfaction of this need, by leading too many of us, in the excitement of the chase, to neglect our duty of more general exposition. Not only those to whom this book is primarily addressed, but his immediate colleagues in the field of cancer research also, are accordingly under a special debt to Dr. Wolf for providing, in short compass and eminently readable form, this unified and lucid account. That he is well qualified to do so is shown by his own contributions, made both in this country and in the United States.

A great part of the relevant work carried out in the past thirty years has been concerned with the discovery of chemical agents, both naturally occurring and purely synthetic, having the capacity to induce cancer under experimental conditions. Dr. Wolf has done ample justice to this important field, as also to the related problems of chemical constitution and biological action. At the same time his book reflects the change of emphasis of the past few years, as a result of which much more attention is being devoted to mechanisms of action, for example through studies of the chemical reactivity and metabolic fate of carcinogens, the contributions of the French school, and the discovery and significance of carcinogenic activity in many nitrogen mustards and other biological alkylating agents. All these advances are now leading to very greatly increased confidence that the elucidation of the carcinogenic process will in fact lead, as had been hoped, to the means of its chemical or enzymatic control. Dr. Wolf's book therefore appears at an appropriate moment in the development of the subject, and is warmly to be commended as an admirable summary of the main experimental facts, for its balanced interpretation, and as a source not only of information but of stimulus as well. It will perhaps be specially welcomed by those wishing to acquaint themselves, without too great difficulty, with a field of research which, if it has of necessity developed along highly specialized lines, is never-theless of the utmost importance towards the ultimate solution of the greatest problem confronting medicine. No other subject quite combines, in the same degree, the thrill of discovery and the prospect of beneficient application. So far as concerns the experimental reproduction of the disease and the understanding of the biological process involved, no more useful or more succinct general account can be recommended than that in the pages which follow.

May, 1952   ALEXANDER HADDOW
Chester Beatty Research Institute,
The Royal Cancer Hospital,
(Institute of Cancer Research, University of London),
London, S.W.3.

Preface

The final aim of cancer research or oncology is to elucidate the cause of the disease and, hence, find a rational basis for its therapy and prevention. The problem has become complex, however, and its roots have spread into many areas of scientific investigation. A most important approach to oncology is chemical: studies of the chemical induction of cancer, of the chemical nature of tumors and of tumor-host relationships, and of investigations on the chemo- and immunotherapy of tumors.

The modern era of chemical oncology opened with the identification and syntheses in the 1930's of well-defined organic compounds that produced tumors at will and with some degree of specificity with respect to tissue, animal strain, and species. By means of the different tumor-inducing (carcinogenic) compounds—precision tools in the hands of the biologist, pathologist, and biochemist—one can interfere with the normal life of cells and turn them into tumor cells (carcinogenesis). It is now well established that chemical carcinogens interact with various vital cell components: proteins and nucleic acids. As a result of these interactions gradual change takes place in the molecular organization and chemical functioning of the cells in the target tissue, leading ultimately to uncontrolled growth and the emergence of malignant tumors. The nature of this change, its relation to the carcinogen and to the emergence of spontaneous cancer (the disease), is the problem of the chemical induction of cancer.

The idea of writing a second edition of Wolf's "Chemical Induction of Cancer" was conceived at the completion of an extensive review article on the "Molecular Geometry and Mechanisms of Action of Chemical Carcinogens," which appeared in 1962 in "Progress in Drug Research." This and other review articles and books which appeared on chemical carcinogenesis in recent years were addressed mainly to the specialist and assumed a thorough familiarity with the component terminologies. Yet the cancer problem, apart from its clinical aspects, is so closely related to the fundamental questions of growth control and differentiation that it presents a challenging interest for all students of biology. Actually, the study of the chemical induction of tumors has become a widely traveled crossroad for many scientific and technological disciplines such as biochemistry, organic chemistry, pharmacology, toxicology, industrial and preventive medicine, pathology, cytology, biophysics, quantum mechanics, cybernetics, and air and water pollution and food additive testing and evaluation studies. Moreover, aside from the difficulties of a complex and multicentric terminology, the voluminous literature on the structure-activity relationships, testing procedures, and modes of action of these chemical agents is widely scattered in scientific periodicals.

This work on chemical carcinogenesis was written for two groups of readers as different in background as the physician, biologist, pathologist, and biochemist who have often left the modern concepts of structure and electronic valence theory of organic chemistry far behind them, and the synthetic organic chemist and physicist who have usually little or no foundation in biology and biochemistry. Sections 2, 3, and 8 were specifically intended to bridge these gaps by introducing or reviewing concepts and terminologies at a depth sufficient to enable the reader to follow the exposition of the molecular characteristics and of the modes of action of chemical carcinogens. Supplementary information is given in Notes in these and other sections at the ends of major subsections. In Section 2 our most important aim was to convey—in a nutshell—the spirit and fascination of the structural concepts of organic chemistry, rather than to follow at every point the official nomenclature to the letter. Thus, for didactic reasons we often used alternative names (not exactly conforming to established rules but terminologically unequivocal) in order to emphasize some structural feature or formal generic relationship to other compounds.

While to some the background information given in Sections 2 and 3 on organic chemistry and modern valence theory may appear to be overextensive at first glance, the authors believe that it truly represents the minimum elements necessary for gaining an intelligent insight into the structure-activity relationships of the different classes of carcinogens. The effort which has gone into these chapters is also amply justified by the expectedly greater number of biologically oriented readers who because of the nature of their scientific disciplines may be drawn to the study of chemical carcinogens. On the other hand, those interested in chemical oncology who have little biological background should profit specifically not only from the introduction to cell structure and function in Section 8, but also from the very practical accounts in Section 4 which guide the reader through the steps for the biological testing of a chemical agent for carcinogenic activity.

The inclusion of background information and specific information in the same work has the added advantage of enabling the reader to survey the field of chemical carcinogenesis without immediately referring to other works. It is the authors' belief that the study of tumors and tumor induction is now entering a phase in which it will be increasingly recognized as that field of molecular biology concerned with cellular regulatory mechanisms; hence, the need for an integrated treatise on the structure-activity relationships, modes of action, and testing techniques of the chemical tools of such studies.

An attempt has been made to present the subject in the form of a coherent story, to discuss experiments and observations in the light of hypotheses or theories which they support or oppose, and to discern interrelations between theories and patterns or structures of knowledge as they are built up or emerge. The scope of the work has been limited to the experimental induction of tumors by extrinsic chemical means. By extrinsic are meant those substances not derived from the organism itself, such as the sex hormones, but chemicals of known structure synthesized in the laboratory or isolated from plants or lower organisms. Nevertheless, certain aspects of the hormonal induction of tumors are discussed so far as they touch on the possible biosynthesis of carcinogens in the organism and on the carcinogenic activity of certain synthetic organic compounds which also have hormone action. Selected readings, arranged in sequence of increasing difficulty, and source books are given at the ends of certain major sections for further study.

March, 1968   Joseph C. Arcos
                                    Mary F. Argus
                                    Seamen's Memorial Research Laboratory
                                    U.S. Public Health Service Hospital
                                    New Orleans, Louisiana

                                    George Wolf
                                    Department of Nutrition and Food Science
                                    Massachusetts Institute of Technology
                                    Cambridge, Massachusetts

Acknowledgments

While there are only three names which appear on the title page, this book has in truth many authors. A great number of co-workers and colleagues here and abroad contributed to this endeavor with advice, by supplying specific pieces of information and certain figures and photomicrographs, by reading and criticizing sections of the manuscript, by letting us see in advance unpublished work and providing bibliographic sources not available locally, and with a tremendous amount of editing and typing necessary to bring this work to good haven. The authors want to thank in particular Drs. Louis C. Cusachs and Richard H. Steele for discussing certain aspects of valence theory and Dr. Kenneth F. Burns for supplying a number of hard-to-come-by specific data on the biology of laboratory animals; Dr. George E. Palade who sent us a series of excellent electron micrographs and gave us his kind permission to reproduce them; Dr. Erik Arrhenius who also willingly sent us some of his electron micrographs and from whose discussions we profited a great deal; Drs. Cornelia Hoch-Ligeti and Hans Hoch who kindly accepted the thankless and important task of reading, criticizing, and editing Section 4 on the general characteristics and pathology of tumors and testing of carcinogens; Dr. R. L. Flurry, Jr. who unstintingly and kindly gave his expert advice on certain aspects of wave mechanics and who performed an invaluable "pruning and weeding-out-job" in reading and criticizing Section 2 and especially Section 3; Thomas J. Morgavi and Arthur A. Mott who contributed enthusiastically with discussions and practical techniques for working out the radiofrequency resonant circuit analog of bonding and antibonding molecular orbitals; Dr. Steven P. H. Mandel who spent several trying hours in clarifying our views of some aspects of biostatistics; Drs. L. M. Black, Charles E. Dunlap, Jan Hamer, Michael Klein, and George Karreman who advised us on some points concerning the bibliography and techniques; Dr. N. Rashevsky who contributed an interesting interpretation and mathematical analysis of certain aspects of molecular geometry as they affect the carcinogenic activity of polycyclic aromatics. For the very high standard of the artwork and illustrations the credit goes to Donald M. Alvarado, Head of the Department of Medical Illustration, Louisiana State University Medical School, who must also be thanked for his inexhaustible patience and good humor in face of our innumerable requests for changes and additions on supposedly finished material. The photographic work was carried out by Eugene R. Miscenich in his usual excellent and professional manner.

We are grateful to Sir Alexander Haddow for encouragement and for providing us with recent volumes of the *British Empire Cancer Campaign*

Annual Reports which permitted us to keep abreast of impressive and original British contributions still "fresh from the bench." Doctors John H. and Elizabeth K. Weisburger, Sam Sorof, James M. Price, Allan H. Conney, Harry S. Gelboin, John J. Roberts, Eula L. Bingham, Maximo Valentinuzzi, Raymond Daudel, Eric Reid, Samuel S. Epstein, Bernard Pullman, and a number of other colleagues willingly complied with our insistent requests for reprints and unpublished manuscripts.

A great deal of our gratitude is due to Anne-Marie Mouledoux, B.S. and Joyce B. Mathison, B.A. for the painstaking and very careful editorial work well beyond the call of duty, for organizing the material, for much pertinent criticism on substance, form, and style, for deciphering and rough-typing the long-hand original, and much dreary proofreading; Judith Fabian, B.S., Mattie J. Tison, B.S., Georgia M. Bryant, B.A., and James A. Bemis, B.A. must also be credited with some of this work. Steven A. Fattel, B.S., Robert F. Patterson, B.S., and Antoinette M. Mano who carried out excellently the demanding work of typing the final manuscript, believe, and with good reason, that the times of slavery are not yet over. Miss Frances R. Winter is warmly thanked for her perseverant efforts to provide us with reprints of the pertinent recent literature necessary for this work.

We are deeply indebted to the National Cancer Institute, U.S. Public Health Service, which has supported so generously our research for many years and made possible the authors' original contributions cited in a number of sections of these volumes. It is owing to the support of this Agency that we could acquire—and we hope we were successful in conveying—a panoramic view of this vast scientific field.

The above list would, however, by far not be complete without naming those who have created in the first two authors' laboratory the framework of scientific freedom which made this work possible; our thanks and gratitude thus go to Dr. John J. Walsh and Dr. George E. Burch for their support, friendship, and encouragement during all phases of preparation of this work.

The staff of Academic Press is thanked for its kind understanding and patience with the difficult problem of numerous deadlines, for advice, support, and cooperation.

Contents

3. The Nature of Intra- and Intermolecular Forces

Part II
THE NATURE OF TUMORS.
CONCEPTS AND TECHNIQUES OF TESTING CHEMICAL AGENTS
FOR CARCINOGENIC ACTIVITY

4. General Characteristics of Tumors and the Testing of Carcinogens

1 | Introduction

Normal versus neoplastic cells. The most significant characteristic of living matter is its high degree of organization, serving to maintain and perpetuate itself. This organization is attained through growth and differentiation: first, by the highly organized and orderly accumulation of matter in the formation of the cell, the unit of living matter; second, by organized growth through strictly controlled and severely limited division of cells to form tissues; third, by the precisely timed differentiation of growing and dividing cells into specialized organs. Growth is controlled, and differentiation takes place, through the action of yet scantily known forces or properties within each cell, probably connected with the functions of the hereditary substance of the chromosomes. Tumor growth (also loosely termed "neoplastic growth" or "neoplasia") is unique as a manifestation of living matter in that it escapes this purposeful organization which characterizes a living organism. The subservience of the part to the survival of the whole is abolished; "the somatic cell, as it were, reasserts its individuality" (Haddow). The tumor cell, though originally derived from a normal cell, has irreversibly escaped the control of those forces which govern normal cell growth. It grows and divides at a rate and in a manner in no way serving the needs of the organism as a whole, but rather at its expense, until the organism succumbs. The tumor in a sense is not a "hostile parasite," since it stems directly from a normally growing cell. Carcinogenesis and tumor growth represent the singular phenomenon of a trend toward a condition of disorder and de-differentiation, and disorganization through an invasion by intensely alive cells created by the living system itself.

"Cancer is pathologically unique," writes Berenblum. It cannot be classed with any of the many other known diseases; it seems to be closely related to, and spring directly from, the fundamental processes of life itself. "The zoological distribution of the disease—and the occurrence of somewhat analogous tumours in plants—is so wide as to lead us to suspect that the neoplastic change . . . has in its nature something fundamental in biology, and is one to which almost every cell is liable in appropriate circumstances" (Haddow).

The problem of carcinogenesis has, therefore, a wider and more general importance than solely a rational therapy of neoplasia. Its solution requires answers to the questions: What makes a tissue grow in one particular way and no other, and why is growth arrested at one particular point and no other? What are the forces and properties of the cell which permit control and organization of growth? A disturbance of these forces or properties is set up in the cancer cell. A comparison between normal and tumor growth, between the normal and the tumor cell, and the discovery of the essential way in which they differ, may lead to a recognition of these forces and properties of cells—the very core and essence of living matter. For these reasons it may well be that at some later time the study of tumors will be recognized as the field of molecular biology concerned with the cellular regulatory mechanisms.

An investigation of normal or tumor-bearing organisms can be undertaken at various levels: it may concern itself with gross morphological changes of tissues or organs; with morphological changes of single cells, or parts of cells (*e.g.*, the nucleus); or looking closer still, with the molecular (or chemical) approach which traces differences in cells to differences in chemical constitution or spatial arrangement of the molecules which make up the cells. In the present state of knowledge, the molecular level is the most fundamental, because at this level biological observations can be most fully explained and organized into laws. Hence the chemical approach to the problem of cancer has the greatest significance. Put into the language of chemistry, the problem would be posed thus: in which way (qualitatively and quantitatively) do the molecules and their interactions in the tumor cell differ from those in the normal cell? What constitutes the essential chemical character of the tumor cell? These questions are closely linked to the problem of the properties of growth control and differentiation (lost by the tumor cell), since in the final analysis the governing and controlling factors of normal cells are chemical in nature.

Discovery of chemical carcinogens. The first reference to chemically induced cancer was made by Percivall Pott in his *Chirurgical Observations* (London) at a remarkably early date (1775). He considered contamination by soot to be the cause of cancer of the scrotum common among chimney sweeps. For about a century this remained the only known form of cancer traced to an environmental cause. In 1875, however, von Volkmann described industrial skin cancer contracted through contact with coal tar, and in 1876 Bell discovered "paraffin cancer" due to shale oil. Later, with the rise of industrialization, many cases of tumor induction by mineral oil, tar, or soot were described, notably "mule spinners' cancer" among cotton spinners in Lancashire, due to the mineral oil used as a lubricant (1887). It is curious that the obvious sequel to these observations, the experimental reproduction of this form of the disease, was not achieved until 1915, despite several earlier attempts. In this year a discovery was made which proved to be of momentous value for the study of chemical carcinogenesis. Malignant skin tumors (epitheliomas) were produced by coal tar application on the ears of rabbits by Yamagiwa and Ichikawa. In 1918 Tsutsui produced skin tumors in mice by painting the skin of mice with a solution of the carcinogen, a method still in use for the testing of possibly carcinogenic compounds. An ether extract of soot was shown to be carcinogenic by Passey in 1922.

The next step was to be the isolation and identification of the particular compounds responsible for the carcinogenic properties of soot, tar, and mineral oil. This task began in 1921 with the demonstration by Bloch and Dreifuss that the active component of coal tar showed the chemical behavior of an aromatic hydrocarbon. The pioneer task to fractionate the coal tar and ultimately to isolate the active material was begun that same year by a group of English investigators, led by Cook, Kennaway, and Hieger. This work resulted in the reporting in 1933 of the identification of 3,4-benzopyrene as the first carcinogenic hydrocarbon of known structure isolated from coal tar. The difficult problem of isolation under the contemporary circumstances is illustrated by the fact that 2 tons of tar were used as starting material. "In the arduous nature of the task and the success which crowned it, only one analogous and equally dramatic example comes to mind, and that is the isolation of radium from pitchblende by the Curies," wrote Greenstein. The isolation and identification of 3,4-benzopyrene as a carcinogen became the signal for the synthesis and testing in the subsequent years of a great variety of polycyclic aromatic hydrocarbons and their analogs.

The discovery of the second large group of chemical carcinogens, the aminoazo dyes, may be traced back to the observation in 1934 of Yoshida in Japan that subcutaneous injection or feeding of o-aminoazotoluene to rats and mice produced, after a long period of time, malignant liver tumors in these animals. Three years later Kinosita reported that a related compound, 4-dimethylaminoazobenzene, used then as a coloring matter (known as "Butter Yellow") for consumable fats, was even more active as a hepatic carcinogen. 4-Dimethylaminoazobenzene and its derivatives are currently used tools to induce liver tumors in experimental animals.

Until about 1950 the classification of chemical carcinogens was relatively simple since the very great majority of the compounds could be grouped either as aromatic polycyclic hydrocarbons and their analogs, as azo dyes, or as aromatic amines (the identification of many aromatic amines as carcinogens began in the decade preceding 1950). Since 1950, however, there was a considerable increase not only in the number but also in the *variety* of structural types of chemical agents, as well as an increase in the variety of other means that have been found to produce neoplasia. It is probably not exaggerated to say that at the present time the number of known ways of tumor induction is over one thousand and includes such heterogeneous factors as chemical compounds of known structure, chemical agents of unknown composition, carcinogenic viruses, physical agents, and various types of experimentally induced hormonal imbalances. It is possible that under certain conditions, in some species and toward some tissue practically any agent may prove to be carcinogenic to some degree. This is well shown, for example, by the production of sarcomas (tumors of connective tissue) in rats by subcutaneously implanted foreign materials (synthetic high polymeric substances, ivory, glass, various metals, asbestos, etc.) and by injection of the earlier used blood plasma extender, polyvinylpyrrolidone, and the intriguing finding of the sarcomatogenic activity in the rat of sub-cutaneously injected *concentrated* solutions of glucose or sodium chloride.

Significance of the study of chemical carcinogenesis. In the early decades of enthusiasm which followed the discovery of the polycyclic hydrocarbon and azo dye carcinogens most chemical oncologists entertained the belief that the testing of a sufficiently great number of different compounds would permit the recognition of some special molecular characteristic, common to all carcinogens and critical for tumor induction. Once such a common molecular property was established the nature of the mechanism of chemical carcinogenesis would somehow become evident. Yet, ironically, the con-siderable body of scientific knowledge resulting from this search and present-ing an almost complete picture of the relation between molecular structure and carcinogenic activity in certain classes of compounds has not elucidated the way in which these compounds bring about malignancy. At first it might appear, therefore, that the investigation of the relation of structure and activity has been a failure because its main objective, the elucidation of the mode of action of the carcinogens, has not been accomplished.

This is, however, not altogether true. Apart from the recognition of many human occupational cancer hazards and the synthesis of standardized tumor-inducing agents of graded potencies for studies with experimental animals, many fertile and stimulating hypotheses on the mechanism of action of these compounds have evolved.

Moreover, the skill of the organic chemist, industrial mass production, and modern advertising techniques bring daily, to the manufacturers of goods for human consumption, agents by which the attractiveness, texture, efficiency of production, and storage stability of food materials and other consumable products may be improved. It is imperative, therefore, to maintain and rapidly expand a body of knowledge which can serve as a basis for the evaluation of the degree of harmlessness, with respect to carcinogenicity, of products destined for direct or indirect human usage. This constitutes another reason for the continuing interest in the study of chemical carcinogenesis, in particular for new and rapid testing procedures and the structure-activity relationships of emerging new classes of carcinogens.

The chief reason for this interest is, however, that no clear-cut separation is possible between the study of structure-activity relationships of chemical carcinogens and the biochemistry of cancer, which ultimately must determine and catalog the subtle molecular and organizational differences between normal and tumor cells, and the mechanisms by which these differences are brought about.

In a modern perspective it is not actually surprising that *alone* neither the investigations of the structure-activity relationships and of the conditions modifying these relationships, nor the study of the pathology of microscopically discernible cellular and tissue alterations during carcinogenesis, nor the determination of changes of various individual enzyme levels during the process, could yield information on the molecular mechanism or mechanisms by which these compounds bring about the neoplastic change. The difficulty in attaining an "understanding" of the carcinogenic process at some general level lies, *in fact*, not so much in the nature of its complexity but in the logical habit of trying to define a complex biological event in terms of its single compartmentalized aspects rather than in terms of relationships and transmission of information. We must now turn our attention to the interrelatedness of cellular and organismic processes, to the significance of the feedback principle for the interpretation of cellular and tissue homeostasis.

The innumerable facets of chemical functioning of the cell, that is its biochemical properties, are the expression of a highly complex molecular organization. No change in functioning can occur without change in the underlying molecular machinery. It follows that changes in the microscopic morphology and biochemistry of the cell during the process of carcinogenesis reflect profound alterations in the structure and spatial relationships of its macromolecular components (proteins, nucleic acids, and high molecular weight lipids), marking the elimination of the precisely timed control systems of its interlocking biochemical processes. Indeed there is a vast body of evidence indicating that in living systems at all levels of organization, from highly differentiated multicellular organisms down to comparatively simple unicellular organisms or single cells of tissues, countless channels of mutual control—in a constant give and take of chemical stimuli —are operative between the component parts. The steady-state of tissue growth in developed multicellular organisms, maintaining the rate of cell division at the replacement level, depends precisely on the integral and efficient functioning of such feedback control networks. A widely differing variety of physical, chemical, and biological agents can interact with cellular macromolecules and bring about modifications of structure and, thus, function. Hence interactions with carcinogens cannot fail to affect the network of control which is the very basis of tissue homeostasis.

The very diversity of the chemical agents that induce tumors indicates that no molecular parameters, critical for carcinogenic activity, may be defined which are valid for *all* molecular types and in *all* experimental situations. Therefore no specific type of interaction may be pinpointed which is common to all chemical carcinogens. It follows that the exact relationships of structure and activity must be studied and defined for each class of chemical carcinogens separately. The only common denominator among these agents is that of being able to interact with cellular components by means of the whole spectrum of different types of valence forces, ranging from covalent bonds to weak van der Waals interactions. The significance of this for a general mechanism of carcinogenesis is that as a consequence of interaction with carcinogens, alterations of structure occur in nucleic acids and proteins, leading to the loss of feedback channels of cellular metabolic control.

SELECTED READING FOR SECTION 1

GENERAL

1. Whyte, L. L.: "Accent on Form. An Anticipation of the Science of Tomorrow." Harper, New York, 1954, 198 pp.
2. Bates, M.: "Man in Nature." Prentice-Hall, Englewood Cliffs, New Jersey, 1965, 116 pp.
3. Bornemisza, S. T.: "The Unified System Concept of Nature." Vantage Press, New York, 1955, 137 pp.
4. Hardin, G. J.: "Nature and Man's Fate." Holt, Rinehart & Winston, New York, 1959, 375 pp.
5. Oberling, C.: "The Riddle of Cancer." Yale University Press, New Haven, Connecticut, 1944, 196 pp.
6. Shimkin, M. B.: "Science and Cancer," U.S. Public Health Service Publication No. 1162, Washington D.C., 1964, 137 pp.
7. Haddow, A.: The production of cancer by chemical compounds. *Endeavour* **2**, 27–33 (1943).
8. Smithers, D. W.: "On the Nature of Neoplasia in Man." Livingstone, Edinburgh, 1964, 176 pp.
9. Stone, K.: "Evidence in Science." John Wright, Bristol, England, 1966, 123 pp.

10. Ingle, D. J.: "Principles of Research in Biology and Medicine." Lippincott, Philadelphia, Pennsylvania, 1958, 123 pp.
11. Wilson, E. B., Jr.: "An Introduction to Scientific Research." McGraw-Hill, New York, 1952, 375 pp.

ON SOME ENVIRONMENTAL AND SOCIETAL COROLLARIES

1. Carson, R.: "Silent Spring." Houghton, Boston, Massachusetts, 1962, 368 pp.
2. Lewis, H. R.: "With Every Breath You Take." Crown, New York, 1965, 333 pp.
3. Mintz, M.: "The Therapeutic Nightmare." Houghton, Boston, Massachusetts, 1965, 590 pp.

1.1   Some Specific Bibliographic Tools of Chemical Oncology

The first year of appearance follows the title of the journal or serial publication; the languages of publication of the periodicals are given in parentheses. The full-length original articles appearing in the periodicals represent at most only one half of the total number of papers published in experimental oncology. The other half is widely scattered among specialized periodicals of pathology, experimental medicine, public health, biology, biochemistry, chemistry, and biophysics, and among general scientific periodicals such as *Nature, Science, Naturwissenschaften,* and *Experientia.*

A.   PERIODICALS

1. *Journal of the National Cancer Institute,* 1940. Published by U.S. Public Health Service (English).
2. *Cancer,* 1948. Published by American Cancer Society (English).
3. *Cancer Research,* 1941. Published by American Association for Cancer Research (English). *Cancer Research* is the successor of the *American Journal of Cancer,* 1931–1940, which in turn was the successor of the *Journal of Cancer Research,* 1916–1930.
4. *Proceedings of the American Association for Cancer Research,* 1953/1954 (English; abstracts of papers presented at the annual meetings of the Association).
5. *British Journal of Cancer,* 1947 (English).
6. *Acta Unio Internationalis contra Cancrum,* 1936–1964. Published in Belgium by International Union Against Cancer (English and French; full-length publication of a selection of papers from the quadrennial meetings of the Union).
7. *International Journal of Cancer,* 1965. This new journal is the successor of the *Acta Unio Internationalis contra Cancrum* (English and French).

9. Hartwell, J. L.: "Survey of Compounds Which Have Been Tested for Carcinogenic Activity." U.S. Public Health Service Publication No. 149, Washington D.C., 1951.
10. Greenstein, J. P.: "Biochemistry of Cancer." Academic Press, New York, 1954.
11. Cowdry, E. V.: "Cancer Cells." Saunders, Philadelphia, Pennsylvania, 1955.
12. Pullman, A., and Pullman, B.: "Cancérisation par les Substances Chimiques et Structure Moléculaire." Masson, Paris, 1955.
13. Rhoads, C. P., Editor: "Antimetabolites and Cancer." American Association for the Advancement of Science, Washington D.C., 1955.
14. Kopac, M. J., et al.: Cancer cytology and cytochemistry. Ann. N. Y. Acad. Sci. **63**, 1031–1462 (1956).
15. Shubik, P., and Hartwell, J. L.: "Survey of Compounds Which Have Been Tested for Carcinogenic Activity." U.S. Public Health Service Publication No. 149, Supplement I. Washington D.C., 1957.
16. Rhoads, C. P., et al.: Subcellular particles in the neoplastic process. Ann. N.Y. Acad. Sci. **68**, 245–656 (1957).
17. Biesele, J. J.: "Mitotic Poisons and the Cancer Problem." Elsevier, Amsterdam, 1958.
18. Boyland, E., Editor: Causation of cancer. Brit. Med. Bull. **14**, 73–192 (1958).
19. Blum, H. P.: "Carcinogenesis by Ultraviolet Light." Princeton University Press, Princeton, New Jersey, 1959.
20. Eckardt, R. E.: "Industrial Carcinogens." Grune & Stratton, New York, 1959.
21. Homburger, F., Editor: "The Physiopathology of Cancer." Hoeber-Harper, New York, 1959.
22. "Radiation Biology and Cancer" (Papers presented at the 12th Annual Symposium on Fundamental Cancer Research, Houston, Texas, 1958). University of Texas Press, Austin, Texas, 1959.
23. Wolstenholme, G. E. W., and O'Connor, M., Editors: "Carcinogenesis—Mechanisms of Action," Ciba Foundation Symposium. Little, Brown, Boston, Massachusetts, 1959.
24. "Cell Physiology of Neoplasia" (Papers presented at the 14th Annual Symposium on Fundamental Cancer Research, Houston, Texas, 1960). University of Texas Press, Austin, Texas, 1960.
25. Nowinski, W. W., Editor: "Fundamental Aspects of Normal and Malignant Growth." Elsevier, Amsterdam, 1960.
26. Pincus, G., and Vollmer, E. P., Editors: "Biological Activities of Steroids in Relation to Cancer." Academic Press, New York, 1960.

27. Aisenberg, A. C.: "The Glycolysis and Respiration of Tumors." Academic Press, New York, 1961.
28. Bergel, F.: "Chemistry of Enzymes in Cancer." Thomas, Springfield, Illinois, 1961.
29. Clark, R. L., Editor: "Cancer Chemotherapy." Thomas, Springfield, Illinois, 1961.
30. Harris, R. J. C., Editor: "Biological Approaches to Cancer Chemotherapy." Academic Press, New York, 1961.
31. Hieger, I.: "Carcinogenesis." Academic Press, New York, 1961.
32. Arcos, J. C., and Arcos, M.: Molecular geometry and mechanisms of action of chemical carcinogens. *Progr. Drug Res.* **4**, 407–581 (1962).
33. Brennan, M. J., and Simpson, W. L., Editors: "Biological Interactions in Normal and Neoplastic Growth." Henry Ford Hospital Symposium. Little, Brown, Boston, Massachusetts, 1962.
34. Busch, H.: "An Introduction to the Biochemistry of the Cancer Cell." Academic Press, New York, 1962.
35. Clayson, D. B.: "Chemical Carcinogenesis." Little, Brown, Boston, Massachusetts, 1962.
36. "The Molecular Basis of Neoplasia" (Papers presented at the 15th Annual Symposium on Fundamental Cancer Research, Houston, Texas, 1961). University of Texas Press, Austin, Texas, 1962.
37. Petrov, N. N., Editor: "Cancer—A General Guide to Research and Treatment." Macmillan, New York, 1962.
38. Ross, W. C. J.: "Biological Alkylating Agents." Butterworths, London, 1962.
39. Scott, T. S.: "Carcinogenic and Chronic Toxic Hazards of Aromatic Amines." Elsevier, Amsterdam, 1962.
40. Bauer, K. H.: "Das Krebsproblem." Springer, Berlin, 1963.
41. Clemmesen, J., Editor: "Cancer of the Urinary Bladder," Symposium organized by International Union Against Cancer. *Acta Unio Intern. Contra Cancrum*, Separatum, **18**, No. 4. Hafner, New York, 1963.
42. Furst, A.: "Chemistry of Chelation in Cancer." Thomas, Springfield, Illinois, 1963.
43. Boyland, E., Editor: Mechanisms of carcinogenesis: chemical, physical and viral. *Brit. Med. Bull.*, **20**, 87–166 (1964).
44. Clar, E.: "Polycyclic Hydrocarbons," 2 vols. Academic Press, New York, 1964.
45. Emmelot, P., and Mühlbock, O., Editors: "Cellular Control Mechanisms and Cancer," Conference organized by International Union Against Cancer. Elsevier, Amsterdam, 1964.
46. Hueper, W. C., and Conway, W. D.: "Chemical Carcinogenesis and Cancers." Thomas, Springfield, Illinois, 1964.

47. Plattner, P. A., Editor: "Chemotherapy of Cancer." Elsevier, Amsterdam, 1964.
48. Proceedings of the European Society for the Study of Drug Toxicity, Vol. III: "Evaluation of the Potential Carcinogenic Action of a Drug," International Congress Series No. 75. Excerpta Medica Foundation, New York, 1964.
49. Volkin, E., Editor: Symposium on Molecular Action of Mutagenic and Carcinogenic Agents. *J. Cellular Comp. Physiol.*, **64**, Suppl. 1, 1–191 (1964).
50. Day, E. D.: "The Immunochemistry of Cancer." Thomas, Springfield, Illinois, 1965.
51. Mitchell, J. S., Editor: "The Treatment of Cancer—with Special Reference to Radiotherapy and Chemotherapy." Cambridge University Press, London and New York, 1965.
52. Montgomery, J. A.: On the chemotherapy of cancer. *Progr. Drug Res.*, **8**, 431–507 (1965).
53. Reid, E.: "Biochemical Approaches to Cancer." Pergamon Press, New York, 1965.
54. Ambrose, E. J., and Roe, F. J. C.: "The Biology of Cancer." Van Nostrand, Princeton, New Jersey, 1966.
55. Daudel, P., and Daudel, R.: "Chemical Carcinogenesis and Molecular Biology." Wiley (Interscience), New York, 1966.
56. "Developmental and Metabolic Control Mechanisms and Neoplasia." (Papers presented at the 19th Annual Symposium on Fundamental Cancer Research, Houston, Texas, 1965). Williams & Wilkins, Baltimore, Maryland, 1966.
57. Doerr, W., Linder, F., and Wagner, G.: "Aktuelle Probleme aus dem Gebiet der Cancerologie." Springer, New York, 1966.
58. Gause, G. F.: "Microbial Models of Cancer Cells." Saunders, Philadelphia, Pennsylvania, 1966.
59. Heinmets, F.: "Analysis of Normal and Abnormal Cell Growth." Plenum Press, New York, 1966.
60. Kark, W.: "A Synopsis of Cancer—Genesis and Biology." Williams & Wilkins, Baltimore, Maryland, 1966.
61. Kimmerle, G.: "Beryllium." Vol. XXI of the series "Handbook of Experimental Pharmacology." Springer, New York, 1966.
62. Loveless, A.: "Genetic and Allied Effects of Alkylating Agents." Pennsylvania State Univ. Press, University Park, Pennsylvania, 1966.
63. Montagna, W., and Dobson, R., Editors: "Carcinogenesis." Vol. VII of "Advances in the Biology of the Skin." Pergamon, New York, 1966.
64. Schnitzer, R. J., and Hawking, F., Editors: "Experimental Chemotherapy." Vol. IV, Part I: "Chemotherapy of Neoplastic Diseases." Academic Press, New York, 1966.

65. Holzer, H., and Holldorf, A. W., Editors: "Molekulare Biologie des Malignen Wachstums." Springer, New York, 1966.
66. U.S. Natl. Acad. Sci. Food Protection Committee: "Toxicants Occurring Naturally in Foods," Natl. Acad. Sci. Publication No. 1354. Washington, D.C., 1966.
67. Truhaut, R., Editor: "Potential Carcinogenic Hazards from Drugs." UICC Monograph No. 7. Springer, New York, 1967.
68. Deichmann, W. B., and Lampe, K. F., Editors: "Bladder Cancer—A Symposium" (Fifth Inter-American Conf. Toxicol. & Occupational Med.) Aesculapius, Birmingham, Alabama, 1967.
69. Wynder, E. L., and Hoffmann, D.: "Tobacco and Tobacco Smoke: Studies in Experimental Carcinogenesis." Academic Press, New York, 1967.
70. "Carcinogenesis: A Broad Critique" (Papers presented at the 20th Annual Symposium on Fundamental Cancer Research, Houston, Texas, 1966). Williams & Wilkins, Baltimore, Maryland, 1967.
71. Goldstein, A., Aronow, L., and Kalman, S. M.: "Principles of Drug Action—The Basis of Pharmacology," Chapter 11: "Chemical Carcinogenesis." Harper & Row (Hoebner), New York, 1967.
72. "The Proliferation and Spread of Neoplastic Cells" (Papers presented at the 21st Annual Symposium on Fundamental Cancer Research, Houston, Texas, 1967). Williams & Wilkins, Baltimore, Maryland, 1968.

Part I

Molecular Architecture and the Physical Bases of Molecular Forces

2 Some Fundamentals of Organic Chemistry: Structural Concepts

2.1 Alkanes. Isomerism. Substitution Reactions. The Tetrahedral Carbon Atom

2.1.1 STRUCTURE OF ALKANES. ISOMERISM

Hydrocarbons belong to that class of organic substances which contain atoms of carbon and hydrogen only. The simplest hydrocarbon is methane:

CH_4

Molecular
formula

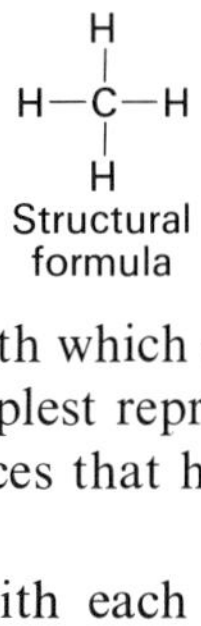

$$H-\overset{\displaystyle H}{\underset{\displaystyle H}{C}}-H$$

Structural
formula

The number of atoms of hydrogen or chlorine with which one atom of an element can combine is termed *valence*. In the simplest representation of a chemical bond, a dash or a dot stands for the forces that hold two atoms together.

The four-valent carbon atoms can combine with each other to form chains. Straight-chain hydrocarbons are also called *normal alkanes* (normal is abbreviated as *n*), for example:

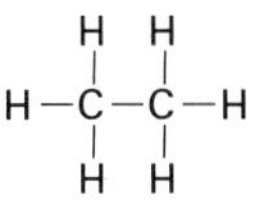

CH_3-CH_3
ethane

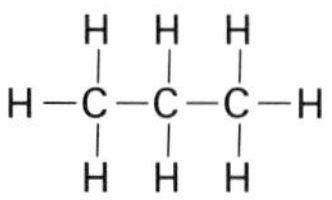

$CH_3-CH_2-CH_3$
propane

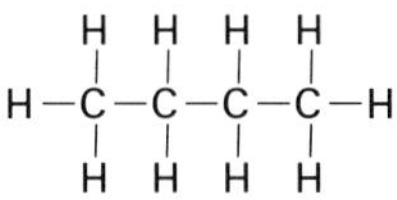

$CH_3-CH_2-CH_2-CH_3$
n-butane

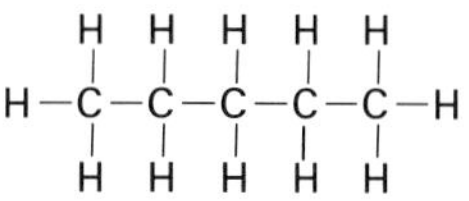

$CH_3-CH_2-CH_2-CH_2-CH_3$
n-pentane

The combination of carbon atoms can continue further, forming much longer chains: C_6, hexane; C_7, heptane; C_8, octane; C_9, nonane; C_{10}, decane; etc. The physical properties of the compounds change with the number of C atoms: methane is a gas, heptane a liquid, and eicosane (C_{20}) a solid at room temperature.

Beyond propane branched chains may be built up. To distinguish the branched-chain alkanes from the *n*-alkanes, the names of the former are preceded by the prefix *iso* (for isomer), for example:

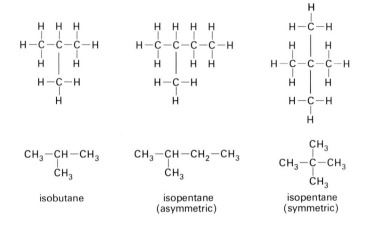

$$CH_3-CH-CH_3$$
$$\quad\quad\;\; |$$
$$\quad\quad\;\; CH_3$$

isobutane

$$CH_3-CH-CH_2-CH_3$$
$$\quad\quad\;\; |$$
$$\quad\quad\;\; CH_3$$

isopentane
(asymmetric)

$$\quad\quad CH_3$$
$$\quad\quad\;\; |$$
$$CH_3-C-CH_3$$
$$\quad\quad\;\; |$$
$$\quad\quad CH_3$$

isopentane
(symmetric)

One way of distinguishing between the two isopentanes may be based on the symmetry of the two structures. The first is the asymmetric isopentane, the second the symmetric isopentane or neopentane. The prefix *neo* indicates the presence of a carbon atom attached by all four valences to other carbon atoms. The number of ways of building up differently branched carbon skeletons and, thus, the number of possible isomers, rapidly increases with the number of carbon atoms. There are four isohexanes, eight isoheptanes, and seventeen isooctanes. Alkanes are also called *paraffins*, and have the general molecular formula C_nH_{2n+2}. The formula shows that, for example, normal alkanes differ from each other only in the number of $-CH_2-$ groups in the molecule. Such a group of compounds is termed a *homologous series* and its members are called *homologs*.

Isomerism holds not only for the alkanes, but it is a general concept of organic chemistry. All compounds having the same molecular formula, irrespective of their structural formulas, are isomers. For example,

$$CH_3-O-CH_3 \quad \text{and} \quad CH_3-CH_2-OH$$

dimethyl ether ethyl alcohol

are isomers, since both have the molecular formula C_2H_6O. It can be readily seen that for elaborate giant molecules the number of possible isomers may be astronomical.

2.1.2   REACTIONS OF ALKANES

The hydrogen atoms in alkanes may be replaced by halogen atoms and other more complex chemical groupings. These are called *substitution reactions*. For example:

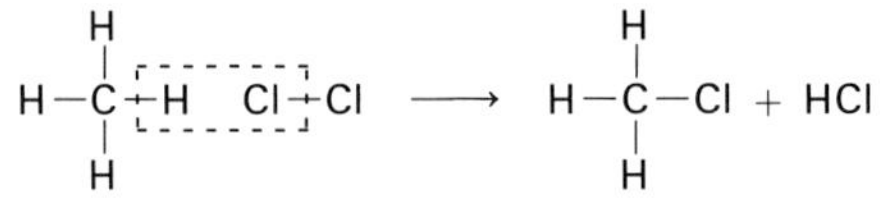

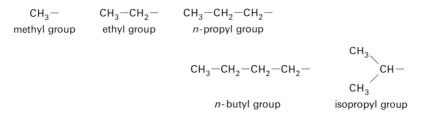

methyl chloride

Further substitution leads successively to CH_2Cl_2 (dichloromethane), $CHCl_3$ (chloroform), and CCl_4 (carbon tetrachloride). Substitution of the longer chain *n*-alkanes yields, for example:

CH_3-CH_2-Cl $CH_3-CH_2-CH_2-Cl$ $CH_3-CH_2-CH_2-CH_2-Cl$
ethyl chloride   *n*-propyl chloride   *n*-butyl chloride

The generic name of such compounds is *alkyl chlorides*. The terms for the hydrocarbon moieties (*alkyl groups*) are derived from the roots of the respective hydrocarbon with the suffix -*yl*, such as:

CH_3- CH_3-CH_2- $CH_3-CH_2-CH_2-$
methyl group   ethyl group   *n*-propyl group

$$CH_3-CH_2-CH_2-CH_2-$$

$$\begin{array}{c} CH_3 \\ \diagdown \\ CH- \\ \diagup \\ CH_3 \end{array}$$

n-butyl group   isopropyl group

The term amyl is used instead of pentyl, then hexyl, heptyl, etc. Groups representing normal chains (*only*) may be abbreviated using the molecular formula, such as:

C_2H_5- C_3H_7- C_4H_9-
ethyl   *n*-propyl   *n*-butyl

To indicate the position of substitution on the alkanes, notations such as the following are used:

$Cl-CH_2-CH_2-Cl$ CH_3-CHCl_2 $Cl-CH_2-CH_2-CH_2-Cl$
1,2-dichloroethane   2,2-dichloroethane   1,3-dichloropropane

$CH_3-CHCl-CH_3$ $NO_2-CH_2-CH_2-CH_2-CH_3$ $CH_3-CH_2-SO_3H$
isopropyl chloride   1-nitro-*n*-butane   ethylsulfonic acid
or 2-chloropropane

The $-CH_2-$ group is often designated as the *methylene group*, thus dichloromethane may also be called methylene dichloride. An analogous terminology is unfortunately also in use for longer carbon chains; for example $-CH_2-CH_2-$ is termed an ethylene group and $-CH_2-CH_2-CH_2-$ a propylene group. However, this terminology applied to groups higher than one carbon is equivocal. Thus, for example, ethylene dichloride designates $Cl-CH_2-CH_2-Cl$, while dichloroethylene is the term for a dichloro-substituted alkene such as $Cl-CH=CH-Cl$ (see Section 2.2). Only the term methylene may be used unequivocally. Long polymethylene segments of complex molecules are often represented as $-(CH_2)_n-$ where "n" stands for the number of $-CH_2-$ groups in a row. Defining the alkane moieties as "alkyl groups" represents a considerable refinement of the terminology of organic chemistry. Thus, for example, the asymmetric isopentane may also be called 2-methyl butane or dimethyl-ethylmethane, while the symmetric isopentane or neopentane is also tetra-methylmethane.

A typical reaction of alkyl halides is that they are readily hydrolyzed by boiling with dilute aqueous sodium hydroxide. This replaces the halogen atom with a hydroxyl group. For ethyl bromide the reaction may be represented as follows:

$$CH_3-CH_2 \dashv Br \qquad Na \dashv OH \longrightarrow CH_3-CH_2-OH + Na-Br$$
ethyl alcohol

Ethyl alcohol can be reconverted to ethyl bromide by reacting the former with H—Br in the presence of a strong dehydrating agent:

$$CH_3-CH_2 \dashv OH \qquad H \dashv Br \xrightarrow{H_2SO_4} CH_3-CH_2-Br + H_2O$$

Treatment of an alkyl halide with zinc powder in presence of acid (which liberates hydrogen) regenerates the parent alkane:

$$CH_3-CH_2 \dashv Br \qquad H \dashv H \longrightarrow CH_3-CH_3 + H-Br$$

A reaction of the alkyl halides, which has been used for the systematic synthesis of alkanes, is the Wurtz–Fittig reaction. This consists of the reaction of these halides with metallic sodium in anhydrous ethyl ether, whereby sodium halide is formed and the alkyl groups join to form larger alkanes, for example:

$$CH_3-CH_2 \dashv Br \qquad Na \quad Na \qquad Br \dashv CH_2-CH_3$$
$$\longrightarrow CH_3-CH_2-CH_2-CH_3 + 2Na-Br$$

The Wurtz–Fittig reaction is an example of a *condensation reaction*, meaning the joining of small chemical groupings to form a larger molecule with simultaneous elimination of certain atoms (here bromine), often the elements of water, of haloacids, or of other small molecules.

Alkyl halides are important intermediates in organic synthesis, since the halogen substituent may be exchanged with a great variety of chemical groupings. For example:

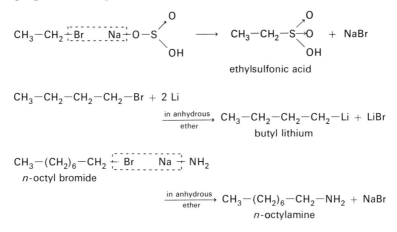

ethylsulfonic acid

$$CH_3{-}CH_2{-}CH_2{-}CH_2{-}Br + 2\,Li \xrightarrow[\text{ether}]{\text{in anhydrous}} CH_3{-}CH_2{-}CH_2{-}CH_2{-}Li + LiBr$$

butyl lithium

$$\underset{n\text{-octyl bromide}}{CH_3{-}(CH_2)_6{-}CH_2{-}Br} + Na{-}NH_2 \xrightarrow[\text{ether}]{\text{in anhydrous}} CH_3{-}(CH_2)_6{-}CH_2{-}NH_2 + NaBr$$

n-octylamine

The arrows between S and O atoms in molecules in the first equation denote coordinate bonds (see Section 3.1.2.7). The $-NH_2$ in *n*-octylamine represents an amino group.

2.1.3 The Tetrahedral Carbon Atom. Molecular Conformations. Optical Isomerism

The planar, two-dimensional representation of carbon compounds as used above and as it is used conventionally is, however, not a correct picture of their actual molecular geometry. In fact, the four bonds that the carbon atom forms with hydrogen, bromine, or any other element are equivalent and are directed toward the corners of a regular tetrahedron. Hence, the carbon atom may be visualized as being in the center of the tetrahedron, and the angle between any pair of valences is 109° 28′ (Fig. 1).

Now, it follows from the tetrahedral valence angles of the carbon atom that the true representation of a fully extended carbon chain is that of a "zigzag" line, with the hydrogen atoms being above and below the plane of the paper (Fig. 2). Longer chains may be folded in various ways as long as the correct valence angles are maintained. These different possible ways of folding of the chains are termed *conformations*. However, in spite of the possibility of these different ways of folding, some conformations are more likely to exist than others. In certain conformations some atoms of the chain are more crowded than in other conformations. Moreover, some conformations will not follow the geometric requirements of the tetrahedral carbon atom and slight distortion of the valence angles will result. Crowding of atoms which are not bonded to each other will cause repulsion. This repulsion and the strain on the valence angles raise the energy of the molecule, hence making that conformation less stable. Figure 2 illustrates the case of *n*-hexane in fully extended and other conformations.

An important consequence of the tetrahedral nature of the carbon atom is molecular asymmetry which results when the four valences are occupied by

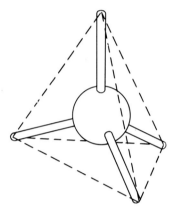

Fig. 1. A representation of the tetrahedral orientation of the valence axes in the carbon atom.

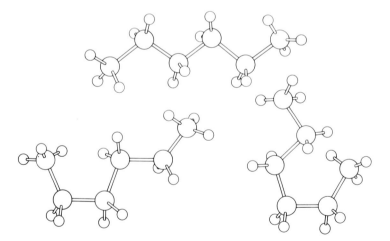

Fig 2. Three possible molecular conformations of *n*-hexane. The figure at the top shows the fully extended conformation, and the two figures at the bottom from left to right represent increasingly "crowded" conformations.

four different chemical groupings. The schematic representation in Fig. 3 shows that there are two possible arrangements of four different substituents relative to each other. These two possible arrangements, called *configurations*, are mirror images since no translational movements or rotations (having as center the carbon atom) can make them superimposable. Carbon atoms which have four different substituents are called *asymmetric carbon atoms*, sometimes indicated by an asterisk ($-\overset{|}{\underset{|}{C}}*-$). The two forms of a compound corresponding to the two configurations of an asymmetric carbon atom are called *enantiomers* or *enantiomorphs*. *Enantiomorphism* is a particular kind of isomerism.

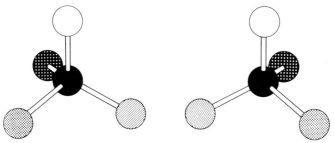

Fig. 3. The two "mirror-image" configurations of a carbon atom with four different substituents (asymmetric carbon atom).

A unique property of compounds containing an asymmetric carbon atom is that they are optically active, which means that they rotate the plane of polarization of plane-polarized light. Hence the two enantiomeric forms are also called *optical isomers* or *optical antipodes*. The two large classes of biologically important optically active substances are the amino acids and the carbohydrates.

An optically active substance which rotates the plane of polarization toward the right is *dextrorotatory* (denoted with " + ") and one which rotates it toward the left is *levorotatory* (denoted with " − "). The extent and direction of *optical rotation* (measured in angle degrees and expressed as *specific rotation*) is an important characteristic of substances containing asymmetric carbon atoms. The two optical isomers of a given optically active substance have specific rotation equal in absolute value but opposite in sign. Except for the behavior toward polarized light, the chemical and other physical properties of enantiomers are generally, but not always, exactly identical.

Which of the two possible configurations actually corresponds to the dextrorotatory and which one to the levorotatory form has been established for a few substances and is known as the *absolute configuration*. Conventions have been established for certain substances: when a certain chemical group is pictured on the right in the structural formula it is designated as the D form; when the same grouping is pictured on the left, the formula is designated as the L form. The use of the terms D and L does not necessarily correspond to the direction of optical rotation, so that it is possible to have a D form with a negative " − " rotation or an L form with a positive " + " rotation.

When equal amounts of the two enantiomers of a substance are mixed, the optical rotations of opposite sign cancel each other and the mixture, called a *racemic mixture* or a *racemate*, is optically inactive and is designated as the DL form. It is interesting that while the physical properties of the component enantiomers are on the whole identical, those of the racemic mixture are different from the ones of the individual enantiomers. The organic synthesis of a compound containing an asymmetric carbon atom always results in the formation of a racemic mixture. Different laboratory procedures have been established to separate racemic mixtures into optical isomers.

More than one asymmetric carbon may be present in a molecule and the number of possible isomers rapidly increases by increasing the number of asymmetric centers. Since every asymmetric carbon contributes with two isomeric possibilities, the total number of possible isomers for a molecule containing $nC*$ is 2^n. The presence of two or any even number of asymmetric carbons can give rise to the optically inactive *meso* configuration. The two possible enantiomers and the meso configuration of a substance containing paired asymmetric centers are *steric isomers* or *stereoisomers*, meaning that they all have the same gross structure and differ only in configuration. In the meso configuration the optical inactivity is due to the fact that the optical activities of the individual asymmetric centers cancel each other within the molecule. Consequently unlike from a racemate, no optically active stereoisomers may be separated from a meso compound.

2.1.4 ALICYCLIC HYDROCARBONS AND THE BAEYER STRAIN THEORY

By elimination of the terminal hydrogen atoms, the ends of hydrocarbon chains may be joined to form ring compounds. These are the *alicyclic hydrocarbons*. Because of the geometric requirements of the tetrahedral carbon atom (to avoid distortion of the valence angles) the 5- and 6-membered rings are the most stable.

cyclopentane   cyclohexane

For the same reason these rings are buckled and not planar as the conventional representation would indicate (Fig. 4). Cyclohexane is ordinarily in the most stable "chair" conformation.

In contrast to the 5- and 6-membered ring systems, in the 3- and 4-membered compounds there is considerable distortion of the tetrahedral angles. The angle is 90° in cyclobutane and 60° in cyclopropane. These large deviations are reflected in the considerable chemical instability of cyclopropane and cyclobutane. For example, by mild heating, cyclopropane readily undergoes what is called an *intramolecular rearrangement* to give propylene (see Section 2.2):

$$CH_2 \diagdown \diagup ... \qquad H_2C-CH_2 \longrightarrow CH_2=CH-CH_3$$

$$\text{propylene}$$

The terminology of derivatives of alicyclic compounds follows that of the straight-chain and branched-chain alkanes. Thus we may have cyclohexyl chloride, cyclopentyl bromide (*not* cycloamyl), etc.

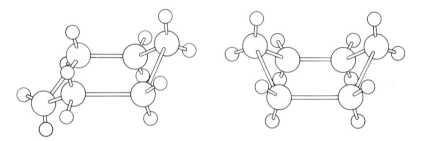

Fig. 4. The two possible conformations of cyclohexane. The "chair" conformation (left) and the "boat" conformation (right).

The great chemical stability of cyclohexane and cyclopentane, and the decreased stability as the number of $-CH_2-$ groups in the ring is decreased, follow the rule known as the *Baeyer strain theory*. Baeyer noted in 1885 that the valence angles of the tetrahedral carbon atom (109° 28′) lie between the values of angles in the regular pentagon (108°) and the regular hexagon (120°). Hence 5- and 6-membered rings form most readily and are most stable. Different chemical or physicochemical influences which favor the tetrahedral angle between carbon valences promote ring formation and enhance chemical stability. That factors other than purely geometric ones are involved is indicated by the much greater frequency of occurrence of 6-membered rings as compared to 5-membered rings. On the other hand, many compounds are known which contain large rings with up to 30 or more carbon atoms. In these rings, however, the valence angles are not strained because the carbon atoms do not lie in one plane and the rings assume various buckled conformations. An important consequence of the Baeyer strain theory is that suitable reactive groups at 5 or 6 carbon distance from one another (1,5 and 1,6 positions on a carbon chain) readily react *intramolecularly*, resulting in ring closure. An example of this is the formation of valerolactone (in Section 2.3.5).

2.2 Alkenes and Alkynes. Chemical Properties of Double and Triple Bonds

2.2.1 ALKENES

Two carbon atoms can combine with each other in a way by which each satisfies two instead of only one of the valences of the other, and form a double bond. The simplest compound of this type is ethylene:

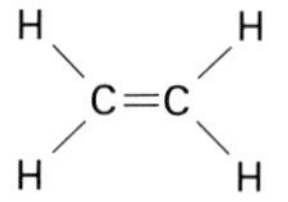

$$\begin{array}{c}
H H \\
\diagdown \diagup \\
C=C \\
\diagup \diagdown \\
H H
\end{array} \qquad \text{or} \qquad CH_2=CH_2$$

The group or radical corresponding to ethylene is the *vinyl* group; a corresponding halide is vinyl chloride $CH_2=CHCl$.

A double bond can also be incorporated into longer carbon chains, such as:

$CH_2=CH-CH_3$ $CH_2=CH-CH_2-CH_3$ $CH_2=CH-CH_2-CH_2-CH_3$
propene or propylene   n-butene-1   n-pentene-1

The terminology clearly shows here that the suffix -*ene* indicates the presence in the molecule of a double bond; the number that follows designates the *lower* numbered of the two carbon atoms involved in the double bond. The definition of the position of this bond is necessary since for compounds containing as few as four carbon atoms, such as n-butene, two isomers are possible:

$CH_2=CH-CH_2-CH_3$ $CH_3-CH=CH-CH_3$
n-butene-1 or 1-butene   n-butene-2 or 2-butene

The term *alkene* denotes the hydrocarbons containing double bonds. Alkenes are also called *olefins*. They may be represented by the general formula C_nH_{2n}.

The group corresponding to propenyl-2 ($-CH_2-CH=CH_2$) is termed *allyl* and the group corresponding to butenyl-2 ($-CH_2-CH=CH-CH_3$) is termed *crotyl*.

For the alkenes the number of possible isomers is increased by the fact that both the position of the double bond and the branching of the chain may vary. There is only one isobutene; however, three alkenes corresponding to the asymmetric isopentane are possible:

$$CH_2=\overset{\underset{|}{CH_3}}{C}-CH_3 \qquad CH_2=\overset{\underset{|}{CH_3}}{C}-CH_2-CH_3 \qquad CH_3-\overset{\underset{|}{CH_3}}{C}=CH-CH_3$$

isobutene or   2-methylbutene-1   2-methylbutene-2
isobutylene

$$CH_3-\overset{\underset{|}{CH_3}}{CH}-CH=CH_2$$

2-methylbutene-3

No alkene corresponding to neopentane can exist, since each valence of the central carbon is linked to another carbon atom.

Alkenes containing two, three, four, or more double bonds are termed diene, triene, tetraene, and polyene, respectively. The simplest diene is butadiene and the simplest triene is hexatriene:

$$CH_2=CH-CH=CH_2 \qquad CH_2=CH-CH=CH-CH=CH_2$$

butadiene   hexatriene

The double bonds in butadiene and hexatriene are *conjugated double bonds*, meaning that they regularly alternate with single bonds. When a conjugated chain is interrupted by a $-CH_2-$ group, the double bonds are said to be *nonconjugated* or *isolated*:

$$CH_2=CH-CH_2-CH=CH_2 \qquad CH_2=CH-CH_2-CH=CH-CH=CH_2$$

a nonconjugated diene   a partially conjugated triene

Double bonds may also be *cumulated*, meaning that they directly follow one another, for example as in carbon suboxide:

$$O=C=C=C=O$$

2.2.2 GEOMETRIC ISOMERISM

The double bond and the tetrahedral orientation of valences of the carbon atom give rise to the phenomenon called *geometric isomerism* or *cis-trans isomerism*. This may be illustrated by the following example. There is free rotation around a single bond and consequently there is only one *n*-butane, in spite of the fact that different molecular formulas may be written:

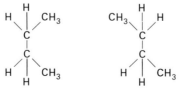

Around a double bond, however, rotation is restricted. One cannot pass from *cis*-2-butene to *trans*-2-butene

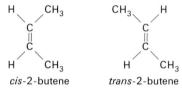

cis-2-butene   trans-2-butene

without breaking one of the two bonds. This would require more energy than is available to the molecule at ordinary temperatures. Two geometric isomers always result when a hydrogen on each carbon involved in a double bond is substituted. An often cited example is the pair, maleic acid (the cis compound) and fumaric acid (the trans compound). The spatial (or *steric*) closeness of the acidic carboxyl groups in the former is clearly indicated by the fact that it readily undergoes an intramolecular condensation reaction, with loss of the elements of water to yield an internal anhydride. Fumaric acid, where the two carboxyl groups

are sterically apart, does not form an internal anhydride.

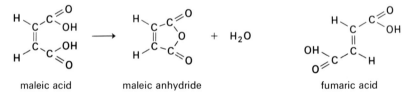

maleic acid   maleic anhydride   fumaric acid

The physical characteristics of cis and trans isomers are always different and so is much of their chemical behavior.

2.2.3 ALKYNES

Two carbon atoms can also combine with each other so that they satisfy three of the valences of each other to form a triple bond. Acetylene or ethyne $(H—C \equiv C—H)$ is the parent compound of this series, called the *acetylenes* or *alkynes*. The class of alkynes is represented by the general formula C_nH_{2n-2}. It follows from the geometry of the carbon atom that the acetylenic linkage does not give rise to cis-trans isomerism.

Just as the double bond, the triple bond may be incorporated into carbon chains and may occur singly or conjugated with other acetylenic linkages or with double bonds, for example:

$$HC \equiv C - CH_3 \qquad HC \equiv C - CH_2 - CH_3 \qquad HC \equiv C - C \equiv CH \qquad HC \equiv C - CH = CH_2$$

propyne or   1-butyne or   butadiyne or   butenyne or
methylacetylene   ethylacetylene   diacetylene   vinylacetylene

The group $HC \equiv C-$ is termed *ethinyl* and the group $HC \equiv C - CH_2-$
propargyl.

2.2.4   REACTIONS OF ALKENES AND ALKYNES

The double and triple bonds are endowed with special properties. Both
readily take up atoms or groups and thus revert to the single bond. Hence,
both bonds are also called "unsaturated" as opposed to the single bond,
which is "saturated." Below are given some typical reactions of ethylene
and acetylene:

$$CH_2 = CH_2 \xrightarrow{H_2} CH_3 - CH_3 \qquad HC \equiv CH \xrightarrow{H_2} CH_2 = CH_2 \xrightarrow{H_2} CH_3 - CH_3$$

$$CH_2 = CH_2 \xrightarrow{Br_2} CH_2Br - CH_2Br \qquad HC \equiv CH \xrightarrow{Br_2} CHBr = CHBr \xrightarrow{Br_2} CHBr_2 - CHBr_2$$

$$CH_2 = CH_2 \xrightarrow{HBr} CH_3 - CH_2Br \qquad HC \equiv CH \xrightarrow{HBr} CH_2 = CHBr \xrightarrow{HBr} CH_3 - CHBr_2$$

$$CH_2 = CH_2 \xrightarrow[H_2SO_4]{H-OH} CH_3 - CH_2 - OH$$

catalyst   ethyl alcohol

$$HC \equiv CH \xrightarrow[H_2SO_4 + Hg^{++}]{H-OH} [CH_2 = CH - OH] \xrightarrow{rearrangement} CH_3 - C \overset{O}{\underset{H}{\big<}}$$

catalyst   vinyl alcohol   acetaldehyde
                  (unstable)

$$CH_2 = CH_2 \xrightarrow{HO-Cl} HO - CH_2 - CH_2 - Cl$$

ethylene chlorohydrin

$$CH_2 = CH_2 + H - O - S \overset{ONa}{\underset{O}{\big<}} \longrightarrow CH_3 - CH_2 - S \overset{ONa}{\underset{O}{\big<}} O$$

sodium ethyl sulfonate

$$CH_2 = CH_2 + H_2O + \quad [O] \quad \longrightarrow HO - CH_2 - CH_2 - OH$$

provided by a *mild*   ethylene glycol,
oxidizing agent, such   a dialcohol
as dilute potassium
permanganate

Such reactions are called *addition reactions*, meaning the addition of elements
or groups of a molecule to a double or triple bond. The addition of bromine
to the ethylenic linkage occurs so readily that it may be used for the rapid
quantitative determination of double bonds.

Attention is called now, in the above group of reactions, to the stepwise
addition of hydrogen bromide to acetylene. It will be noted that in the

second step addition of hydrogen bromide to bromoethylene (or vinyl bromide) resulted in the formation of 1,1-dibromoethane only, and not in the production of 1,2-dibromoethane, or of an equal mixture of the two dibromo derivatives. This is a typical example of reactions which follow the *Markownikoff rule*. This rule states that in the addition of a haloacid to an ethylenic linkage, bearing a halogen substituent at one of the carbon atoms, the halogen moiety of the haloacid will be linked to the carbon having the halogen substituent (mechanism in Section 3.1.2.4).

If an ethylenic linkage is treated with a *strong* oxidizing agent then, instead of the formation of a dialcohol similar to ethylene glycol, there is rupture of the double bond and oxidation of the carbon atoms to acidic carboxyl groups, for example:

$$CH_3-CH=CH-CH_3 \xrightarrow{\text{oxidant}} 2\ CH_3-C{\overset{\displaystyle O}{\underset{\displaystyle OH}{<}}}$$

In the sole case of the two-carbon alkene, ethylene, the reaction will not stop at the acid stage but will proceed to carbon dioxide because of the easy oxidizability of formic acid:

$$CH_2=CH_2 \xrightarrow{\text{oxidant}} 2\ H-C{\overset{\displaystyle O}{\underset{\displaystyle OH}{<}}} \xrightarrow{\text{oxidant}} 2\ CO_2 + 2\ H_2O$$

formic acid

The halogenated alkanes may be readily reconverted to the unsaturated alkenes and alkynes by treatment with alcoholic potassium hydroxide, which removes from the molecules the elements of haloacids. The importance of this reaction for organic synthesis is illustrated by the following examples:

$$CH_3-CH=CH-CH_3 \xrightarrow{Br_2} CH_3-\underset{\underset{Br}{|}}{CH}-\underset{\underset{Br}{|}}{CH}-CH_3$$

$$\xrightarrow[\text{alcohol}]{KOH} CH_2=CH-CH=CH_2 + 2\ HBr$$

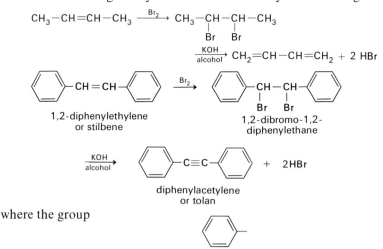

1,2-diphenylethylene
or stilbene

1,2-dibromo-1,2-
diphenylethane

diphenylacetylene
or tolan

+   2HBr

where the group

represents a *phenyl* group (see Section 2.4.1).

The hydrogens in acetylene have acidic properties. Passing acetylene gas into ammoniacal cuprous or silver solutions yields, as precipitates, the red cuprous acetylide and the white silver acetylide, respectively. Sodium acetylide is readily formed by passing acetylene into molten metallic sodium. The monoacetylides have the general formula $CH \equiv C-Me$; both hydrogens may be substituted, however. Treatment of the acetylides with acid regenerates acetylene. Acetylides are also formed by homologs of acetylene.

Conjugated double-bonded systems show a different reactivity than single or nonconjugated ethylenic linkages, which is that the most reactive points of such systems are the two ends of the conjugated chain. Consequently addition reactions will proceed at these points, for example:

$$CH_2=CH-CH=CH-CH=CH_2 \xrightarrow{Br_2} Br-CH_2-CH=CH-CH=CH-CH_2-Br \xrightarrow{Br_2}$$

$$\underset{\underset{Br}{|}}{CH_2Br-CH}-CH=CH-\underset{\underset{Br}{|}}{CH}-CH_2Br \xrightarrow{Br_2} CH_2Br-CHBr-\underset{\underset{Br}{|}}{CH}-\underset{\underset{Br}{|}}{CH}-CHBr-CH_2Br$$

This special reactivity behavior of conjugated double-bonded systems became the basis of an important organic synthetic technique, the Diels–Alder diene addition. The structural variety of compounds which may be built up by this procedure is illustrated by the following examples:

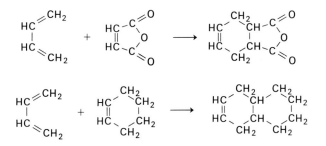

2.2.5 POLYMERIZATION. THE POLYISOPRENES

The 2-methyl derivative of butadiene, isoprene, is an important molecular building block in the biosynthesis of many natural products, for example, in natural latex and terpenes. Latex, the raw material for rubber, is the result of the *linear* double bond addition of many isoprene molecules to one another. *Terpenes* are compounds in which the isoprene building blocks combine by double bond addition to form various cyclic molecules. A process whereby many molecules, having *more than one reactive center*, can combine with one another to form chains or branched networks is called *polymerization*. The final products of such a process are called *polymers* and the compounds, the molecules of which combine to make up the polymer, are called *monomers.* Combinations of only two, three, or four molecules of the monomer are termed dimer, trimer, and tetramer. When a synthetic high polymer is formed from only one monomer it is termed a *homopolymer.* When molecules of two or more *different types* of monomer combine randomly to make up molecular chains or networks, the final product is a *heteropolymer.* Monomers having different types of reactive chemical groupings other than double bonds may polymerize; polymerization by double bond addition is only one of the several possibilities.

Returning to our original example, natural latex is a homopolymer of isoprene (where "*n*" denotes an indefinite but large number of monomer units):

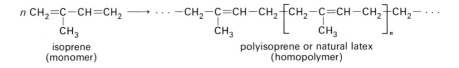

isoprene
(monomer)

polyisoprene or natural latex
(homopolymer)

A typical terpene, limonene (present in turpentine), may be regarded as a cyclic dimer of isoprene. A hypothetical route of the synthesis of limonene would be:

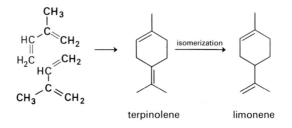

terpinolene   limonene

Actually, *cracking* (treatment by heat and pressure, resulting in breaking up of a molecule into smaller molecules representing fragments) of limonene gives isoprene in good yield, by breaking up the limonene molecule into two molecules of isoprene.

An important group of high molecular weight polyenes related to the terpenes is the *carotenoids.* These compounds are terpenic in that they may be formally regarded as the results of polymerization of isoprene, but in a specifically oriented fashion. They are highly colored unsaturated substances, soluble in oils, fats, and solvents for fats, and are found in many animal and plant products. Typical carotenoids are lycopene (the red coloring substance in tomatoes) and carotene (the coloring substance in carrots). Carotene is closely related to and is used for the synthesis of vitamin A.

2.3   Some Important Functional Groups and Their Reactions

The term "functional group" is a loose but convenient one; it denotes small chemical groupings conferring to molecules their special reactivity. In alkanes, bearing as substituent a halogen or alkali metal atom, a sulfonic, hydroxyl, amino or other group, the chemical reactivity of these groups is indeed much greater than that of the chemically rather inert carbon chain. The definition of "functional group" has its limitations, however, when we consider the alkenes and alkynes. For example, the bromo substituent in bromoethylene is much more resistant to hydrolysis than in ethyl bromide. Yet in mono-halogenated ethylenes the "unsaturated" double bond may still be quite reactive. Thus, because of their reactivity to combine with other groups to form larger atomic assemblages, double bonds and triple bonds are also regarded as functional groups when considering larger molecules. Compounds which contain unsaturated double or triple bonds and another reactive functional group, give the chemical reactions of both.

2.3.1   ALCOHOLS AND HYDROPEROXIDES

Alcohols may be derived from alkanes or alkenes by replacing one or more hydrogen atoms with *hydroxyl groups*. The terminology of alcohols may be derived from the terms of the respective hydrocarbons with the suffix *-ol*. Thus we say methyl alcohol or methanol, ethyl alcohol or ethanol (the latter commonly called "alcohol"), propyl alcohol or propanol, etc. However, for the C_5 alcohol the term amyl alcohol is more generally used than pentanol.

Alcohols may be *primary, secondary (sec)*, or *tertiary (tert)* depending on whether the carbon atom to which the hydroxyl group is linked is attached to one, two, or three carbon atoms. For example:

$$CH_3-OH \qquad CH_3-CH_2-OH \qquad CH_3-CH_2-CH_2-OH$$

are primary alcohols, while

$$CH_3-\underset{\underset{OH}{|}}{CH}-CH_3 \qquad CH_3-CH_2-CH_2-\underset{\underset{OH}{|}}{CH}-CH_3$$

are secondary alcohols, or written a different way:

$$CH_3-CH(OH)-CH_3 \qquad CH_3-CH_2-CH_2-CH(OH)-CH_3$$

isopropyl alcohol   *asym*-isoamyl alcohol
or pentanol-2

The compounds:

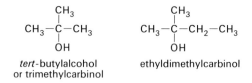

tert-butylalcohol   ethyldimethylcarbinol
or trimethylcarbinol

are tertiary alcohols. As the examples indicate, tertiary alcohols are conveniently designated as *carbinols* (meaning the central $\overset{\smile}{=}$C—OH segment of the molecule).

Alcohols may be monobasic, dibasic (also called *diols* or *glycols*), tribasic (also called *triols*), or polybasic (also called *polyols*), meaning that one, two, three, or more hydroxyl groups are attached to the carbon chain. Thus, the same molecule may contain primary, secondary, and tertiary alcoholic hydroxyl groups. Below are given the formulas of a few well-known polybasic alcohols:

CH_2—OH	CH_2—OH	CH_2—OH	CH_2—OH
CH_2—OH	CH_2	CH—OH	CH—OH
	CH_2—OH	CH_3	CH_2—OH
ethylene glycol	1,3-propanediol	1,2-propanediol	1,2,3-propanetriol or glycerol

$$CH_3$$
$$CH_3-\overset{|}{C}-CH-CH_2-OH$$
$$\quad\;\; HO\;\; OH$$
3-methyl-1,2,3-butanetriol

$$\cdots -CH_2(-\overset{|}{C}H-CH_2-)_n\overset{|}{C}H-CH_2-\cdots$$
$$\qquad\qquad OH \qquad\quad\; OH$$
poly(vinyl alcohol)

An important class of substances that belong to the polyols are the *carbohydrates* or *sugars*, having the general formula $C_n(H_2O)_n$. Carbohydrates containing only one polyol grouping in their molecule are called *monosaccharides* (*e.g.*, glucose). The backbone of most monosaccharides is either a 5-carbon chain (*pentoses*) or a 6-carbon chain (*hexoses*).

Usually organic compounds cannot bear two or three hydroxyls on the same carbon. With a few exceptions such compounds immediately lose water to yield aldehydes, ketones, or acids (Sections 2.3.2 and 2.3.3):

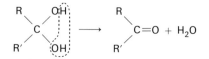

where R′=H for aldehydes, R′= alkyl for ketones, and R′=OH for acids.

Hydroperoxides may be formally regarded as monoalkyl-substituted hydrogen peroxide. The general formula of the hydroperoxides is

$R-O-O-H$, where R stands for an alkyl group. Hydroperoxides may be prepared from the corresponding alcohols by oxidation under specific conditions.

2.3.1.1 Reactions of Alcohols

Since alcohols may be formally regarded as monoalkyl-substituted water, it is not unexpected then that they react with alkali metals to liberate hydrogen and form the respective alkali alcoholate. For example:

$$2 \ CH_3-OH + 2 \ Na \longrightarrow 2 \ CH_3-ONa + H_2$$
sodium methoxide

The CH_3O- is termed a methoxy group, C_2H_5O- ethoxy, C_3H_7O- propoxy, and C_4H_9O- butoxy; in general these are *alkoxy* groups. The reactivity of alcohols toward alkali metals decreases with the lengthening of the carbon chain.

Because of the alkoxy group attached to an alkali metal, alcoholates may serve as synthetic intermediates:

$$CH_3-CH_2-O\dashv Na \quad Cl\dashv CH_2-CH_3 \longrightarrow CH_3-CH_2-O-CH_2-CH_3 + NaCl$$
diethyl ether

$$CH_3-CH_2-O\dashv Na \quad Cl\dashv \underset{\underset{O}{\|}}{C}-CH_3 \longrightarrow CH_3-CH_2-O-\underset{\underset{O}{\|}}{C}-CH_3$$
acetyl chloride   ethyl acetate

The alcoholic hydroxyl may be replaced by a halogen atom by reacting an alcohol with a haloacid in presence of a dehydrating agent (Section 2.1.2), or with a phosphorus halide:

$$3 \ R-OH + PBr_3 \longrightarrow 3 \ R-Br + H_3PO_3$$

Alcohols may be converted to alkenes by loss of the hydroxyl group and one hydrogen in the presence of dehydrating agents or a catalyst. For example:

$$\underset{\underset{H}{}}{CH_2}-\underset{\underset{OH}{}}{CH_2} \xrightarrow[\substack{\text{or } Al_2O_3 \text{ catalyst;} \\ H_2O \text{ vapor; } 350°C}]{H_2SO_4; \ >200°C} CH_2{=}CH_2 + H_2O$$

Under less drastic conditions ethanol gives diethyl ether:

$$\begin{array}{c} CH_3-CH_2{-}OH \\ CH_3-CH_2{-}OH \end{array} \xrightarrow[\substack{\text{or } Al_2O_3 \text{ catalyst;} \\ 250°C}]{H_2SO_4; \ 130{-}140°C} CH_3-CH_2-O-CH_2-CH_3$$

Passing from primary, to secondary, to tertiary alcohols, replacement of the hydroxyl by a halogen, and dehydration becomes progressively easier. Reactivity toward alkali metals to form alcoholates changes inversely.

An interesting reaction of 1,2,3-propanetriol (glycerol) is the loss of two molecules of water when heated with a mild dehydrating agent to yield acrolein, an unsaturated aldehyde (aldehydes, see Section 2.3.2):

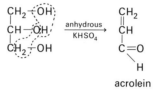

acrolein

Note that acrolein (or acrylic aldehyde) represents the aldehyde of the allyl moiety (see Section 2.2.1). The corresponding unsaturated alcohol is indeed allyl alcohol. However, for the respective aldehydes and acids the terms are acrylic aldehyde (acrolein) and acrylic acid (compare with butyl alcohol and butyric acid, Section 2.3.3).

2.3.2 Aldehydes and Ketones

Aldehydes (from the contraction of *al*cohol *dehyd*rogenatus) are the products of mild oxidation (dehydrogenation) of primary alcohols. For example, mild oxidation of ethanol with air in presence of a catalyst gives acetaldehyde:

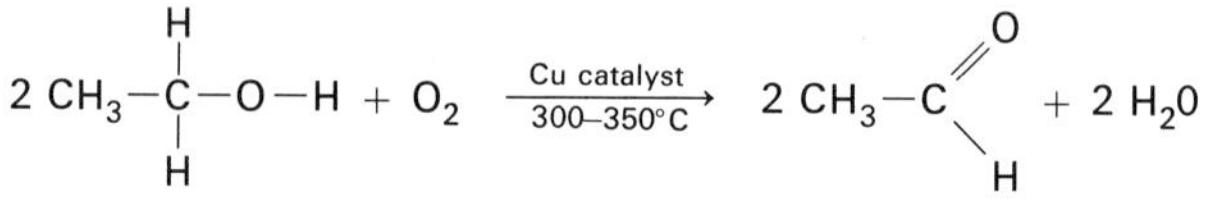

$$2\ CH_3-\underset{\underset{H}{|}}{\overset{\overset{H}{|}}{C}}-O-H + O_2 \xrightarrow[300–350°C]{Cu\ catalyst} 2\ CH_3-C\overset{\displaystyle O}{\underset{\displaystyle H}{\diagup}} + 2\ H_2O$$

The *aldehyde group*

may also be represented as —CHO.

Except for formaldehyde (obtained in a similar way from methanol) and acetaldehyde, the common names of the higher aldehydes are similar to the ones of the corresponding alcohols up to C_5: propionaldehyde (C_3), butyraldehyde (C_4). However, the n-C_5 aldehyde is known as n-valeraldehyde, the n-C_6 aldehyde as caproic aldehyde, the n-C_8 aldehyde as caprylic aldehyde. In addition to the common names of the aldehydes, a systematic nomenclature is also used in which the name of an aldehyde is derived from the name of the corresponding alkane with the suffix -al. Thus we say methanal, ethanal, propanal, n-butanal, n-pentanal, etc. Formaldehyde is sometimes represented by its molecular formula CH_2O.

Ketones are the products of oxidation (dehydrogenation) of secondary alcohols. Ketones may be regarded as aldehydes in which the hydrogen atom of the aldehyde group has been replaced by an alkyl substituent. For example, mild oxidation of isopropyl alcohol gives dimethyl ketone or acetone, the simplest ketone:

$$CH_3-\underset{\underset{H}{|}}{\overset{\overset{OH}{|}}{C}}-CH_3 \xrightarrow{\text{oxidant}} CH_3-\underset{}{\overset{\overset{O}{||}}{C}}-CH_3$$

In the systematic nomenclature the names of ketones are formed from the corresponding alkane with the suffix -one, followed or preceded by a number denoting the position of the *carbonyl group* or *keto group*

$$-\underset{\underset{O}{||}}{C}-$$

in the carbon chain. Thus acetone is propanone-2, 2-propanone, or simply propanone since 1-propanone cannot exist. There is only one butanone, since butanone-2 and butanone-3 are identical. However, beginning with C_5 the denoting of the position of the keto or ketone group is meaningful since there are two pentanones:

$$CH_3-\underset{\underset{O}{||}}{C}-CH_2-CH_2-CH_3 \qquad CH_3-CH_2-\underset{\underset{O}{||}}{C}-CH_2-CH_3$$

methyl-n-propyl ketone   diethyl ketone or
or pentanone-2   pentanone-3

For designating more complex ketones, the groups on both sides of the $\underset{}{\overset{}{C}}=O$ group are defined; for example isopropyl-tert-butyl ketone:

$$\underset{\underset{CH_3}{}}{\overset{\overset{CH_3}{\diagdown}}{H-C}}-\underset{\underset{O}{||}}{C}-\underset{\underset{CH_3}{|}}{\overset{\overset{CH_3}{|}}{C}}-CH_3$$

Tertiary alcohols may not be oxidized further without cleavage to smaller molecules representing segments of the original carbon skeleton.

2.3.2.1   Reactions of Aldehydes and Ketones

Aldehyde and keto groups may undergo addition and condensation reactions:

addition reactions

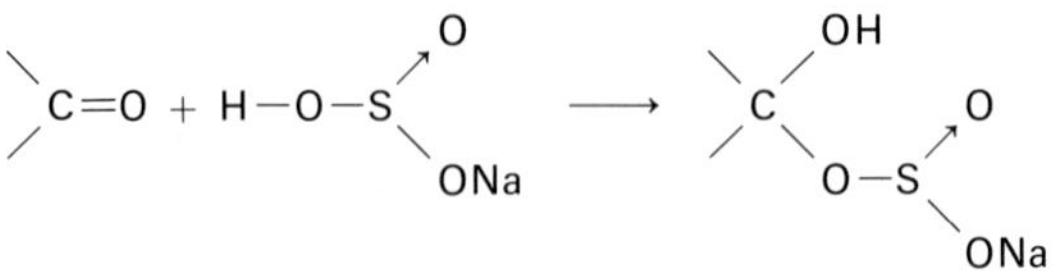

$$\text{\Large$>$}\!C{=}O + H{-}O{-}S\!\!\begin{array}{c}O\\ \\ONa\end{array} \longrightarrow \text{\Large$>$}\!C\!\!\begin{array}{c}OH\\ \\O{-}S\end{array}\!\!\begin{array}{c}O\\ \\ONa\end{array}$$

a bisulfite addition
product or bisulfite
adduct

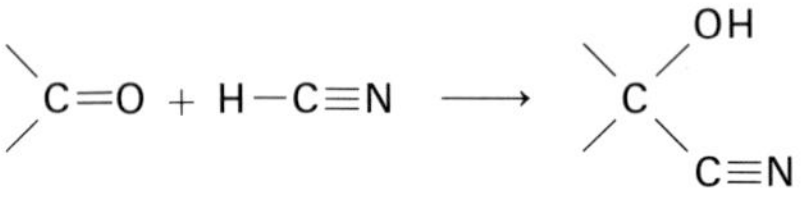

$$\text{\Large$>$}\!C{=}O + H{-}C{\equiv}N \longrightarrow \text{\Large$>$}\!C\!\!\begin{array}{c}OH\\ \\C{\equiv}N\end{array}$$

a cyanohydrin

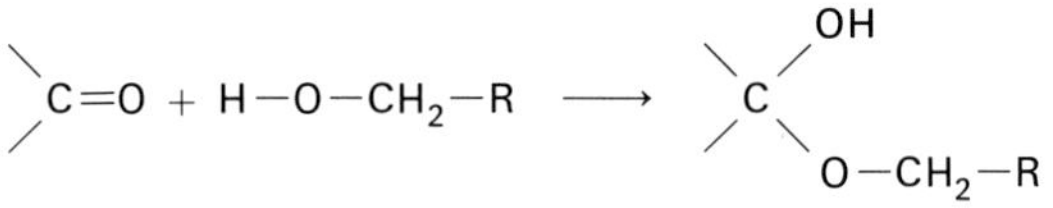

$$\text{\Large$>$}\!C{=}O + H{-}O{-}CH_2{-}R \longrightarrow \text{\Large$>$}\!C\!\!\begin{array}{c}OH\\ \\O{-}CH_2{-}R\end{array}$$

a primary   a hemiacetal or
alcohol   lactol

condensation reactions

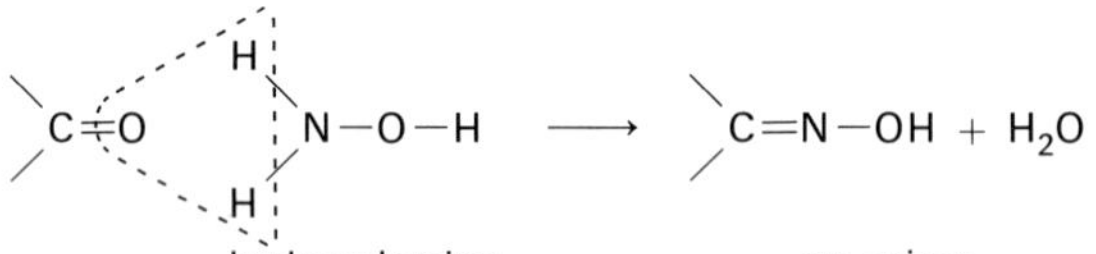

$$\text{\Large$>$}\!C{=}O \quad H \atop N{-}O{-}H \atop H \longrightarrow \text{\Large$>$}\!C{=}N{-}OH + H_2O$$

hydroxylamine   an oxime
(aldoxime or ketoxime)

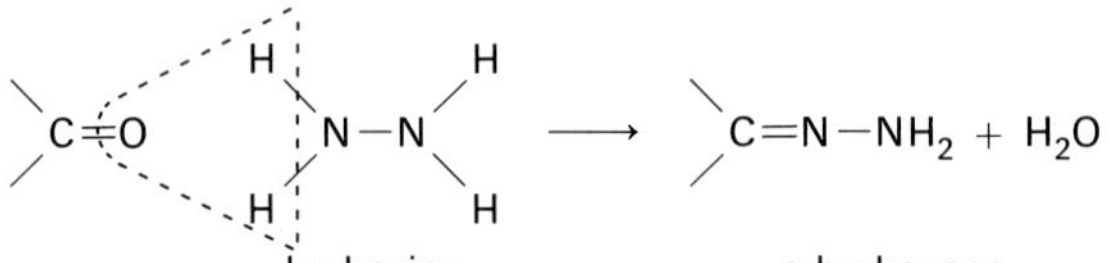

$$\text{\Large$>$}\!C{=}O \quad \begin{array}{c}H \quad H\\ N{-}N\\ H \quad H\end{array} \longrightarrow \text{\Large$>$}\!C{=}N{-}NH_2 + H_2O$$

hydrazine   a hydrazone

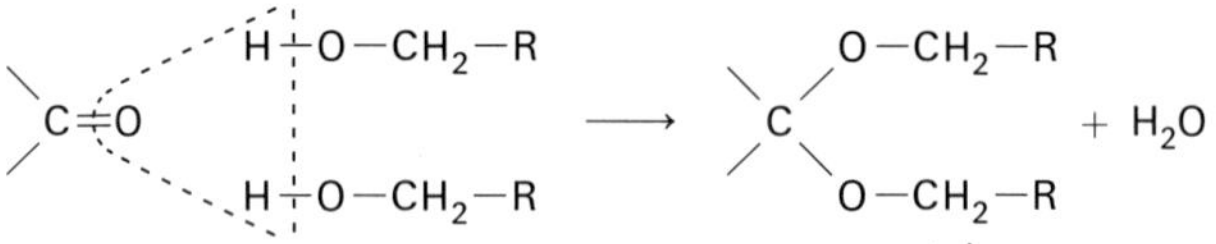

$$\text{\Large$>$}\!C{=}O \quad \begin{array}{c}H{+}O{-}CH_2{-}R\\ H{+}O{-}CH_2{-}R\end{array} \longrightarrow \text{\Large$>$}\!C\!\!\begin{array}{c}O{-}CH_2{-}R\\ O{-}CH_2{-}R\end{array} + H_2O$$

an acetal

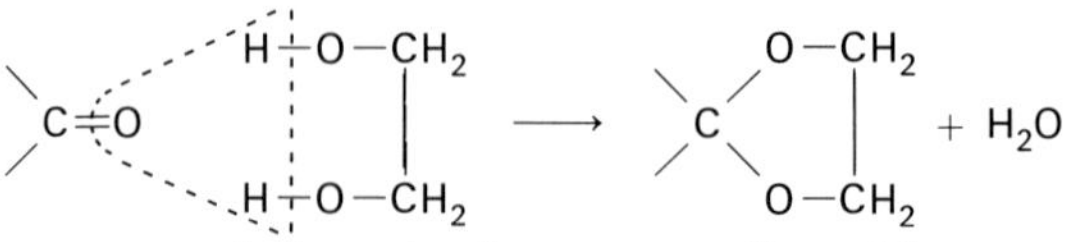

$$\text{\Large$>$}\!C{=}O \quad \begin{array}{c}H{+}O{-}CH_2\\ H{+}O{-}CH_2\end{array} \longrightarrow \text{\Large$>$}\!C\!\!\begin{array}{c}O{-}CH_2\\ O{-}CH_2\end{array} + H_2O$$

ethylene glycol   a cyclic acetal
or other   or a
vicinal diols   dioxolane

An important group of cyclic hemiacetals is the great majority of the naturally occurring monosaccharides (see also Section 2.3.1). In fact most monosaccharides contain, in addition to the alcoholic hydroxyls, either an aldehyde group (*aldoses*), or a keto group in the 2 position in the carbon chain (*ketoses*). Thus, following the Baeyer strain theory (Section 2.1.4), in pentoses and hexoses cyclic hemiacetal formation is favored, for example:

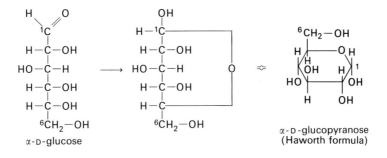

α-D-glucose

α-D-glucopyranose
(Haworth formula)

Two or more monosaccharide molecules may combine, by elimination of the elements of water, through two acetal hydroxyls, or through acetal and alcoholic hydroxyl pairs to form *disaccharides*, *trisaccharides*, or *polysaccharides*. For example, cellulose is the linear and starch the branched polysaccharide of glucose. Such an inter-saccharide linkage, which actually bears a formal resemblance to an ether linkage (Section 2.3.4), is called a *glycoside linkage*. There is a group of natural compounds called in general terms *glycosides*, in which glucose or another monosaccharide is linked by a glycoside linkage to a great variety of non-sugar compounds. Many of the glycosides have pharmacological importance, for example, the digitalis-type cardiac glycosides. The non-sugar moiety of a glycoside is called its *aglycon*.

2.3.2.2   Polycarbonyl Compounds. Keto-Enol Tautomerism

More than one aldehyde or keto group may be present in a molecule. Such compounds are termed di-, tri-, or polycarbonyl compounds. The simplest dialdehyde is glyoxal which consists of two aldehyde groups joined directly together. The simplest diketone is diacetyl ($CH_3-\overset{\displaystyle O}{\underset{\displaystyle \|}{C}}-$ denotes an acetyl group) or 2,3-butanedione. The relative position of the two keto groups may also be denoted by the Greek letters α, β, γ. δ.

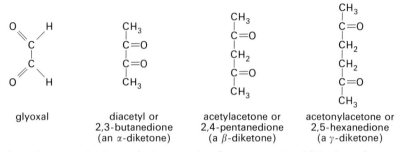

| glyoxal | diacetyl or 2,3-butanedione (an α-diketone) | acetylacetone or 2,4-pentanedione (a β-diketone) | acetonylacetone or 2,5-hexanedione (a γ-diketone) |

Acetylacetone is the typical example of compounds which show *keto-enol tautomerism. Tautomerism* is the phenomenon whereby an organic compound shows reactivity properties corresponding to two different structural formulas. Acetylacetone can react according to the following structural formulas in equilibrium:

$$CH_3-\overset{\overset{O}{\|}}{C}-CH_2-\overset{\overset{O}{\|}}{C}-CH_3 \rightleftharpoons CH_3-\overset{\overset{OH}{|}}{C}=CH-\overset{\overset{O}{\|}}{C}-CH_3$$

"keto" form   "enol" form

Acetylacetone actually shows the properties of both a diketone and an unsaturated alcohol (in "enol," *en* stands for double bond and *ol* for alcohol): it forms oximes and hydrazones (like a diketone), but it also readily takes up bromine (like an unsaturated compound) and reacts with metallic sodium by liberating hydrogen gas (like an alcohol). Compounds containing the $-CH_2-\overset{\overset{\|}{C}}{\underset{O}{}}-$ group generally show keto-enol tautomerism. The phenom-

enon has great synthetic significance because the alkali enolates condense with alkyl halides in the following way:

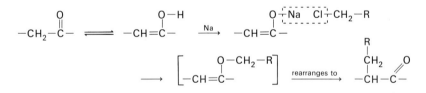

The procedure may be repeated to substitute the second hydrogen on the carbon.

2.3.3 ORGANIC ACIDS. ACYL CHLORIDES, ANHYDRIDES, AMIDES, AND NITRILES. PERACIDS

Organic acids are the terminal stage in the oxidation of the corresponding primary alcohols. Thus, oxidation of both aldehydes and alcohols yields organic acids. Ketones may not be oxidized further without disruption of the carbon skeleton.

Treatment of acetaldehyde or ethanol by a strong oxidant yields acetic acid:

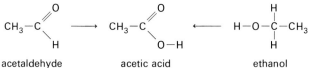

| acetaldehyde | acetic acid | ethanol |

The *carboxyl group*

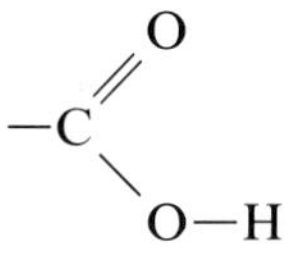

may also be represented as —COOH.

Similarly, oxidation of methanol or formaldehyde gives formic acid, oxidation of n-propanol or propionaldehyde gives propionic acid, etc. The higher straight-chain acids (*fatty acids*) are commonly termed butyric (C_4), valeric (C_5), caproic (C_6), oenanthic (C_7), caprylic (C_8), pelargonic (C_9), capric (C_{10}) acid, etc. In the systematic nomenclature the names of the acids are formed from the respective hydrocarbon terms with the suffix -*oic*. Thus we have methanoic, ethanoic, propanoic, butanoic acid, etc. The alkali salts (generally Na or K) of long-chain fatty acids are the *soaps*.

When two or more carboxyl groups are present in the molecule, we have dibasic (dicarboxylic), tribasic (tricarboxylic), or polybasic acids. The simplest dicarboxylic acid, oxalic acid (or ethanedioic acid), is obtained by joining two carboxyl groups. Higher n-chain dibasic acids result from inserting one or more —CH_2— groups between the two carboxyls, such as:

HOOC—CH_2—COOH	malonic or propanedioic acid
HOOC—CH_2—CH_2—COOH	succinic or butanedioic acid
HOOC—$(CH_2)_3$—COOH	glutaric or pentanedioic acid

Direct halogenation of the fatty acids always substitutes on the carbon skeleton in the position adjacent (or α) to the carboxyl group, for example:

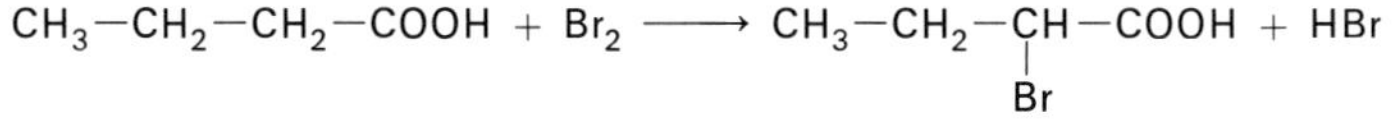

$$CH_3-CH_2-CH_2-COOH + Br_2 \longrightarrow CH_3-CH_2-\underset{\underset{Br}{|}}{CH}-COOH + HBr$$

α-bromobutyric acid

Halogenation in the α-position increases the acidity of the fatty acids. Halogenated acids, such as monochloro-, dichloro-, and trichloroacetic acid, are stronger acids than acetic acid. An α-bromo or iodo group may in turn be readily replaced by an amino group (—NH_2). α-Amino derivatives of several mono- and dibasic acids are building blocks of a biologically important group of substances, the proteins. The biologically important amino acids are listed in Section 8.1.*

The hydroxyl in the carboxyl group may be replaced by a halogen atom from phosphorus halides or thionylchloride, yielding *acyl halides*:

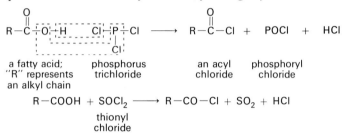

| a fatty acid; "R" represents an alkyl chain | phosphorus trichloride | an acyl chloride | phosphoryl chloride |

$$R-COOH + SOCl_2 \longrightarrow R-CO-Cl + SO_2 + HCl$$

thionyl chloride

An *acyl group* is the moiety of an organic acid without the carboxylic hydroxyl. Thus, acetyl chloride, propionyl bromide, butyryl chloride, etc., are acyl halides. The acyl halides are powerful intermediates to introduce acyl groups into various molecules (*e.g.*, amines, alcohols, phenols).

Hypothetically, *organic anhydrides* may be regarded as resulting from the elimination of the elements of one molecule of water from two carboxyl groups of organic acids:

$$R-C \diagup^O_{\diagdown O-H} \quad H-O \diagdown_{\diagup} C-R \longrightarrow R-\overset{O}{\overset{\|}{C}}-O-\overset{O}{\overset{\|}{C}}-R + H_2O$$

In practice anhydrides are synthesized by reaction of the acyl halide with an alkali salt of the acid:

$$R-CO-Cl \quad Na-OOC-R \longrightarrow R-CO-O-CO-R + NaCl$$

This procedure permits the synthesis of mixed anhydrides, joining different acyl groups.

Acyl halides and anhydrides are easily hydrolyzed, which regenerates the free acid:

$$R-CO-Cl + H_2O \longrightarrow R-COOH + HCl$$
$$R-CO-O-CO-R + H_2O \longrightarrow 2 R-COOH$$

The ease of hydrolysis decreases with the lengthening of the "R" chain.

Acyl chlorides react with alcohols and mercaptans (thioalcohols, where sulfur replaces oxygen in the hydroxyl group) to form esters and thioesters:

$$R-CO-Cl \quad H-O-R' \longrightarrow R-COO-R' + HCl$$
$$R-CO-Cl \quad H-S-R' \longrightarrow R-COS-R' + HCl$$

* Sections 5, 6, and 7 appear in Volume II; Sections 8 and 9 and the Appendixes appear in Volume III.

Amides and *nitriles* are successive stages in the dehydration of ammonium salts of organic acids. For example, stepwise dehydration of ammonium acetate yields first acetamide:

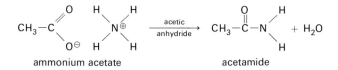

ammonium acetate   acetamide

In ammonium acetate ($CH_3—COO^{\ominus}$ $NH_4^{\oplus}$) the $CH_3—COO$ and NH_4 moieties are linked together by an *ionic bond* represented by $\ominus$ and $\oplus$ charges (Sections 2.3.6.1, 3.1.2.1, 3.1.2.3, and 3.1.2.6).
   Dehydration of acetamide yields acetonitrile:

acetonitrile

Starting with acids other than acetic acid, we may form amides such as formamide, propionamide, butyramide. The

$$-\underset{\underset{O}{\|}}{C}-NH- \qquad \text{or} \qquad -CO-NH-$$

linkage, also known as *amide linkage* or *peptide linkage*, will be encountered again in Section 8.1 dealing with the structure of proteins. Also, amide linkages can manifest keto-enol type tautomerism, called *lactam-lactim tautomerism*:

$$-NH-\underset{\underset{O}{\|}}{C}- \; \rightleftharpoons \; -N=\underset{\underset{OH}{|}}{C}-$$

Organic acids form derivatives analogous to amides with hydrazine ($NH_2—NH_2$) and are termed *hydrazides.*
   The nitrile of formic acid, formylnitrile, is the same as hydrocyanic acid ($H—C{\equiv}N$). The C_3 term is propionitrile, then butyronitrile, valeronitrile, etc. The synthetic importance of nitriles is due to the fact that they may be hydrolyzed to the ammonium salt, from which the free acid may be liberated. Since nitriles may also be regarded as alkyl cyanides, it may be readily seen that the introduction of the $—C{\equiv}N$ group on different carbon skeletons allows the synthesis of complex organic acids otherwise difficultly accessible.

For example:

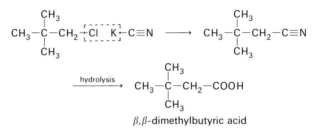

$$CH_3-\overset{\overset{\displaystyle CH_3}{|}}{\underset{\underset{\displaystyle CH_3}{|}}{C}}-CH_2\overline{\dashv Cl \quad K\dashv}C\equiv N \longrightarrow CH_3-\overset{\overset{\displaystyle CH_3}{|}}{\underset{\underset{\displaystyle CH_3}{|}}{C}}-CH_2-C\equiv N$$

$$\xrightarrow{\text{hydrolysis}} CH_3-\overset{\overset{\displaystyle CH_3}{|}}{\underset{\underset{\displaystyle CH_3}{|}}{C}}-CH_2-COOH$$

β,β-dimethylbutyric acid

Organic acids may be oxidized with hydrogen peroxide to *peracids*, which are currently used in many oxidative syntheses requiring agents milder than H_2O_2. The peracids, which may be regarded as monoacylated hydrogen peroxides, have the general formula:

$$R-C\overset{\displaystyle O}{\underset{\displaystyle O-O-H}{\diagdown}}$$

The aldehyde, keto, and carboxyl groups may coexist in the same molecule with other functional groups: hydroxyl, sulfonic, or amino groups, double or triple bonds, etc. Thus, we may have hydroxy acids, keto acids, amino acids, different types of unsaturated acids, etc. Maleic and fumaric acids (discussed with respect to geometric isomerism in Section 2.2.2) are examples of possible coexistence of carboxyl groups and other functional groups in the same molecule. Such compounds, containing a combination of different types of functional groups, show chemical properties reflecting all the functional groups present. This illustrates the practically infinite variety of organic compounds which may be built up.

2.3.4 ETHERS, EPOXIDES, AND ENDO OXIDES

An ether is formed by the condensation of two molecules of alcohol with elimination of water. For example:

$$CH_3-CH_2-O\overline{\dashv H \quad H-O\dashv}CH_2-CH_3 \xrightarrow[\text{or Al}_2O_3]{H_2SO_4} CH_3-CH_2-O-CH_2-CH_3 + H_2O$$

diethyl ether or "ether"

The orientation of this reaction depends on the conditions of the reaction (temperature, concentration of sulfuric acid, presence or absence of super-heated steam when using Al_2O_3 as dehydrating catalyst). It was shown in Section 2.3.1.1 that, depending on the conditions, ethanol may yield ethylene by losing one molecule of water per molecule of ethanol, or diethyl ether by losing one molecule of water per two molecules of ethanol.

Another method of preparation of diethyl ether, due to Williamson, is the condensation of sodium ethoxide (sodium alcoholate) with ethyl iodide:

$$CH_3-CH_2-O \dashv Na \quad I \vdash CH_2-CH_3 \longrightarrow CH_3-CH_2-O-CH_2-CH_3 + NaI$$

The Williamson synthesis, which is also proof of structure of the ethers, may be used for the preparation of different sorts of symmetric (with respect to the $-O-$ linkage or *ether linkage*) or asymmetric (mixed) ethers.

The nomenclature of ethers is based on designating the two molecular groupings on the two sides of the ether linkage, followed by "ether." Thus, we say, for example, dimethyl ether, diethyl ether, methylethyl ether, dipropyl ether, isopropyl-*n*-butyl ether, *tert*-butyl methyl ether, etc.

The ether linkage in the lower molecular weight ethers is not split by hydrochloric acid. An appreciable amount of dry HCl gas may be dissolved in ethers because of the formation of *oxonium salts* (see Section 2.3.6.1). However, hydroiodic acid (and hydrobromic acid somewhat less readily) splits the ether linkage with the formation of an alcohol and an alkyl halide. For example:

$$(C_2H_5)_2O + HI \longrightarrow C_2H_5-OH + C_2H_5-I$$

The intramolecular ethers of vicinal diols are called *epoxides*. The simplest epoxide is ethylene oxide formed by treating ethylene chlorohydrin with calcium hydroxide:

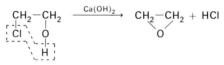

More than one epoxide group may be present in a molecule and the epoxide group may be present together with other functional groups. For example:

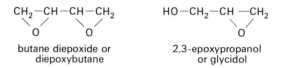

butane diepoxide or   2,3-epoxypropanol
diepoxybutane   or glycidol

The ether linkage may also be present in a molecule as an intramolecular cross-link, if the strain on the valence angles of the carbon atoms of the molecular skeleton is not too great. Such ether linkages may occur within alicyclic rings. Compounds bearing such an ether linkage are called *endo oxides*. A simple endo oxide is cyclohexane-1,4-endo oxide; a well-known natural substance of this type is *cantharidin* (isolated from Spanish flies):

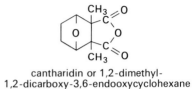

cyclohexane-1,4-endo oxide
or 1,4-endooxycyclohexane

cantharidin or 1,2-dimethyl-
1,2-dicarboxy-3,6-endooxycyclohexane

In such endo oxides the cyclohexane skeleton is in the "boat" conformation (Section 2.1.4) to accommodate the ether linkage between the 1 and 4 carbon atoms.

An interesting internal diether of ethylene glycol is diethylene oxide or dioxane:

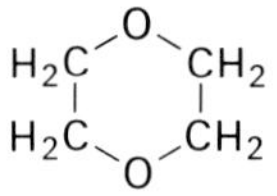

The "open" ethers and also dioxane, where no strain is imposed on the valence angles of the carbon and oxygen atoms, are quite stable compounds. The ether linkage in these may not be cleaved by hydrolysis, but, as we have seen, may be split by hydroiodic acid.

Following the Baeyer strain theory (Section 2.1.4), because of strain on the valence angles and on the bond lengths, endo oxides and especially the epoxides are much more unstable and reactive than "open" ethers or dioxane. Thus, just as cyclopropane is changed to propylene, heat causes intra-molecular rearrangement of ethylene oxide to acetaldehyde:

$$CH_2\!-\!CH_2 \longrightarrow CH_3\!-\!CHO$$
$$\diagdown\!O\!\diagup$$

Because of their reactivity, epoxides are valuable synthetic intermediates. Unlike diethyl ether, ethylene oxide reacts with hydrochloric acid to form ethylene chlorohydrin. Epoxides form addition compounds with a great variety of organic compounds having reactive hydrogen atoms. For example, ethylene oxide can yield the following:

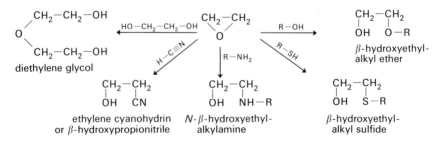

diethylene glycol

ethylene cyanohydrin
or β-hydroxypropionitrile

N-β-hydroxyethyl-
alkylamine

β-hydroxyethyl-
alkyl sulfide

β-hydroxyethyl-
alkyl ether

Ethers form explosive peroxides with hydrogen peroxide or on prolonged standing in air. Ether peroxides may be regarded as dialkylated hydrogen peroxides.

2.3.5   ESTERS AND LACTONES

Esters are the products of condensation of organic or inorganic acids with alcohols. A well-known ester, used as a common solvent, is ethyl acetate:

$$CH_3-CH_2-O+H \quad H-O-\overset{O}{\underset{}{\diagdown}}C-CH_3 \rightleftharpoons CH_3-CH_2-O-\overset{}{\underset{\overset{\|}{O}}{C}}-CH_3 + H_2O$$

the ethyl ester of acetic
acid or ethyl acetate

The $-O-\overset{}{\underset{\overset{\|}{O}}{C}}-$ (or $-OOC-$) group in esters is called an *ester linkage.*

The formation of esters by this reaction is a typical equilibrium reaction, as indicated by the $\rightleftharpoons$ symbol. Equilibrium reactions follow the chemical kinetic *law of mass action* (see Suppletory Note* for Section 2.3).

Esters are also formed by the reaction of acyl chlorides and alcohols. This reaction (in contrast to the reaction with free acids) is not reversible. The general reaction may be represented as:

$$R-O+H \quad Cl+\overset{}{\underset{\overset{\|}{O}}{C}}-R' \longrightarrow R-O-\overset{}{\underset{\overset{\|}{O}}{C}}-R' + HCl$$

The common names of esters are derived by combining the term for the alcoholic alkyl group moiety with the root of the acyl term followed by the suffix *-ate*, for example, methyl formate, methyl butyrate, butyl butyrate, ethyl valerate. The systematic nomenclature is derived in a similar manner: methyl methanoate, methyl butanoate, ethyl pentanoate, etc. Similarly the esters of inorganic acids are designated: methyl sulfate, dimethyl sulfate, ethyl sulfate, ethyl phosphate, tributyl phosphate, etc. The lower dialkyl sulfates are often used as energetic alkylating agents:

$$2\,R-COO-Na + (CH_3)_2SO_4 \longrightarrow 2\,R-COO-CH_3 + Na_2SO_4$$

An important group of naturally occurring esters are the *fats*, which are triesters (sometimes called triglycerides) of glycerol with long straight-chain monobasic acids (hence the term fatty acids used for the entire series). Esters of higher alcohols and higher acids (approximately $C_{15}-C_{30}$) are the *waxes*.

* Suppletory Note on page 63.

A biologically important group of organic-inorganic mixed triglycerides is the *phosphatides* or *phospholipids* which play a role in the permeability properties of membraneous structures in living organisms. The two well-known groups of phospholipids are the *lecithins* and *cephalins*, which may be represented by the general formulas:

$$CH_2-OOC-R$$
$$CH-OOC-R'$$
$$CH_2-O-\overset{\nearrow O}{\underset{OH}{P}}-O-choline$$

lecithins

$$CH_2-OOC-R$$
$$CH-OOC-R'$$
$$CH_2-O-\overset{\nearrow O}{\underset{OH}{P}}-O-colamine$$

cephalins

The structural formula of choline is given in Section 2.3.6.1. Colamine is β-aminoethanol $(NH_2-CH_2-CH_2-OH)$, and R and R' represent the alkyl moieties of fatty acids which may be identical or different. The phosphatides represented here are the α-isomers. The β-isomers are also known, in which the choline- or colaminephosphoric acid group esterifies the secondary hydroxyl. The fats and phosphatides together constitute the class of the *lipids*. Fats are soluble in oils and in many organic solvents, and are insoluble in water (*i.e.* are *hydrophobic*). Many phosphatides are not, strictly speaking, soluble in water in the sense of producing in it a complete molecular dispersion; they can nevertheless absorb a large amount of water (*i.e.*, are *hydrophilic*) while maintaining ordered molecular arrays (*micelles*; see Sections 3.3.2.1 and 3.3.2.2).

Unlike ethers, esters may undergo hydrolysis in the presence of bases or acids which splits the ester linkage and regenerates the alcohol and acid:

$$C_2H_5-O \cdots \overset{\overset{O}{\diagdown}}{\underset{H}{\overset{}{C}}} \cdots \overset{}{\underset{OH}{}} C-CH_3 \xrightarrow{NaOH} C_2H_5-OH + CH_3-COONa$$

A reaction similar to the hydrolysis of esters is *alcoholysis*. The ester of one alcohol (of alkyl residue $R-CH_2-$) can be transformed into that of another alcohol (of alkyl residue $R'-CH_2-$), by prolonged reaction of the original ester with the R'-alcohol, in the presence of a trace of acid or alcoholate of R' as catalyst:

$$R-CH_2-OOC-alkyl + R'-CH_2-OH$$

$$\xrightarrow{R'-CH_2-ONa} R'-CH_2-OOC-alkyl + R-CH_2-OH$$

In general it is easier to replace a higher alcohol by a lower one.

The reactivity of esters is further increased if the ester linkage is part of a strained ring. In this respect there is similarity between esters and ethers.

Intramolecular esters of hydroxyacids are termed *lactones*. The ring of the simplest lactone, β-propiolactone, may be more readily opened by reaction with methanol or ethanol than the alcohol moiety of straight-chain *n*-propionic esters may be exchanged:

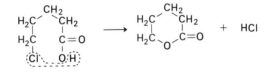

Expectedly, the behavior of lactones follows the Baeyer strain theory. The reactivity of the lactonic ester bond decreases and the stability of the lactone increases when the lactone ring is an unstrained 6-membered ring (see Section 2.1.4). This is shown by the fact that δ-halogen *n*-valeric acid is readily cyclized to valerolactone upon heating:

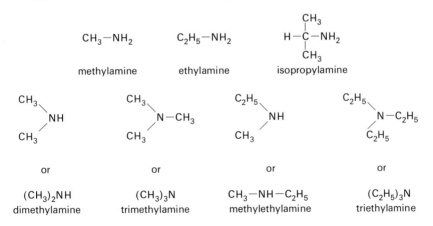

2.3.6 AMINES

Amines are obtained by replacing the hydrogen atoms in ammonia with organic groupings. Simple amines are obtained by substituting one or more hydrogen atoms of ammonia with an alkyl group. These are named by adding the suffix -*amine* to the names of the alkyl groups. For example:

$$CH_3-NH_2 \qquad C_2H_5-NH_2 \qquad H-\overset{\displaystyle CH_3}{\underset{\displaystyle CH_3}{C}}-NH_2$$

methylamine   ethylamine   isopropylamine

CH_3	CH_3	C_2H_5	C_2H_5
NH	N—CH$_3$	NH	N—C$_2$H$_5$
CH$_3$	CH$_3$	CH$_3$	C$_2$H$_5$
or	or	or	or
$(CH_3)_2NH$	$(CH_3)_3N$	$CH_3-NH-C_2H_5$	$(C_2H_5)_3N$
dimethylamine	trimethylamine	methylethylamine	triethylamine

The above are, however, only representative examples since ammonia may be substituted with a practically limitless variety of organic groupings.

Depending on whether one, two, or all three hydrogens are substituted, the amines may be *primary*, *secondary*, or *tertiary* amines. Furthermore, the only two or all three substituents may be identical groups, or they may be entirely different (mixed amines).

The atomic assemblage

$$-N\begin{matrix} H \\ \diagup \\ \diagdown \\ H \end{matrix} \qquad \text{or} \qquad -NH_2$$

is termed an *amino group*. However, when in an $-NR_2$ group the R_2 substituents are small groupings, and the whole $-NR_2$ group is a relatively small part of a larger molecule, it is still convenient to use the term amino, such as dimethylamino or diethylamino group, etc.

When more than one amino group is present, the compounds are termed diamines, triamines, tetramines, etc. Some biologically occurring diamines are:

$$H_2N-(CH_2)_4-NH_2 \qquad\qquad\qquad H_2N-(CH_2)_5-NH_2$$
tetramethylenediamine or   pentamethylenediamine or
putrescine   cadaverine

In nature, putrescine and cadaverine are the products of bacterial decay of animal proteins. Two higher amines have been isolated from sperm:

$$H_2N-(CH_2)_3-NH-(CH_2)_4-NH_2 \qquad H_2N-(CH_2)_3-NH-(CH_2)_4-NH-(CH_2)_3-NH_2$$
spermidine   spermine

The $-NH-$ group, as in the above formulas, is called an *imino group*. An imino group may also replace one or more $-CH_2-$ groups in alicyclic compounds. When these amines are substituted on the nitrogen atom, the name of the substituent will be preceded by $N-$, to distinguish this substitution from substitution on the carbon skeleton. Furthermore, to define the position of a substituent on the carbon skeleton, the atoms are numbered beginning with the nitrogen atom such as:

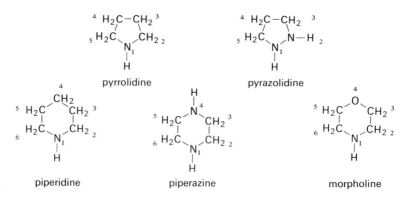

pyrrolidine   pyrazolidine

piperidine   piperazine   morpholine

By alkyl substituting the imino groups, we may have structures of the type:

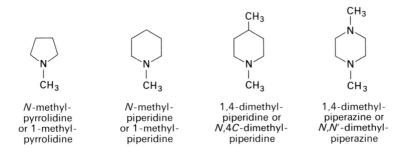

| N-methyl-
pyrrolidine
or 1-methyl-
pyrrolidine | N-methyl-
piperidine
or 1-methyl-
piperidine | 1,4-dimethyl-
piperidine or
N,4C-dimethyl-
piperidine | 1,4-dimethyl-
piperazine or
N,N'-dimethyl-
piperazine |

In the amines the basic properties of ammonia are maintained and often enhanced. The methylamines and ethylamines are stronger bases in solution than ammonia. The amines react with acids in the same way that NH_3 does, forming salts such as NH_4Cl, RNH_3Cl, R_2NH_2Cl, R_3NHCl. Ammonia and the amines add certain alkyl halides to give derivatives having one more alkyl group than the starting compounds. The last stage in the alkylation of ammonia is called a *quaternary ammonium* compound.

2.3.6.1 The Nature of Quaternary Ammonium Compounds. Amine Oxides. Oxonium Salts

The salification of an amine may be represented as follows:

$$\begin{matrix} CH_3\!\!\searrow \\ CH_3\!-\!N \\ CH_3\!\!\nearrow \end{matrix} + HCl \longrightarrow \left[\begin{matrix} CH_3\!\!\searrow \\ CH_3\!-\!N \to H \\ CH_3\!\!\nearrow \end{matrix} \right]^{\oplus} Cl^{\ominus}$$

In ammonium compounds the halogen is linked to nitrogen by an ionic bond (see Sections 3.1.2.1, 3.1.2.3 and 3.1.2.6). The fourth substituent (hydrogen in this case) is linked to nitrogen by a *dative bond* or *coordinate bond* (see Section 3.1.2.7). This type of bond is designated by the symbol "→" to distinguish it from the *covalent bond* represented by the dash or dot.

Also in alkyl halide addition compounds of amines, such as:

$$\begin{matrix} CH_3\!\!\searrow \\ CH_3\!-\!N \\ CH_3\!\!\nearrow \end{matrix} + CH_3\!-\!I \xrightarrow{\text{in ethanol}} \left[\begin{matrix} CH_3\!\!\searrow \\ CH_3\!-\!N \to CH_3 \\ CH_3\!\!\nearrow \end{matrix} \right]^{\oplus} I^{\ominus}$$

the fourth alkyl is attached to nitrogen by a coordinate bond and iodine is attached by an ionic bond.

The ammonium salts of different alkylamines may be hydrolyzed to the corresponding mono-, di-, tri-, or tetraalkylammonium hydroxides. Just as the halogen atom in the alkylammonium halides, the hydroxyl group in the corresponding hydroxides is linked to the nitrogen by an ionic bond. The quaternary ammonium hydroxides are strong bases. A biologically important quaternary ammonium hydroxide is choline, trimethyl-β-hydroxyethyl-ammonium hydroxide:

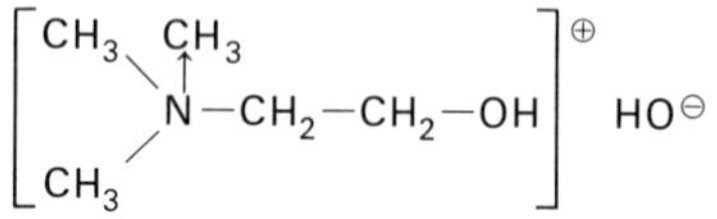

$$\left[\begin{array}{c} CH_3 \quad CH_3 \\ N-CH_2-CH_2-OH \\ CH_3 \end{array}\right]^{\oplus} \quad HO^{\ominus}$$

choline

Nitrogen does not have five valences in the same sense that carbon is quadrivalent. The tetra-substituted ammonium ion is tetrahedral (like the carbon atom) and the halogen or hydroxyl is linked to it only by electrostatic attraction which is the ionic bond. The tetrahedral nature of the tetra-substituted ammonium ion was shown by the resolution of asymmetrically substituted ammonium compounds into optically active enantiomeric forms.

Oxidation of tertiary amines leads to *amine oxides*, in which the oxygen atom is linked to the nitrogen by a coordinate bond. Several amine oxides form stable hydrates:

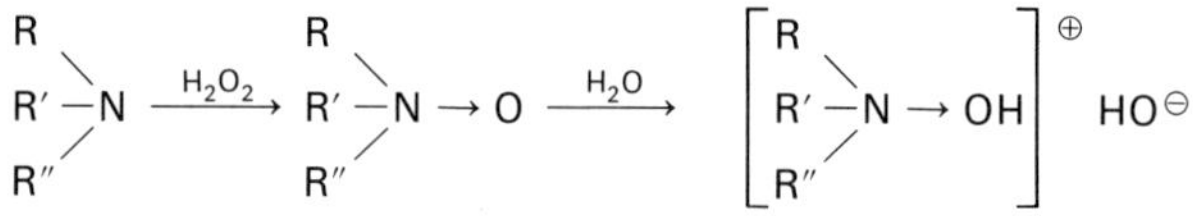

$$\begin{array}{c} R \\ R'-N \\ R'' \end{array} \xrightarrow{H_2O_2} \begin{array}{c} R \\ R'-N \rightarrow O \\ R'' \end{array} \xrightarrow{H_2O} \left[\begin{array}{c} R \\ R'-N \rightarrow OH \\ R'' \end{array}\right]^{\oplus} \quad HO^{\ominus}$$

Such hydrates have been separated into enantiomers which indicates that the positions of the two hydroxyls are not equivalent. The amine oxides may be easily reduced to yield the initial tertiary amines.

Oxygen and sulfur can also establish coordinate bonds. Both elements are bivalent and consequently any additional linkage involves coordinate and ionic bonds. The *oxonium salts* of ethers (Section 2.3.4) have accordingly the following general structure, where "X" stands for the moiety of XH acid:

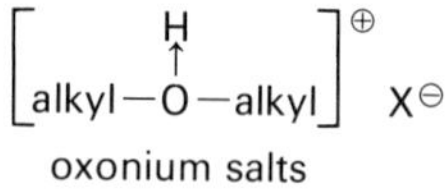

$$\left[\begin{array}{c} H \\ \uparrow \\ alkyl-O-alkyl \end{array}\right]^{\oplus} \quad X^{\ominus}$$

oxonium salts

2.3.6.2 Some Methods of Preparation of Primary Amines

Primary amines may be obtained from amides of organic acids. Hydrogen liberated from sodium metal plus absolute ethanol in the very reaction mixture reduces an amide to an amine having the same number of carbon atoms as the starting acylamide:

$$4\ C_2H_5-OH + 4\ Na \longrightarrow 4\ C_2H_5-ONa + 2\ H_2$$
$$R-CO-NH_2 + 2\ H_2 \longrightarrow R-CH_2-NH_2 + H_2O$$

Another method, known as *Hofmann's degradation*, yields amines having a carbon skeleton one carbon shorter. A summary equation of this complex reaction is:

$$R-\underset{\underset{O}{\|}}{C}-NH_2 \xrightarrow[\text{or HOBr}]{\text{HOCl}} R-NH_2 + CO_2 + HCl \text{ (or HBr)}$$

Similarly as acylamides, nitriles may be reduced to primary amines:

$$R-C{\equiv}N + 2\,H_2 \longrightarrow R-CH_2-NH_2$$

Primary amines may also be prepared by condensation of alkyl halides with sodium amide (see Section 2.1.2) or with potassium phthalimide (*Gabriel's phthalimide synthesis*):

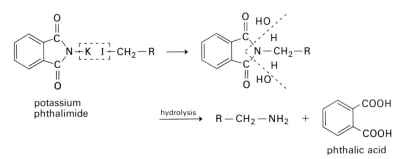

N-K I-CH2-R
HO
H
N-CH2-R
H
HO
potassium
phthalimide
hydrolysis
R-CH2-NH2 +
COOH
COOH
phthalic acid

The conversion of other nitrogen-containing functional groups to primary amino groups is discussed in Section 2.3.7.1.

2.3.6.3 *Some Reactions of the Amines*

The primary and secondary amines may be alkylated as illustrated in the following where "X" stands for —Cl, —Br, or —I:

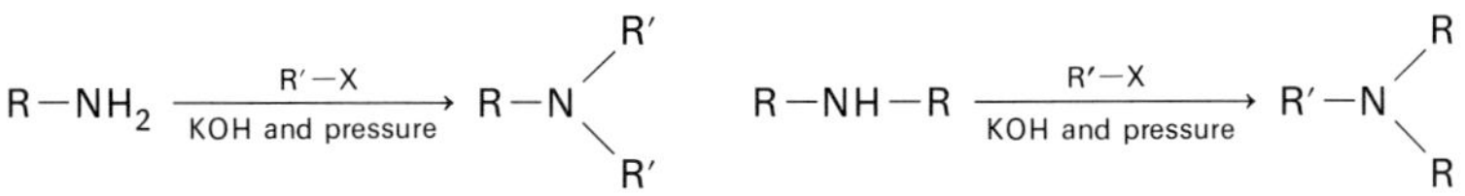

R-NH2
R'-X
KOH and pressure
R-N
R'
R'
R-NH-R
R'-X
KOH and pressure
R'-N
R
R

or acylated (using acyl chlorides or anhydrides):

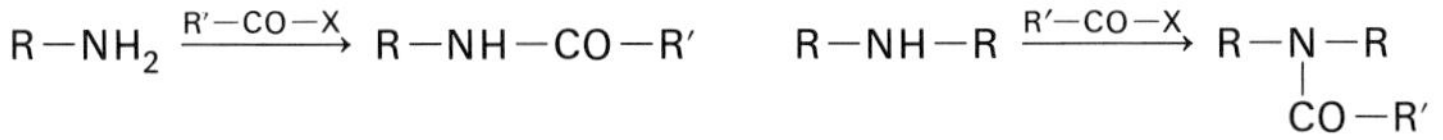

R-NH2
R'-CO-X
R-NH-CO-R'
R-NH-R
R'-CO-X
R-N-R
CO-R'

which results in *N*-monoalkyl or *N,N*-dialkyl derivatives of acylamides (Section 2.3.3).

The vicinity of two carbonyl groups confer acidic properties to the imino group; the hydrogen of the latter group may be replaced by alkali metals, which renders such imines valuable for organic synthesis. One diacylimide, phthalimide, showing this property has been cited in the previous section in connection with the preparation of primary amines (Gabriel's synthesis). Also in the 5-membered ring compound, succinimide, and in the 6-membered glutarimide, the nitrogen-linked hydrogen may be replaced by an alkali metal.

The primary amino group can undergo several interesting reactions. On reacting with nitrous acid it is replaced by an alcoholic hydroxyl:

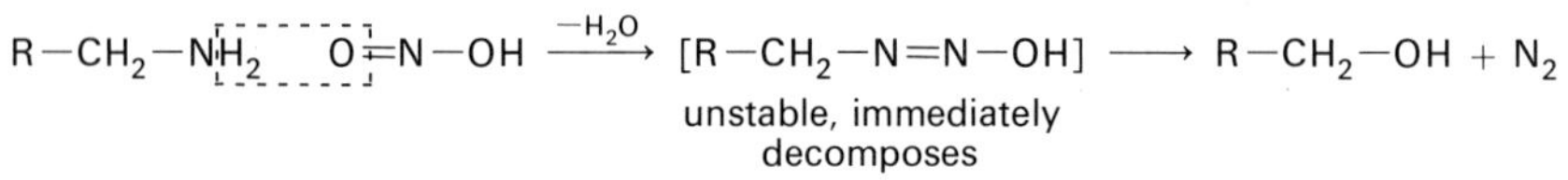

$$R-CH_2-NH_2 \quad O=N-OH \xrightarrow{-H_2O} [R-CH_2-N=N-OH] \longrightarrow R-CH_2-OH + N_2$$

unstable, immediately
decomposes

Condensation of primary amines with aldehydes gives *Schiff bases*:

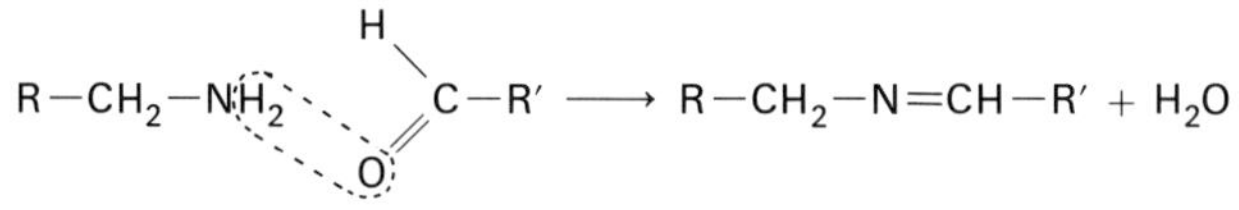

$$R-CH_2-NH_2 \cdots \underset{O}{\overset{H}{\underset{\big|}{C}}}-R' \longrightarrow R-CH_2-N=CH-R' + H_2O$$

which are very sensitive to acid and may be readily reconverted to the amine and the aldehyde on acid hydrolysis. The $-N=CH-$ double bond in Schiff bases can be hydrogenated to give the expected secondary amine.

With chloroform and a strong base, primary amines give *carbylamines* (or *isonitriles*) of characteristically disagreeable odor:

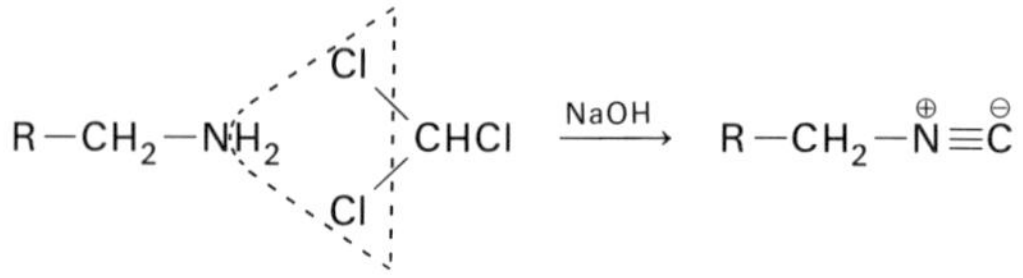

$$R-CH_2-NH_2 \quad \overset{Cl}{\underset{Cl}{\big\backslash}} CHCl \xrightarrow{NaOH} R-CH_2-\overset{\oplus}{N}\equiv\overset{\ominus}{C}$$

The secondary amines react with nitrous acid by forming *N-nitrosamines* or *nitrosamines*:

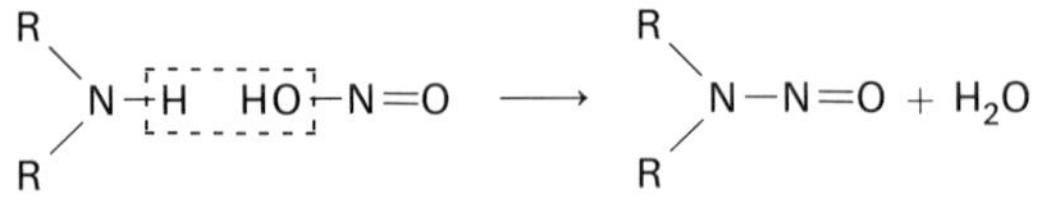

$$\underset{R}{\overset{R}{\big\backslash}}N-H \quad HO-N=O \longrightarrow \underset{R}{\overset{R}{\big\backslash}}N-N=O + H_2O$$

Both secondary and primary amines may be oxidized by monopersulfuric acid (H_2SO_5) and certain other mild oxidizing agents to the corresponding *N-hydroxyamines* or *hydroxylamines*:

$$R-NH-OH \quad \text{and} \quad \underset{R}{\overset{R}{\big\backslash}}N-OH$$

On heating, quaternary alkyl ammonium halides dissociate to the tertiary amine and alkyl halide, and hydroxides dissociate to the tertiary amine and alcohol. Thus, thermal dissociation may be used to regenerate the tertiary amine from a quaternary halide or hydroxide (an important reaction based on this property is *exhaustive methylation*). For example, heating of tetra-methylammonium hydroxide regenerates trimethylamine and methanol:

$$(CH_3)_4N^{\oplus} \; ^{\ominus}OH \longrightarrow (CH_3)_3N + CH_3-OH$$

However, if one of the alkyl groups is an ethyl or a higher group, the reaction takes a different orientation (here R = H for ethyl and R = alkyl for a higher alkyl):

$$R-CH_2-CH_2-\overset{\overset{\displaystyle CH_3}{|}}{\underset{\underset{\displaystyle CH_3}{|}}{N^{\oplus}}} \quad ^{\ominus}OH \longrightarrow R-CH=CH_2 + (CH_3)_3N + H_2O$$

2.3.7   OTHER NITROGEN- AND SULFUR-CONTAINING GROUPS

2.3.7.1   *Nitrogen-Containing Groups*

Nitro compounds ($-NO_2$ for *nitro* group) may be prepared by direct nitration of hydrocarbons with nitric acid in the presence of sulfuric acid as a dehydrating agent:

$$R\!-\!\!\overset{\ulcorner\;\;\;\;\;\;\;\;\;\;\urcorner}{H} \quad \overset{\ulcorner}{HO}\!-\!\overset{\overset{\displaystyle O}{\uparrow}}{N}\!\!=\!\!O \xrightarrow{\;H_2SO_4\;} R-NO_2 + H_2O$$

The ease of replacement of a hydrogen by a nitro group increases from primary, to secondary, to tertiary carbon.

Nitroalkanes have also been prepared by the reaction of alkyl halides with silver nitrite.

$$CH_3\!-\!\!\overset{\ulcorner\;\;\;\;\;\;\;\urcorner}{I} \quad \overset{\ulcorner}{Ag}\!-\!O\!-\!N\!\!=\!\!O \longrightarrow CH_3\!-\!\overset{\overset{\displaystyle O}{\uparrow}}{N}\!\!=\!\!O + AgI$$

With ethyl iodide, however, an equal mixture of the nitro compound and the isomeric nitrite (that is, ester of nitrous acid) is formed:

$$CH_3\!-\!CH_2\!-\!\!\overset{\ulcorner\;\;\;\;\;\;\;\urcorner}{I} \quad \overset{\ulcorner}{Ag}\!-\!O\!-\!N\!\!=\!\!O \longrightarrow$$

$$\begin{array}{l} CH_3\!-\!CH_2\!-\!\overset{\overset{\displaystyle O}{\uparrow}}{N}\!\!=\!\!O \\ 50\% \end{array} \quad + AgI$$

$$CH_3\!-\!CH_2\!-\!O\!-\!N\!\!=\!\!O$$
$$50\%$$

As the alkyl chain of the halide is lengthened the proportion of the nitrite product of the reaction increases. Esters of nitrous acid are obtained exclusively by treatment of alcohols with alkali salts of nitrous acid and sulfuric acid:

$$2\ C_2H_5-OH + 2\ KNO_2 + H_2SO_4 \longrightarrow 2\ C_2H_5-O-NO + K_2SO_4 + 2\ H_2O$$
$$\text{ethyl nitrite}$$

Nitroso compounds with a carbon-linked *nitroso* (—N=O) group may be obtained by mild oxidation of primary amines with monopersulfuric acid (H_2SO_5):

$$R-CH_2-NH_2 \xrightarrow{\ H_2SO_5\ } R-CH_2-N=O$$

The nitroso or nitro group when linked to a primary or secondary carbon gives a keto-enol type tautomerism (Section 2.3.2.2):

$$\underset{\displaystyle R-CH-N=O}{\overset{\displaystyle NO_2}{\big|}} \rightleftharpoons \underset{\displaystyle R-C=N-OH}{\overset{\displaystyle NO_2}{\big|}}$$
$$\text{nitrolic acid}$$

$$\overset{\displaystyle O}{\underset{\displaystyle R-CH_2-N=O}{\big\uparrow}} \rightleftharpoons \overset{\displaystyle O}{\underset{\displaystyle R-CH=N-OH}{\big\uparrow}}$$
$$\text{nitronic acid}$$

The acidic "aci" tautomers of nitrolic acids form highly colored salts.

The nitro and nitroso groups may be readily reduced to an amino group. For example, with Zn + HCl:

$$R-NO_2 \xrightarrow{\ Zn\ +\ HCl\ } R-NH_2$$

This reaction is especially important for obtaining aromatic amines (Section 2.4.1.2).

Hydroxamic acids may be prepared by oxidation of N-monoalkylhydroxylamines:

$$R-CH_2-NH-OH \longrightarrow \underset{\displaystyle R-C=N-OH}{\overset{\displaystyle OH}{\big|}}$$

Hydroxamic acids can also be obtained by oxidation of aldoximes (oximes of aldehydes). Mild reduction of the carbon-linked nitroso group at neutral or alkaline pH gives N-monoalkylhydroxylamines or N-hydroxyalkylamines, such as:

$$C_2H_5-NO \xrightarrow[\ H_2O\ ]{\ zinc\ dust\ } C_2H_5-NH-OH$$
$$\text{ethylhydroxylamine}$$

The nitrosamines, containing a nitrogen-linked nitroso group, have been discussed in Section 2.3.6.3.

Azo or *diazo compounds*, characterized by the —N=N— linkage, are rare among the alkanes, alkenes, alkynes, and their various derivatives. The most important, in view of the present subject, are the *diazoalkanes*. The simplest diazoalkane is diazomethane, a yellow gas, which may be prepared by the decomposition of *N*-nitroso-*N*-methylurea (or of *N*-nitroso-*N*-methyl ethyl-carbamate) with alkali:

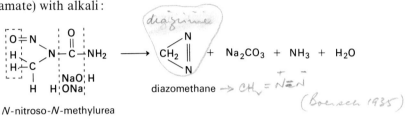

N-nitroso-*N*-methylurea

Diazomethane has the molecular formula CH_2N_2. Higher diazoalkanes, diazoethane, diazopropane, etc., frequently represented by the general formula

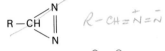

(or according to modern interpretation R—CH=$\overset{\oplus}{N}$=$\overset{\ominus}{N}$), have been prepared in a similar way, as well as by the oxidation of hydrazones of n-chain aldehydes.

Diazoalkanes are energetic alkylating agents. Diazomethane is extensively used (in ether solution) for methylating various organic compounds having reactive hydrogens, such as alcohols, acids, amines, phenols, and mercaptans, following the general reaction:

$$R—H + CH_2N_2 \longrightarrow R—CH_3 + N_2$$

It also reacts with aldehydes and ketones because of the keto-enol tautomerism of these compounds:

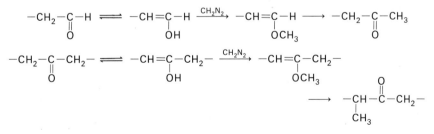

Azoxy derivatives of alkanes, characterized by the

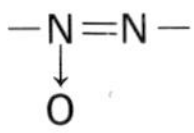

$$-N=N-$$
$$\downarrow$$
$$O$$

linkage, have been prepared by condensation of hydroxylamine derivatives and nitroso compounds:

$$R-NH-OH \quad HO-N=CH- \xrightarrow{NaOH} R-N=N-CH_2-$$
$$\underset{O}{|}$$

The formation and different reactions of the nitrile ($-C\equiv N$) group have already been shown in the preceding sections. Hydrocyanic acid (or hydrogen cyanide), which is the nitrile of formic acid, is a tautomeric substance:

$$H-C\equiv N \; \rightleftharpoons \; H-\overset{\oplus}{N}\equiv\overset{\ominus}{C}$$

isonitrile form

However, the alkyl derivatives of both the nitrile and the isonitrile (carbylamine) are stable; heating to 250°C is necessary to cause the rearrangement of isonitriles to nitriles. Nitriles are obtained by condensation of alkyl halides with KCN, while condensation with AgCN gives mainly isonitriles. The structure of nitriles (that is, the existence of the C—C bond between the carbon skeleton and the nitrile C atom in R—C≡N) is proven by the fact that hydrolysis gives the corresponding carboxylic acids. The structure of isonitriles (that is, the existence of the C—N bond between the carbon skeleton R and the isonitrile N) is shown by the reaction:

$$R-\overset{\oplus}{N}\equiv\overset{\ominus}{C} \xrightarrow{Br_2} R-N=CBr_2 \xrightarrow{hydrolysis} R-NH_2 + CO_2 + 2\,HBr$$

alkylimino-
carbonyl halide

primary
amine

Mild oxidation of isonitriles gives *isocyanates* ($-N=C=O$), and treatment with sulfur yields *isothiocyanates*, also called mustard oils ($-N=C=S$).

2.3.7.2 Sulfur-Containing Groups

The simplest sulfur-containing functional group is the $-SH$ group, called the *sulfhydryl group*. Sulfhydryl compounds are also termed *mercaptans*. Simple alkyl mercaptans may be prepared by condensation of alkyl halides with KSH or NaSH, or by addition of H_2S to alkenes:

$$R-CH_2-Cl \quad K-SH \longrightarrow R-CH_2-SH + KCl$$

$$CH_2=CH_2 + H_2S \longrightarrow CH_3-CH_2-SH$$

Mercaptans form metal derivatives called *mercaptides* or *thiolates* (analogous to alcoholates). They show great affinity for mercury, with which they give R—S—Hg—S—R or R—S—Hg—Cl type compounds. Mercaptans may be condensed with aldehydes and ketones to *mercaptals* and *mercaptols* in the presence of HCl. An important reaction of mercaptans is the formation of addition compounds with double or triple bonds:

$$-CH{=}CH{-} + R{-}SH \longrightarrow \underset{\underset{S-R}{|}}{-CH{-}CH_2{-}}$$

Oxidation of mercaptans by air at alkaline pH, by potassium ferricyanide $[K_3Fe(CN)_6]$, or by other mild agents yields the corresponding *disulfides*:

$$2 R{-}SH + [O] \longrightarrow R{-}S{-}S{-}R + H_2O$$

The $-S{-}S{-}$ bond is called a *disulfide bond* or *disulfide bridge*. The above reaction is readily reversed by reducing agents. The easy passage between the sulfhydryl and the disulfide forms is highly significant in biological systems.

Under certain conditions exchange may occur between a disulfide and a sulfhydryl compound following the reaction:

$$R{-}SH + R'{-}S{-}S{-}R' \longrightarrow R{-}S{-}S{-}R' + R'{-}SH$$

This is called a *sulfhydryl-disulfide interchange* (see also Section 3.1.2.6). Various agents can promote or inhibit this interchange. For example, certain types of radiation promote this interchange because of loosening of the S—S bond; trace amounts of H_2O_2 have been found in some instances to promote interchange catalytically. Agents which tie up the —SH group (such as $HgCl_2$ or R—Hg—Cl) will inhibit interchange. Such conditions of molecular geometry which cause strain on the S—S bond will act favorably on disulfide interchange. Disulfide interchange and the formation of disulfide bridges are of great importance for the maintenance of internal structure of complex protein molecules, for various types of enzyme and hormone action, for the compounding of proteins into living tissue fabrics, in the molecular mechanism of cell division, etc.

Stages of further oxidation of the sulfhydryl group are:

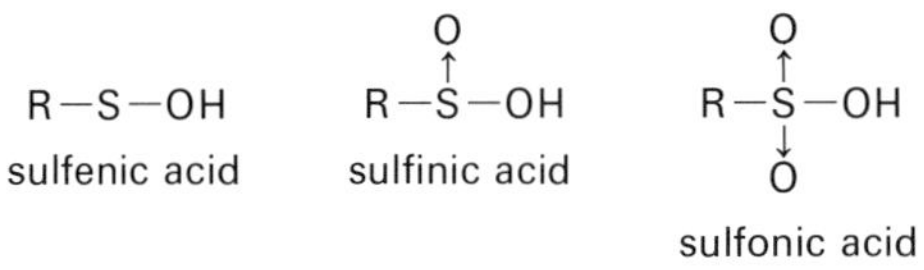

$$
\begin{array}{ccc}
 & O & O \\
 & \uparrow & \uparrow \\
R{-}S{-}OH & R{-}S{-}OH & R{-}S{-}OH \\
 & & \downarrow \\
 & & O \\
\text{sulfenic acid} & \text{sulfinic acid} & \\
 & & \text{sulfonic acid}
\end{array}
$$

Since sulfur can only establish two covalent bonds, the additional oxygen atoms in the sulfinic and sulfonic acid groups are linked to sulfur by co-ordinate bonds (Section 3.1.2.7).

Sulfenic acids or their derivatives have not been isolated; however, their existence is inferred from the reversible hydrolysis of the S—S bond at alkaline pH:

$$R{-}S{-}S{-}R \underset{}{\overset{H_2O}{\rightleftharpoons}} R{-}S{-}OH + R{-}SH$$

Strong oxidizing agents convert the $-SH$ group directly to an $-SO_3H$ group; the reaction may not be arrested at the intermediate $-SO_2H$ stage because of its ease of oxidation:

$$R-SH + 3[O] \longrightarrow R-SO_3H$$

Just as the carboxylic acids form acyl halides, the organic sulfonic acids form sulfonyl halides, esters, and amides:

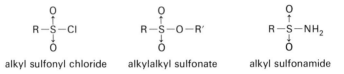

alkyl sulfonyl chloride   alkylalkyl sulfonate   alkyl sulfonamide

Reduction of the sulfonyl chlorides by zinc dust gives the sulfinic acids:

$$R-SO_2 \fbox{$Cl \quad H$} + H \xrightarrow[H_2O]{Zn} R-SO_2H + HCl$$

The sulfonamides, unlike the acylamides, behave as acids and are soluble in alkalies.

Alkyl sulfides or *thio ethers* may be obtained following the general reaction:

$$R-S \fbox{$Na \quad I$} R \longrightarrow R-S-R + NaI$$

The alkyl sulfides form addition compounds, called *sulfonium compounds*, similar to the ammonium compounds.

Mild or vigorous oxidation converts the thio ethers to *sulfoxides* or to *sulfones*, respectively:

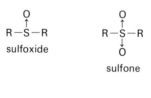

Thiocarbonyls ($-\overset{S}{\underset{\|}{C}}-$) result from the replacement of the oxygen with a sulfur atom in the carbonyl group. The diamide of thiocarbonic acid $[S=C(OH)_2]$ is thiourea ($NH_2-\overset{}{\underset{\|}{C}}-NH_2$). Thiocarboxylic acids may be

prepared by reacting an acyl chloride with NaSH:

$$R-CO \fbox{$Cl \quad Na$} SH \longrightarrow R-\overset{O}{\overset{\|}{C}}-SH \underset{\text{equilibrium}}{\overset{\text{tautomeric}}{\rightleftharpoons}} R-\overset{S}{\overset{\|}{C}}-OH$$

Thiocarbonyls have a greater tendency to keto-enol tautomerism than the corresponding carbonyl compounds. This molecular rearrangement results in the appearance of sulfhydryl groups, for example:

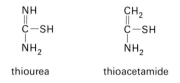

thiourea	thioacetamide

This is indicated by the fact that they may be methylated by diazomethane to the *S*-methyl compounds. Also, thiourea may be oxidized to the disulfide compound or to sulfinic acid.

2.3.8   SOME DERIVATIVES OF THE CARBONIC ACIDS

Carbonic acid and orthocarbonic acid, which correspond to the mono- and dihydrate of carbon dioxide, do not exist in the free state:

carbonic acid	orthocarbonic acid

However, esters of orthocarbonic acid (orthocarbonates) and various derivatives of carbonic acid are known.

Although carbon tetrachloride (CCl_4) corresponds formally to the tetrachloride of orthocarbonic acid, it does not form orthocarbonates which are obtained by other synthetic routes. The acyl chloride of carbonic acid, carbonyl chloride, or phosgene ($COCl_2$), however, reacts as expected. It can react with one or two molecules of an alcohol, depending on whether the reaction takes place in the cold or at higher temperature:

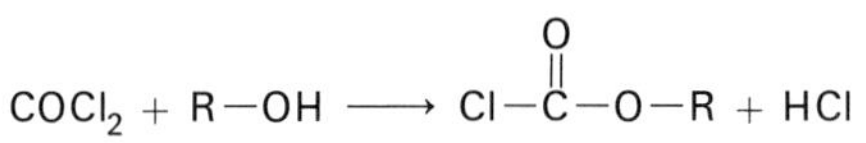

$$COCl_2 + R-OH \longrightarrow Cl-\overset{\overset{\displaystyle O}{\|}}{C}-O-R + HCl$$

chlorocarbonic
esters

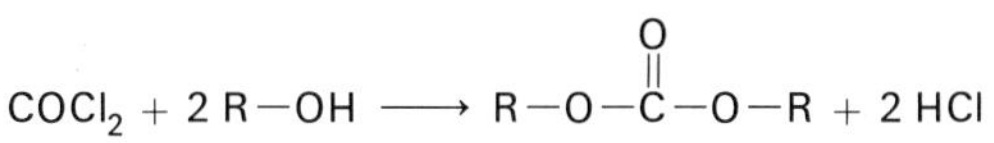

$$COCl_2 + 2\,R-OH \longrightarrow R-O-\overset{\overset{\displaystyle O}{\|}}{C}-O-R + 2\,HCl$$

alkyl carbonates

With ammonia it yields the diamide of carbonic acid known as *urea*:

$$COCl_2 + 2\ NH_3 \longrightarrow NH_2-\overset{\overset{\displaystyle O}{\|}}{C}-NH_2 + 2\ HCl$$
$$\text{urea}$$

Using primary or secondary amines instead of ammonia, the corresponding symmetric *N,N'*-dialkyl or *N,N,N',N'*-tetraalkylureas are obtained. Urea shows keto-enol tautomerism. The amino groups of urea behave as primary amino groups; urea reacts with nitrous acid:

$$HO-N\dasheq O \qquad H_2N-\overset{\overset{\displaystyle O}{\|}}{C}-NH_2 \qquad O\dasheq N-OH \longrightarrow CO_2 + 3\ H_2O + 2\ N_2$$

and can undergo Hofmann's degradation reaction (see Section 2.3.6.2):

$$NH_2\!\dashv\!CO\!\dashv\!NH_2 \longrightarrow NH_2-NH_2 + KBr + CO_2$$
$$K\!\dashv\!O\!\dashv\!Br \qquad\qquad \text{hydrazine}$$

The imide of urea is *guanidine*, usually available as the hydrochloride $(NH_2)_2C{=}NH{\cdot}HCl$. The univalent group corresponding to guanidine is called the *guanidyl* or *guanidino* group.

On heating with NH_4Cl, only one chlorine of phosgene reacts:

$$COCl_2 + NH_4Cl \longrightarrow NH_2-CO-Cl + 2\ HCl$$
$$\text{carbamyl}$$
$$\text{chloride}$$

The resulting compound, carbamyl chloride, may be regarded as the acyl chloride of aminoformic acid, or the amide of chloroformic acid, or the acyl chloride of aminocarbonic or *carbamic acid*. Because of the reactive chlorine, carbamyl chloride can undergo condensation reactions with primary or secondary amines to give monoalkyl- or asymmetric dialkylureas. Reaction of carbamyl chloride with hydroxylamine (NH_2-OH) gives hydroxyurea. The hydrazide of carbamic acid is *semicarbazide* ($NH_2-NH-CO-NH_2$). Upon hydrolysis carbamyl chloride yields CO_2 and NH_4Cl, since carbamic acid is unstable in the free state.

The esters of carbamic acid are the *urethans*, which may be prepared by condensation of carbamyl chloride with alcohols (with elimination of HCl) or by reacting urea with alcohols at high temperature (resulting in replacement of one $-NH_2$ group by an alkoxy group and liberation of ammonia). The urethans show the reactions of esters and of acid amides. The *N*-monoalkylurethans show the reactions of esters and acid amides and give *N*-nitroso and *N*-nitro derivatives (see Section 2.3.6.3).

SUPPLETORY NOTE FOR SECTION 2.3

The law of mass action may be illustrated by the formation of ethyl acetate from ethanol and acetic acid. The rate of the reaction toward the right (that is the formation of ethyl acetate and water) depends on the rate of collisions between molecules of ethanol and acetic acid; however, not all collisions lead to reaction and the proportion of collisions favorable for combination depends on the chemical affinity of the two molecular species to each other. Thus, the velocity of the reaction toward the right depends, first, on the concentrations of the two molecular species (determining the rate of collisions) and, second, on a proportionality constant, called the *velocity constant*, which is a function of the chemical affinities. *The velocity constant holds for a given temperature and experimental conditions.* The velocity V of the formation of ethyl acetate and water (reaction toward the right) may thus be written as:

$$V_r = k_1[C_2H_5-OH] \cdot [CH_3-COOH] \tag{a}$$

where k_1 is the velocity constant and the formulas in brackets denote the concentrations of the reactants.

However, the ethyl acetate and water formed in the process also react with each other, and this regenerates ethanol and acetic acid (reaction shown by the lower arrow in $\rightleftharpoons$ pointing toward the left). This reaction also depends on the rates of collision (*i.e.* on the respective concentrations of ethyl acetate and water), and has a velocity constant k_2 determined by the affinity of ethyl acetate and water to each other. The velocity of the reaction toward the left is, thus:

$$V_l = k_2[CH_3-COO-C_2H_5] \cdot [H_2O] \tag{b}$$

Obviously, then, the reaction toward the right (the formation of ethyl acetate) cannot come to a completion and the change in the concentration of the four molecular species will come to a standstill at the time when the velocities become equal $V_r = V_l$, that is when:

$$k_1[C_2H_5-OH] \cdot [CH_3-COOH] = k_2[CH_3-COO-C_2H_5] \cdot [H_2O] \tag{c}$$

Equation (c) may be rearranged to:

$$\frac{[CH_3-COO-C_2H_5] \cdot [H_2O]}{[C_2H_5-OH] \cdot [CH_3-COOH]} = \frac{k_1}{k_2} = K \tag{d}$$

where the ratio of the two velocity constants equals K, the *equilibrium constant*. Written in a general form, a reversible reaction

$$A + B \underset{k_b}{\overset{k_a}{\rightleftharpoons}} C + D \tag{e}$$

has an equilibrium constant:

$$\frac{[C] \cdot [D]}{[A] \cdot [B]} = \frac{k_a}{k_b} = K \qquad (f)$$

It can be readily seen that the magnitude of K is indicative of the concentrations of the products C and D relative to the concentrations of the reactants A and B, *at equilibrium.* If the value of K is high the concentrations of C and D are comparatively high, and vice-versa.

Consider now Eq. (d). Since K is a constant, the equation directly indicates the way by which the reaction toward the right (formation of ethyl acetate) may be brought to completion despite the tendency to reach equilibrium. If the ethyl acetate and/or the water as they are being formed are somehow eliminated from the reaction medium (*i.e.* the concentrations in the numerator are decreased), the concentrations of ethanol and acetic acid will also decrease accordingly so as to satisfy Eq. (d). This means that the concentrations of ethanol and acetic acid will tend toward zero and the formation of ethyl acetate is brought to completion. This can be accomplished, for example, by adding dropwise an equimolar mixture of ethanol and acetic acid to concentrated sulfuric acid at 140° ; the latter, being an energetic dehydrating agent, will bind the water formed (thus eliminating it from the reaction) and ethyl acetate is distilled off.

2.4 Benzene and the Aromatic Character

The alkanes, alkenes, alkynes, and their various derivatives constitute the class of *aliphatic* compounds. Under certain conditions of molecular geometry, a conjugated double bond system can confer to cyclic carbon chains a special reactivity behavior and a chemical stability approaching that of the alkanes. The structural nature of this large group, called *aromatic* compounds, is the subject of the section on benzene and the aromatic character.

If a 6-membered ring contains *three* conjugated double bonds, the double bonds in this compound have none of the properties of the linear conjugated hexatriene : the double bonds in benzene do not behave as would be expected from those of cyclohexatriene, but as though they were "saturated" (*i.e.*, single bonds).

Of the three compounds:

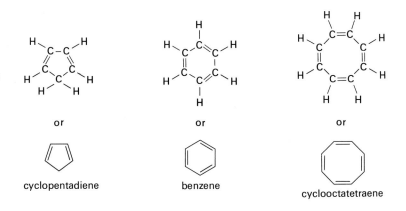

| cyclopentadiene | benzene | cyclooctatetraene |

both cyclopentadiene and cyclooctatetraene show the presence of conjugated double bonds, *e.g.*, both instantaneously decolorize water solutions
of potassium permanganate or bromine, ordinary reagents for unsaturated
compounds. Benzene, which should correspond to cyclohexatriene, does not
react under the same conditions. The presence of double bonds in benzene
becomes evident only under special circumstances.

That benzene, corresponding to the molecular formula C_6H_6, and yet
showing no unsaturated character, has the structure of cyclohexatriene was
proposed by Kekulé. However, it soon became evident that the cyclohexatriene structure, with its double bonds localized at fixed positions in
the molecule, could not be accepted without qualification. According to the
cyclohexatriene structure four disubstituted isomers of benzene should be
possible : substitution on carbons separated from each other by two carbons
(designated 1,4- or *para* disubstitution, abbreviated as *p*), substitution on
carbons separated from each other by one carbon (1,3- or *meta* disubstitution,
abbreviated as *m*), substitution on adjacent carbons linked by a single bond,
and substitution on adjacent carbons linked by a double bond (disubstitution
on adjacent carbons is designated 1,2- or *ortho*, abbreviated as *o*). Experimental evidence indicated, however, that there is only one ortho isomer for a
disubstituted benzene, irrespective of the nature of the substituent.

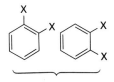

| ortho or 1,2- disubstitution | meta or 1,3- disubstitution | para or 1,4- disubstitution |

Kekulé recognized this difficulty and proposed that the double bonds in benzene oscillate back and forth between two structures:

The double arrow ($\leftrightarrow$) designates the oscillation (or in present-day terminology, *resonance*) between different structures of a compound involving change in the position or positions of double bonds only, without modification of the constituting atoms. This is to be distinguished from a tautomeric equilibrium (denoted by "$\rightleftharpoons$") which involves displacement of hydrogen (*e.g.*, keto-enol tautomerism, see Section 2.3.2.2) or may amount to rearrangement of the molecular skeleton (*e.g.*, nitrile-isonitrile tautomerism).

Others proposed different structures for benzene:

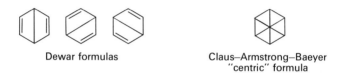

Dewar formulas   Claus–Armstrong–Baeyer
"centric" formula

It is now considered that the actual state of benzene corresponds to resonance involving the two Kekulé, the three Dewar structures, and a great number of polar ionic structures (Section 3.2.2). These different resonating structures are called *limit formulas*, *limit structures*, or *canonical structures*, and the actual molecule may be visualized as an intermediate (the *resonance hybrid*) between all limit structures. The resonance hybrid has, consequently a greater probability of existence, or in other words, is more stable than any of the contributing limit structures.

The exceptional stability and the nonreactivity of the unsaturated system in benzene is due to its particular molecular geometry. Physicochemical measurements indicate that, unlike cyclopentadiene and cyclooctatetraene, benzene is a flat and completely symmetrical molecule. It is this flatness or planarity which is the crucial requirement for resonance.

Because of the fact that benzene does not show the unsaturated character of cyclohexatriene, other notations are also in use which do not show the double bonds:

The first three symbols illustrate well the fact that benzene is a resonance hybrid in which no precise positions can be assigned to the double bonds (Section 3.1.2.2). The use of the simple hexagon can be equivocal, however, when representing certain structures because this symbol formally denotes cyclohexane compounds. By far the most commonly used is still the original Kekulé formulation with the implicit understanding that the three con- jugated double bonds in the hexagonal ring denote the specific aromatic character.

Evidence for the structure of benzene is provided by the fact that it can be formed by the trimerization of acetylene at high temperature, and furthermore, that catalytic hydrogenation of benzene results in cyclohexane:

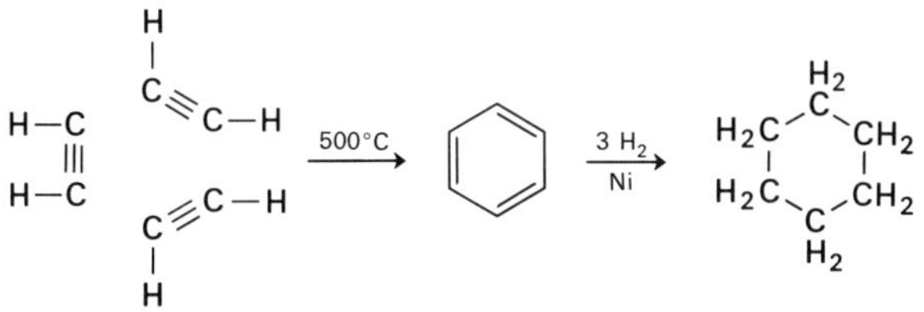

Benzene is the parent structure of all aromatic compounds and forms the basis of an important branch of organic chemistry dealing with compounds composed of such rings. With respect to our specific topic, we have mentioned in the introduction that all carcinogenic hydrocarbons are aromatic ring structures.

2.4.1   TYPICAL REACTIONS OF BENZENE

2.4.1.1   Substitution by One Substituent

A great variety of functional groups may be linked to benzene, which then becomes a *phenyl group* symbolized as:

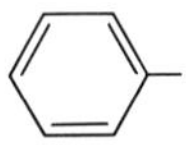

or C_6H_5- or $\Phi-$

The phenyl group and corresponding groups of more complex aromatic ring structures are called by the common name *aryl groups*.

For substitution by chlorine or bromine, ferric halide is required as a catalyst to yield first monochlorobenzene or monobromobenzene. The reaction can proceed further to give the various multi-substituted isomers.

Fuming sulfuric acid converts benzene to benzenesulfonic acid. A nitric acid-sulfuric acid mixture converts benzene to nitrobenzene:

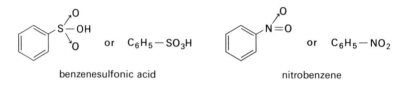

benzenesulfonic acid   nitrobenzene

Benzene may be readily condensed, with elimination of water, with aldehydes to form diphenylmethane derivatives:

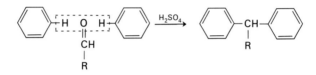

and with alcohols to form alkyl benzenes:

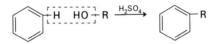

A difference between aliphatic and aromatic compounds is that an aromatic ring may be readily linked to mercury. With benzene the reaction is as follows:

$$C_6H_6 + Hg(OOC-CH_3)_2 + C_2H_5-OH$$
mercuric acetate

$$\xrightarrow{-H_2O} C_6H_5-Hg-OOC-CH_3 + C_2H_5-OOC-CH_3$$
phenylmercuric acetate   ethyl acetate

A most important reaction of aromatic compounds is the *Friedel–Crafts reaction*. In the presence of anhydrous aluminum trichloride in diethyl ether, dioxane, or other similar anhydrous solvents, benzene and higher aromatics undergo condensation and addition reactions with a great variety of compounds. In this way different functional groups may be linked to aromatic nuclei. Typical products that may be obtained from benzene by the Friedel–Crafts reaction are:

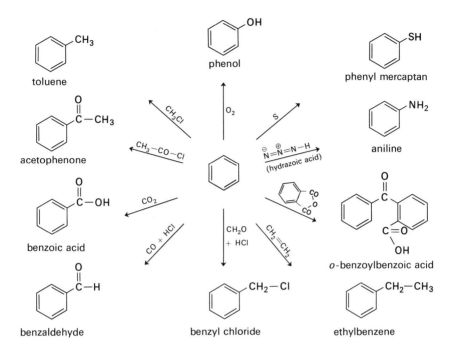

Simple alkyl groups or more complex aliphatic chains attached to benzene or other aryl groups are called *side chains*.

The chemical behavior of the substituents is modified by the aryl group. Halogenation of toluene in the presence of ultraviolet light results in the stepwise substitution of the hydrogens of the methyl group. For example, chlorination yields first benzyl chloride C_6H_5—CH_2—Cl (*benzyl* for the C_6H_5—CH_2— group), then benzal chloride C_6H_5—$CHCl_2$ (*benzal* or *benzylidene* for the C_6H_5—CH= group), and finally benzotrichloride. In the presence of ferric halide catalyst and the absence of light, the nucleus is substituted in preference to the methyl group. The strength of the halogen-aryl bond is much greater than that of the halogen-alkyl bond. Benzyl chloride may be hydrolyzed readily to benzyl alcohol just as, for example, ethyl chloride is hydrolyzed to ethyl alcohol. However, chlorobenzene does not hydrolyze to phenol under the same experimental conditions; hydrolysis takes place only under much more drastic conditions. The fluorine-aryl bond in fluorobenzene is even more stable; in fact, certain reactions tending to remove the fluorine substituent split the ring itself.

The presence of an aryl substituent considerably decreases the acidity of the carboxyl group. Thus, benzoic acid, which may be regarded as phenyl-formic acid, is a considerably weaker acid than formic acid. The ability of an aryl to weaken the acidity of the carboxyl decreases with the interposition of CH_2 groups; phenylacetic acid is not a much weaker acid than acetic acid. The acyl group of benzoic acid is termed *benzoyl*; the amide of benzoic acid is benzamide.

Aromatic compounds hydroxylated in the ring are *phenols*. The acidic character manifested by the low aliphatic alcohols (replacement of hydrogen by alkali metals) is even more pronounced in phenols. Certain halogen and nitro derivatives of phenol are strong acids. Phenyl methyl ether (methoxybenzene) is known as anisole and phenyl ethyl ether (ethoxybenzene) as phenetole.

Substitution by aryl groups decreases the basic character of ammonia. For example, *aniline* (phenylamine) is a much weaker base than the corresponding molecular weight monoalkylamine; however, aniline does form a stable salt with hydrochloric acid. With diphenylamine the hydrochloride, which may be formed in anhydrous media, spontaneously decomposes to the free amine and hydrochloric acid upon dissolution in water. Triphenylamine does not form the hydrochloride under any circumstances. Alkyl substitution of aniline, however, increases basicity; *N,N*-dimethylaniline is a stronger base than aniline. This parallels the situation with ammonia and alkylamines (Section 2.3.6).

2.4.1.2 *Diazotization and the Azo Compounds*

An important difference in the chemical behavior of alkyl-bound and aryl-bound primary amino groups resides in their reaction with nitrous acid. Primary alkylamines are immediately decomposed by this reagent with liberation of nitrogen and the replacement of the amino by a hydroxyl group to give the corresponding alcohol. With primary arylamines, however, the intermediate compound, called a *diazonium compound*, is relatively stable. The reaction by which a diazonium compound is formed is termed *diazotization*. With aniline the reaction is as follows:

$$\Phi-NH_2 \xrightarrow[\text{HCl}]{\text{KNO}_2} \Phi-N\!\underset{\lfloor_____\rfloor}{H_2 \qquad O}\!=\!N-OH \longrightarrow \Phi-N=N-OH \Longrightarrow \left[\Phi-\underset{N}{\overset{|||}{N}}\right]^{\oplus} OH^{\ominus}$$

benzenediazonium
hydroxide

$$\xrightarrow{\text{HCl}} \left[\Phi-\underset{N}{\overset{|||}{N}}\right]^{\oplus} Cl^{\ominus} \Longrightarrow \Phi-N=N-Cl$$

benzenediazonium chloride

The diazonium hydroxides are strong bases. The stability of the diazonium compound increases with the size and complexity of the aryl moiety. The importance of diazonium compounds lies in the fact that they undergo the *coupling reaction* with a variety of organic compounds having a reactive, mobile hydrogen substituent, and form highly colored *azo compounds*:

$$aryl-N=N \dashv Cl \qquad H \vdash aryl \longrightarrow aryl-N=N-aryl$$

The —N=N— group is called an *azo linkage*. Unlike similar derivatives in the aliphatic series, the aromatic azo compounds are in general highly stable substances. Different phenols and tertiary arylamines have been commonly used as coupling partners to form a considerable variety of azo compounds. In these cases coupling takes place practically exclusively in the position para to the amino or hydroxyl group. With benzenediazonium chloride and phenol or dimethylaniline the following compounds are obtained:

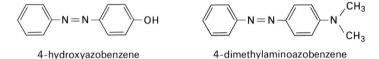

4-hydroxyazobenzene   4-dimethylaminoazobenzene

If in the process of diazotizing an amine, an insufficient amount of nitrous acid (KNO_2 + HCl) is added, the diazotized portion of the amine couples with the amino group of the nondiazotized amine, to give *diazoamino* compounds having the general formula:

$$aryl-NH-N=N-aryl$$

Formally, the parent compound of aromatic azo compounds is *azobenzene*. Azobenzene itself may not be prepared by direct coupling since diazonium compounds do not couple with benzene. It may be obtained by an indirect procedure, which is also used to obtain more complex azo compounds, by condensation of a primary amine and a nitroso compound:

The numbering of azobenzene, for defining the position of substituents, begins at the branching of the azo linkage to the ring. When substituents are present on both rings, the second ring is numbered 1′, 2′, etc., and by convention is termed the "prime" ring.

Coupling of a diazonium compound is usually the procedure for the preparation of unsymmetric (with respect to a line bisecting the —N=N— group) azo compounds. The preparation of symmetric azo compounds is often readily accomplished by alkaline reduction of the appropriate nitro derivative. For example, azobenzene, which is the simplest of the symmetric aromatic azo compounds, may be obtained by reduction of nitrobenzene. Depending on the experimental conditions, alkaline reduction of $\Phi—NO_2$ yields, in fact:

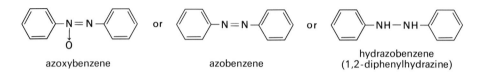

azoxybenzene   azobenzene   hydrazobenzene
(1,2-diphenylhydrazine)

Acid reduction of nitrobenzene (or any of the above intermediates) gives aniline (*cf.* Section 2.3.7.1):

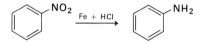

The 1,2-diarylhydrazines, such as hydrazobenzene, undergo, in the presence of strong mineral acids, an intramolecular rearrangement called the *benzidine rearrangement*:

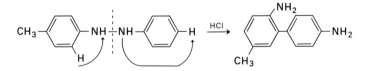

benzidine
(4,4′-diaminobiphenyl)

When one or both para positions are blocked by a strongly linked substituent (for example, alkyl), the reaction which will take place will be, respectively, a *half-semidine* (or *o-p*-semidine) *rearrangement*:

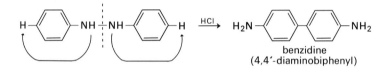

or a *semidine* (or *o-o*-semidine) *rearrangement*:

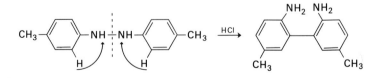

2.4.1.3 Substitution by More Than One Substituent

The presence of a substituent in the benzene ring or in more complex aromatic structures has an orienting effect on the positions of further substitutions. In view of the orienting effect *in benzene*, the different functional groups may be *ortho-para directing* or *meta directing*. For example, $-SO_3H$, $-NO_2$, $-CHO$, $-COOH$, $-CN$, $-NR_3^{\oplus}$ are meta directing; while $-OH$, $-NH_2$, $-alkyl$, $-\Phi$ are ortho-para directing. The relative proportions of the ortho and para isomers formed depend on the nature of the entering group. In higher aromatic ring systems the orientation of substituents becomes much more complex.

A disubstituted benzene group is sometimes termed a *phenylene group*; it must be defined whether *o*, *m*, or *p*. A trisubstituted benzene derivative may be *vicinal* (1,2,3-isomer), *symmetrical* (1,3,5-isomer), or *asymmetrical* (1,2,4-isomer):

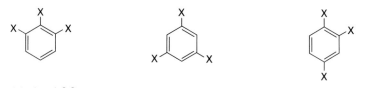

| vicinal or 1,2,3- | symmetrical or 1,3,5- | asymmetrical or 1,2,4- |

The previously defined terms (*o*, *m*, and *p*) for disubstituted isomers may also be used when the two substituents are different (since the terms denote relative positions in a symmetrical molecule), for example, *o*-chloronitrobenzene, *p*-chlorobenzenesulfonic acid, *p*-nitrosodimethylaniline. However, with three substituents, the terms vicinal, symmetrical, or asymmetrical can only be used when all three substituents are the same. Otherwise the position of the substituents must be defined by numbers. For example, 1-chloro-3,5-dinitrobenzene, 1,2-dinitro-4-chlorobenzene, 1-chloro-2-bromo-3-benzenesulfonic acid, 1-chloro-3,5-benzenedisulfonic acid.

Following are some polysubstituted benzene derivatives known under specific names:

a. alkylbenzenes

   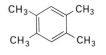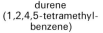

| toluene | *o*-, *m*-, and *p*-xylene | mesitylene (1,3,5-trimethyl-benzene) | durene (1,2,4,5-tetramethyl-benzene) |

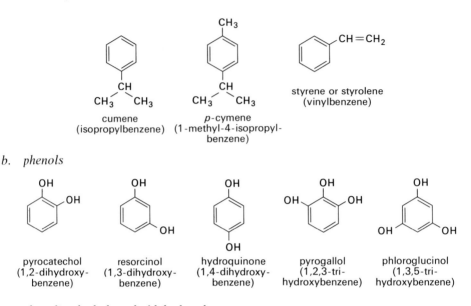

styrene or styrolene
(vinylbenzene)

cumene
(isopropylbenzene)

p-cymene
(1-methyl-4-isopropyl-
benzene)

b. *phenols*

pyrocatechol
(1,2-dihydroxy-
benzene)

resorcinol
(1,3-dihydroxy-
benzene)

hydroquinone
(1,4-dihydroxy-
benzene)

pyrogallol
(1,2,3-tri-
hydroxybenzene)

phloroglucinol
(1,3,5-tri-
hydroxybenzene)

c. *phenolic alcohols and aldehydes; ketones*

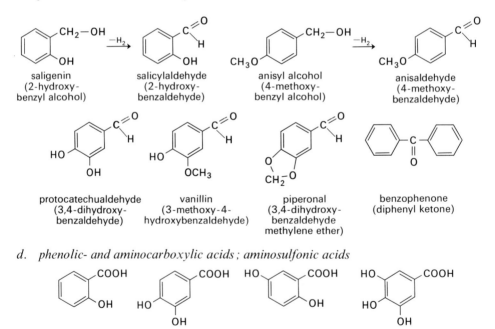

saligenin
(2-hydroxy-
benzyl alcohol)

salicylaldehyde
(2-hydroxy-
benzaldehyde)

anisyl alcohol
(4-methoxy-
benzyl alcohol)

anisaldehyde
(4-methoxy-
benzaldehyde)

protocatechualdehyde
(3,4-dihydroxy-
benzaldehyde)

vanillin
(3-methoxy-4-
hydroxybenzaldehyde)

piperonal
(3,4-dihydroxy-
benzaldehyde
methylene ether)

benzophenone
(diphenyl ketone)

d. *phenolic- and aminocarboxylic acids; aminosulfonic acids*

salicyclic acid
(2-hydroxybenzoic
acid)

protocatechuic acid
(3,4-dihydroxy-
benzoic acid)

gentisic acid
(2,5-dihydroxy-
benzoic acid)

gallic acid
(3,4,5-trihydroxy-
benzoic acid)

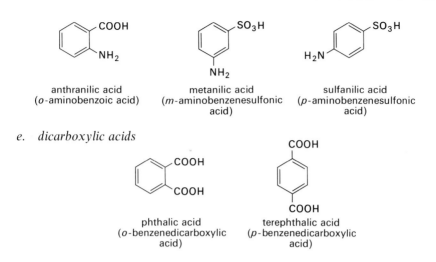

anthranilic acid
(*o*-aminobenzoic acid)

metanilic acid
(*m*-aminobenzenesulfonic acid)

sulfanilic acid
(*p*-aminobenzenesulfonic acid)

e. *dicarboxylic acids*

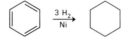

phthalic acid
(*o*-benzenedicarboxylic acid)

terephthalic acid
(*p*-benzenedicarboxylic acid)

2.4.1.4 *Reactions Abolishing the Aromatic Character*

Benzene may be hydrogenated in the presence of nickel catalyst at 200°C under pressure, to yield cyclohexane:

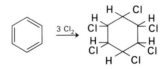

and chlorinated or brominated in the presence of strong ultraviolet irradiation to give the respective hexahalogen cyclohexane:

The most interesting of the reactions of benzene compounds involving the aromatic character is the formation of quinones. The simple quinones of benzene may be regarded as diketo cyclohexadienes. Quinones may be *o*- or *p*-quinones. *m*-Quinones cannot be formulated and, in fact, do not exist. The two quinones of benzene are consequently:

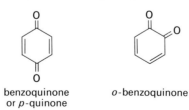

benzoquinone
or *p*-quinone

o-benzoquinone

Benzoquinone may be formed by the vigorous oxidation of aniline or phenol. Reduction of benzoquinone gives hydroquinone (Section 2.4.1.3) with reestablishment of the aromatic structure:

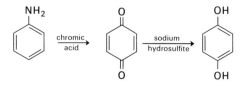

o-Benzoquinone is prepared by mild oxidation of pyrocatechol, the corresponding ortho diphenolic compound:

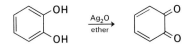

The reactions of benzoquinone show the presence of the keto groups and of the unsaturated double bonds. It undergoes the Diels–Alder diene addition with butadiene (Section 2.2.4) and forms oximes with hydroxylamine. The monooxime of benzoquinone is tautomeric with *p*-nitrosophenol:

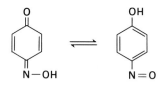

With regard to our specific subject it is important to note that benzoquinone reacts with $-NH_2$ and with $-SH$ groups. This type of reaction may be exemplified in the following manner:

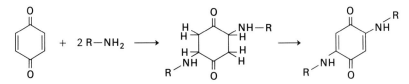

The intermediate is reoxidized to the 2,5-disubstituted quinone by excess quinone (which is thereby reduced to hydroquinone).

2.4.2 HOMOLOGS AND BENZOLOGS OF BENZENE. HETEROCYCLIC ANALOGS

It is often convenient to make a distinction between homologs and benzologs of benzene. The different mono- and polyalkyl derivatives of

benzene are its homologs. Higher derivatives, which result from the attach-
ment of one or more benzene rings may be considered as composed of several
aromatic rings, and are called *benzologs* of benzene. Among the benzologs
of benzene one may distinguish *noncondensed* and *condensed* (or *annelated*)
polycyclic systems.

2.4.2.1 Noncondensed Polycyclic Systems

Linking of two or more benzene rings to each other by single bonds
leads to the *polyphenyl* compounds: biphenyl, the terphenyls, the quater-
phenyls, etc. The numbering of biphenyl is indicated below:

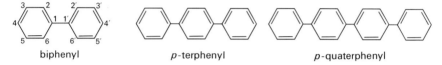

biphenyl   *p*-terphenyl   *p*-quaterphenyl

The univalent group corresponding to biphenyl (C_6H_5—C_6H_4—) is called
xenyl. A well-known amine of the biphenyl series is *benzidine*, or 4,4′-
diaminobiphenyl (Section 2.4.1.2).

Benzene rings may also be linked to each other in a branched fashion,
such as in 1,3,5-triphenylbenzene:

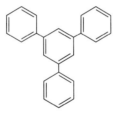

The 1,2-diphenyl derivative of ethylene is known as *stilbene*. (The numbering of the rings and the designation of the ethylenic carbons are indicated in
the formula):

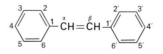

Stilbene may be regarded as a phenyl derivative of styrene (Section 2.4.1.3).
Like styrene, stilbene is an unsaturated compound. The intercyclic double
bond may undergo addition reactions similar to simple alkenes (Section
2.2.4). Stilbene is a *structural analog* of (or is *isosteric* with) azobenzene
(Section 2.4.1.2), since the two compounds are similar in the general arrangement of the atoms, in molecular size and shape, and differ only in the replacement of the —CH= groups in the former by —N= in azobenzene.

Triphenylmethane (or *tritane*) $[(C_6H_5)_3C\!-\!H]$ is the parent compound of an important class of dyes. The univalent group corresponding to triphenylmethane is called the *trityl group* $[(C_6H_5)_3C\!-\!]$. The simplest triphenylmethane dyes are monoaminated:

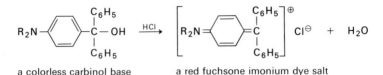

a colorless carbinol base   a red fuchsone imonium dye salt

Increasing the number of *p*-amino or *p*-dialkylamino groups results in deepening of the color of the dye salt:

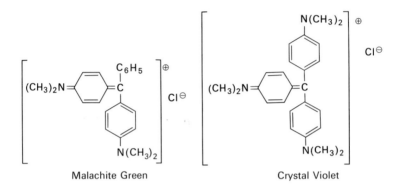

Malachite Green   Crystal Violet

Such compounds which exhibit a quinone-like double bond arrangement are termed *quinoid* or *quinonoid*. The relation between color, resonance, and chemical structure is discussed in Section 3.2.3.

2.4.2.2 Condensed Polycyclic Systems

The simplest bicyclic ring system is *indene*, comprised of fused benzene and cyclopentadiene moieties. In indene the unsaturated character of the cyclopentadiene moiety is manifest. However, bromine addition to indene gives only a dibromide, since one of the two double bonds of cyclopentadiene is at the same time part of the aromatic ring:

indene

Fluorene, which corresponds to the fusion of one benzene ring with indene, may also be regarded as 2,2'-methylene-bridged biphenyl or as diphenylene-methane. In fact, both 2-methylbiphenyl and diphenylmethane lose hydrogen at high temperature to yield fluorene:

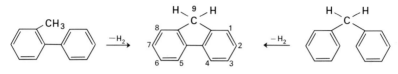

Hydroxy derivatives of fluorene, whether the hydroxy group is linked to the methylene bridge or to the aromatic nuclei, are called *fluorenols*. The 9-fluorene ketone is *fluorenone*.

The simplest benzolog of benzene is *naphthalene*, composed of two fused or *condensed* benzenic nuclei. The increase in the number of double bonds considerably increases the number of possible limit formulas. Thus, the structure of naphthalene may be written following three Kekulé and thirty-nine Dewar structures; the number of polar ionic limit formulas is consider-able for naphthalene (Section 3.2.2).

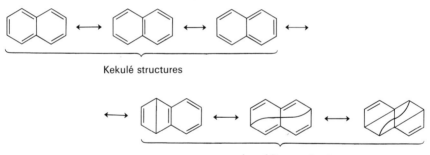

Kekulé structures

examples of Dewar structures

Naphthalene may be hydrogenated under much milder conditions than benzene. Thus, hydrogen liberated by sodium metal from ethanol hydrogen-ates naphthalene in the 1,4-positions:

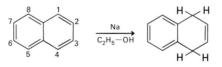

The resulting 1,4-dihydronaphthalene is a typical unsaturated compound. It can take up bromine to give 2,3-dibromotetrahydronaphthalene, which may be dehydrobrominated to regenerate the initial naphthalene:

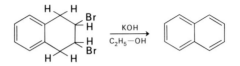

The structure of naphthalene is further indicated by the fact that its oxidation yields 1,4-naphthoquinone and, under more drastic conditions, phthalic acid. The presence of two benzene rings sharing adjacent carbon atoms is thereby proven:

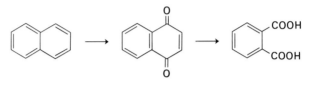

1,4-naphthoquinone
or α-naphthoquinone

Such a procedure, whereby a compound of unknown structure is oxidatively fragmented to yield a known compound or compounds, thus giving information on the structure, is called *oxidative degradation.*

Vitamins K_1 and K_2 are derivatives of 2-methyl-1,4-naphthoquinone (known as menadione), substituted at the 3-position with partially saturated linear polyisoprene chains of different lengths; menadione itself has vitamin K activity. 1,2,3,4-Tetrahydronaphthalene (known as tetralin) and decahydronaphthalene (decalin) are used as solvents.

Hydrogenation of naphthalene to the 1,4-dihydro derivative indicates that the 1- and 4-positions, also known as the α-positions, are particularly reactive. In fact, monochlorination, mononitration, or monosulfonation gives overwhelmingly or exclusively the α-monosubstituted isomer: 1-chloro- or 1-nitronaphthalene or 1-naphthalenesulfonic acid. Naphthalene derivatives substituted in the 2- or 3-positions (also known as the β-positions) are prepared by indirect methods. The univalent group corresponding to naphthalene is a *naphthyl group.* Thus, one may have α-naphthyl- or β-naphthyl- (for example, α-naphthylamine or β-naphthylamine). The two monophenols of naphthalene are α-naphthol and β-naphthol. The carboxylic acids of naphthalene (the benzologs of benzoic acid) are termed *naphthoic acids.*

The positions of substitution in di- or polysubstituted naphthalenes are designated by numbers, for example, 2-amino-1-naphthol, 1-amino-4-naphthalenesulfonic acid, 1,4,6-naphthalenetrisulfonic acid. However, 2,6- and 1,8-disubstitution is also designated by special terms, *amphi-* and *peri-.*

Note that in addition to a 1,4- and 1,2-naphthoquinone, an *amphi*-naphtho-
quinone may be formulated and, in fact, does exist:

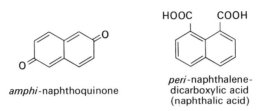

amphi-naphthoquinone

peri-naphthalene-
dicarboxylic acid
(naphthalic acid)

Various polysubstituted aminonaphthalenesulfonic or aminonaphthol-
sulfonic acids are extensively used for the preparation of complex azo dyes.

Cross-linking of the peri position in naphthalene by an ethane bridge
results in *acenaphthene*. The term *ace* is often used in the terminology of
condensed polycyclic systems, denoting a $-CH_2-CH_2-$ group which
cross-links a ring structure at certain points and thereby establishes a new
5- or 6-membered ring. Acenaphthene is correctly *peri*-acenaphthene. At high
temperature the ace bridge in acenaphthene loses hydrogen to yield *acenaphthylene*. Condensation of one more benzene nucleus to the peri bridge
gives *fluoranthene*. Fluoranthene may also be regarded as 1,9-benzofluorene.

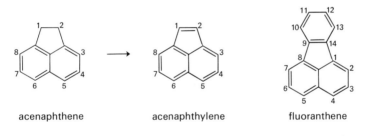

acenaphthene   acenaphthylene   fluoranthene

Mild oxidation of acenaphthene or of acenaphthylene gives a 1,2-diketone,
acenaphthenequinone. More vigorous oxidation splits the ace bridge to
yield *peri*-naphthalenedicarboxylic acid.

Condensation of further benzene rings with naphthalene in *linear direction*
gives the family of compounds called the *acenes*; for example:

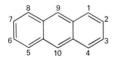

anthracene

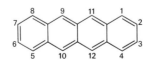

naphthacene
(or tetracene)

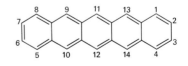

pentacene

With increase of the molecular complexity the number of possible resonant limit formulas increases; the simplest acene, anthracene, has the following Kekulè structures:

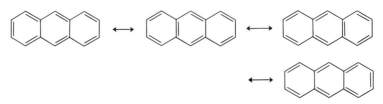

and a great number of Dewar structures and ionic limit structures.

The structure of anthracene is demonstrated by the fact that it may be obtained from benzyl chloride by the Friedel–Crafts reaction, followed by a dehydrogenation:

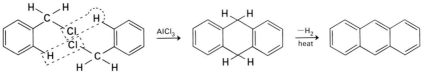

9,10-dihydroanthracene

The central 9 and 10 positions, also called *meso* or *mesoanthracenic positions*, are the most reactive positions to oxidation, reduction, and substitution by halogen. Toward sulfonation, however, the 1- and 2-positions are the reactive ones. Most derivatives of anthracene are prepared by indirect procedures, passing through the 9,10-diketone, known as *anthraquinone*. Anthraquinone may be obtained by strong oxidation of anthracene or by ring closure (*intramolecular cyclization*) of o-benzoylbenzoic acid (Section 2.4.1.1):

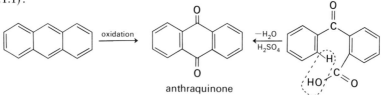

anthraquinone

The semiquinone of anthracene is *anthrone*, which is tautomeric with anthranol:

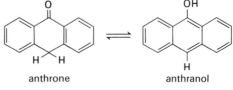

anthrone   anthranol

The 9,10-diol, which is the hydroquinone of anthraquinone, is known as anthrahydroquinol. Anthracene derivatives, hydroxy-substituted *in the lateral rings*, are more often termed hydroxyanthracenes than anthrols, and the position or positions of substitution are defined by numbers.

A peculiar property of anthracene is its reaction with maleic anhydride. This is an example of the fact that in complex polycyclic hydrocarbons, in spite of the resonance, certain positions may show unsaturated character to some degree. The presence or absence of such reactive positions depends on the molecular geometry. The reaction of anthracene with maleic anhydride is a typical Diels–Alder addition (Section 2.2.4) which clearly indicates the presence of a conjugated diene between the 9 and 10 positions, as it is actually pictured by the Kekulé formulas:

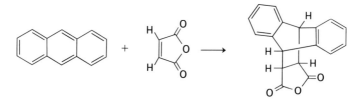

Condensation of benzene rings with naphthalene in *angular* direction gives the family of compounds called the *phenes*. The simplest phene is phenanthrene, which may be regarded as 1,2-benzonaphthalene or as dehydro-2,2'-acebiphenyl:

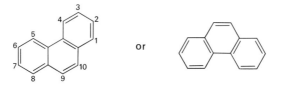

or

The positions 9 and 10 in phenanthrene correspond in several respects to the similarly numbered positions in anthracene. Hence they are also called the *meso* positions. The term *mesophenanthrenic* position must be used to distinguish it from a *mesoanthracenic* position when both are present in a complex hydrocarbon. The univalent group corresponding to phenanthrene is the *phenanthryl group*, preceded by a number defining the position of linkage.

Mild reduction of phenanthrene yields 9,10-dihydrophenanthrene. Oxidation gives the 9,10-diketone, phenanthrenequinone. More vigorous oxidation splits the ace bridge to yield the 2,2'-biphenylcarboxylic acid, called diphenic acid.

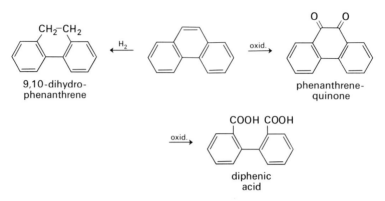

9,10-dihydro-
phenanthrene

phenanthrene-
quinone

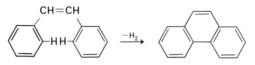

diphenic
acid

The structure of phenanthrene is further substantiated by the fact that it may be obtained by dehydrogenation of *cis*-stilbene:

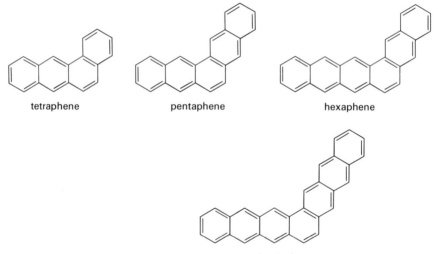

Linear addition of further benzene rings to the lateral rings of phenanthrene gives higher phenes:

tetraphene   pentaphene   hexaphene

heptaphene

Tetraphene, which is 2,3-benzophenanthrene, may also be regarded as, and in fact is generally termed *1,2-benzanthracene*. It is the simplest condensed polycyclic hydrocarbon which has both mesoanthracenic and mesophenanthrenic positions (or as they are sometimes called, "regions").

Condensation of a benzene ring with phenanthrene at the 9,10-position corresponds to *triphenylene*, an interesting molecule with three symmetry axes. Triphenylene may also be regarded as *o*-phenylene-2,2'-biphenyl:

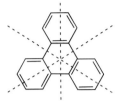

In all condensed aromatic polycyclic hydrocarbons the number of resonant limit structures increases with the complexity of the molecule (Section 3.2.2). The terminology of higher polycyclic systems will be discussed in the introductory section of the chapter on the structure and carcinogenic activity of polycyclic hydrocarbons (Section 5.1.1.1).

2.4.2.3 Heterocyclic Systems

Heterocyclic compounds result by replacing one or more carbon atoms in cyclic hydrocarbons with elements other than carbon, most often nitrogen, oxygen, or sulfur. Heterocyclic compounds may be aliphatic or aromatic in character. For example, the cyclic amines listed in Section 2.3.6 are aliphatic heterocyclic compounds. The most important 5-membered aromatic heterocyclic systems are:

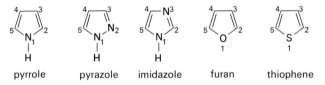

pyrrole   pyrazole   imidazole   furan   thiophene

Pyrrole enters into the composition of a biologically important class of compounds, the *porphyrins*, which are complex tetrapyrrole derivatives. For example, chlorophyll and ferrous protoheme (the porphyrin moiety of hemoglobin) are porphyrin derivatives. Other porphyrin derivatives play important roles as respiratory catalysts in the cell, as the working moiety of vitamin B_{12}, etc. (see later in Table VII, Section 3.1.2.8). Another group of tetrapyrrole derivatives, the *phthalocyanines*, show close structural similarity to the porphyrins and are also highly colored. The phthalocyanines are distinguished by their extreme chemical stability and hence are used as pigments in paints.

To distinguish compounds containing cyclic structures constructed of carbon only, from heterocyclic compounds, the former are called *homocyclic* compounds. Cyclopentadiene is the homocyclic analog of pyrrole, furan, and thiophene. However, this analogy is only formal, since the double bonds in these three heterocyclic compounds have nearly the same inactivity as in benzene, while cyclopentadiene behaves as an unsaturated diene. This is due to the fact that atoms capable of forming onium compounds (ammonium, oxonium, sulfonium) can, to an extent, replace a carbon–carbon double bond. Because of involvement in the resonance, the ability of the heteroatoms to form onium compounds largely disappears. The compound resulting from replacement of one —CH= group in benzene by —N= is pyridine. Replacement of two —CH= groups by —N= in ortho, meta, and para gives in this order pyridazine, pyrimidine, and pyrazine:

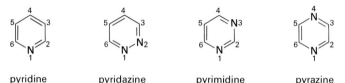

pyridine   pyridazine   pyrimidine   pyrazine

Pyrrole and the above 6-membered nitrogen-containing heterocyclics are weak bases. Catalytic hydrogenation abolishes the aromatic character, and the resulting cyclic secondary mono- and diamines are strong bases (e.g., pyrrolidine, piperidine, and piperazine in Section 2.3.6).

Many heterocyclic compounds have condensed ring systems with one benzene ring fused to a heterocyclic ring. Some condensed heterocyclic ring systems, which are of interest in view of our topic, are:

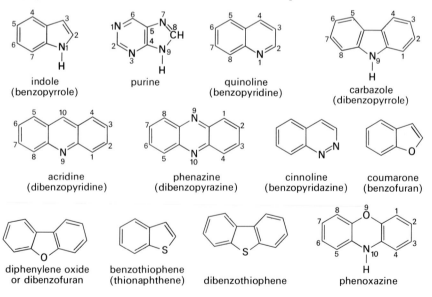

indole   purine   quinoline   carbazole
(benzopyrrole)   (benzopyridine)   (dibenzopyrrole)

acridine   phenazine   cinnoline   coumarone
(dibenzopyridine)   (dibenzopyrazine)   (benzopyridazine)   (benzofuran)

diphenylene oxide   benzothiophene   dibenzothiophene   phenoxazine
or dibenzofuran   (thionaphthene)

A large family of diverse types of complex basic plant compounds, the *alkaloids*, contain nitrogen as part of aromatic or nonaromatic heterocyclic rings. The nitrogen is in many instances tertiary, being at the site of fusion of two or three rings.

SELECTED READING FOR SECTION 2

1. Herz, W.: "The Shape of Carbon Compounds." Benjamin, New York, 1963, 152 pp.
2. Whitmore, F. C.: "Organic Chemistry," 2 vols. Dover, New York, 1961, 1005 pp.
3. Traynham, J. G.: "Organic Nomenclature: A Programmed Introduction." Prentice-Hall, Englewood Cliffs, New Jersey, 1966, 129 pp.
4. Fieser, L. F., and Fieser, M.: "Organic Chemistry." Reinhold, New York, 1956, 1118 pp.
5. Roberts, J. D., and Caseiro, M. C.: "Basic Principles of Organic Chemistry." Benjamin, New York, 1965, 1315 pp.

3   The Nature of Intra- and Intermolecular Forces

3.1   The Nature of Valence

3.1.1   THE NUCLEUS. THE STRUCTURE OF ATOMIC SHELLS. ELECTRON ORBITALS

3.1.1.1   *The Nucleus*

The first comprehensive model of atomic structure is due mainly to the work of Rutherford and Bohr. Almost all of the atomic mass is carried in a central atomic particle called the *nucleus*. The most important particles making up the nucleus are the *protons* carrying a positive charge, and the *neutrons* carrying no electric charge. Protons and neutrons are also termed *nucleons*. A neutron and a proton have approximately the same mass. Except the atomic nucleus of ordinary hydrogen (containing one proton and no neutron), the nuclei of all elements in the Periodic Table are composed of protons and an equal or slightly larger number of neutrons. The packing of protons and neutrons in the atomic nuclei is not random but follows definite structural patterns and is a factor of nuclear stability. The number of protons in the nucleus (indicating the number of positive charges) is called the *atomic number* and this defines the position of an element in the Periodic Table.

The *mass number* gives the sum of the number of protons and neutrons in the nucleus and represents the approximate nuclear mass. There is for each element a given proportion of protons and neutrons which has over-whelmingly the widest distribution in nature. However, varieties exist which differ in the number of neutrons in the nucleus. Forms of elements which have the same number of protons but a different number of neutrons are called *isotopes*. In some cases this deviation in the number of neutrons causes nuclear instability resulting in gradual disintegration of the element with emission of radiation. Besides the common type of hydrogen containing one proton only (designated as $_1H^1$), for example, one variety is known containing one neutron in addition to the proton (deuterium, designated as $_1H^2$), and another containing two neutrons (the radioactive tritium: $_1H^3$). Other examples are the common $_6C^{12}$ and the isotopic radioactive $_6C^{14}$, the common $_7N^{14}$ and the isotopic $_7N^{15}$. In these symbols the subscript denotes the atomic number and the superscript the mass number.

3.1.1.2   The Bohr–Sommerfeld Model of Electron Shell Structure. The Quantum Numbers

In an electrically neutral atom the positive charges of the nucleus are balanced by the negative charges of the *electrons* surrounding it. The number of electrons surrounding the nucleus is therefore the same as the number of protons; the atomic number defines consequently the number of electrons as well. In the original model of successive electron shells proposed by Bohr the electrons, regarded as particles, move around the nucleus in well-defined orbits.

The Bohr model was eminently successful in giving the first rational explanation for the wavelengths of the emission spectrum lines of hydrogen, observed by Balmer in the visible, by Paschen in the infrared, and by Lyman in the ultraviolet region. Figure 5 shows the orbits in the hydrogen atom according to the Bohr model and the spectrum lines of the Balmer series designated as H_α, H_β, H_γ, H_δ. The Bohr orbits represent a sequence of increasing energy levels (characterized by the integers $n = 1, 2, 3, 4, 5\ldots$, called *quantum numbers*) which the electron may occupy. The quantum numbers define the distance of these orbits from the center of the atom because the angular momentum $m \cdot v \cdot r$ of the electron can take on only discrete values following the relation:

$$m \cdot v \cdot r_n = n\frac{h}{2\pi} \tag{1}$$

where h is Planck's constant (6.6×10^{-27} erg $\cdot$ sec), m the mass of the electron (9.1×10^{-28} gm resting mass), v the velocity of the electron, and r_n the radius of an orbit defined by a quantum number n. It follows that the electrons may occupy only certain permissible energy levels in the atom; these energy levels are said to be *quantized*.

According to the Bohr model no electromagnetic radiation is emitted as long as the electron is stationary in any one orbit. However, in a flame or electric arc the atoms may be brought into states of high energy (excited states), corresponding to displacement of the electrons to higher orbits.

Atoms in excited states emit radiations of characteristic wavelengths when the electrons return to orbits of lower energy. The energy difference between the higher and lower orbits, and the frequency v (number of oscillations completed in one second) of the radiated light energy, are related by the equation:

$$E' - E = h \cdot v \tag{2}$$

where E' and E represent the respective energy levels of a higher and a lower orbit. The difference energy is carried away by the elementary light corpuscle,

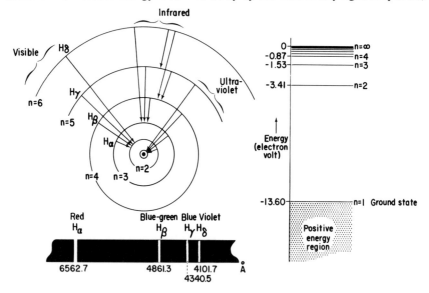

Fig. 5. The quantized circular electron orbits of the hydrogen atom following the Bohr atom model, and the electron transitions between orbits causing the appearance of the Balmer (in the visible), Paschen (in the infrared), and Lyman (in the ultraviolet) spectrum line series. The spectrum lines of the Balmer series are designated as H_{α}, H_{β}, H_{γ}, and H_{δ}. For the calculation of the spectrum line frequencies from the orbital quantum numbers n, see Suppletory Note 1. The energy levels of the quantized orbits are given in electron volts (1 eV = 23.06 kcal/mole).

the photon $h \cdot v$. However, electron energy "jump" may occur between different pairs of orbits in different individual atoms simultaneously, consequently a spectrum containing several discrete lines is produced (such as the Balmer series in Fig. 5) (see Suppletory Note 1*).

The Bohr theory proved very fruitful in interpreting in a first approximation the structure of simple atoms, particularly hydrogen. It did account also for the spectra of alkali metals which are, like hydrogen, in the first group of the Periodic Table. However, the Bohr theory could not account

* Suppletory Notes for Section 3.1 begin on page 142.

for certain phenomena observed with the hydrogen spectrum and it was definitely unsatisfactory for the interpretation of the spectra of more complex atoms. Thus, when the spectral lines of hydrogen were examined with spectroscopes of much higher resolution some were found to be actually composed of several very close lines. By putting the source of emission under the action of a magnetic field it was found that this separation of the spectral lines of hydrogen and other elements is considerably enhanced so that they can be readily observed; other spectral lines which normally appear as single are split into groups of closely spaced lines (Zeeman effect). It appeared then that the Bohr orbits contain actually several suborbits (called now *subshells*) representing close, discrete, energy levels. An n quantum number characterizes actually the *average* energy level of all subshells of a given Bohr orbit. The number n is henceforth called the *principal quantum number*. The orbits (now called *shells*) characterized by the principal quantum numbers are alternately called K, L, M, N, O, P, and Q *shells* (K for $n = 1$, L for $n = 2$, M for $n = 3$, etc.).

The Bohr model was refined further by Sommerfeld. To account for the close but *discrete energy levels*, he assigned to each shell a number of subshells equal to n. Thus, the $n = 1$ level (*ground state*) contains one spherical subshell, the $n = 2$ level one spherical and one elliptical subshell, the $n = 3$ level one spherical subshell and two elliptical subshells of different shapes, etc. (Fig. 6). These subshells within each shell are characterized by the *azimuthal quantum number l*, which can take on only integral values. Thus

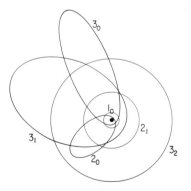

Fig. 6. The quantized elliptical electron orbits of the Sommerfeld atom model. The quantum number n determines the average energy of the electron shell. The azimuthal quantum number l (subscript) determines the shape of the subshells within each shell following the relation $b/a = (l + 1)/n$, where b and a are the half of the minor axis and the half of the major axis of an orbit, respectively. Thus, within a given shell the eccentricity of the elliptical subshells increases with the decrease of the azimuthal quantum number; the flattest orbit within a given shell corresponds to $l = 0$.

l defines now the permissible angular momenta which are $l \cdot (h/2\pi)$. [The angular momentum $m \cdot v \cdot r$ is a vector quantity (see Suppletory Note 2) and the simplest way to represent it is by an arrow drawn along the axis about which the rotation occurs. Because of the angular momentum an orbital subshell may be regarded as a gyroscope; Fig. 7A.] The *maximum* value of l is derived from the principal quantum number following the relation $l = n - 1$; thus the values of l for a given shell are $0, 1, 2, 3 \ldots n - 1$. For example, the N shell ($n = 4$) contains four subshells which are distinguished by the azimuthal quantum numbers 0, 1, 2, and 3. The total *number* of azimuthal quantum numbers assigned to a shell always equals the number of subshells in that shell. Electrons for which $l = 0, 1, 2, 3$ are, respectively, called s, p, d, f electrons following the early spectroscopists' terminology to indicate the character of lines in emission spectra (sharp,

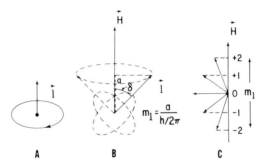

Fig. 7. A. The orbital electron as a gyroscope. The arrowhead on the circular orbit indicates the orbital motion of the electron. The vertical arrow represents the angular momentum vector $\vec{l}$. B. The precession of the orbital electron gyroscope produced by an external magnetic field $\vec{H}$. The angle of precession is δ, and the projection of the angular momentum vector on the axis of the magnetic field is a. The angle δ is quantized so that the possible values of the magnetic quantum numbers m_l are integers. C. Some quantized orientations of the angular momentum vector relative to the magnetic field axis, and the corresponding magnetic quantum numbers.

principal, *diffuse*, *fundamental*). For example, a $1s$ electron is an electron in the K ($n = 1$) shell for which $l = 0$, a $2p$ electron is one in the L ($n = 2$) shell for which $l = 1$, a $4d$ electron is one in the N ($n = 4$) shell for which $l = 2$.

Two further quantum numbers are necessary to characterize the possible states of an electron in the electron shells. The Zeeman effect and experiments by Stern and Gerlach indicated that in a magnetic field (independently of the field strength) the planes of the electron subshells (the planes of the suborbits) can occupy only certain permissible positions relative to the direction of the field. This may be explained as follows: an electron in a circular path is equivalent to a circular current creating a *magnetic moment*, the direction of which coincides with the vector of the angular momentum. (The magnetic moment is the product of the strength of the magnetic poles of a magnet and the distance between the poles. A circular current is said to have a magnetic moment $\vec{M}$ when it creates the same magnetic field as a permanent magnet of moment $\vec{M}$.) An external field $\vec{H}$ exercises therefore a torque on the "orbital-gyroscope" (Fig. 7A) by acting on the magnetic moment. The result is the precession around the axis of the external field. The angle δ of this precession can take on, however, discrete values only. The *Larmor rule* states that δ can have only such values that the projection of the angular momentum on the axis of the field is an integral multiple of $h/2\pi$ (Fig. 7B); this multiplier m_l, called the *magnetic quantum number,* quantizes the spatial orientation of the subshells. The *number* of m_l values is obtained from the azimuthal quantum number following the relation $m_l = 2l + 1$; the actual values of m_l may range from $-l$ to $+l$. For example, for $l = 0$, $m_l = 0$; for $l = 1$, $m_l = -1, 0, +1$; for $l = 2$, $m_l = -2, -1, 0, +1, +2$ (Fig. 7C).

Figure 7B indicates actually that the magnetic quantum number defines the magnitude of a component of the angular momentum in the direction of the magnetic field. The actual value of the magnetic moment may be calculated from this component by means of a proportionality constant (see Suppletory Note 3) because the directions of the angular momentum and magnetic moment vectors coincide. The magnetic quantum numbers m_l for given values of l maintain their significance even in the absence of any deliberately applied strong magnetic field since the magnitude of the angle of precession δ is totally independent of the field intensity.

The introduction of a fourth quantum number became necessary because in many instances the n, l, and m_l quantum numbers could account for only one half of the number of spectral lines which could be observed with high resolution spectroscopes. Uhlenbeck and Goudsmit have shown that the total number of lines could be explained by considering the electrons to be spinning and, thus, creating a magnetic moment of their own. This magnetic moment (spin moment) may be parallel or antiparallel to the magnetic moment of the subshell. The corresponding *spin magnetic quantum number* m_s has only one magnitude, but because of the two possible directions of the spin, it can have two signs $m_s = +\frac{1}{2}$ or $-\frac{1}{2}$ (see Suppletory Note 4).

3.1.1.3   *The Electron Waves of de Broglie. The Heisenberg Uncertainty Principle. Wave Mechanics*

Considerable refinement in the concepts of the structure of electronic shells began with the realization that the electrons have both corpuscular and wave properties. The wave nature of the electron was put forward on theoretical grounds by de Broglie and demonstrated experimentally a few years later by Davisson and Germer.

The theory of de Broglie was closely patterned on Einstein's theory of light according to which both a momentum and a wavelength must be ascribed to the elementary light corpuscle, the photon. Thus, if the equation describing the photon energy and the equation describing the energy of material particles:

$$E = h \cdot v \qquad \text{and} \qquad E = m \cdot c^2$$

are combined and solved for m, we get:

$$m = \frac{hv}{c^2}$$

where c is the velocity of light. Multiplying both sides of the equation with the expressions of velocity, for corpuscles and waves, respectively, we get the momentum $m \cdot v$ of the photon:

$$m \cdot v = \frac{hv}{c^2} \cdot c, \qquad \text{that is} \quad m \cdot v = \frac{hv}{c} \tag{3}$$

However, remembering that the relation of the wavelength, frequency and propagation velocity is $c = \lambda \cdot v$, then substituting in Eq. (3), and solving for λ:

$$\lambda = \frac{h}{m \cdot v} \tag{4}$$

Following the theory of de Broglie, an identical relation holds for the electron; that is, an electron of mass m and velocity v represents *at the same time* a wave of wavelength λ. Thus, the concept of a particle-like electron circulating in well-defined orbits can be replaced by the representation of the electron as a three-dimensional "standing-wave" pattern. The idea of permissible and forbidden electron orbits introduced by Bohr becomes now a consequence of the concept of a well-defined electron wavelength. Thus, the only permissible orbits are those into which the electron wave will just "fit in"; in other words the circumference of the permissible orbits must be integral multiples of the electron wavelength:

$$2\pi r_n = n \cdot \lambda \tag{5}$$

A two-dimensional schematic representation of permissible and forbidden orbits is given in Fig. 8.

The intuitive but arbitrary postulate of Bohr that the angular momentum of the circulating electron can only take on values which are the integral multiples of $h/2\pi$ [see Eq. (1)] follows naturally from Eqs. (4) and (5). Solving these two equations for the momentum and for the wavelength, respectively, we get:

$$m \cdot v = \frac{h}{\lambda} \quad \text{and} \quad \lambda = \frac{2\pi r_n}{n}$$

Substituting for λ in the expression of the momentum:

$$m \cdot v = \frac{n \cdot h}{2\pi r_n}$$

from which we find Eq. (1) of the angular momentum

$$m \cdot v \cdot r_n = n \frac{h}{2\pi}$$

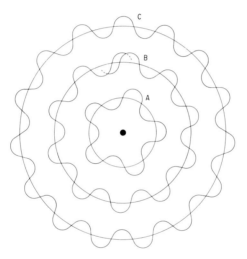

Fig. 8. A representation of electron standing waves in atomic orbits following de Broglie. The orbits A and C represent permissible orbits, and B illustrates a forbidden orbit.

Another reason why the corpuscular representation of the electrons moving in precise atomic orbits has been replaced by a wave-like representation is that it is *a priori* impossible to assign an exact physical position to an electron which would be expectable according to the corpuscular theory. This follows from the *Heisenberg Uncertainty Principle* (see Suppletory Note 5):

$$\Delta x \cdot \Delta m v_x \approx h \tag{6}$$

which states that the simultaneous determination of both the position x

(relative to an x coordinate axis) and the momentum $m \cdot v_x$ of a particle (moving along the x axis) involves an uncertainty Δ, and that the product of the two errors may not be less than h, the constant of Planck. This limitation of the precision of simultaneous measurements is negligible in the macroscopic world because of the very small value of h. It results, however, in considerable uncertainty when measurements are carried out on the scale of subatomic dimensions. Also, following the Uncertainty Principle there is an incompatibility between the known atomic electron energy levels and the energy levels which may be calculated by assuming a more closely defined position for an electron (see Suppletory Note 6).

Wave mechanics, founded by de Broglie, Schrödinger, Heisenberg, Pauling, and others, represents the further development of the theory of electron shells. In wave mechanics the corpuscular concept of the electron is totally abandoned and replaced by a mathematical expression, known

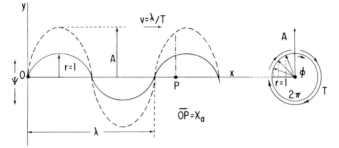

Fig. 9. Wave motion and "circle of reference" of a simple harmonic motion. The amplitude of the motion (the *maximum* displacement in the direction of the y axis) is A, the amplitude function is ψ, the wavelength λ, the propagation velocity v, and the distance from the origin at an arbitrary point P is x_a.

as an amplitude function or *wave function* (usually represented as ψ), which describes the three-dimensional wave amplitude pattern of the electron. The meaning of the wave function is explained in Suppletory Note 7 using the representation of a simple oscillatory motion and its circle of reference (Fig. 9). The significance of the wave function for wave mechanics may be understood as follows: It is known from the physics of wave motions that just as the energy of a simple mechanical harmonic motion is proportional to the square of its amplitude, the intensity of a light wave passing through a unit of space is proportional to the square of its amplitude. However, because of the dual (wave and corpuscular) nature of light the intensity of the wave is also proportional with the number of photons. By analogy it will be assumed that the number of electrons present in a definite region of space is proportional to the square of the amplitude ψ of the wave associated to the electrons by virtue of the Eq. (4).

Now, when only one electron is considered, the intensity ψ^2 of the electron wave cannot be regarded as proportional to the *number* of electrons, since only one electron is present. The ψ^2 of the wave of an electron is interpreted as being proportional to the *probability dP* of finding the electron in a definite small unit portion of space; this probability is also proportional to the volume dv of the considered unit portion of space. Thus, the probability has the form:

$$dP = \psi^2(x, y, z) \cdot dv \tag{7}$$

from which:

$$\frac{dP}{dv} = \psi^2(x, y, z) \tag{8}$$

where x, y, and z represent the fact that the electron wave is three-dimensional and its intensity must, therefore, be known for all three coordinates defining the space dv. The ratio dP/dv represents, thus, the *probability density* of the presence of the electron. This has two implications. First, that $\psi^2 = 0$ corresponds to the total absence of electrons. Second, that there is a unit probability (or certainty) of an electron, having the wave function ψ, being present in that space which is the sum of all small dv unit volumes considered. This second implication, called the *normalization condition* of the wave function, is mathematically expressed as:

$$\int \psi^2 \, dv = 1 \tag{9}$$

It should be retained for future reference that what is commonly called "electron density" is truly the probability density of electron presence.

The ψ amplitude functions for any particular atom are obtained by solving a differential equation (Schrödinger equation) which involves the total energy and the potential energy of the electron; the number of permissible shells and subshells is delimited by the fact that the Schrödinger equation has valid solutions only for certain values of the total energy (see Suppletory Note 8). In wave mechanics the existence of discrete electron energy levels follows naturally from the mathematical form of the Schrödinger equation. Solution of this equation for the simplest case, the hydrogen atom, yields the same expression for the possible energy levels of the electron as the Bohr theory [see Suppletory Note 1, Eq. (i)]. For more complex atoms and energy levels higher than $n = 1$ the characteristic values of ψ depend, furthermore, on the quantum numbers l, m_l and m_s.

3.1.1.4 The Exclusion Principle of Pauli. The Periodic System of Elements

The four quantum numbers n, l, m_l, and m_s define the possible atomic electron energy levels. However a unifying principle was still needed since otherwise it might have been supposed, for example, that since the K shell represents the lowest energy level, all electrons in a neutral unexcited atom would be present in that shell. This unifying principle is known as the *Pauli Exclusion Principle* which states that *no two electrons in any atom can have the same four quantum numbers*. In other words if two electrons have identical quantum numbers n, l, and m_l, they must have different spin magnetic quantum numbers m_s. Since there are only two values for m_s ($+\frac{1}{2}$ and $-\frac{1}{2}$), it follows that any subshell can contain only two electrons with identical n, l, and m_l quantum numbers. Two such electrons are called by virtue of their opposite spins *coupled* or *paired*, and are symbolized as ↑↓. Two electrons having identical spins ↑↑ (or ↓↓) are called *unpaired*, and, following the Exclusion Principle, they must differ in at least one of the three quantum numbers n, l, and m_l. (The significance of opposite spins for electrons having the same n, l, and m_l quantum numbers is further discussed in Section 3.1.2.1.)

There are two additional restrictions on the successive filling up of the atomic shells with electrons. The first restriction is that the lowest energy (more stable) subshells are filled up in preference to the higher energy subshells; this is in line with the fact that any physical or chemical system tends to change toward the lowest possible energy level. In polyelectronic atoms, however, there is a partial inversion in the order of energies of subshells in neighboring higher shells, which is paralleled by the order of filling with electrons. The order of energies of subshells in polyelectronic atoms is the following:

$$1s < 2s < 2p < 3s < 3p < 3d \approx 4s < 4p < 4d$$
$$\approx 5s < 5p < 6s < 5d < 4f < 6p < 7s < 6d < 5f$$

Because of this partial inversion, no electrons enter into a d subshell until the s subshell of the next higher shell has been filled. Similarly the f subshells receive no electrons before several lower subshells in higher shells are filled. These irregularities are due to the fact that shapes of the d and f subshells (see Section 3.1.1.5) are such that they extend far beyond the lower subshell of higher shells.

The second restriction is called *Hund's rule* or the *rule of maximum multiplicity*. This rule states that when several electrons occupy subshells of the same l quantum number, then the most stable arrangement corresponds to a distribution where the electrons occupy the greatest possible number of subshells and have parallel (*i.e.*, "unpaired") spins, as long as this last requirement does not come in opposition with the Exclusion Principle. In other words in the successive filling of the subshells, before any pairing of the electrons takes place, the subshells must be occupied as much as possible by single electrons. For example, if in a shell the s subshell and the three p subshells are filled, additional electrons will successively occupy the five

Table I—Part 1
The Electron Configurations of Elements

Period	Element	Shell: Subshell: Atomic No.	K 1s	L 2s 2p	M 3s 3p 3d	N 4s 4p 4d 4f	O 5s 5p 5d	P 6s
I	H	1	1					
	He	2	2					
II	Li	3	2	1				
	Be	4		2				
	B	5	*Helium Core 2 electrons*	2 1				
	C	6		2 2				
	N	7		2 3				
	O	8		2 4				
	F	9		2 5				
	Ne	10		2 6				
III	Na	11	2	2 6	1			
	Mg	12			2			
	Al	13		*Neon Core 10 electrons*	2 1			
	Si	14			2 2			
	P	15			2 3			
	S	16			2 4			
	Cl	17			2 5			
	A	18			2 6			
IV	K	19	2	2 6	2 6	1		
	Ca	20				2		
Transition Metals, first series	Sc	21				1 2		
	Ti	22				2 2		
	V	23		*Argon Core 18 electrons*		3 2		
	Cr	24				5 1		
	Mn	25				5 2		
	Fe	26				6 2		
	Co	27				7 2		
	Ni	28				8 2		
	Cu	29	2	2 6	2 6 10	1		
	Zn	30				2		
	Ga	31				2 1		
	Ge	32		*Cu⁺ Core 28 electrons*		2 2		
	As	33				2 3		
	Se	34				2 4		
	Br	35				2 5		
	Kr	36				2 6		

(continued)

Table I—Part 1—continued
The Electron Configurations of Elements

Period	Element	Atomic No.:	K	L		M			N				O			P
		Shell:	K	L		M			N				O			P
		Subshell:	1s	2s	2p	3s	3p	3d	4s	4p	4d	4f	5s	5p	5d	6s
V	Rb	37	2	2	6	2	6	10	2	6			1			
	Sr	38											2			
	Y	39									1		2			
	Zr	40									2		2			
	Nb	41			Krypton Core						4		1			
	Mo	42			36 electrons						5		1			
	Tc	43									6		1			
	Ru	44									7		1			
	Rh	45									8		1			
	Pd	46									10					
	Ag	47	2	2	6	2	6	10	2	6	10		1			
	Cd	48											2			
	In	49											2	1		
	Sn	50			Ag⁺ Core								2	2		
	Sb	51			46 electrons								2	3		
	Te	52											2	4		
	I	53											2	5		
	Xe	54											2	6		
VI	Cs	55	2	2	6	2	6	10	2	6	10		2	6		1

Transition Metals, second series: Y, Zr, Nb, Mo, Tc, Ru, Rh, Pd

Ag⁺ Core 46 electrons

Xenon Core 54 electrons

d subshells singly, and will have unpaired spins. The pairing of electrons and spins will begin only with the "fitting in" of the sixth electron. This rule is due to the fact that the mutual repulsion of electrons, occupying singly subshells of same energy, is less if they have unpaired spins.

Using the conceptual framework given by the four quantum numbers and their relationships, the Pauli Exclusion Principle, the Hund's rule, and the order of energies of the subshells, the electronic configuration of any neutral atom may be described. Table I, Part 1 gives the electronic configuration of neutral atoms of the elements up to the atomic number 55 (cesium). Hydrogen has only one electron which is therefore in the 1s subshell. The 1s subshell is filled in helium, which has two electrons. In lithium which has three electrons, two electrons fill the 1s subshell (helium core) and 1 electron is in the 2s subshell. In beryllium, having four electrons, both the 1s and 2s subshells are filled. Between boron and neon (where the 1s and 2s subshells are filled) the additional electrons fill up successively the three available $2p$ subshells (denoted as p_x, p_y, and p_z, see Section 3.1.1.5). In boron the single p electron is in the p_x subshell; in carbon the two p electrons are "unpaired" and are in the p_x and p_y subshells, respectively; nitrogen contains three "unpaired" electrons distributed evenly among the p_x, p_y, and p_z orbitals. "Pairing" begins with oxygen in which $2p_x$ contains two electrons of opposite spins, and $2p_y$ and $2p_z$ contain one "unpaired" electron each.

Elements of Period III have the K and L shells filled (neon core) and further electrons enter into the successive subshells of the M shell. Instances of elements showing inversion of the filling order begin to appear in Period IV with potassium, the first element having an argon core. In this manner it is possible to estimate the number of electrons that enter into the different subshells and thus describe the electronic configuration of the elements. It can be seen that the total number of electrons that can occupy a given shell is $2n^2$, where n is the principal quantum number (*rule of Stoner*).

The electronic configuration is often given in shorthand notation in which each subshell is described by the principal quantum number, the subshell type, and a superscript to the latter denoting the number of electrons in the subshell. Table I, Part 2 illustrates the distribution of electrons with their

Table I—Part 2

The Electron Configurations of Elements

(First and Second Period)

Element	Orbitals filled					Configuration
	$1s$	$2s$	$2p_x$	$2p_y$	$2p_z$	
H	↑	○	○	○	○	$1s$
He	↑↓	○	○	○	○	$1s^2$
Li	↑↓	↑	○	○	○	$1s^2, 2s$
Be	↑↓	↑↓	○	○	○	$1s^2, 2s^2$
B	↑↓	↑↓	↑	○	○	$1s^2, 2s^2, 2p$
C	↑↓	↑↓	↑	↑	○	$1s^2, 2s^2, 2p^2$
N	↑↓	↑↓	↑	↑	↑	$1s^2, 2s^2, 2p^3$
O	↑↓	↑↓	↑↓	↑	↑	$1s^2, 2s^2, 2p^4$
F	↑↓	↑↓	↑↓	↑↓	↑	$1s^2, 2s^2, 2p^5$
Ne	↑↓	↑↓	↑↓	↑↓	↑↓	$1s^2, 2s^2, 2p^6$

respective spins and the shorthand notation of the electronic configuration for the elements of Periods I and II.

The examination of Table I, Part 1 shows that the periodicity of properties of the elements, which is the basis of the Periodic Table, derives from the periodicity with which the outermost subshells of the atoms possess electrons in the same subshell types. Thus, for example, Li, Na, K, and Rb all have one electron in an s-type subshell; fluorine, chlorine, and bromine all have five electrons in a p-type subshell. Since the electrons in the outermost shell interact to the greatest extent when chemical bonds are formed between atoms, they are often referred to as *valence electrons*.

3.1.1.5 The Shapes of Atomic Orbitals

A consequence of the normalization condition [Eq. (9)] of the wave function is that, for an electron in any energy state, there is a small but finite probability that it may be found in *any* particular point in the space considered. Therefore, following the wave-mechanical conception, the *total* charge of an electron around the nucleus may not be encompassed by a sharply defined spatial contour (similar to the two-dimensional planar orbits of the Bohr-Sommerfeld model). Rather, the electron may be regarded as a diffuse three-dimensional cloud, the density of which at each point (defined by the x, y, z coordinates) is proportional to $\psi^2(x, y, z)$.

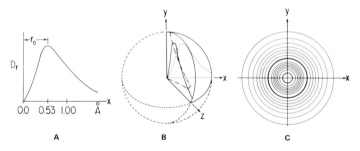

Fig. 10. The *radial* electron probability D_r of a $1s$ electron as a function of the distance from the nucleus. A gives the distribution obtained for any one direction (for example, x). This distribution is *independent* from the direction; thus, the same distribution is obtained along any one radius. The radial electron probability distribution along three perpendicular radii (for example, the x, y, z coordinate axes) is shown in B. The cross-section of this spherical electron distribution at a x–y plane is represented in C; the dark circle in C shows the maximum of D_r (at r_0).

Figure 10A shows the distribution of the *radial* electron probability (Suppletory Note 9) of a $1s$ electron. It will be noted that the *radial* electron probability has a maximum at a certain distance from the nucleus, then it slowly decreases but actually never reaches zero. The distribution of a $1s$ electron is *independent* of the spatial orientation of the radius. In other words it is spherically symmetrical. The same distribution will hence be found along any arbitrary radius (such as the three perpendicular coordinate axes x, y, z) as shown in Fig. 10B. Figure 10C shows the cross-sectional contours of this probability distribution. The distance from the nucleus where the probability is maximum is about 0.53 Å, which is the same value that is obtained by the Bohr theory for the $n = 1$ orbit (see Suppletory Note 1).

Now for the purpose of graphic representation it is customary to draw a boundary surface which will represent a region in space that includes a specific fraction (usually 90%) of the electron probability ψ^2. The $1s$ electron energy level can therefore be represented as a spherical shell having such a radius that the boundary surface includes an electron probability (or "electron density") of 0.90 (Fig. 11). Such a three-dimensional electron density distribution pattern is called an *orbital*. We will say that this is the volume occupied by the electron. The $2s$, $3s$, $4s$, etc., orbitals are all spherical

Fig. 11. The shape of a $1s$ orbital. The center of the sphere coincides with the origin of the three coordinate axes. The radius of the sphere, the boundary surface of which includes an electron density of 0.90, is taken as unity: $r_0 = \sqrt{1}$ (for comparing the radial extensions of orbitals belonging in the same electron shell).

except that the respective r_0 values are increasingly larger as they belong to shells of increasingly higher energy.

In contrast to the s subshells, the probability distributions of the p, d, and f subshells are strongly dependent on direction and have, thus, quite different geometries. A p orbital is represented by two equal spheroidal volumes; there are three equivalent p orbitals (denoted as p_x, p_y, p_z) the axes of which are oriented at right angles to one another (Fig. 12). The existence of three p orbitals with different spatial orientation is due to quantization by the magnetic quantum number m_l, which for a p electron ($l = 1$) can have the three values $-1, 0, +1$. The p orbitals in the different shells have essentially identical shapes, but have higher energy levels and greater geometric dimensions in the higher shells.

The shapes of the d orbitals are even more complex. There are five d orbitals since a d electron ($l = 2$) can have five values for the magnetic

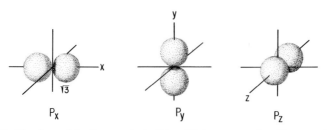

Fig. 12. The shape of the three equivalent $2p$ orbitals, p_x, p_y, and p_z. The axes of the p orbitals lie at right angles to one another. The radial extension of all three $2p$ orbitals is $\sqrt{3}$, taking the radial extension of the $2s$ orbital as unity ($r_0 = \sqrt{1}$). The radial extension is the maximum extension of an orbital from the origin of the three axes, which origin coincides with the center of the atom. The radial extension of an s orbital is, thus, the same as the radius of the sphere, while the radial extension of a p orbital corresponds to the diameter of one of the spherical lobes.

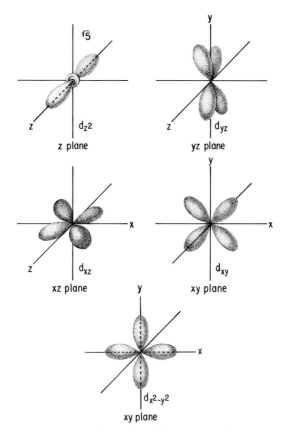

Fig. 13. The shapes of the five $3d$ orbitals. The radial extension of the simplest of these orbitals, d_{z^2} (for $m_l = 0$) is $\sqrt{5}$, taking the radial extension of the $3s$ orbital as unity ($r_0 = \sqrt{1}$).

quantum number ($m_l = -2, -1, 0, +1, +2$). Figure 13 shows the five $3d$ orbitals. Except for one of them (d_{z^2}), d orbitals represent two dumbbell-shaped volumes; these are tangent at the origin, oriented at right angles to one another, and lie in one plane. The notations indicated in the figure give the spatial relationships of these orbitals with respect to the three coordinate axes. Thus, for the orbital d_{z^2} ($m_l = 0$), the notation indicates that the length-wise axis of the orbital coincides with the z axis. The symbols d_{xz} and d_{yz} (for $m_l = \pm 1$) represent the fact that the two orbitals lie in the xz and yz planes, respectively. For d_{xy} and $d_{x^2-y^2}$ ($m_l = \pm 2$), the notations indicate that the first orbital occupies the xy plane, while the second is positioned so that the two axes of the dumbbells (which are at right angles with respect to each other) coincide with the x and y coordinate axes.

3.1.2   The Structure and Nature of Bonding Orbitals

3.1.2.1   Overlapping of Orbitals: Covalent Bond Formation. Molecular Orbitals. The σ Bond. Bond Strength. The Octet Rule

A covalent single bond, which was represented in Section 2 by a dash or a dot, corresponds to the overlapping of two atomic orbitals (where each orbital contains one lone electron) of neighboring atoms; covalent bond formation may also be regarded as the fusion of two "electron clouds." Because of this overlapping or fusion what was before two individual atomic orbitals becomes now a single *molecular orbital* (sometimes called *bonding orbital*) to which applies the same rule as for the atomic orbitals, namely that two electrons in the same orbital must have paired spins (↑↓). At first glance it would appear then that the force holding the atomic nuclei together is the attraction between the opposite spin magnetic moments of the two electrons as shown in Fig. 14. However, the calculations show that the force which actually maintains covalent bonds is the *resonance energy* which arises as a result of a special wave-mechanical phenomenon, the *electron exchange* (see Section 3.2.1). The binding energy arising from the spin mag-netic moment attraction cannot be separately accounted for, and it should be regarded as "merging" into the resonance energy. Nonetheless, Fig. 14 provides a useful nonmathematical representation that two electrons can occupy a given orbital and have attraction between them. Two electrons *at most* may be involved in the formation of a covalent single bond.

Figure 15 illustrates the formation of a hydrogen molecule from two hydro-gen atoms. Bond formation involves here the two $1s$ electrons, which have, therefore, in the resulting H—H molecule opposite spins. Of particular interest for the chemistry of organic compounds is the fact that bond for-mation can also involve an s and a p orbital or two p orbitals, where each combining atomic orbital contains one lone electron; in the resulting molecular orbital the two electrons have paired spins. Figure 16 illustrates bond formation between hydrogen and a given p orbital of another atom. These types of bonds which exemplify the covalent single bonds are called σ bonds (sometimes they are called σs bonds, σp bonds, or σsp bonds to designate the type of electrons which are involved). The reason that there is no complete merging of atoms is that electrostatic repulsive forces are also

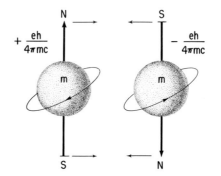

Fig. 14. A pictorial representation of the pairing of electrons having opposite spins. The opposite spins give rise to antiparallel spin magnetic momenta (see Suppletory Note 3). The reader must be cautioned here: this representation should not be regarded as a true picture of reality but merely as a "teaching aid" helping to visualize that *two* electrons may be present in an orbital and that two electrons are involved in the formation of a covalent single bond. The energy holding two atoms together in such a bond is actually due to the electron-exchange phenomenon or resonance (Section 3.2.1).

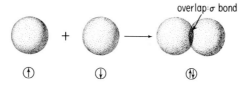

Fig. 15. Bond formation between two s orbitals. The orbital overlap represents a σs bond.

acting. First, there is repulsion between the two positively charged nuclei and, second, there is repulsion between the two electrons themselves (this electrostatic repulsion is to be distinguished from the attraction due to the opposite spin magnetic moments shown in Fig. 14). At a certain inter-nuclear distance, which is different according to the type of atoms involved, a balance is struck between the forces of attraction and repulsion.

The overlapping of atomic orbitals shows an approximate parallelism with the stability of a covalent bond: the greater the overlapping the stronger the bond. The region of overlap (which appears in Figs. 15 and 16 as more darkly shadowed) represents the region in space where values of the wave functions of the two orbitals coincide; i.e., the overlapping is a measure of interpenetration of the two electron clouds. Therefore, in this region the electron probability density will be greater than the probability density of either of the two atomic orbitals. Hence, the molecular orbital of a given electron may be considered as the *linear combination of the atomic orbitals* (LCAO) involved in bonding. The method, based on this principle, to calculate molecular orbitals is called the *LCAO method* or *MO* (molecular orbital) *method.* Thus, following the LCAO method, the wave function of the molecular orbital of a diatomic molecule is the sum of the two atomic wave functions:

$$\psi_{+\text{molecule}} = C_1\psi_1 + C_2\psi_2 \tag{10}$$

where the coefficients C_1 and C_2 represent the respective contributions of the atomic orbitals ψ_1 and ψ_2 to the molecular orbital; C_1 and C_2 are

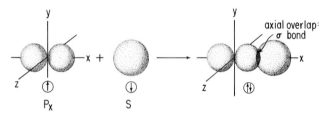

Fig. 16. Bond formation between a *p* orbital and an *s* orbital. The orbital represents a σsp bond. In σ-bond formation involving one or two *p* orbitals, there is always axial overlapping, i.e., the bond axis coincides with the orbital axis.

equal for molecules which are symmetrical with respect to the center of the bond (such as H_2) and unequal for molecules which are unsymmetrical. Since the square of the wave function is a measure of the electron probability density (Section 3.1.1.3), in a molecular orbital we have:

$$\psi_{+\text{molecule}}^2 = (C_1\psi_1 + C_2\psi_2)^2 = C_1^2\psi_1^2 + C_2^2\psi_2^2 + 2\,C_1C_2\psi_1\psi_2 \tag{11}$$

where the term $2\,C_1C_2\psi_1\psi_2$ gives the electron probability density in the region of the overlap. Since the term $\psi_1\psi_2$ represents the overlap of the two atomic orbitals, $\int \psi_1\psi_2\,dv$ denoted as S (in this instance S_{12}) means the total overlapping considered in the sum of all small dv unit volumes making up the total space. Thus S is called the *overlap integral.* Obviously, the value of S will vary (from 0 to unity) with the shapes of the atomic orbitals which overlap, and with the interatomic distances (e.g., for H_2, $S_{12} \approx 0.73$, and for aromatic π bonds, $S \approx 0.25$).

During the formation of a bond, energy is released. This same energy, called the *bond energy*, must be communicated to dissociate the overlapping orbitals. For this reason, bond energies are always given with a negative sign, indicating the fact that the bonded state is a lower energy (more stable) state than the energy state of two separated atoms. The bond energy (generally expressed in kilocalories per mole) is therefore a measure of the stability of a bond. In the calculations of the bond energies (E_+) by the LCAO method, the total energy is usually expressed as the sum of the two unit terms α and β, such as:

$$E_+ = \frac{2\alpha + k\beta}{1 + S} \tag{12}$$

In the so-called "zeroth" approximation of the LCAO method, S is taken equal to zero so that:

$$E_+ = 2\alpha + k\beta \tag{13}$$

The unit α is known as the *Coulomb integral*. It is a measure of the electron-attracting power (the electronegativity, see Section 3.1.2.3) of an atom. In other words, it is the energy unit of an electron considered to be in the electrostatic field of only one atom, *i.e.*, in a pure atomic orbital. The value of α will, therefore, be different depending on the type of atoms involved in bonding. Now, the bond involves two electrons, each in the atomic orbital of another atom. Hence the term 2α in Eq. (13). The unit β is called the *resonance integral* and it is the energy unit of an electron in the field of the two atoms involved in bonding. The value of β varies with the electronegativity of the two atoms and is a function of the overlap integral. In carbon-carbon bonds β is a function of only the interatomic distance. Both α and β are negative (to yield negative E_+ values) and k is a coefficient describing the number of β units which compose E_+. In calculations of π bonds (Sections 3.1.2.2 and 3.2.2) the resonance integral is frequently taken as $\beta \approx -18\ \text{kcal/mole}$ (assuming $S = 0$). Because α is the electron energy in a pure atomic orbital, in the calculations of π bonds of carbon compounds 2α is conveniently taken as the zero level of the energy, and the bond energies are expressed in β units only.

The relative spatial position of two atomic orbitals "fusing" into a molecular orbital (*i.e.*, the direction of a bond) will always be such as to result in maximum overlapping for a given internuclear distance. This follows from the aforementioned facts that (a) maximum overlapping corresponds to maximum bond strength, which is to say to the lowest energy level (as compared to the energy level of the two orbitals when apart), and (b) any physical and chemical system tends to occupy the lowest possible energy level. Now, this is of no consequence for bonds involving only s orbitals because s orbitals are spherically symmetrical; thus σs bonds have no angular dependence (Fig. 15). It is, however, very important in the formation of σp or σsp bonds (*e.g.*, Fig. 16) because the axes of the three p orbitals form right angles.

Experimental results substantiate the fact that between σp bonds and between σsp bonds the valence angles are 90°; a 90° valence angle is often found in compounds of elements of Group 5 of the Periodic Table. The experimentally determined bond angles are 93° for phosphine (PH_3), 92° for arsine (AsH_3), and 91° for stibine (SbH_3). For ammonia (NH_3), the bond angle is, however, 107°; this increase is generally ascribed to repulsion between the hydrogen atoms which carry a partial positive charge because of partial polarization of the bonds (see Section 3.1.2.3). The large value for the valence angle of water (104.5°) may be attributed to the same cause. An alternative explanation for the valence angles of ammonia is based on the hybridization of orbitals (Section 3.1.2.2).

Upon examining Table I, Part 1, we find that the elements neon, argon, krypton, xenon, and radon (the latter having the atomic number 86) all possess eight electrons (*octet*) in the outer electron shell; helium has two electrons (*doublet*) in its shell. These elements are very unreactive toward combination with other elements (hence the term *noble gases*), which indicates that these electronic configurations are particularly stable ones. In fact, the type of combinations in which atoms can participate is governed by and large by the tendency to gain or approach the nearest "noble gas configuration" (doublet or octet) as the result of this combination.

Atoms can gain or approach the noble gas configuration by (a) gain or loss of electrons, and (b) the *sharing of electrons*. The first case, where an electron is detached from one atom and placed in the orbital of another atom is exemplified by lithium chloride. In LiCl the lithium atom abandoned one electron to acquire the stable helium core, and the departing electron is taken up by the chlorine atom which thus acquires the stable argon core. By this electron transfer, however, the electrically neutral Li atom loses one negative charge and will have, therefore, an excess of one positive charge (positive ion); on the other hand, the electrically neutral Cl atom acquires an excess of one negative charge (negative ion). The combination in LiCl is maintained by electrostatic attraction between the oppositely charged ions $Li^{\oplus}$ and $Cl^{\ominus}$. This type of bond is called an *electrovalent* or *ionic bond* (see also Sections 3.1.2.3 and 3.3.5).

The second case is where an electron pair (necessarily of opposite spins) is shared by two atomic nuclei (the σ bond). Thus, in the aforementioned formation of a hydrogen molecule from two hydrogen atoms (Fig. 15) both atomic nuclei *equally share* the electron doublet and thereby both acquire the stable, helium-type electron shell configuration. Another example is the formation of NH_3, where the electron of one hydrogen atom forms a "paired" electron doublet with the lone electron in each $2p$ orbital of nitrogen.

The L shell of nitrogen being thus filled, the N atom acquires a completed neon core while each of the three H atoms acquires a helium core: bonding between the N atom and the three H atoms is due to the sharing of the three electron doublets. In carbon, nitrogen, oxygen, phosphorus, and sulfur, which are the common constituents of organic compounds of biological interest, electron sharing may continue till there is a maximum of eight electrons, or four doublets, in the outer shell (*octet rule*; see also in Sections 3.1.2.5 and 3.1.2.7).

3.1.2.2 Hybrid Atomic Orbitals. The π Bond

The concept of the simple atomic orbitals described in the previous section is incomplete, however, for explaining the tetravalence and the tetrahedral nature of the carbon atom, and other characteristics of certain types of covalent bonds. Table I indicates, for example, that carbon has the $1s$ and $2s$ orbitals filled and should exhibit therefore a covalence of two, corresponding to one electron each in the $2p_x$ and $2p_y$ orbitals. Yet, carbon exhibits tetravalence in the overwhelming majority of its compounds (however, bivalent carbon compounds are also known, *e.g.*, CO and iso-nitriles). Now, it could be assumed that part of the energy released during the formation of the four covalent bonds is utilized to "raise" one $2s$ electron to the unoccupied, higher energy $2p_z$ orbital (which is the same as saying that the C atom is brought to an "excited state"):

$$C(2s\,(\uparrow\downarrow)\quad 2p\,(\uparrow)\,(\uparrow)\,(\bigcirc)\,) \longrightarrow C(2s\,(\uparrow)\quad 2p\,(\uparrow)\,(\uparrow)\,(\uparrow)\,)$$

This assumption cannot, however, account for the observed experimental facts. Since p_x, p_y and p_z form right angles with each other, it would be expected then that three of the four valences of carbon are separated by 90° and that the fourth valence has no angular dependence (since the $2s$ orbital has a spherical symmetry). This would be totally contradictory with the tetrahedral configuration of CH_4, CCl_4, etc. (which has been demonstrated beyond any possible doubt), and could not account for the phenomenon of optical isomerism (see Section 2.1.3).

This difficulty was resolved by Pauling and Slater who introduced the concept of *hybridization of atomic orbitals*. The carbon atom orbitals that are actually involved in the formation of chemical bonds are neither pure s nor pure p orbitals, but combined orbitals or *hybrids*. Hybridization involves the determination of the angular directions in which the linear combination of wave functions of the one $2s$ and three $2p$ orbitals give higher values than the magnitude of single s and p orbitals. It is truly surprising that this purely theoretical procedure indicated indeed the existence of four equivalent hybrid orbitals of a maximum relative extension of 2 (taking the radius of the 2s orbital as unity), differing only in the angular directions of this maximum extension so that the four orbitals are directed toward the corners of a regular tetrahedron. Thus, the axes of the four hybrid orbitals are oriented at angles of 109° 28′ relative to each other, which is the valence angle found in simple single-bonded carbon compounds (Section 2.1.3). This process, called *tetrahedral hybridization*, is represented as sp^3 in shorthand notation; this notation indicates that the hybridization involves one s and three p orbitals.

In other types of carbon compounds hybridization may involve the 2s orbital and only two or only one of the three 2p orbitals. Hybridization of 2s, $2p_x$ and $2p_y$, called *trigonal hybridization* and represented as sp^2, yields three hybrid orbitals which lie in one plane and are oriented at 120° angles relative to each other; the unchanged $2p_z$ orbital is oriented perpendicularly above and below the sp^2 plane. Hybridization of 2s and $2p_x$, called *digonal hybridization* and represented as sp, yields two hybrid orbitals the axes of which form a 180° angle; the two hybrid orbitals are oriented perpendicularly to both faces of the plane constituted by the $2p_y$ and $2p_z$ orbitals. A schematic representation of the formation of sp, sp^2, and sp^3 hybrid orbitals is given in Fig. 17.

Following the *Hultgren theorem*, for any given shell the *relative* maximum extension of any type of orbital (nonhybridized or hybridized) equals the square root of the number of orbitals of that type. Thus for the successive orbital types, the relative extensions are $\sqrt{1}$ for s, $\sqrt{3}$ for p, $\sqrt{4}$ for sp^3, $\sqrt{5}$ for d, and so forth. For other orbitals hybridized from s and p the extension approaches $\sqrt{4}$ with the increase of the p orbital character, $\sqrt{3.74}$ for sp and $\sqrt{3.97}$ for sp^2. The relative maximum extensions and the bond angles of simple and hybrid orbitals are tabulated in Table II.

An orbital having a specific angular orientation and extending far from the nucleus may be expected to be spatially more favored for bonding than an orbital extending less far or having spherical symmetry. Hence, the relative maximum extension of an orbital is a direct measure of the overlapping

Table II
Relative Maximum Extension (Overlapping Power) of Orbitals. Bond Angles

Orbital:	s	p	sp	sp^2	sp^3
Relative maximum extension:	1.000	1.732	1.932	1.991	2.000
Angle between directions of maximum extension (bond angle):	—	90°	180°	120°	109° 28′

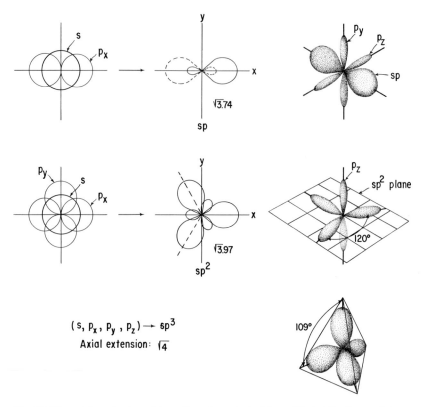

Fig. 17. Digonal (or *sp*), trigonal (or *sp²*), and tetrahedral (or *sp³*) hybridization, and the two- and three-dimensional representations of the respective hybrid orbitals. The relative radial extensions of the hybrid orbitals (taking for $2s$, $r_0 = \sqrt{1}$) are given.

power, that is, of the strength of the σ bond (for a given bond length) which may be established by that orbital.

The hybridization of orbitals is also of importance for the explanation of the properties of ammonia and quaternary amines. Table I, Part 1 indicates that each of the three $2p$ orbitals of nitrogen contains one unpaired electron which would permit the establishment, for example, of three s—p bonds (as in NH_3), three p—p bonds (as in NF_3), or three p—sp^3 bonds [as in $N(CH_3)_3$]. However, we have seen in the preceding section that the valence angles of ammonia show a large discrepancy from that which could be expected on the basis of pure s—p bonding orbitals. One explanation which fits closely with the observed 107° valence angle is that the three p orbitals involved in bonding are actually not pure p orbitals but are hybridized with the $2s$ orbital to four sp^3 orbitals (being at 109° 28′ to one another), and the unshared electron pair occupies one of the four hybrid orbitals (Fig. 18).

Another advantage of this concept is that it is in accordance with the tetrahedral nature of the ammonium ion and the optical isomerism observed in asymmetrically substituted ammonium compounds. The presence of the unshared electron pair in an sp^3 orbital is reflected by the ease with which ammonia establishes coordinate bonds (Section 2.3.6.1). The mechanism of coordinate bonding can now be shown by the example of the formation of NH_4Cl from NH_3 and HCl (Fig. 18). In HCl the bond between the H and

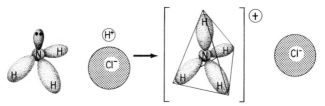

Fig. 18. A representation of the four sp^3 hybrid orbitals of ammonia and of its salification by HCl. In free ammonia the free electron doublet is shown to occupy the hydrid orbital lobe at the top in the figure. The three N—H lobes are shown as being larger because they include the $H^\oplus$ nuclei.*

Cl atoms is an ionic bond; the lone electron of the hydrogen atom is trans-ferred to the chlorine atom, whereby the former atom becoming an un-neutralized hydrogen nucleus or proton ($H^\oplus$) acquires a positive charge, and the latter atom having its $3p_z$ orbital filled with the extra electron (to yield a completed argon core) acquires a negative charge ($Cl^\ominus$). Now, in the presence of NH_3 the proton will be bonded to the N atom by the unshared electron pair (on the apex of the tetrahedron in Fig. 18); the bonding is due to the sharing of the electron pair whereby the proton acquires a filled helium core electron configuration. However, while NH_3 has no *full* electric charge, the ammonium ion resulting from the combination acquires one full positive charge because of the bonding of the proton having one full positive charge (for the partial electric charge of ammonia, see Section 3.1.2.3). Thus, the bond holding the ammonium and chloride ions together is an electro-static ionic bond: $NH_4^\oplus Cl^\ominus$. The mechanism of bonding in quaternary alkyl ammonium halides is identical (see also Section 2.3.6.1).

* The above sp^3 hybrid orbital model of NH_3 proposed originally by J. E. Lennard-Jones and J. A. Pople may have to undergo modification, however. R. J. Gillespie reviewed [*J. Chem. Educ.*, **40**, 295 (1963)] the evidence suggesting that the orbital containing the nonbonding lone electron pair is actually larger than the orbitals containing bonding doublets. This is ascribed to the *contraction* of the electron cloud in the bonding orbitals owing to attraction by the proton, thus allowing a greater expansion of the electron cloud of the free doublet. The contraction of the three bonding orbitals and expansion of the nonbonding orbital constitutes an alternate explanation for the deviation of NH_3 from the perfect tetrahedral valence angle.

Unlike in nitrogen, there is no hybridization of s and p orbitals in phosphorus, arsenic and antimony. This is indicated by the slight basicity or the total lack of basicity of PH_3, AsH_3, and SbH_3 (because of the absence of an electron pair in an sp^3 orbital of high overlapping power) and by the valence angles very close to those of pure p orbitals (see preceding section). In most compounds, however, bonding occurs through orbitals hybridized to some extent.

In addition to s and p orbitals, d orbitals may also concur in hybridization, which can then involve a variety of orbital combinations. Hybridization of d orbitals is of importance for bond formation through "expanded octets" (Section 3.1.2.7) and in the formation of metal coordination compounds (Section 3.1.2.8).

The sp^2 and sp hybrid orbitals are used for the formulation of double and triple bonds. Ethylene may be represented as shown in Fig. 19A–D. The three sp^2 orbitals (which lie in one plane and at 120° angle to one another) of each of the two carbon atoms bind the four hydrogen atoms and provide the inter-carbon bond; all these bonds are σ bonds. In addition to these bonds, the two nonhybridized $2p_z$ orbitals (at 90° angles relative to the plane of the sp^2 orbitals) overlap sidewise. The *sidewise overlapping* of p orbitals constitutes what is known as a π bond. This sidewise fusion of two p orbitals is often represented as a wide, crescent-shaped orbital extending on both sides of the C—C σ bond and is called a π *orbital*. Thus, a C=C bond always consists of the combination of a σ bond and a π bond and hence is often called a σ-π *bond*. Axial (or endwise) overlapping provides more interpenetration of orbitals than sidewise overlapping. The σ bonds are therefore stronger bonds than π bonds. This is shown by the fact that the bond strength for a C—C bond is 81.6 kcal/mole and for a C=C bond 146.1 kcal/mole; thus the π bond contributes an increment of the order of 64 kcal/mole only.

The sidewise overlap in π bonds is the cause of the restricted rotation about the double bonds in alkenes, and thus, of the phenomenon of geometric isomerism (Section 2.2.2). In fact, for maximum sidewise overlap (lowest energy level) in a π bond the p orbitals must be parallel to each other; it may be readily visualized that this is achieved when the two sp^2 orbital planes of the two carbon atoms involved in the π bonding coincide, in other words when the molecule is coplanar. Any twisting of the molecule about the σ-bond axis would decrease π-bond overlap and hence would require more energy than is available to the molecule at ordinary temperatures. Similar reasoning reveals that rotation about a simple σ bond is possible because it does not involve change in the extent of orbital overlap.

The electronic formulation of benzene is shown in Figs. 19E and F. All six carbon atoms are sp^2 hybridized, and the bonds in the hexagonal skeleton

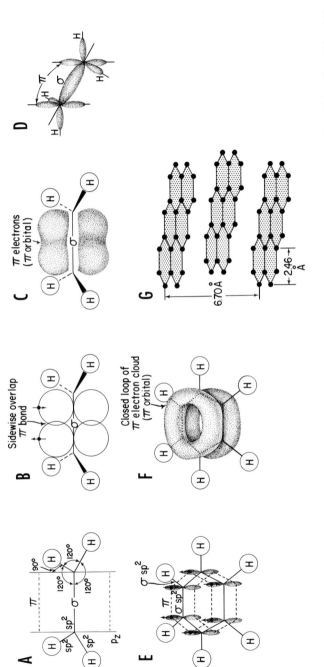

Fig. 19. A–D. The bond types and valence angles in ethylene, the two-dimensional and three-dimensional representations of the π bond. E and F. The bond types and valence angles in benzene, and the three-dimensional representation of the delocalized π-electron cloud. G. A segment of the lamellar polynuclear structure of graphite is shown.

are $sp^2 - sp^2$ σ bonds, which accounts for the perfect hexagonal symmetry of the molecule and for the 120° C—C—C valence angles. All six non-hybridized $2p_z$ orbitals point in a direction perpendicular to the plane of the hexagonal skeleton and form π bonds by sidewise overlapping. Since lateral overlapping is possible *on either side* of each carbon atom because of the cyclic structure, the orientations of the spin moments of the electrons occupying the $2p_z$ orbitals are regularly alternated. However coupling of opposite spin moments can involve only two electrons. It is therefore assumed that the possible types of interactions between $2p_z$ orbitals of opposite spins are rapidly alternating (resonance in aromatic compounds; see Section 3.2.2). This implies that no π-electron pair can be properly assigned to any one carbon-carbon bond (compare Section 2.4), but rather the entire system of π electrons forms a doughnut-shaped cloud (π orbital) extending over the whole molecule, and the π orbital is divided by the plane of the hexagonal σ-bonded ring into two equal parts. Hence the π bonds in benzene are also called *delocalized* or *mobile bonds*. This term indicates that the movement of the π electrons is not restricted to the space between two neighboring atoms. In contrast, the double bonds in alkenes are called *localized* and the reactivity of the bonds is due precisely to the localization of the π electrons.

Because the movement of the localized π electrons is restricted, they do not influence importantly the electron distribution of bonds in other parts of the molecule. On the other hand, in delocalized π-electron systems the π-electron cloud extends undivided over the whole molecule and any electron displacement at one point is readily transmitted to other points (*mesomeric effect*, see Section 3.2.2). The delocalization of π electrons holds not only for benzene but also for its annelated benzologs (the condensed polycyclic aromatic hydrocarbons) and in general for all uninterrupted conjugated systems. The electric semiconductivity of the higher polycyclic hydrocarbons and the electric conductivity of graphite (Fig. 19G) is due to the delocalized π-electron cloud transmitting the electron flow.

A little reflection will reveal then the reason of the unsaturated character of cyclooctatetraene (Section 2.4). Since the angles of the regular octagon are 135°, the eight sp^2 hybridized carbon atoms having a valence angle of 120° cannot be accommodated in one molecular plane. Accordingly, cyclooctatetraene has a conformation similar to the "boat" conformation of cyclohexane (Section 2.1.4); two opposite pairs of carbon atoms are in one plane and the other opposite pairs are in another plane because of the "cis"-type puckering of the ring. Therefore the $2p_z$ orbitals cannot form π-bonds "on both sides" and the pairing of these orbitals is strictly "one-sided" or localized; hence, the absence of the aromatic character.

Acetylene and its homologs are formulated with sp hybridized carbon atoms (Fig. 20), which accounts well for the rod-like shape of these molecules.

The figure shows that the binding of the two hydrogen atoms and the inter-carbon bond is assured by the two sp orbitals. The nonhybridized $2p_y$ and $2p_z$ orbitals of the two carbon atoms overlap sidewise to form two π bonds. The distribution of the π electrons about the σ-bond axis may be represented as a tunnel-like cloud. The bond strength of $C\equiv C$ is 192 kcal/mole, indicating that the increment provided by one π bond is lower in triple-bonded than in double-bonded carbon compounds.

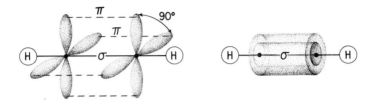

Fig. 20. The bond types, valence angles, and the cylindrical π-electron cloud of acetylene.

3.1.2.3 *Partial Polarization of Bonds. Dipole Moment. Electronegativity of Elements and Groups*

In Section 3.1.2.1 it was shown that in forming a single bond two atoms may gain or approach a "noble gas configuration" by either transfer of an electron, as in $Li^{\oplus}Cl^{\ominus}$ (ionic bond), or by equal sharing of an electron pair, as in the H—H molecule (covalent bond). These two bonding types are, however, truly the limiting cases of single bond formation. In reality, single bonds are seldom such pure bond types. In many cases the actual bond is neither purely ionic nor purely covalent but an intermediate type, called *heteropolar* or *semipolar bond*. This is due to the fact that while the two atoms still share the bonding electron pair, they have an unequal affinity for electrons, which results in a displacement of the doublet toward the atom of greater electron affinity (*unequal sharing*). In unequal sharing the two coefficients C_1 and C_2, which in Eq. (10) represent the respective contributions of the two orbitals for bonding, will have consequently different values.

The transition from pure covalent to pure ionic bond is illustrated in Fig. 21. A pure covalent bond is electrically neutral because the positive charge of each nucleus is fully neutralized by the equivalent negative charge

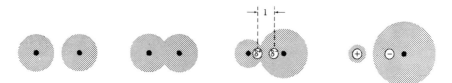

Fig. 21. The figure represents from left to right: two separate atomic orbitals; two fused atomic orbitals with equal sharing of the total electron charge, which results in a nonpolar covalent bond; two fused atomic orbitals with unequal sharing of the electron charge, which results in a partially polarized covalent bond having partial charges δ^+ and δ^-; an ionic bond, which does not involve orbital overlap and is maintained by electrostatic attraction due to the transfer of one full electron charge from one atom to the other.

of the surrounding electron cloud; this amounts to saying that the centers of the positive and negative charges coincide. In ionic bonding, on the other hand, there is a complete separation of the centers of the charges, and the two ions (if both are monovalent) carry a full electron charge of ± 1. In the case of unequal sharing the centers of positive and negative charges no longer coincide. However, they are not fully separated and so the charge of the molecule amounts to only a fraction of unit electron charge. These *partial charges* are symbolized by δ^+ and δ^-. Bonds having unequal sharing of electrons are also called *partially polarized bonds*.

Molecules which have partial separation of charges within them are oriented in an electric field; the charges are randomly distributed between uncharged condenser plates, and are lined up (polarized) when the plates are charged. In other words they behave like electric dipoles (Fig. 22). Therefore,

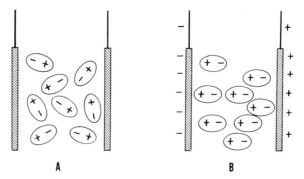

Fig. 22. The random distribution of polar molecules between uncharged condenser plates (A) and the oriented alignment of the molecules between charged condenser plates (B).

experimental evidence for unequal electron sharing and *polarity* of molecules is gained by measuring their *dipole moments* μ (see Suppletory Note 10).

The definition of the dipole moment is analogous to the definition of the magnetic moment (Section 3.1.1.2): the dipole moment is the product of the magnitude of the electric charge and the distance between the two charges. Moreover, in the expression of the dipole moment of molecules the symbol δ is introduced, since the electric charge that is separated is less than the full electron charge ($\delta < 1$). Thus

$$\mu = \delta \cdot e \cdot l \tag{14}$$

where e is the unit charge of an electron and l the distance separating the charges. Dipole moments are given in electrostatic units or Debye units (1 debye $= 10^{-18}$ esu). The Debye unit D is of this magnitude because $e = 4.80 \times 10^{-10}$ esu and interatomic distances are always of the order 10^{-8} cm; consequently $10^{-10} \times 10^{-8} = 10^{-18}$. A totally nonpolar substance is one with a moment of 0.00 D, such as CH_4, straight-chain paraffins, benzene, CCl_4, BF_3.

It may be readily realized from Fig. 21 that a dipole moment has a direction, in other words it is a vector quantity (see Suppletory Note 2), the direction of which coincides with the line connecting δ^+ and δ^-. Because the arrowhead of the dipole moment vector points in the direction of *greater* electron density, to know the actual direction in which the vector points it must be established which of the two atoms involved in the bond has the greater affinity for the electron doublet. The relative affinity of an element to electrons is known as its *electronegativity*. This means that an atom of this element will acquire a greater share of negative charge when combined with an atom of a less electronegative element. The electronegativity of elements will be discussed later in this section.

In simple diatomic molecules the dipole moment reflects clearly the moment due to one unequally shared electron doublet. For example, the dipole moment of hydrogen fluoride (1.91 D) reflects the unequal sharing of the H—F bond. In polyatomic molecules, however, the actually measurable dipole moment is a *vectorial sum* or *difference* of partial moments (called *bond moments*), which are due to the inequalities of electron distribution in different bonds of the molecule (for the addition and subtraction of vectors see Suppletory Note 2). It follows from this that the absence of dipole moment does not rule out the existence of highly polar bonds in a molecule since in the case of symmetrically arranged equivalent polar bonds the dipole moments mutually cancel each other (*e.g.*, CCl_4, BF_3).

The bond moment cannot always be obtained by measuring the dipole moment of a diatomic compound (as in the aforementioned case of HF and the other halo acids). For example, the O—H bond moment is calculated from the molecular dipole moment of water. The very polarity of water indicates that the molecule is not linear as H—O—H (since then the two equivalent O—H bond moments would cancel each other), but angular

Since the interbond angle of water is known, from other physicochemical measurements, to be 104.5° and because the molecular dipole moment (1.84 D) is the vectorial sum of two equivalent vectors, the magnitude of the O—H bond moment may be determined by using the formula in Suppletory Note 2 (in this case $\vec{a} = \vec{b}$, $\vec{c} = 1.84\ D$, and $\alpha = 104.5°$; solving for $\vec{a}$ we get $\mu_{O—H} = 1.51\ D$). In a similar way the S—H bond moment has been determined from the dipole moment and the interbond angle of

Again, the bond moment of the N—H bond was determined from the total moment of ammonia (1.46 D) and the known H—N—H bond angle (107°).

Once a bond moment is obtained from one compound it may then be applied to "resolve" the measured dipole moments of other compounds. For example, the C—O bond moment can be determined from the dipole moment of CH_3—O—H if the C—O—H valence angle is known, since the O—H bond moment is now established. Some representative bond moments are:

Bond:	C—H	N—H	S—H	C—N	C—O	C=O
Moment (D):	0.30	1.31	0.68	1.00	1.20	2.7

For vector calculations it is often convenient to assign moments to functional groups as a whole. These *group moments* represent the sum of individual bond moments. The interaction of group moments is illustrated by the example of *o*-, *m*-, and *p*-dinitrobenzene and *o*-, *m*-, and *p*-aminobenzoic acid (Fig. 23). Benzene is a nonpolar molecule; introduction of one —NO_2 group creates a group moment of 4.10 D. If a second nitro group is introduced, three isomers are possible which have the dipole moments: 6.00 D for *o*-, 3.80 D for *m*-, and close to 0.00 D for *p*-dinitrobenzene. Summation of two nitro group moments will result in decrease of the total dipole moment in the order ortho, meta, para. In contrast, in the case of aminobenzoic acid the

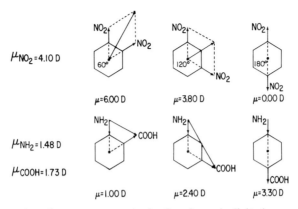

$\mu_{NO_2} = 4.10\ D$

$\mu = 6.00\ D$ $\mu = 3.80\ D$ $\mu = 0.00\ D$

$\mu_{NH_2} = 1.48\ D$

$\mu_{COOH} = 1.73\ D$

$\mu = 1.00\ D$ $\mu = 2.40\ D$ $\mu = 3.30\ D$

Fig. 23. Summation of group moments in the three isomeric dinitrobenzenes and amino-benzoic acids.

total dipole moment increases in this order of the isomers. This is due to the fact that the group moments of the $-NH_2$ group (1.48 *D*) and of the $-COOH$ group (1.73 *D*) are opposite in direction, which results in the total moment having the maximum value in the para isomer.

Earlier in this section it was pointed out that the polar character of a bond is due to the unequal electronegativity of the two atoms involved. The electronegativity, *i.e.*, the electron-attracting power, is a potential energy and the electronegativity values represent this energy level in electron-volt units. That the elements have different electronegativities is owing to the fact that the valence electrons in the outermost shell are actually reached by only a portion of the nuclear attraction. This is because interposed between the valence electrons and the nuclei are situated the filled nonvalence electron cores which act as a shield and exert a *screening effect* on the nuclear charge. Since the screening effect is roughly proportional with the number of non-valence electrons shielding the nuclear charge and since the electron-attracting power of the nucleus is proportional to the total nuclear charge (*i.e.*, the atomic number), the electronegativity of elements within each period of the Periodic Table increases in general with the difference between the atomic number and the number of nonvalence electrons. Furthermore, since the attraction exerted on the valence electrons also depends on their average distance from the nucleus, the maximum electronegativity within the periods gradually decreases toward the higher periods because of the increase of *size* of the shielding nonvalence electron core (Fig. 24).

Different atomic parameters have been proposed as the basis for the scale of electronegativities. The most frequently utilized electronegativity

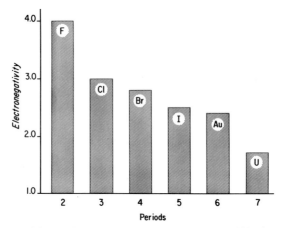

Fig. 24. Decrease of the maximum electronegativity of elements within the successive periods of the Periodic Table.

scale, due to Pauling, is based on the increment of bond energies owing to the partial polarization of bonds. (Another, less often used measure of electronegativity of an atom is the half of the sum of the ionization potential plus the electron affinity; see Section 3.3.3.) If a bond between atoms A and B is truly covalent then its bond energy is an intermediate between the bond energies of the bonds A—A and B—B. Bonds formed between atoms of the same kind, such as H—H, are essentially covalent. The bond energy E_{AB} of a true covalent bond is, therefore, the arithmetic or geometric mean of the bond energies E_{AA} and E_{BB} so that

$$E_{AB} \approx \frac{E_{AA} + E_{BB}}{2} \approx \sqrt{E_{AA} \cdot E_{BB}}$$

However, in partially polarized bonds there results a bond energy increment Δ_{AB} which is due to the electrostatic attraction between the partial electric charges. This energy difference Δ_{AB} between the calculated E_{AB} value and the experimentally found energy of the A—B bond (determined from the heat of formation) is directly proportional to the square of electronegativity difference between atoms A and B:

$$\Delta_{AB} = 23.06 \, (X_A - X_B)^2 \text{ kcal/mole} \tag{15}$$

The proportionality factor 23.06 represents the number of kilocalories equivalent to one electron-volt energy change per gram molecule; this proportionality constant is introduced because bond energies are usually given in kilocalories per mole while $X_A - X_B$ represents energy measured in electron volts.

Table III
Electronegativities of Some Common Elements

H 2.1						
Li 1.0	Be 1.5	B 2.0	C 2.5	N 3.0	O 3.5	F 4.0
Na 0.9	Mg 1.2	Al 1.5	Si 1.8	P 2.1	S 2.5	Cl 3.0
K 0.8	Ca 1.0			As 2.0	Se 2.4	Br 2.8
						I 2.5

Electronegativity values are expressed in a scale between 0 and 4. This scale is obtained by assigning to fluorine, the most electronegative element, a value of 4.0. For example, it is found for HF that $X_A - X_B = \sqrt{\Delta_{AB}/23.06}$ = 1.9. Therefore, since hydrogen has a *lesser* attraction for electrons than fluorine, this value is *subtracted* from the assigned electronegativity of fluorine; thus the electronegativity of hydrogen is $4.0 - 1.9 = 2.1$. In general, nonmetals have electronegativity values above 2, amphoteric elements have values around 2, and metals less than 1.8 down to as low as 0.7. The advantage of using this electronegativity scale is that negative values are avoided. The electronegativities of some common elements are given in Table III. It must be emphasized that the electronegativities of the elements are not constant values but may vary to some extent with the nature of the combination in which the element is involved. Furthermore, among the metals the electronegativity generally increases with the valence number of the atom; for example $Fe^{\oplus\oplus}1.8$, $Fe^{3\oplus}1.9$; $Cu^{\oplus}1.9$, $Cu^{\oplus\oplus}2.0$; $Sn^{\oplus\oplus}1.8$, $Sn^{4\oplus}1.9$. An explanation for this is that with the increase of the valence number there is loss of electron(s) from lower orbitals (see Table I, Part 1) resulting in the decrease of the screening effect.

Using the electronegativity values the percentage ionic character of bonds may be calculated. Semiempirical relationships to calculate the percentage ionic character of a bond have been proposed by Pauling and by Smyth. According to Smyth the percentage ionic character of a bond A—B is given by the equation:

$$A - B = 0.16(X_A - X_B) + 0.035(X_A - X_B)^2 \tag{16}$$

If the absolute value of the difference $|X_A - X_B|$ is zero units, the ionic character is 0%; 0.38 units corresponds to 5%, $0.67 \cong 10\%$, $1.24 \cong 25\%$, $2.08 \cong 50\%$, and $2.80 \cong 75\%$.

It is especially important for the understanding of the nature of organic compounds that the electronegativity of an atom varies with its state of hybridization; thus the electronegativity of the carbon atom increases with the predominance of the s-orbital character. The explanation of this lies in the fact that within the same electron shell the s orbital has a notably shorter radial extension than the p orbitals (Table II); hence the nuclear attraction is more effective at the level of the s orbital. Therefore, electronegativity of a carbon atom increases with the percentage of s-orbital character such as $sp = 50\% > sp^2 = 33\% > sp^3 = 25\%$. An interesting consequence of this is that the hydrogen atoms of acetylene may be directly substituted by metal atoms (Section 2.2.4), while the hydrogen atoms of methane cannot be substituted directly. The mobility of hydrogen in acetylene is due to displacement of the electron doublet in the C—H bond toward the more electronegative sp carbon; this confers mobility to the proton, $i.e.$, acid character to the molecule:

$$\overset{\delta^-}{2\ HC}\equiv\overset{\delta^+}{C\!\!\!\rightharpoondown H} + Na-Na \longrightarrow \overset{\delta^-}{2\ HC}\equiv\overset{\delta^+}{C\!\!\!\rightharpoondown Na} + H-H$$

Here the symbol $\rightharpoondown$ represents displacement of the doublet toward the C atom. The effect of electronegativity and bond polarization on the acidity of organic compounds is discussed further in Sections 3.1.2.4 and 3.2.4.

The effect of an electronegative atom in a molecule is not limited to the bonds directly adjacent to it. The effect reverberates throughout the whole structure and its intensity decreases with the distance from the electronegative atom. The *rule of Walsh* states that when in a compound, such as methane, or in general in a compound

one of the hydrogens (or X) is replaced by a more electronegative element, the electronegativity of the carbon atom increases relative to the other three hydrogen atoms (or to R_1, R_2, and R_3). Inversely the electronegativity of the carbon atom decreases if the new substituent is less electronegative than the previous one. Consequently, just as a scale has been established for the electronegativity of elements, a relative order of electronegativities may be assigned to substituent groups, such as:

$$-NO_2 > -SO_2OR > -SO_2R > -CN > -COOR > -CHO > -COR$$

Furthermore, the electronegativities of alkyl groups have been found (from the measurements of the ionization potentials of the respective alkyl chlorides) to decrease in the following order:

$$-H > -CH_3 > -C_2H_5 > -n\text{-}C_3H_7 > -tert\text{-}C_4H_9$$

Interpretation of the rule of Walsh yields the same order of electronegativities for the latter groups.

3.1.2.4 Transmission of Polarization Within a Molecule: Inductive Effect. The Acidity of Organic Compounds

The phenomenon, that the bond polarization caused by an electronegative element or group is transmitted through chains of atoms and reverberates through the whole molecule, is known as the *inductive effect*. By convention, atoms or groups which are more electronegative than hydrogen (such as the halogens, and the series of substituent groups listed in the previous section: $-NO_2$, $-SO_2OR$, $-SO_2R$, etc.) are said to exhibit a *negative* inductive effect $(-I)$; such an atom or group is sometimes called a *key atom* or a *key group*. Groups which are less electronegative than hydrogen (such as the alkyl groups) display *positive* inductive effect $(+I)$.

Electron shifts due to inductive effect are represented either by arrowheads $(\rightarrow)$ or by triangular arrows $(\Longleftarrow)$; in the former representation the arrowhead points in the direction of electron displacement, whereas when the latter symbol is used the width of the triangular arrow follows the electron density, i.e., the wide end is toward the greater density. For example, the partial polarization of the C—Cl bond in methyl chloride may be represented as $Cl \leftarrow CH_3$ or as $Cl \Longleftarrow CH_3$.

The transmission of the polarizing effect through the chains of atoms is reflected by the increase of the dipole moment with the chain length:

$$\overset{\delta^-}{Cl} \Longrightarrow \overset{\delta^+}{CH_3} \qquad \overset{\delta^-}{Cl} \Longrightarrow CH_2 \Longrightarrow \overset{\delta^+}{CH_3} \qquad \overset{\delta^-}{Cl} \Longrightarrow CH_2 \Longrightarrow CH_2 \Longrightarrow \overset{\delta^+}{CH_3} \qquad \cdots$$

$$\xleftarrow{\quad} I_1 \xrightarrow{\quad} \qquad \xleftarrow{\quad} I_2 \xrightarrow{\quad} \qquad \xleftarrow{\qquad} I_3 \xrightarrow{\qquad} \qquad \cdots$$

$$\mu = 1.83D \qquad 2.00D \qquad 2.13D \qquad \lim \mu_{C_n} = 2.20D$$

since the dipole moment increases with the distance separating the partial charges. However, the fact that with the further increase of the chain length the dipole moments reach a constant limiting value $(\lim \mu_{C_n})$ indicates that the inductive effect slowly fades with the distance from the electronegative atom.

A consequence of the negative inductive effect is that when more electronegative key atoms replace hydrogens in molecules, the valence electrons from the nearby atoms are pulled toward the key atoms, for example:

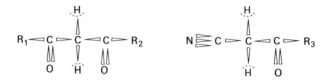

This results in the considerable weakening of the C—H bonds in the CH_2 group so that the latter becomes able to liberate protons, i.e., $H^\oplus$ ions. Following the Brönsted concept of acidity (Section 3.2.4), this amounts to saying that the compound acquires acidic properties. If the proton is released in such a compound (as in the presence of alkali metals) the CH group retaining the electron doublet will be negatively charged; the structure represents then the tautomeric form of the enolate ion (Section 2.3.2.2):

$$R_1-\overset{\oplus}{\underset{\underset{O}{\|}}{C}}-\overset{\ominus}{\underset{\underset{H}{|}}{C}}-\underset{\underset{O}{\|}}{C}-R_2 \rightleftharpoons R_1-\underset{\underset{\ominus O}{\|}}{C}=\underset{\underset{H}{|}}{C}-\underset{\underset{O}{\|}}{C}-R_2 \longleftrightarrow R_1-\underset{\underset{O}{\|}}{C}-\underset{\underset{H}{|}}{C}=\underset{\underset{O_\ominus}{|}}{C}-R_2$$

Because of the inductive effect, substitution with a highly electronegative atom, such as fluorine or chlorine, considerably strengthens the acidity of aliphatic organic acids and, as expected, the increment is so much greater the closer the electronegative substituent is to the carboxyl group; this is an example of the $-I$ effect. Acidity also increases with the number of electronegative substituents.

Inversely, upon replacement of the carbon-bound hydrogen atom in formic acid with alkyl groups, the acid strength *decreases* to an extent which is proportional with the chain length. The acid strength decreases in the same order as the electronegativity of the alkyl groups decreases. This is an example of the $+I$ effect. The $-I$ and $+I$ effects, causing, respectively, weakening and strengthening of the binding of the proton, may be represented as:

$$Cl \Rightarrow CH_2 \Rightarrow C\overset{\displaystyle O \Rightarrow H}{\underset{\displaystyle O}{\diagdown}} \qquad \text{and} \qquad CH_3-CH_2-CH_2 \Rightarrow C\overset{\displaystyle O-H}{\underset{\displaystyle O}{\diagdown}}$$

The influence of the $+I$ and $-I$ effects on the acid strength (as dissociation constant) of some typical fatty acids is shown in Table IV.

Table IV
Dissociation Constants of Some Fatty Acids

Acid		Dissociation constant
Formic	H—COOH	21.0×10^{-5}
Acetic	CH_3—COOH	1.9×10^{-5}
Propionic	CH_3—CH_2—COOH	1.4×10^{-5}
Butyric	CH_3—CH_2—CH_2—COOH	1.5×10^{-5}
α-Chlorobutyric	CH_3—CH_2—CHCl—COOH	140.0×10^{-5}
β-Chlorobutyric	CH_3—CHCl—CH_2—COOH	8.9×10^{-5}
γ-Chlorobutyric	CH_2Cl—CH_2—CH_2—COOH	2.6×10^{-5}

Substitution by electronegative groups has an opposite effect on base strength than on acid strength. Because the basicity of amines depends on the availability of the free electron doublet on the nitrogen atom, withdrawal of this doublet towards an electronegative substituent will lower basicity; for example, $(CF_3)_3N$ has no basic properties at all. Conversely, replacement of the hydrogen atoms in ammonia with alkyl groups will heighten basicity because the alkyl groups have lower electronegativity than hydrogen; the methylamines, ethylamines, etc., are consequently stronger bases than ammonia.

The term "key atom" or "key group" for substituents displaying $-I$ effect denotes the ability of such a substituent to "loosen" the octet of the carbon atom with which it is linked. Reactions of compounds of this type often involve, therefore, reactive intermediates resulting from total dissociation of the bond. For example:

$$\begin{array}{c} R_1 \\ R_2 {-}\overset{\delta+}{C} {=}\overset{\delta-}{O}{-}R_4 \\ R_3 \end{array} \longrightarrow \left[\begin{array}{c} R_1 \\ R_2 {-}\overset{\oplus}{C} \quad {}^{\ominus}O{-}R_4 \\ R_3 \end{array} \right]$$

The "loosening" of the octet of the adjacent carbon atom by a halogen is the underlying cause of the mechanism of the well-known Markownikoff rule (Section 2.2.4). For example, the addition of HCl to $CH_2{=}CHBr$ proceeds according to the mechanism:

$$\overset{\delta-}{Br} {-} \overset{\delta+}{CH} {=} \overset{\delta-}{CH_2} \xrightarrow{H^\oplus} Br{-}\underset{\oplus}{CH}{-}CH_3 \xrightarrow{Cl^\ominus} CHBrCl{-}CH_3$$

3.1.2.5 The Lewis–Langmuir–Eistert Symbolism

The two-dimensional structural formulas of organic chemistry, as we developed them in Section 2, show quantitatively the locations of the atomic nuclei. In order to visualize the approximate spatial skeleton of the molecules

Table V

Configuration of Valence Electrons of Some Common Elements

H·							He:
Li·	·Be·	·B·	·Ċ·	·N̈:	·Ö·	:F̈·	:N̈e:
Na·	·Mg·	·Ȧl·	·Sï·	·P̈:	·S̈·	:Cl·	:Ȧr:
K·	·Ca·		·Ge·	·Äs:	·S̈e·	:Br·	:Kr:
Rb·						:Ï·	:Xe:

we had to learn to read three-dimensionality into these formulas. It was just as necessary to develop the modern theory of valence which enables us to read into the valence bonds (which we have symbolized as dashes or dots) the spatial distribution and mobility of valence electrons, in order to represent the geometry and reactivity of molecules. However, with compounds of any complexity the routine use of orbital representation is too cumbersome. It is, therefore, necessary to develop a simple symbolism which, while giving a picture that "freezes" moving electrons, can still provide information about the distribution of valence electrons whenever the brief representation of this distribution is necessary. The development of such a symbolism, which actually preceded the development of modern valence theory, is due to Lewis, Langmuir, and Eistert.

According to this symbolism the elements are shown with their valence electrons only and each electron is represented by a dot (for this reason, in order to avoid the confusion of a valence bond with the symbol of an electron, covalent bonds are always represented as dashes and not dots whenever the Lewis–Langmuir–Eistert symbolism is used). An electron doublet is represented either as a bar or as two closely positioned dots, indicating that the two electrons belong in the same orbital. An element having a full octet electron configuration is shown as being surrounded by four doublets. Lone valence electrons are shown as isolated dots (they are not grouped either together or with doublets), indicating that each occupies singly an unfilled orbital. Table V shows the representation of some common elements following this symbolism. Since an electron doublet may also be represented by a bar, ·N̈: may also be written as ·N̈|, ·Ö· as ·Ō·, :Cl· as |Cl·, :N̈e: as |N̄e|, etc. A chloride ion is represented as :Cl:$^\ominus$ or as |Cl|$^\ominus$, and a sodium ion as Na$^\oplus$ since the single valence electron which would be shown in this symbolism is lost. For special representational purposes bond polarization (between two elements A and B) is sometimes shown as A: B equivalent to A ⊳ B or A ← B (or A :B equivalent to A ⊲ B or A → B). A nonpolarized covalent bond A—B is, therefore, A:B. Formulas represented following the Lewis–Langmuir–Eistert symbolism are often termed "Lewis structures."

3.1.2.6   Covalent and Ionic Bonds. Radicals and Free Radical Reactions

The symbolism described makes it apparent that covalent bond formation and ionic bond formation are *electron-pairing* and *electron-unpairing* type reactions, respectively. The general form of these reactions is:

$$A \cdot + \cdot B \longrightarrow A : B \quad \text{and} \quad A \cdot + \cdot B \longrightarrow A^{\oplus} + :B^{\ominus}$$

For example:

$$H \cdot + \cdot H \longrightarrow H : H \qquad |\overline{Cl} \cdot + \cdot \overline{Cl}| \longrightarrow |\overline{Cl} : \overline{Cl}|$$

$$Li \cdot + \cdot \overline{\underline{Cl}}| \longrightarrow Li^{\oplus} \, {}^{\ominus}|\overline{\underline{Cl}}| \qquad 2 \, |\overline{\underline{Cl}} \cdot + \cdot Mg \cdot \longrightarrow |\overline{\underline{Cl}}|^{\ominus} \, {}^{\oplus}Mg^{\oplus} \, {}^{\ominus}|\overline{\underline{Cl}}|$$

If energy is communicated to a covalent bond (*e.g.*, chlorine is irradiated by ultraviolet light), the molecules dissociate into atoms or *free radicals*; any atom or group of atoms that contains one or more unpaired electrons is called a free radical. Free radicals can be produced by ionizing radiations, electric discharges, or at high temperatures in flames. Small molecular weight free radicals are highly reactive and consequently have very short life spans at room temperature (of the order of 10^{-2}–10^{-3} seconds); they unite with each other or may displace other groups in compounds present in the medium. For example, when a mixture of hydrogen and dry chlorine is irradiated, at first the chlorine radicals formed react with nondissociated hydrogen:

$$|\overline{\underline{Cl}} \cdot + H : H \longrightarrow |\overline{\underline{Cl}} : H + H \cdot$$

The liberated hydrogen radicals then react, in turn, with nondissociated chlorine:

$$H \cdot + |\overline{\underline{Cl}} : \overline{\underline{Cl}}| \longrightarrow |\overline{\underline{Cl}} : H + |\overline{\underline{Cl}} \cdot$$

Once initiated, the cycle is repeated again and again with explosive rapidity until all hydrogen and chlorine are united to HCl. This is an example of a *free radical chain reaction*. Many polymerization reactions for the preparation of synthetic high polymers involve free radical chain reactions.

Other free radical reactions are known which are not chain reactions (a chain reaction means that the total reaction involves a series of steps each of which generates a reactive intermediate that brings about the next step). The Wurtz–Fittig reaction (Section 2.1.2) is an example of such a reaction having a nonchain free radical mechanism:

$$2 \; CH_3-CH_2 \vdots \; \overline{Cl}| \; + \; Na \vdots Na \longrightarrow 2[CH_3-CH_2 \cdot] \; + \; 2Na \cdot \; +2|\overline{Cl} \cdot$$

ethyl
radical

$$\longrightarrow CH_3-CH_2:CH_2-CH_3 + 2Na^{\oplus} \; ^{\ominus}|\overline{Cl}|$$

Free radical reactions probably play an important role in the mechanism by which radiations induce damage in living organisms. It was briefly mentioned in Section 2.3.7.2 that radiations promote the interchange of sulfhydryl-disulfide groups which are important for the maintenance of structures and for the function of proteins. The enhancement is due to the fact that the interchange proceeds *via* free radical mechanism. The products which may be formed in sulfhydryl-disulfide interchange depend on the relative rates of recombination of the reactive intermediates. If the rates are not very different, all possible recombinations take place, such as:

$$R_1-S \vdots S-R_2 + R_3-S \vdots H \longrightarrow R_1-S:S-R_3 + R_2-S:S-R_3 + R_1-S:S-R_2$$
$$+ R_1-S:S-R_1 + R_2-S:S-R_2 + R_3-S:S-R_3 + R_1-S:H + R_2-S:H + R_3-S:H$$

This amounts to saying that in a protein, containing several disulfide and sulfhydryl groups, many new S—S bonds formed during random recombinations are different from the ones in the native protein.

However, not only S—S bonds but any other bond may be opened by high-energy radiations. It is well known that in synthetic high polymers, such as polyethylene and polyvinyl chloride, X-rays and γ-rays produce free radical carbon-chain fragments. These reactive intermediates establish random cross-links between the carbon chains of the high polymer, conferring insolubility and infusibility, increase of the tensile strength and of the resistance to swelling, etc., to the material; these are technologically desirable goals. On the other hand, in biological macromolecules radiation-induced cross-links are undesirable as they are accompanied by drastic change or loss of function, such as the radiation-induced inactivation of enzymes or the bridge formation and clumping in chromosomes.

3.1.2.7   *Exceptions to the Octet Rule: Incomplete and Expanded Octets.*
Coordinate Bonds. The One-Electron Bond

The octet rule, as it has been defined in Section 3.1.2.1 must now undergo some modifications. Even though the tendency to acquire the closest stable "noble gas" electron configuration is the driving force in the formation of covalent and ionic bonds, instances are known where atoms are surrounded by less than four doublets. Atoms of this type are said to have *incomplete octets*. Hydrogen must be disregarded since the single doublet required for the completeness of its electron shell does, in fact, confer to it the electron configuration of the closest "noble gas," helium; the case of hydrogen constitutes, therefore, an implicit corollary of the octet rule. Atoms with incomplete octets are encountered in the second, third, and fourth periods, for example:

$$H_5C_2:Be:C_2H_5 \qquad |\overline{F}:B:\overline{F}| \qquad |\overline{O}:\overline{S}:\overline{O}| \qquad |\overline{O}:\overline{Cl}:\overline{O}|$$

diethyl	boron	sulfur	chlorine
beryllium	trifluoride	trioxide	dioxide

Many of the compounds formed are very stable and are electrically neutral. Consequently, molecular species with incomplete octets should not be classified together with the highly reactive ionic intermediates formed during reactions such as a positively charged *carbonium ion*:

$$R_1 : \overset{\overset{\textstyle R_2}{..}}{\underset{\oplus}{C}} : R_3$$

Another group of exceptions to the octet rule is the compounds with *expanded octets*. In fact, the octet rule applies *strictly* only to the second period of the Periodic Table, that is to those elements which have no more than four orbitals available (Table I, Part 1). Many highly stable compounds are known, however, where the central atom has a higher valence number than that which could be predicted from the octet rule. Atoms with expanded octets are encountered in the third and subsequent periods. For example:

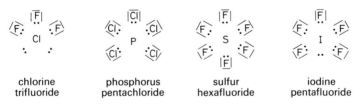

chlorine	phosphorus	sulfur	iodine
trifluoride	pentachloride	hexafluoride	pentafluoride

Now, inspection of the electronic configurations (in Table I, Part 1) shows that beginning with the third period, the elements contain a number of unfilled peripheral orbitals. Thus, elements of the third period have none of the five $3d$ orbitals filled in the shell M. Similarly, the $4d$ and $4f$ orbitals assigned to the shell N in the fourth period are empty, and so on for higher shells. Covalent binding by atoms with expanded octets is accounted for by assuming that the supplementary doublets occupy these unfilled orbitals. Therefore, elements of the second period may not have a valence number higher than 4 because they do not have unfilled orbitals which may accommodate supplementary doublets. This is spectacularly illustrated by the example of nitrogen and phosphorus. Both elements have five electrons in the outer shell: nitrogen has two electrons in the $2s$ orbital and 3 lone electrons in each of the three $2p$ orbitals ($\cdot\ddot{\text{N}}\cdot$); phosphorus has two electrons in the $3s$ orbital and 3 lone electrons in each of the three $3p$ orbitals ($\cdot\dot{\text{P}}\cdot$). However, while

$$|\overline{\text{Cl}}\text{:}\ddot{\text{N}}\text{:}\overline{\text{Cl}}|$$
$$|\overline{\underset{..}{\text{Cl}}}|$$

does not react further with chlorine ($\cdot\overline{\text{Cl}}|$),

$$|\overline{\text{Cl}}\text{:}\overset{..}{\text{P}}\text{:}\overline{\text{Cl}}|$$
$$|\overline{\underset{..}{\text{Cl}}}|$$

yields readily PCl_5.

The nature of coordinate bonds and coordination compounds follows directly from the concepts of incomplete and expanded octets. A coordinate bond may be formed between two atoms if one has a free doublet (donor) and the other an incomplete octet (acceptor). For hydrogen, in which the electron shell is complete with two electrons (helium), the requirement of "incomplete octet" for coordinate bonding means incomplete doublet, that is an $H^{\oplus}$ ion. The formation of a coordinate bond is represented generally as:

$$\text{A: + B} \longrightarrow \text{A} \rightarrow \text{B} \quad \text{or} \quad \text{A + :B} \longrightarrow \text{A} \leftarrow \text{B}$$

where the head of the arrow representing the valence bond points from the donor in the direction of the acceptor atom. The following types of coordinate bonds may be distinguished:

1. "Onium" type. The concept of onium type coordinate bond has been encountered in Sections 2.3.6.1 and 3.1.2.2, and the orbital representation of the formation of $NH_4^{\oplus}Cl^{\ominus}$ was given in Fig. 18. In the Lewis–Langmuir–Eistert symbolism this may be described as:

$$H_3N: \; + \; H^{\oplus}|\overline{\text{Cl}}|^{\ominus} \; \longrightarrow \; \left[H-\underset{\underset{\displaystyle H}{|}}{\overset{\overset{\displaystyle H}{|}}{N}}\rightarrow H \right]^{\oplus} \; |\overline{\text{Cl}}|^{\ominus}$$

An essentially identical mechanism describes the formation of the quaternary tetraalkylammonium halides, for example:

$$(CH_3)_3N: \; + \; \overset{\delta+}{H_3C}\!=\!\!\overset{\delta-}{\overline{\text{Cl}}}| \; \longrightarrow \; \left[H_3C-\underset{\underset{\displaystyle CH_3}{|}}{\overset{\overset{\displaystyle CH_3}{|}}{N}}\rightarrow CH_3 \right]^{\oplus} \; |\overline{\text{Cl}}|^{\ominus}$$

The reaction implies a reactive intermediate carbonium ion (a methonium ion $H_3C^\oplus$).

In spite of the fact that one bond out of the four in the ammonium ion is a coordinate bond, once the ammonium ion is formed the two types of bonds are indistinguishable since we have seen (Sections 2.3.6.1 and 3.1.2.2) that the ion has a tetrahedral configuration which is symmetrical. Consequently it is more correct to represent the ions as:

$$
\left[\begin{array}{c} H \\ | \\ H-N-H \\ | \\ H \end{array} \right]^{\oplus}
\quad \text{or} \quad
\left[\begin{array}{c} R \\ | \\ R-N-R \\ | \\ R \end{array} \right]^{\oplus}
$$

which shows four identical bonds. Nonetheless, it must be borne in mind that the "coordinate character" of one bond did not disappear, it has only been evenly distributed among the four bonds. The lesser stability of the "coordinate character" equivalent to one bond becomes manifest when the energy of such a compound is raised. Thus, it is well known that ammonia gas may be readily liberated by warming a solution of ammonium hydroxide. Also, we have seen in Section 2.3.6.3 that, upon heating, the quaternary tetraalkylammonium halides dissociate into trialkylamine and alkyl halide.

If one of the substituents of a quaternary ammonium ion contains an acid group (*e.g.*, carboxyl or sulfonic) an internally neutralized compound results:

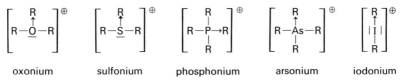

Compounds of this type, which show the behavior of both acids and bases, are called *amphoteric* or *amphiprotic*. An important group of amphoters, the α-amino acids, are amino derivatives of acetic acid substituted on the α-carbon (Section 2.3.3 and listed in Section 8.1*).

Elements other than nitrogen, having free electron doublets, can form onium type coordinate bonds. The oxonium salts have been briefly mentioned in Sections 2.3.4 and 2.3.6.1. The following onium type cations are commonly known:

$$
\left[\begin{array}{c} R \\ | \\ R-O-R \end{array} \right]^{\oplus}
\quad
\left[\begin{array}{c} R \\ \uparrow \\ R-S-R \end{array} \right]^{\oplus}
\quad
\left[\begin{array}{c} R \\ | \\ R-P{\rightarrow}R \\ | \\ R \end{array} \right]^{\oplus}
\quad
\left[\begin{array}{c} R \\ \uparrow \\ R-As-R \\ | \\ R \end{array} \right]^{\oplus}
\quad
\left[\begin{array}{c} R \\ | \\ I \\ | \\ R \end{array} \right]^{\oplus}
$$

oxonium   sulfonium   phosphonium   arsonium   iodonium

* Sections 5, 6, and 7 appear in Volume II; Sections 8 and 9, and the Appendixes appear in Volume III.

A most common instance of the oxonium ion is the formation of *hydronium ions.* Hydrogen ions are always present in water, combined with undissociated water molecules:

$$H:\overline{\underline{O}}:H + H^\oplus \longrightarrow \left[H:\overset{H}{\underset{\cdot\cdot}{O}}:H \right]^\oplus$$

hydronium
ion

2. Amine-oxide type. This type of coordinate bond has been mentioned in Section 2.3.6.1. The formation of an amine oxide is formulated as:

$$\begin{array}{c} R_1 \\ R_2\!-\!N: \\ R_3 \end{array} + \cdot\overline{\underline{O}}\cdot \longrightarrow \begin{array}{c} R_1 \\ R_2\!-\!N\!\rightarrow\!\overline{\underline{O}}| \\ R_3 \end{array}$$

Because of the much greater electronegativity of oxygen than of either a hydrogen atom or an alkyl group, the four valences in amine oxides are not all equivalent. Electron density is displaced toward oxygen, the N→O bond is highly polarized and for this reason it has often been called a "semi-polar bond." The N→O bond is *not* a double bond as it has sometimes been incorrectly termed in the past, since a double bond implies the sharing of *two* doublets. The correct representation of the nitroso and nitro groups, containing double bonded and coordinately bonded oxygen atoms, is therefore:

$$R\!-\!\overline{N}\!=\!O \quad \text{and} \quad R\!-\!N\!\!\begin{array}{c} \nearrow O \\ \searrow O \end{array}$$

Also sulfur, phosphorus, arsenic, and iodine form amine oxide type coordinate bonds. The correct representation of sulfoxides, of sulfones, and of the respective acid groups is as follows:

$$\begin{array}{ccccc} |\overline{\underline{O}}| & |\overline{\underline{O}}| & \nearrow O \diagdown & OH & OH \\ \uparrow & \uparrow & \diagup & \diagup & \diagup \\ R\!-\!S\!-\!R & R\!-\!S\!-\!R & R\!-\!S\!-\!OH & R\!-\!P\!\rightarrow\!\overline{\underline{O}}| & R\!-\!As\!\rightarrow\!\overline{\underline{O}}| \\ & \downarrow & \diagdown & \diagdown & \diagdown \\ & |\overline{\underline{O}}| & \diagdown O \diagup & OH & OH \end{array}$$

Also iodine can form a coordination bond with oxygen; $R\!-\!\overline{\underline{I}}\!\rightarrow\!\overline{\underline{O}}|$ is termed an iodoso compound, *e.g.,* iodosobenzene.

3. Fluoroborate type. Hydrogen fluoride (and other halohydric acids) reacts with BF_3 to form fluoroboric acid. In this combination the $|\overline{F}|^\ominus$ ion acts as electron donor and fills the incomplete octet of the boron atom:

$$\begin{array}{c} |\overline{F}| \\ |\overline{F}: B \\ |\overline{F}| \end{array} + |\overline{F}|^\ominus H^\oplus \longrightarrow \left[\begin{array}{c} |\overline{F}| \\ |\overline{F}: B\!\leftarrow\!\overline{F}| \\ |\overline{F}| \end{array} \right]^\ominus H^\oplus$$

fluoroborate
ion

Just as $NH_4^\oplus$, the $BF_4^\ominus$ ion has a tetrahedral symmetry and the two types of bonds are indistinguishable. By way of the same bonding mechanism, BF_3 is capable of forming some interesting addition compounds with ethers and amines:

$$
\begin{array}{cc}
\begin{array}{c}
|\overline{F}|\ \ R \\
\ \ |\ \ \ | \\
|\overline{F}-B{\leftarrow}O| \\
\ \ |\ \ \ | \\
|\overline{F}|\ \ R
\end{array}
&
\begin{array}{c}
|\overline{F}|\ \ R \\
\ \ |\ \ \ | \\
|\overline{F}-B{\leftarrow}N-R \\
\ \ |\ \ \ | \\
|\overline{F}|\ \ R
\end{array}
\end{array}
$$

   In addition to incomplete and expanded octets, another type of exception to the octet rule is the covalent *one-electron bond* or *covalent bond by singlet*. A group of compounds of this type is the boron hydrides. The simplest of them, B_2H_6, contains eight bonds in the molecule but only twelve valence electrons (2×3 from the two boron atoms and 6×1 from the six hydrogen atoms). The electronic structure of B_2H_6 is:

$$
\begin{array}{c}
H \cdot\ \cdot H \cdot\ \cdot H \\
B\quad\ \ B \\
H^{\cdot\cdot}\ H^{\cdot\ \cdot}\ H^{\cdot\cdot}
\end{array}
$$

The two boron atoms each bind two hydrogens by normal covalent bonding (by doublet). These two BH_2 moieties are held together by $\cdot H \cdot$ bridges in which the B—H bonds may be regarded as one-electron singlet bonds.* Another example for the singlet bond is the hydrogen molecule-ion. Experimental evidence indicates that the neutral $H:H$ molecule may lose one electron to become a hydrogen molecule-ion $(H \cdot H)^\oplus$ in which the two nuclei are held together by one electron only. The fact that two nuclei can be held together by just *one* electron is consistent with the statement in Section 3.1.2.1 that the bond energy of a covalent bond cannot be attributed to attraction between spin magnetic moments. Figure 14 was used as a mnemonic aid for visualizing electron pairing in nonmathematical terms. In the one-electron bond there is evidently no way to conceive such a pairing, and so simple electromagnetic considerations cannot even help to visualize this singlet covalent bond. The phenomenon of resonance to which is due the cohesion of the one-electron bond will be discussed in Section 3.2.1.

3.1.2.8   Coordination Compounds. The Geometry of Coordination Symmetry: Electrostatic Basis of Valence Angles

   Incomplete and expanded octets and the coordinate bond play an important role in the formation of *complex* or *coordination compounds*. A

---

   * However, according to Longuet-Higgins it is more correct to look upon the hydrogen bridge in B_2H_6, in the sense of the molecular orbital method, as a delocalized electron cloud of two electrons held together by the embedded proton charge.

coordination compound contains a *central metal atom* surrounded by a cluster of *coordinating atoms* or *groups* (also called *donor* atoms or groups, or *ligands*). The central atom together with the ligands surrounding it constitute the *coordination sphere*. The number of atoms or groups surrounding the central atom in the coordination sphere is called the *coordination number* or *coordination index*. The most common coordination numbers are 4 and 6. However, complexes having coordination numbers 2, 3, 5, and greater than 6 are also known. Complex ions with coordination number 2 are, for example:

$$[H_3N:\rightarrow Ag\leftarrow:NH_3]^{\oplus} \quad \text{and} \quad [N\equiv C:\rightarrow Ag\leftarrow:C\equiv N]^{\ominus}$$

Table VI shows the structure of a few typical coordination compounds having coordination numbers 4 and 6.

The linking of the ligands to the central atom is a phenomenon essentially identical to the filling of incomplete octets and to the formation of expanded octets, in that the central atom can accept electrons up to the complete filling of all the unfilled orbitals assigned to its period in the Periodic Table. The relative stabilities of complexes of some typical coordinating metals decrease in the order: Hg > Be > Cu > Ni > Co > Pb > Zn > Cd > Fe > Mn > Mg > Ca. Since the ligand plays the role of electron donor, it can be any ion or molecule which has some atom or group having one or more free doublets; for example, cyanide ion $^{\ominus}$:C≡N, halide ions $|\underline{X}|^{\ominus}$, oxygen type donors $\overline{O}R_2$ and $\overline{S}R_2$, and nitrogen type donors $\overline{N}R_3$, $\overline{As}R_3$, and $\overline{P}R_3$.

The coordination number of the central atom is determined by three parameters:

1. The Effective Atomic Number (EAN). The central atom may accept electrons from donor atoms or groups up to the atomic number of the next higher "noble gas" (*rule of Sidgwick*). This number is called the *effective atomic number* (EAN). This is actually a different way of saying that the octet can be "expanded" up to the point where all the unfilled orbitals of the electron shell are filled. The *maximum* coordination number of a metal ion is, therefore, *half* of the difference between the EAN and the number of electrons in the metal ion (half, since every coordinate bond requires the sharing of *two* electrons). This delimits the maximum number of ligands which may be coordinated around the central atom. The number of actually coordinated ligands may, however, be less, and this depends on the "charge density" of the central atom and the tendency of the coordination sphere to attain optimum symmetry.

Consider the complex ions in Table VI. The $[BeF_4]^{2\ominus}$ is formed by the union of $|\underline{F}|^{\ominus\oplus}Be^{\oplus\ominus}|\underline{F}|$ and $2\,Na^{\oplus\ominus}|\underline{F}|$. The surrounding $4\,|\underline{F}|^{\ominus}$ donate

Table VI

Coordination Index and Symmetry of Some Complex Compounds

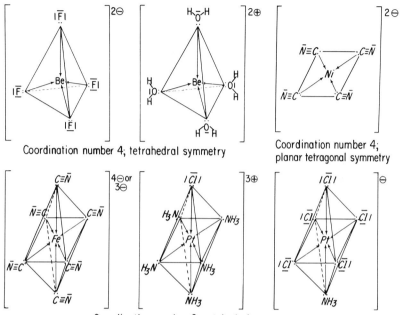

Coordination number 4; tetrahedral symmetry

Coordination number 4; planar tetragonal symmetry

Coordination number 6; octahedral symmetry

4 doublets whereby $Be^{2\oplus}$ reaches the stable neon configuration; beryllium has, therefore, a coordination number of 4. Since the sum of negative charges of the ligands are in excess of 2 over the positive charges of the metal, the complex anion carries 2 negative charges. In contrast, when $Be^{2\oplus}$ is hydrated in solution by coordinating 4 water molecules (which are neutral) the resulting complex ion, in which the coordination number of Be is also 4, carries two positive charges $[Be(H_2O)_4]^{2\oplus}$.

The coordination number of $Fe^{2\oplus}$ is 6, which is half of the difference between the number of its electrons (24) and the atomic number of the next "noble gas," krypton (36). Combination of $Fe^{2\oplus}$ and 6 $(CN)^{\ominus}$ results in four net negative charges in $[Fe(CN)_6]^{4\ominus}$. Oxidation of $[Fe(CN)_6]^{4\ominus}$ to $[Fe(CN)_6]^{3\ominus}$ causes deviation from the EAN since the latter ion possesses only 35 electrons (compare to krypton: 36). This results in the tendency of the $[Fe(CN)_6]^{3\ominus}$ ion to act as an electron acceptor, *i.e.*, an oxidizing agent.

The coordination number of $Pt^{4\oplus}$ is 6, which is half of the difference between the number of its electrons (74) and the number of electrons of the next "noble gas," radon (86). Depending on the type of ligands, the complex ion may be a cation or an anion. Coordination of one $|\overline{Cl}|^{\ominus}$ and five NH_3 molecules (carrying no ionic charge) by $Pt^{4\oplus}$ results in three net positive ionic charges in the complex $[Pt(NH_3)_5Cl]^{3\oplus}$. On the other hand, coordination of five $|\overline{Cl}|^{\ominus}$ and one NH_3 results in one net negative charge in the complex $[PtCl_5NH_3]^{\ominus}$.

Coordination by $Ni^{2\oplus}$ constitutes one of the number of exceptions to the EAN concept. From the difference of the number of electrons in $Ni^{2\oplus}$ (26) and its EAN (krypton core = 36 electrons) the coordination number should be 5. Yet, the experimentally found coordination numbers of $Ni^{2\oplus}$ are 4 and 6, the former corresponding to an EAN = 34 (as in $[Ni(CN)_4]^{2\ominus}$ shown in the upper right corner of Table VI) and the latter to an EAN = 38. This exception is an example where the tendency to reach optimum symmetry overrules the tendency to attain the electron core corresponding to the EAN; in fact, the optimum arrangements of both 4 and 6 ligands are of higher symmetry than that of a 5-ligand coordination sphere (see below in this section).

The type of coordination compounds discussed above carry excess positive or negative charges [*formal charge* (see Suppletory Note 11)] and are, thus, electrolytes. Many complexes are known which are nonelectrolytes, *e.g.*, $Ni(:C=\overset{\frown}{O})_4$, $Fe(:C=\overset{\frown}{O})_5$.

2. *The charge density of the central atom.* The charge density is the ratio: number of positive charges/ionic radius in angstrom units. The metals that form the most stable complexes are those which have a large positive charge compared to the size of the ion; it is under these conditions that the attraction between the nucleus of the central atom and the electron doublets "donated" by the ligands will be the greatest. This is another way of saying that all other conditions being equal the more electronegative metal will form more stable complexes (compare Section 3.1.2.3). For complex formation the charge density must be at least 1.80; some ions may have charge density values as high as 6.5. Low charge density provides the explanation why metal ions such as $Na^{\oplus}$, $K^{\oplus}$, and $Rb^{\oplus}$ (ratios: 1.05, 0.75, and 0.68) do not act as coordinating centers in spite of the availability of unfilled orbitals, while $Mg^{\oplus\oplus}$ and $Ca^{\oplus\oplus}$ (ratios: 3.1 and 2.0) form stable complexes. Lithium ion is in an intermediate position with its ratio of 1.67; a few stable complexes of lithium, for example:

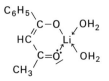

lithium benzoylacetonate dihydrate

are, in fact, known. Lithium is, thus, the first element in the Periodic Table showing maximum valency (by coordination) compatible with the number of unfilled orbitals of the period. The tendency of lithium to coordinate is also indicated by the much larger hydration sphere (Section 3.4.4) of $Li^{\oplus}$ than of the other alkali metal ions.

3. The ratio of the metal and ligand radii. The EAN and the charge density give information about the maximum multiplicity and the magnitude of the attractive forces coordinating the ligands. However, the actual number of ligands which may be accommodated around the metal ion will also depend on the relative size of the ligands and the metal ion. If the metal ion is very small and the ligands are large, fewer ligands can be accommodated around the metal than would be possible with smaller ligand size. Therefore, for the optimum accommodation (maximum close packing) of a given number of ligands the ratio of the metal and ligand radii must be at a certain value. This means that, given a minimum charge density of about 2.0, the *actual* coordination number increases with the increase of the radius ratio up to the value of the maximum coordination number. For example, for a ratio 0.15–0.22 the number of ligands which may be symmetrically accommodated around the center cannot be higher than 3; for an actual coordination number of 6, the ratio must be as high as 0.41–0.59.

A ligand group or molecule may contain one or more electron-donor atoms and is named accordingly *unidentate* or *multidentate* (literally, having one or many teeth). Multidentate ligands may be bi-, tri-, tetra-, penta-, and hexadentate and are called *chelates*. The whole complex which includes a metal is a *metal chelate*. A typical feature of metal chelate structure is the formation of a 5- or 6-membered ring in accordance with the Baeyer strain theory (Section 2.1.4), hence the term "chelate" (meaning the claw of a crab) because of the pincer-like inclusion of the metal. Some typical chelates are shown in Table VII. Tetradentate metal chelates of certain derivatives of porphine play a variety of important biological roles as the functional working moieties of oxygen transfer agents and biocatalysts (*e.g.*, the chlorophylls, vitamin B_{12}, and ferrous protoheme in hemoglobin).

In a particularly interesting group of metal complexes the ligands are unsaturated or aromatic compounds, and it is a portion of the π-electron cloud which is "donated" to the central atom. Binding is established by an oriented deformation of the π-electron cloud and overlapping with the orbitals of the metal. Such coordination compounds, called π *complexes*, are exemplified in Table VIII. In many cases it is difficult to determine, however, whether or not an adduct is a true π complex (*i.e.*, whether the metal is in an equidistant position relative to the two carbon atoms of the π bond).

Table VII

Structures of Some Multidentate Metal Chelates

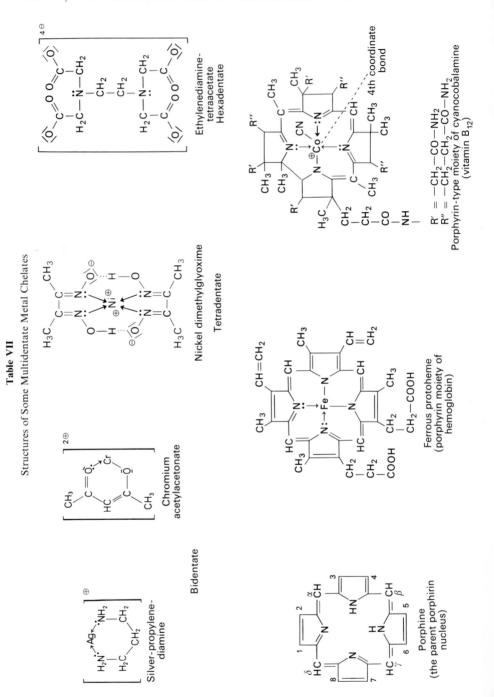

Geometric and electrostatic considerations indicate that the experimentally observed symmetries of complexes are actually the most likely
arrangements for the numbers of ligands present. Since the electron pairs
(representing the coordinate bonds) exert repulsion on each other, they
will occupy a distribution in space which will minimize repulsion; this is
achieved by distancing each other as far as possible. Now, if the electron

Table VIII
Some π-Electron Coordination Compounds

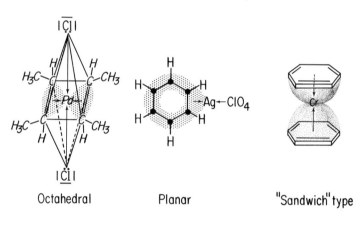

| Octahedral | Planar | "Sandwich" type |

pairs about an atom are regarded as mobile negative charges on a spherical
surface, then the maximum distance of separation of the charges corresponds
to a maximum angle of the radii connecting the charges with the center of
the sphere. Thus, two charges will tend to move to opposite positions to
achieve minimum repulsion, and the valence angle will be 180° (digonal
symmetry). To be equidistant, three charges will be at 120° to each other in
the equatorial plane of the sphere (trigonal symmetry). Four charges at
equidistant points on the surface of the sphere will be at 109° 28′ relative to
each other, *i.e.*, the valences will be "directed" toward the corners of a
regular tetrahedron (tetrahedral symmetry). In some special instances four
charges may occupy equidistant positions in the equatorial plane of the
sphere at angles of 90° (tetragonal symmetry). Five charges cannot be
arranged so as to be equidistant on the sphere. When six electron pairs are
present, the optimum arrangement to minimize repulsion is that four pairs

are in an equatorial tetragonal plane and the two other pairs are at 90°
angles relative to the plane, one above and one below (octahedral symmetry).
It may be readily seen that identical qualitative considerations explain the
valence angles of the carbon atom. Moreover, as in the carbon atom, the
symmetrical valence distribution of atoms with expanded octets is the
result of the hybridization of all orbitals partaking in bond formation
(mentioned in Section 3.1.2.2).

SUPPLETORY NOTES FOR SECTION 3.1

NOTE 1

The initial form of the Bohr model which can give an approximate
account for the spectrum of hydrogen may be derived by means of a simple
electrostatic theory. The force of attraction between the electron and the
proton may be expressed by Coulomb's Law:

$$F = \frac{e^2}{r_n^2} \tag{a}$$

where e is the charge of the electron or of the proton [4.8×10^{-10} electrostatic centimeter-gram-second (cgs) units] and r_n the distance separating
the charges.

If one considers the electron as a corpuscle, its moving about in a circular
orbit gives rise to a centrifugal force

$$F = m\frac{v^2}{r_n} \tag{b}$$

For the orbiting of the electron in a stationary fashion on any one orbit
the force of attraction must equal the centrifugal force:

$$m\frac{v^2}{r_n} = \frac{e^2}{r_n^2} \quad \text{from which} \quad mv^2 = \frac{e^2}{r_n} \tag{c}$$

Expressing the electron velocity v from Eq. (1), substituting in Eq. (c) and
solving for r_n we get:

$$r_n = n^2 \frac{h^2}{4\pi^2 me^2} \tag{d}$$

Since in Eq. (d) the quantities h, m, and e are constants, the radii of the permissible orbits increase as $1, 4, 9, 16, \ldots$, that is, as the squares of the n quantum numbers. It may be calculated that for the ground level $n = 1$ the radius of the orbit is 0.528 Å.

In order to calculate the frequency of the radiation emitted when the electron passes from a higher to a lower orbit, the energy levels of the orbits must be known. The total energy of the electron is the sum of kinetic and potential energy. From elementary mechanics:

$$E_{kin} = \tfrac{1}{2}mv^2 \tag{e}$$

thus for the electron, substituting from Eq. (c):

$$E_{kin} = \frac{1}{2} \frac{e^2}{r_n} \tag{f}$$

On the other hand, electrostatics shows that the potential energy between two charges equals the product of the charges divided by the distance separating them. Thus for the electron in a given orbit we have:

$$E_{pot} = \frac{-e \cdot +e}{r_n} = -\frac{e^2}{r_n} \tag{g}$$

The total energy of the electron is therefore:

$$E_{total} = E_{kin} + E_{pot} = \frac{1}{2} \frac{e^2}{r_n} + \left(-\frac{e^2}{r_n}\right) = -\frac{1}{2} \frac{e^2}{r_n} \tag{h}$$

Substituting r_n from Eq. (d), since the radius of a given orbit is identical to the distance separating the charges, we get the expression of energy for any one orbit:

$$E_{total} = -\frac{2\pi^2 m e^4}{h^2} \cdot \frac{1}{n^2} \tag{i}$$

For distinguishing between two orbits, let the quantum number of an E' higher orbit be n and the quantum number of an E lower orbit be k. The energy difference between the two orbits is therefore:

$$E' - E = -\frac{2\pi^2 m e^4}{h^2} \cdot \frac{1}{n^2} - \left(-\frac{2\pi^2 m e^4}{h^2} \cdot \frac{1}{k^2}\right) = \frac{2\pi^2 m e^4}{h^2} \cdot \left(\frac{1}{k^2} - \frac{1}{n^2}\right) \tag{j}$$

By substituting $h \cdot v$ for the energy difference [from Eq. (2)] and solving for v we get:

$$v = \frac{2\pi^2 m e^4}{h^3} \left(\frac{1}{k^2} - \frac{1}{n^2}\right) \tag{k}$$

Wave number (number of waves in 1 cm: $v_{cm^{-1}} = 10^7/\lambda_{m\mu}$, since $10^7 \, cm^{-1} = 1 \, m\mu$) equals v divided by c which is the velocity of light $(2.998 \times 10^{10} \, cm/sec)$. When Eq. (k) is expressed in wave number, the quantity $2\pi^2 me^4/ch^3$ is known as the Rydberg constant and has a value of $109,700 \, cm^{-1}$.

Equation (k) gives the frequencies of the emitted spectral lines by substituting for n and k the respective quantum numbers. For example: substitution of 5 and 1, 4 and 1, 3 and 1, 2 and 1 yields the frequencies of the Lyman series (ultraviolet spectrum lines); substitution of 6 and 2, 5 and 2, 4 and 2, 3 and 2 yields the frequencies of the Balmer series (visible spectrum lines); substitution of 6 and 3, 5 and 3, 4 and 3 yields the frequencies of the Paschen series (some of the infrared spectrum lines).

The numerical values of the energy levels of the hydrogen atom in the different orbits can be calculated by substituting the quantum numbers 1, 2, 3, ..., etc., for k and setting n equal to infinity in Eq. (j). These values in electron volts (1 ev $= 23.06 \, kcal/mole$ or $1.6 \times 10^{-12} \, ergs/mole$) represent the energies which must be supplied to the atom (Fig. 5) to place the electron from defined orbits to an infinitely distant level, i.e., to remove it completely (ionization energy).

An important implication of the Bohr model is that in its conceptual framework, atoms do not radiate while electrons are on *stationary* orbits. This represented a sharp break with classical physics, according to which if an electron is regarded as a well-defined material particle orbiting at a velocity v in an orbit of radius r_n then the frequency of orbiting is:

$$v = \frac{v}{2\pi r_n} \tag{l}$$

Therefore, if atoms would behave as ordinary electromagnetic oscillators then the frequencies of the emission bands should correspond to the orbiting frequencies at the permissible stationary orbits. The experimental evidence clearly shows that this is not the case. Yet, paradoxically, the idea of regarding the atoms as electromagnetic oscillators in the classical sense is still quite useful for the simple explanation of molecular phenomena such as resonance (see Suppletory Note 1 for Section 3.2) and light absorption (Section 3.2.3.3).

NOTE 2

There are two kinds of quantities in the physical world: scalars and vectors. A *scalar* has only magnitude determined by unique numbers which can be added, subtracted, etc., following the laws of ordinary arithmetic. A *vector*, on the other hand, is determined by its *magnitude* and by its *direction*. Thus vectors are *oriented quantities*. For example, length, mass, temperature, density, electric charge are scalars; velocity, acceleration, force, electric or magnetic field are vectors. A vector is designated by a straight line with an arrowhead, drawn in the proper direction, with its length to scale. In shorthand notation a vector quantity may be represented as $\vec{E}$ (for electric field), $\vec{p}$ (for momentum), $\vec{M}$ (for magnetic moment), etc.

Because vector quantities also have directions they can only be added, subtracted, etc., as scalars *if they have the same directions*. In any other case, the addition of vectors follows the *parallelogram law*, which is illustrated below:

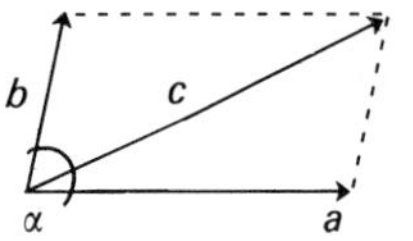

$$\vec{a} + \vec{b} = \vec{c}$$

The value of the *resultant vector* $\vec{c}$ may be determined graphically by drawing the vectors $\vec{a}$ and $\vec{b}$ to scale with their respective directions, or it may be readily calculated with the formula:

$$\vec{c} = \sqrt{(\vec{a})^2 + (\vec{b})^2 + 2\vec{a}\vec{b}\cos\alpha}$$

where α is the angle between the directions of $\vec{a}$ and $\vec{b}$. Thus, the more nearly two vectors point in the same direction, the greater is the magnitude of the resultant vector.

The difference of two vectors is illustrated as:

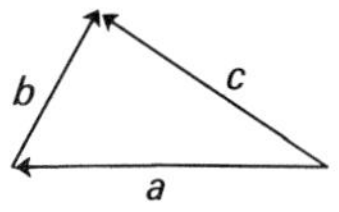

$$\vec{a} - \vec{b} = \vec{c}$$

This indicates that, when subtracting two vectors, the more nearly the two vectors point in exactly opposite directions the smaller will be the difference vector.

For manipulating vectors for the purpose of addition or subtraction, the arrows may be moved *but they must always be kept parallel to their original directions*; in other words, vectors do not change when subjected to translation in the direction or opposite to the direction of the vector, or in a direction perpendicular to the direction of the vector. The *multiplication* of vectors follows more complex laws; this is beyond the scope of our purpose.

NOTE 3

This constant $e/2mc$ may be regarded as equal to the ratio of the magnetic moment $\vec{M}$ of the circulating electron and of the orbit angular momentum $m \cdot v \cdot r = \vec{p}$. This may be demonstrated as follows. The electron in a circular orbit is equivalent to a current around a plane circular area which, according to electromagnetic theory, causes a magnetic moment:

$$\vec{M} = \frac{I \cdot S}{c} \tag{a}$$

where I is the intensity of the current, S the area of the surface, and c the velocity of light. However, the intensity of current is actually the rate of flow of charge $I = e/t$; thus, for the circular path of the electron:

$$\vec{M} = \frac{e \cdot \pi \cdot r^2}{c \cdot t} \tag{b}$$

On the other hand, the angular momentum $\vec{p} = m \cdot v \cdot r$. Furthermore, in a circular motion the velocity may be expressed in terms of angular velocity ω, thus:

$$v = \omega \cdot r \tag{c}$$

where for a given angle Φ of rotation, $\omega = \Phi/t$. (For the definition of ω see Suppletory Note 7.) Since for a whole circular orbit $\Phi = 2\pi$, the angular momentum of the electron may be expressed as:

$$\vec{p} = \frac{2\pi m r^2}{t} \tag{d}$$

Hence, the ratio $\vec{M}/\vec{p}$, called the *gyromagnetic ratio* is:

$$\frac{\vec{M}}{\vec{p}} = \frac{e}{2mc} \quad \text{and} \quad \vec{M} = \vec{p}\frac{e}{2mc} \tag{e}$$

Since the component $\vec{p}$ of the angular momentum in the direction of the magnetic field is $m_l \cdot (h/2\pi)$, then:

$$\vec{M} = m_l \cdot \frac{e \cdot h}{4\pi mc} \tag{f}$$

Thus the magnetic moment varies as integral multiples of the unit $(e \cdot h)/4\pi mc$, known as the *Bohr magneton*.

NOTE 4

The spin magnetic momentum $\vec{M}_s$ is also quantized in Bohr magneton units (see Suppletory Note 3):

$$\vec{M}_s = m_s \cdot \frac{h}{2\pi} \cdot 2 \cdot \frac{e}{2mc} = \pm \frac{e \cdot h}{4\pi mc}$$

since $m_s = \pm\frac{1}{2}$. Note that the factor $2e/2mc$ relating the spin angular moment to the spin magnetic momentum is twice as great as the factor $e/2mc$ relating the orbit angular momentum to the orbit magnetic moment (see Suppletory Note 3).

Note 5

A simple derivation of the Heisenberg Uncertainty Principle is based on the following reasoning. The spatial position of a corpuscle may be determined by measuring its three coordinates x, y, and z. For example, a microscope may be used to measure the position of the corpuscle relative to the x axis. The uncertainty Δx of the actually determined position is due to the limitation of the resolving power of the microscope which in turn is caused by the diffraction of light. The resolving power of the microscope is given by the well-known relation:

$$\Delta x \approx \frac{\lambda}{\sin \alpha} \tag{a}$$

where λ is the wavelength of the light beam and α the half angle of the aperture of the beam focused on the corpuscle. Thus, for a given angle α, the shorter the wavelength the more accurate will be the determination of the position.

The very observation of the corpuscle by means of a beam of light implies, however, that a shock occurred between the corpuscle and a photon resulting in the diffraction of the latter (Compton effect). According to Einstein's theory of light the smaller the wavelength the greater is the momentum of a photon [following Eq. (4)]. Now the exact fraction of this momentum, actually communicated by the photon to the examined corpuscle and causing a change in its initial momentum along the x axis, cannot be known because the direction of the photon trajectory in the angle of aperture of the light beam is undetermined. However, the *maximum* fraction which may be communicated is given by the relation:

$$\Delta m v_x \approx \frac{h \cdot v}{c} \sin \alpha \tag{b}$$

It follows from Eqs. (a) and (b) that the condition which increases the precision of determination of position (decrease of wavelength) will cause a correspondingly increasing imprecision in the determination of the momentum of the corpuscle.

By multiplying Eqs. (a) and (b) with one another we get:

$$\Delta x \cdot \Delta m v_x \approx \frac{\lambda}{\sin \alpha} \cdot \frac{h \cdot v}{c} \cdot \sin \alpha \tag{c}$$

However since $\lambda = c/v$, we find Eq. (6):

$$\Delta x \cdot \Delta m v_x \approx h$$

An identical relation was derived by Bohr and Heisenberg by considering a great number of other measuring systems.

NOTE 6

According to the Heisenberg Uncertainty Principle, a precise position of an electron in an atom would correspond to an energy level 10^6 times higher than the actually known energy levels of the corpuscle. It has been calculated, for example, that if the position of an electron would be known with a certainty of 10^{-12} cm (which is the order of magnitude of the nucleus) then the uncertainty of its momentum would be of the order of 10^{-15} gm cm sec^{-1}. If one considers that the resting mass of the electron is of the order of 10^{-27} gm, this would correspond to an electron kinetic energy of approximately 20 Mev (mega electron volt), which is impossible since energy levels of this order of magnitude are found only in the nucleus.

NOTE 7

The meaning of the "wave function" may best be explained by actually deriving a simple amplitude function. Figure 9 represents the "wave" of an oscillatory motion called *simple harmonic motion* (see also in Suppletory Note 7 for Section 3.2) progressing from the origin O toward the right (dotted line).

Such a wave motion is best examined by means of a geometric construct called a "circle of reference." Consider the circle of reference of unit radius vector $r = 1$ in Fig. 9. If this radius vector rotates around, in one complete rotation it describes a whole cycle, or an angle 360° (which equals 2π). On the other hand, in one complete oscillation or cycle the wave of a simple harmonic motion progresses a distance λ. Consequently, for the radius vector rotation $\lambda = 2\pi$, and the velocity of rotation per unit time, called the *angular velocity*, is $\omega = 2\pi/T$. The angle of rotation of the radius vector at any given time t, called the *phase angle*, is $\Phi = (2\pi/T) \cdot t$.

From the triangle formed by the unit radius vector $r = 1$, its projection on the x axis, and the intercept of the two (designated as ψ_1), $\sin \Phi = \psi_1/1$, from which:

$$\psi_1 = 1 \cdot \sin \Phi = 1 \cdot \sin \frac{2\pi}{T} \cdot t \tag{a}$$

Plotting ψ_1 against t, the sine curve (solid line) in Fig. 9 is obtained. Thus, from the amplitude function (a) the value of ψ_1 for any given time t may be calculated; ψ_1 may take on values between 0 and 1 depending on the phase angle $\Phi = (2\pi/T) \cdot t$ of the motion. Now if the amplitude has the value of A instead of unity, the amplitude function becomes:

$$\psi_A = A \cdot \sin \frac{2\pi}{T} \cdot t \tag{b}$$

represented by the dotted line curve in the figure.

Let us examine now the form of an amplitude function ψ_x describing the amplitude of the oscillations at a point P being at a distance x_a from the origin. If x_a/λ is an integer (which means that x_a is an integral multiple of λ) then the wave train at the point P is exactly in phase with a wave train just leaving the origin. However, at *any arbitrary distance* x_a the value of ψ_x, in addition to depending on the phase angle $(2\pi/T) \cdot t$, also depends on the difference of the phase $(2\pi \cdot x_a)/\lambda$ relative to the phase of the wave at the origin. The total phase angle is then $(2\pi/T) \cdot t \pm (2\pi \cdot x_a)/\lambda$ (depending on the direction of progression of the wave the positive or negative sign is used). Hence the amplitude function ψ_x is:

$$\psi_x = A \cdot \sin 2\pi \left(\frac{1}{T} \cdot t \pm \frac{x_a}{\lambda} \right) \tag{c}$$

However, since the *period* T (the time required to complete one oscillation or cycle) is the reciprocal of the frequency v, the function is usually written as:

$$\psi_x = A \cdot \sin 2\pi \left(v \cdot t \pm \frac{x_a}{\lambda} \right) \tag{d}$$

NOTE 8

A derivation of the Schrödinger amplitude equation proceeds from the expression of energy of the electron. The total energy of the electron is the sum of the kinetic energy and the potential energy:

$$E_{\text{total}} = E_{\text{kin}} + E_{\text{pot}} \tag{a}$$

Regarding the electron as a corpuscle of mass m, its kinetic energy *following classical mechanics* is:

$$E_{\text{kin}} = \tfrac{1}{2}mv^2 \tag{b}$$

where the velocity v must be given relative to the three spatial coordinates:

$$E_{\text{kin}} = \tfrac{1}{2}m(v_x^2 + v_y^2 + v_z^2) \tag{c}$$

Multiplying the numerator and denominator by m and rearranging, we get:

$$E_{kin} = \frac{1}{2m}[(m \cdot v_x)^2 + (m \cdot v_y)^2 + (m \cdot v_z)^2] \tag{d}$$

The terms which represent the momentum of the electron in the direction of the x, y, and z axes, $m \cdot v_x$, $m \cdot v_y$, and $m \cdot v_z$, are now substituted by their equivalent *in wave mechanics*, which are the differential operators:

$$\frac{h}{2\pi(-1)^{1/2}} \cdot \frac{\partial}{\partial x}, \qquad \frac{h}{2\pi(-1)^{1/2}} \cdot \frac{\partial}{\partial y}, \qquad \text{and} \qquad \frac{h}{2\pi(-1)^{1/2}} \cdot \frac{\partial}{\partial z}$$

(An operator is the symbol of a mathematical operation which transforms one function into another one. For example $3x^2$ is the result of the operation of d/dx on x^3, meaning differentiation of x^3 with respect to x. The terms such as $\partial/\partial x$ represent *partial* differential operators. This means that if a function is dependent on two or more variables, such an operator would differentiate the dependent variable only with respect to one independent variable, here x.)

Now,

$$(m \cdot v_x)^2 = \left(\frac{h}{2\pi(-1)^{1/2}} \cdot \frac{\partial}{\partial x} \right)^2 = -\frac{h^2}{4\pi^2} \cdot \frac{\partial^2}{\partial x^2}$$

and similarly for the squares of the momenta $(m \cdot v_y)^2$ and $(m \cdot v_z)^2$. Substituting these operators into Eq. (d) for kinetic energy we obtain the operator corresponding to the kinetic energy, E_{kin} (op):

$$E_{kin}\,(op) = -\frac{h^2}{4\pi^2} \cdot \frac{1}{2m} \left(\frac{\partial^2}{\partial x^2} + \frac{\partial^2}{\partial y^2} + \frac{\partial^2}{\partial z^2} \right) \tag{e}$$

The significance of E_{kin} (op) is twofold: (a) that if we let this operator act on a function (*e.g.*, on ψ of an electron wave), in other words if we perform the mathematical operation (with ψ) outlined in Eq. (e), then we get the *actual value* of kinetic energy (of the electron); (b) that the momentum corresponding to this energy can vary only in $h/2\pi$ units.

Substituting (e) into Eq. (a) and rearranging:

$$\frac{h^2}{8\pi^2 m} \left(\frac{\partial^2}{\partial x^2} + \frac{\partial^2}{\partial y^2} + \frac{\partial^2}{\partial z^2} \right) + (E_{total} - E_{pot}) = 0 \tag{f}$$

Multiplication by $8\pi^2 m/h^2$ and introduction of the amplitude ψ give:

$$\left(\frac{\partial^2 \psi}{\partial x^2} + \frac{\partial^2 \psi}{\partial y^2} + \frac{\partial^2 \psi}{\partial z^2}\right) + \frac{8\pi^2 m}{h^2}(E_{total} - E_{pot})\psi = 0 \tag{g}$$

The triple term

$$\frac{\partial^2}{\partial x^2} + \frac{\partial^2}{\partial y^2} + \frac{\partial^2}{\partial z^2}$$

is known as the *Laplacian operator* and is symbolized by ∇^2. A form in which the Schrödinger equation is often represented is then:

$$\nabla^2 \psi + \frac{8\pi^2 m}{h^2}(E_{total} - E_{pot})\psi = 0 \tag{h}$$

Here $E_{pot} = -(e^2/r_n)$ from Eq. (g) in Suppletory Note 1. The Schrödinger equation has valid solutions for ψ only when E_{total} takes on certain discrete values. For example, the wave function of the $1s$ orbital of the hydrogen atom is:

$$\psi_{100} = \frac{1}{(\pi a^3)^{1/2}} e^{-r/a}$$

where the subscript 100 indicates that it is the ψ for $n = 1$, $l = 0$, $m_l = 0$, e is the basis of the natural logarithm, r the distance from the nucleus, and the constant $a = h^2/4\pi^2 m e^2$.

Another form of the Schrödinger equation is obtained by rearranging Eq. (f) as:

$$E_{total} = -\frac{h^2}{8\pi^2 m}\nabla^2 + E_{pot} = H \tag{i}$$

where H, known as the *Hamiltonian energy operator*, is merely the sum of the kinetic and potential energy of the electron. In terms of this operator the Schrödinger equation is written as:

$$H\psi = E_{total}\,\psi \tag{j}$$

which is its familiar form in molecular orbital calculations.

NOTE 9

The electron probability as a function of the distance from the nucleus is expressed by a radial distribution function. This function is obtained when the term dv for unit volume is replaced in Eq. (7) by a term giving the volume of a spherical shell of unit thickness at a distance r from the nucleus. The volume of such a shell is given by the expression $4\pi r^2\,dr$, where $4\pi r^2$ is the surface of a sphere of radius r, and dr the thickness of the shell. Thus, the radial electron probability D_r is given by:

$$D_r = 4\pi r^2 \psi^2(x, y, z)\,dr$$

NOTE 10

The determination of the dipole moment is carried out by measuring the dielectric constant and calculating the dipole moment from it. The dielectric constant ε is a coefficient which is a measure of the ability of a substance to increase the capacity C of a condenser to store electric charge Q, when the substance is placed between the condenser plates. This may be explained in the following way. The capacity of a condenser (*e.g.*, in Fig. 22), placed in a vacuum, is given by the expression $C = Q/V$, where V is the potential difference which can be measured between the plates. The meaning of this equation may best be understood by comparing the electric charge to a gas of amount Q, having a pressure V when enclosed in a recipient of storage *capacity* (or volume) C. Thus, for a given value of Q, decrease of V will be an indication of the increase of C and inversely.

A little reflection will indicate that the capacity of the condenser to store electric charge may be increased either (a) by increasing the surface of the plates, or (b) by decreasing the distance between the plates. The latter causes increase of the charge density on the surfaces facing each other (hence decrease of the charge "pressure" V) because of greater localization of the charges due to their mutual attraction. There is also a third way to increase the capacity of the condenser, which is to place between the plates some material, which can either be polarized by the field (*induced* or *distortion polarization*) or which has a dipole moment of its own due to asymmetric electron distribution. This will increase the capacity because a greater number of opposite charges will now face the charges on each plate surface causing an increase of the charge density, which in turn results in decrease of V (for the same value of Q). Therefore, in general, the capacity of a condenser is given by $C = \varepsilon \cdot Q/V$. The ε of vacuum or air is unity. Some typical values at 25°C are: hexane 1.90, CCl_4 2.24, benzene 2.28, chloroform 4.80, ethanol 24.3, nitrobenzene 34.8, water 79.5, acetonitrile 80 (note the much higher dielectric constants of polar liquids).

All materials show some degree of induced polarization, *i.e.*, a dipole moment which is *induced* by an electric field, and this is denoted as P_{ind}. Thus, the total molar polarization P_M of a compound having a *permanent* dipole moment is given by the sum

$$P_M = P_{ind} + P_\mu \qquad (a)$$

where P_μ represents the polarization due to the permanent dipole moment, which is called *orientation polarization*. However, P_{ind} and P_μ can be separated because *the induced polarization is independent from the temperature and depends only on the field strength*. The orientation polarization P_μ is, on the other hand, strongly affected by the temperature. This is because the random thermal agitation of the molecules counteracts their orderly alignment toward the condenser plates, which is to say, the ordering of the permanent dipoles in the field axis. Thus, the magnitude of the P_μ vector which is oriented in the direction of the field is proportional to $\mu^2/3kT$, where k is the Boltzmann constant or universal gas constant R per molecule ($k = R/N = 1.38 \times 10^{-16}$ erg per degree; the Avogadro number $N = 6.02 \times 10^{23}$) and T is the absolute temperature. The term kT represents the kinetic energy of one single dipole of moment μ; the term must be taken three times because the dipole has translational freedom in the 3 dimensions. It is clear that the higher the temperature the lesser is the orientation of the dipoles.

The total molar polarization is given by the Clausius–Mosotti equation as:

$$P_M = \frac{\varepsilon - 1}{\varepsilon + 2} \cdot \frac{M}{d} \tag{b}$$

where M is the molecular weight of the compound and d its density. The ratio M/d is known as the *molar volume*.

Now, electrodynamic theory indicates that a molecule having 3 translational freedoms occupies during thermal agitation all possible positions in rapid succession describing thus the surface area 4π of a sphere of unit radius; accordingly, a polar molecule may be regarded as a spherical charge. However, only one third of that three-dimensional charge is manifest in the direction of the field axis because the latter represents only one dimension. Thus both terms P_{ind} and P_μ are proportional to $4\pi/3$:

$$P_{ind} = \tfrac{4}{3}\pi N\alpha \qquad \text{and} \qquad P_\mu = \tfrac{4}{3}\pi N \cdot \frac{\mu^2}{3kT}$$

where α represents the polarizability, that is the ease by which the distortion of the electron cloud can be brought about. Both P_{ind} and P_μ are multiplied with the Avogadro number to convert molecular quantities into molar quantities. Thus, P_{ind} and P_μ represent the induced and permanent dipole moments of a mole of substance in an electric field of unit strength.

The explicit form of Eq. (a) is, therefore:

$$\frac{\varepsilon - 1}{\varepsilon + 2} \cdot \frac{M}{d} = \alpha(\tfrac{4}{3}\pi N) + \frac{\mu^2}{3kT}(\tfrac{4}{3}\pi N) \tag{c}$$

Since both μ and α are molecular constants, Eq. (c) has the general form:

$$P_M = a + b\,(1/T) \tag{d}$$

and gives a straight line when P_M is plotted against the reciprocal of the absolute temperature $1/T$. Its slope, $b = (4\pi N/9k)\mu^2$, is used to calculate the value of μ. To eliminate the effect of the mutual interaction of the dipoles in the solution (due to their relative concentration), the value of μ is usually determined at several concentrations and extrapolated to infinite dilution. In a similar way α may be determined from the intercept of the curve.

NOTE 11

The *formal charge* of an atom $\oplus$ or $\ominus$ must be clearly distinguished from the partial charge δ^+ or δ^-. The formal charge of an atom is zero if the number of electrons about it equals the number of its positive charges. If the number of positive and negative formal charges in a molecule are equal, the total formal charges add up to zero. The concept of formal charge is important for the discussion of molecules having double or triple bonds.

The difference between formal charge and partial charge is explained as follows. Ammonia has an appreciable dipole moment because of the greater electronegativity of nitrogen than hydrogen (see Section 3.1.2.3); this indicates that the nitrogen in ammonia possesses partial negative charge and the three hydrogen atoms possess partial positive charges. Another compound, BF_3, has no measurable dipole moment in spite of the fact that the electronegativity difference between the boron and fluorine atoms (Table III) indicates that the B—F bonds are highly polarized $\overset{\delta^+}{B}\!=\!\overset{\delta^-}{F}$. The actually measurable dipole moment is zero because the three B—F bonds are symmetrically distributed in one plane (trigonal symmetry), and the bond moments consequently cancel each other. Neither NH_3 nor BF_3 have formal charges; ammonia contains 10 electrons for the total atomic number 10 of the nitrogen and the three hydrogen atoms; boron trifluoride contains 32 electrons for an identical number of total positive charges of one boron and three fluorine atoms.

On the other hand, in an ammonium ion there are 10 electrons for a total of 11 positive charges, indicating an excess of one positive charge. We say that ammonium ion has a formal charge of $+1$. In the fluoroborate ion there are 42 electrons for a total number of 41 positive charges; we say that the fluoroborate ion has a formal charge of -1. The bond moments (internal partial charges) in both $NH_4^\oplus$ and $BF_4^\ominus$ cancel each other, however, because both ions have tetrahedral symmetry.

3.2 Resonance

3.2.1 THE NATURE OF RESONANCE

In Sections 3.1.2.1 and 3.1.2.3 we have seen that, except for the relatively small contributions of bond energy increments in partially polarized bonds, the main component of the bonding energy which constitutes a single covalent bond is due to resonance or electron exchange. The nature of resonance energy can best be illustrated with the one-electron bond in the hydrogen molecule-ion (Section 3.1.2.7).

The hydrogen molecule-ion $(H \cdot H)^{\oplus}$ may be regarded as composed of an isolated hydrogen atom $H_A \cdot$ and a hydrogen ion $H_B{}^{\oplus}$:

$$H_A \cdot \quad H_B{}^{\oplus}$$

(I)

and the state of this system can be described by a wave function ψ_I. However, the arrangement:

$$H_A{}^{\oplus} \quad \cdot H_B$$

(II)

which can be described by the wave function ψ_{II}, has the same energy, and its existence is therefore just as probable. Thus the wave functions ψ_I and ψ_{II} are equally good (or bad) descriptions of the state of the system. In accordance with this, when the interaction energy between a hydrogen atom and a hydrogen ion is calculated by using either ψ_I or ψ_{II}, it is found that the internuclear repulsion increases with the decrease of their distance (dotted line in Fig. 25). However, since arrangements (I) and (II) are equivalent they both may be regarded as contributing to the actual state of the system. Hence, a correct description should take into account both arrangements by adding the two wave functions such as:

$$\psi = C_I \psi_I + C_{II} \psi_{II} \tag{17}$$

where ψ is the resultant wave function (the wave function of the resonance hybrid) and the coefficients C_I and C_{II} represent the extent of contributions of ψ_I and ψ_{II} to the state of the molecule; for totally symmetrical atoms $C_I = C_{II}$. This is the principle of a second method of mathematically describing the formation of the covalent bond [*valence bond method* (*V B*); also called *method of mesomerism*]. The principle of the alternate LCAO method was given in Section 3.1.2.1. Note that Eq. (17) shows a similarity to Eq. (10) in the LCAO method. It is important to realize that this similarity is only a formal one since in Eq. (10) ψ_1 and ψ_2 describe *atomic* orbitals, while ψ_I and ψ_{II} describe contributing *molecular* resonant forms of $(H \cdot H)^{\oplus}$.

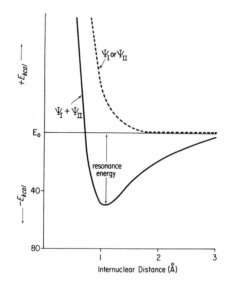

Fig. 25. Energy curves of the hydrogen molecule-ion. The lower curve corresponds to the formation of a stable one-electron bond.

Now, if the resultant wave function ψ is used to calculate the interaction energy, it is indeed found that the energy curve has a pronounced minimum at an internuclear distance of 1.06 Å (solid line in Fig. 25) indicating the formation of a stable one-electron bond in agreement with the experimental finding. This in turn supports the original assumption, namely that both arrangements, (I) and (II), contribute to the actual state of the molecule (the resonance hybrid). In other words, the single electron oscillates back and forth between the two nuclei:

$$[H_A \cdot \quad H_B^{\oplus}] \leftrightarrow [H_A^{\oplus} \quad \cdot H_B]$$

and it is the energy of this oscillation (the *resonance energy* or *exchange energy*) which holds the nuclei together. The energy of the bond and the frequency of the oscillation (*resonance frequency*) are related by the equation $E = h \cdot v$ (used in Section 3.1.1.3); the bond energy of the hydrogen molecule-ion due to resonance is 50 kcal/mole (Fig. 25), from which the resonance frequency of the bond is calculated to be 7×10^{14} per second.

A little reflection will reveal why the one-electron bond is relatively rare. For the electronic oscillation to be at an optimum, the two nuclei should exert equal attraction on the electron, *i.e.*, should have equal or very similar electronegativities (*e.g.*, boron and hydrogen). Greater electronegativity of one atom will tend to stabilize the electron in its vicinity and will thus decrease the frequency of oscillations between the nuclei (and hence the bond energy).

The resonance phenomenon in the electron-pair covalent bond is formulated in a similar way. Let $A^{.1}$ and $^{2.}B$ be two atoms with their respective valence electrons. As long as the two atoms are separate, the electrons $^{.1}$ and $^{.2}$ belonging to different orbitals have unpaired spins (↑) and (↑) which is in accordance with Hund's rule (Section 3.1.1.4). The orbitals of two such electrons cannot interpenetrate since only electrons with paired spins may occupy the same orbital (following the Pauli Exclusion Principle). Thus, as $A^{.1}$ (↑) approaches (↑) $^{2.}B$, the internuclear and interelectronic repulsion forces will prevail, and an energy curve similar to the dotted line in Fig. 25 will be obtained. The two electrons are then said to be in an *antibonding orbital*. On the other hand, if as $A^{.1}$(↑) approaches (↑)^{2}B there is inversion of the spin (to result in $A^{.1}$(↑) and (↓)$^2 B$, or $A^{.1}$(↓) and (↑)$^2 B$) then the two orbitals interpenetrate to form a *bonding orbital* (earlier in Section 3.1.2.1). In the valence bond terminology this is described by saying that electron

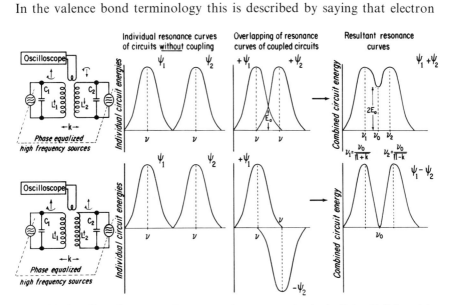

Fig. 26. Coupling of common electromagnetic resonant circuits in "phase" (↑↓) and in "phase opposition" (↑↑). The individual resonance energy curves of the circuits in the non-coupled state, the overlapping of the curves due to coupling, and the mutual resonance curves resulting from summation of the respective individual curves are shown. The coupling coefficient k is the ratio of the *mutual inductance* to four times the geometric mean of the separately measured inductances L_1 and L_2. The mutual inductance arises because of geometric closeness which brings about an overlapping of the magnetic fields of the two coils. Hence, the coupling coefficient increases with the geometric closeness of the two coils, but also varies with their respective positions.

exchange takes place:

$$[A^{\cdot 1} \quad {}^{2 \cdot}B] \longleftrightarrow [A^{\cdot 2} \quad {}^{1 \cdot}B] \longleftrightarrow \ldots$$

The significance of bonding and antibonding orbitals for electron density is discussed in Suppletory Note 1,* and their meaning is explained using the simple electrical analogy of radio-frequency resonant circuits coupled in "phase" and in "phase opposition" (Fig. 26).

Resonant structures having formal charges (see Suppletory Note 11 for Section 3.1), in which both electrons are attached to the same nucleus, also contribute, however, to the state of the H_2 molecule:

$$\ldots \longleftrightarrow [A^{\oplus} \quad {}^{1 \cdot}_{2 \cdot}B^{\ominus}] \longleftrightarrow [{}^{\ominus}A^{\cdot 1}_{\cdot 2} \quad B^{\oplus}]$$

Each resonant limit structure may be described by a wave function, and the wave function of the resonance hybrid is obtained by adding the four wave functions (each multiplied with its coefficient). The interaction energy curve of the neutral hydrogen molecule calculated with the wave function of the resonance hybrid is similar in shape to the solid line curve in Fig. 25, but the minimum is at 0.74 Å internuclear distance.

While differing electronegativities of A and B do increase the participation of charged resonant structures, large differences in electronegativity are compatible with the formation of covalent bond by electron pair. This is due to the fact that in the main contributing structures the two electrons are merely interchanged. In the one-electron bond, which as we have seen is not compatible with a large electronegativity difference, the sole electron would be restricted in the vicinity of the more electronegative atom.

3.2.2 RESONANCE IN ALKENES, AROMATIC COMPOUNDS, AND FREE RADICALS. MESOMERIC EFFECT. HYPERCONJUGATION

The concept of resonance is particularly successful in explaining the properties of unsaturated and aromatic compounds. A generalization of the concept is that there is resonance when two or more structures can be drawn for a compound or when a compound cannot be legitimately represented by a sole structure (*e.g.*, benzene by cyclohexatriene, Section 2.4), but only by a system of several structures (the limit formulas). We say then that the molecule "resonates" between these different structures. The resonant limit formulas have physical significance only in the sense that *each* molecule resonates between these different structures, that is, *each* molecule is a resonance hybrid of the limit formulas. Using a simple analogy, a limit formula does not represent the actual molecule any more than an extreme (or "limit") position of a vibrating reed during vibration represents the whole process of vibration. Nonetheless, the sum of all the positions of

* Suppletory Notes for Section 3.2 begin on page 210.

the reed does describe the process of vibration. It follows that *the resonant limit structures are not chemical entities that may be isolated.* This is also a simple way of distinguishing between limit formulas and tautomeric forms (Section 2.3.2.2) since the latter may be isolated under special experimental conditions. However, in spite of the fact that the resonant limit formulas do not have an actual, measurable physical reality and are fictitious valence schemes and mathematical dodges, they are extremely useful for the explanation of the properties and reactive potentialities of molecules.

According to Section 3.2.1 a good description of a resonance hybrid must take into account all resonant limit formulas which may be written and which may conceivably and *reasonably* contribute to the normal state of a molecule. The wave function of a resonance hybrid is then in general:

$$\psi = C_1\psi_1 + C_{II}\psi_{II} + C_{III}\psi_{III} + \cdots + C_n\psi_n \tag{18}$$

where $\psi_1, \psi_{II}, \psi_{III}, \ldots$ are the wave functions of the limit formulas and the coefficients $C_1, C_{II}, C_{III}, \ldots$ represent the extent of their contribution to the hybrid. For example, if the two Kekulé and three Dewar structures (Section 2.4) are considered to be the only contributing resonant limit formulas of benzene then the wave function of the hybrid is composed by the linear combination of five wave functions. The wave mechanical calculations (VB method) give the following coefficients:

$$\psi_{benzene} = 0.408\psi_1 + 0.408\psi_{II} + 0.177\psi_{III} + 0.177\psi_{IV} + 0.177\psi_V$$

where ψ_1 and ψ_{II} represent Kekulé structures and ψ_{III}, ψ_{IV}, and ψ_V the Dewar structures. From these coefficients the relative contribution of each structure, called the *weight of the structure,* may be calculated as follows:

$$\psi_1 = \psi_{II} = \frac{(0.408)^2}{2(0.408)^2 + 3(0.177)^2} = 0.39$$

and

$$\psi_{III} = \psi_{IV} = \psi_V = \frac{(0.177)^2}{2(0.408)^2 + 3(0.177)^2} = 0.073$$

Each of the Kekulé structures has a weight of 0.39 (39%) and each of the Dewar structures 0.073 (7.3%). Thus the total contribution of the five limit structures is $(2 \times 39\%) + (3 \times 7.3\%) = 100\%$.

The structure of the resonance hybrid is, however, not exactly an intermediate between the structures of the limit formulas in the sense that if the energy levels corresponding to these different structures are calculated it is found that the energy level of the resonance hybrid is *lower* than the energy level of the lowest energy limit structure. The difference energy, which confers an added stability to the resonance hybrid, is called *resonance energy* (see also Section 3.2.1). It is an important fact that *the resonance energy increases with the number of limit formulas which contribute to the hybrid*. The meaning of resonance energy is further illustrated in Suppletory Note 2, where the resonance energy of benzene is calculated from its enthalpy diagram (Fig. 27).

The simplest π-bonded structure for which resonant limit formulas may be drawn up is the ethylenic double bond:

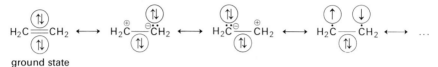

ground state

In the structures having formal charge (ionic limit formulas) two π electrons are displaced together and, therefore, paired spins are maintained (in subsequent examples of ionic limit formulas the free electron doublet will generally not be represented but its presence will be implied on any carbon atom having a negative formal charge). The above biradical structure, unlike the ionic limit formulas, does have a physical reality. This structure represents the *excited singlet state* (not to be confused with the covalent bonding by "singlet," *i.e.*, by one electron, in Sections 3.1.2.7 and 3.2.1) of ethylene, and is also called the *first excited state*. The excited singlet states

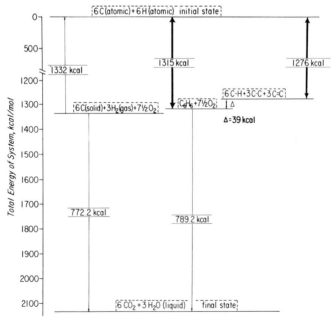

Fig. 27. Calculation of the resonance energy of benzene using an enthalpy diagram.

of molecules are responsible for the light absorption and fluorescence phenomena. This singlet state is a *possible* resonant form in the sense that in all the formulas above the spins are antiparallel and, therefore, the electronic transitions between this singlet, on one hand, and the *ground state* limit formula and the ionic limit formulas, on the other hand, are not "forbidden." By a "forbidden" transition is meant an electronic transition involving the inversion of spin which process has a low probability. However, because the excited singlet state is a high energy state, it is not customary to include it among the limit formulas which represent the ground state of the molecule. The relationships of the electron spin states to the molecular energy levels, and to the phenomena of light absorption, and fluorescence and phosphorescence emission are summarized in Fig. 28 and discussed in Suppletory Note 3.

The ground state is approximated most closely by structures which have the lowest energies. The energy which may be calculated by wave mechanical methods for each of the ionic limit formulas is lower than the energy of the first excited state but higher than the energy of the ground state. This is

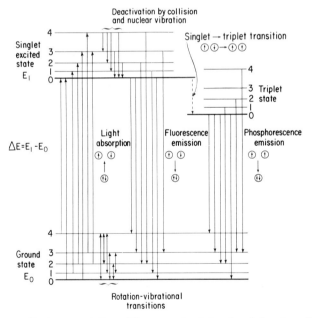

Fig. 28. A generalized representation of the energy levels in π-bonded systems. The ground state, singlet excited state and triplet state energy levels, and the rotation-vibrational sublevels of these states are shown. The groups of electronic transitions (represented by the arrows between the sublevels of different energy states) are responsible for the light absorption, fluorescence emission, and phosphorescence emission phenomena. The transition from the lowest singlet excited level to the lowest triplet level is not accompanied by the emission of radiation.

because the displacement of an electron (as in an ionic limit formula) is a process requiring energy, which energy is thereby "incorporated" into that structure. *Thus, the limit formulas which play a preferential role in the stabilization of the ground state are non-ionic.*

Since the ionic limit formulas represent higher energy levels than the ground state, they are sometimes called "excited" limit formulas. A clear distinction must be made, however, between the "excited" limit formulas which are hypothetical valence schemes, and the first excited state which has a physical reality as shown by the absorption spectra (see Suppletory Note 3 and Section 3.2.3.1). Because the ionic limit formulas have higher energy levels than the ground state they contribute little to the stabilization of that state. On the other hand, *the ionic limit formulas* (because they are energy-rich structures) *play a preferential role in the stabilization of the first excited state.*

This is exemplified with the resonance of butadiene* which may be described as:

$$[\overset{\frown}{CH_2}-CH=CH-\overset{\frown}{CH_2} \longleftrightarrow CH_2\overset{\frown}{=}CH\overset{\frown}{-}CH\overset{\frown}{=}CH_2] \longleftrightarrow \overset{\oplus}{CH_2}\overset{\frown}{-}CH=CH\overset{\frown}{-}\overset{\ominus}{CH_2}$$

ground state

$$\longleftrightarrow \overset{\frown}{CH_2}=CH\overset{\frown}{-}CH=CH_2 \longleftrightarrow \overset{\ominus}{CH_2}-CH=CH-\overset{\oplus}{CH_2} \longleftrightarrow \cdots$$

where each curved arrow shows the displacement of *one* electron. Thus, these ionic limit formulas are called "mono-excited." However, mono-excited structures involving only one double bond can also be drawn:

$$CH_2-CH-CH=CH_2 \qquad CH_2=CH-CH-CH_2 \qquad \text{etc.}$$
$$\overset{\oplus}{}\overset{}{}\overset{\ominus}{} \qquad\qquad\qquad \overset{\oplus}{}\overset{}{}\overset{\ominus}{}$$

Moreover, because of the presence of *two* double-bonds, "di-excited" structures may also be formulated, and contribute to a small extent to the resonance hybrid:

$$CH_2-CH-CH-CH_2 \qquad CH_2-CH-CH-CH_2 \qquad CH_2-CH-CH-CH_2 \qquad \text{etc.}$$
$$\overset{\oplus}{}\ \overset{\ominus}{}\ \overset{\oplus}{}\ \overset{\ominus}{} \qquad \overset{\ominus}{}\ \overset{\oplus}{}\ \overset{\oplus}{}\ \overset{\ominus}{} \qquad \overset{\oplus}{}\ \overset{\ominus}{}\ \overset{\ominus}{}\ \overset{\oplus}{}$$

Also triple bonds can take part in resonance because they possess mobile π electrons which are necessary for "conducting the resonance wave." For example, for divinylacetylene the following ionic limit formula may be written:

$$CH_2\overset{\frown}{=}CH\overset{\frown}{-}C\equiv C\overset{\frown}{-}CH\overset{\frown}{=}CH_2 \longleftrightarrow \overset{\oplus}{CH_2}-CH=C=C=CH-\overset{\ominus}{CH_2} \longleftrightarrow \cdots$$

Electronic transitions involving triple bonds always result in the appearance of a cumulated double-bonded system (Section 2.2.1). The above type of

* Actually the diene limit formula contributes by about 70% to the stabilization of the ground state, the "long bond" structure by about 20% and the ionic structures by about 10%. In the first excited state the relative contributions of the diene and "long bond" structures are reversed.

electron displacements involving π electrons only are called π-π *transitions* or π-π *conjugations*.

Passing to higher and higher polyenes, the number of limit formulas and, hence, the total resonance energy increases with the number of double bonds. However, it may be easily conceived that the number of ionic limit formulas increases much faster than the number of non-ionic formulas. Therefore, the part of the total resonance energy contributed by the ionic limit formulas increases much faster than the part contributed by the non-ionic limit formulas. This means, in other words, that the relative contribution of the ionic limit formulas to the resonance hybrid increases with the number of double bonds. Remembering that the non-ionic limit formulas stabilize preferentially the ground state and the ionic limit formulas stabilize preferentially the first excited state and, also, that resonance energy means greater stability, *i.e.*, energy *decrease*, an important consequence of this situation becomes evident: *the energy difference* (transition energy ΔE, Suppletory Note 3 and Fig. 28) *between the ground state* (E_0) *and first excited state* (E_1) *decreases with the increase of the number of double bonds.* The significance of this for the light absorption and color of organic compounds is discussed in Section 3.2.3.

Now, every limit structure represents a certain pattern of π-electron cloud distribution. Thus, the increase of the number of these structures means actually a "spreading" of the π electrons along the chain. As the number of limit structures which parallels the length of the conjugated chain increases, the delocalization of the π electrons becomes more and more pronounced. Thus the π electrons of a longer conjugated chain may be regarded as an uninterrupted fluid cloud (electron gas) extending over the whole molecule; thereby the alternate single bonds acquire some degree of double bond character (see Section 3.2.2.1.1). The canonical structures of butadiene, represented as patterns of π-electron cloud distribution, are shown in Fig. 29.

Some aspects of the resonance of benzene and of polycyclic systems have already been discussed in Sections 2.4 and 3.1.2.2. For these aromatic systems the Kekulé and Dewar formulas represent the ground state. However, just as for the conjugated *chains*, ionic limit formulas may be drawn for the aromatic cyclic systems as well. In fact, benzene can have mono-, di-, and tri-excited forms to a total of 170 ionic limit structures. An accurate calculation of the wave function of the resonance hybrid must take into account the small contributions of the wave functions of all these ionic resonant forms, in addition to the Kekulé and Dewar formulas. The patterns of π-electron cloud distribution in the limit structures of benzene are shown in Fig. 30.

The number of resonant limit structures of conjugated aromatic ring compounds, as those of conjugated aliphatic chains, rapidly increases with the number of double bonds. A large number of limit structures may be

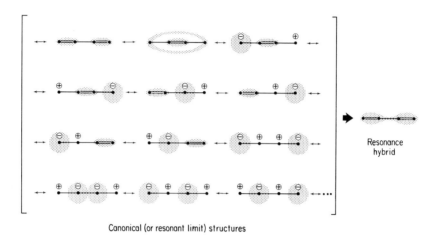

Canonical (or resonant limit) structures

Fig. 29. The pattern of π-electron cloud distribution of the resonance hybrid of butadiene as a resultant of the π-electron patterns of the canonical structures.

written for the higher polyphenyls, acenes, and phenes. Accordingly, the resonance energies of these compounds are high. However, in the higher complex cyclic structures the resonance energy also depends on the *pattern of arrangement of the rings*; for example, the resonance energy of anthracene is 116 kcal/mole and the resonance energy of its angular isomer, phenanthrene, is 130 kcal/mole. The resonance energy is generally somewhat greater in a phene than in an acene with the same number of rings. The number N of non-ionic limit structures of unsubstituted acenes and phenes may be calculated by *Rümer's formula*:

$$N = \frac{n!}{[n/2]![(n/2) + 1]!} \tag{19}$$

where n is the number of carbon atoms in the rings (that is the number of π electrons). The expression $n!$ means the factorial of n; for example, for $n = 6$, $n! = 1 \times 2 \times 3 \times 4 \times 5 \times 6 = 720$.

Resonance is maintained in cyclic aromatic systems if one or more $=CH-$ groups are replaced by a heteroatom having three electrons for covalent bonding. Although by far the most common replacement is by nitrogen (Section 2.4.2.3), a few aromatic compounds are known with arsenic-containing heterocycles. The non-ionic limit formulas of pyridine, for example, are analogous to those of benzene:

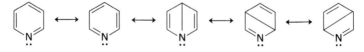

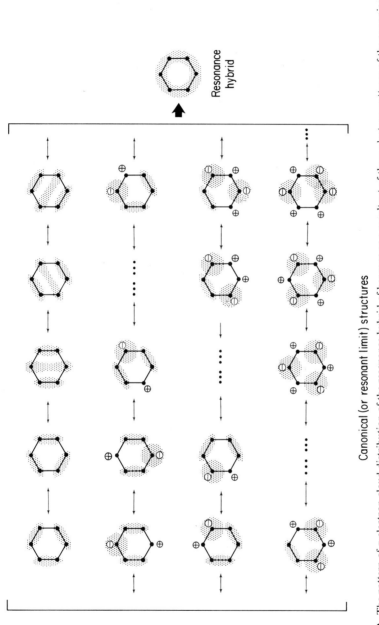

Canonical (or resonant limit) structures

Fig. 30. The pattern of π-electron cloud distribution of the resonance hybrid of benzene as a resultant of the π-electron patterns of the canonical structures.

but the "weights" of the structures are different. The ionic limit formulas have, in general, a much greater "weight" in the heterocyclic compounds than in the hydrocarbons. As the limit structures indicate, the free doublet of nitrogen does not formally participate in the resonance. Oxygen and sulfur, possessing only two electrons for covalent bonding, cannot replace ordinarily a =CH— group in a 6-membered ring. Instances are known, however, where oxygen-containing hexagonal rings show some aromatic character, for example:

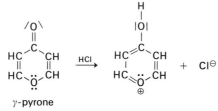

γ-pyrone

Among the 5-membered ring compounds (Section 2.4.2.3) not only the nitrogen-containing heterocyclics but also the oxygen- or sulfur-containing ones show aromatic character. Because of their free doublets the heteroatoms can be regarded as replacing a —CH=CH— group in the localized cyclo-hexatriene form of benzene, i.e., the pentagonal ring will contain a total number of 6 mobile electrons (aromatic sextet), such as:

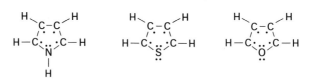

and resonant limit structures may be formulated without difficulty, for example:

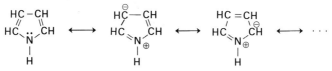

Accordingly, pyrrole is a weaker base than pyridine because, unlike in the latter, the doublet formally participates in the resonance. Blockage of the doublet by salification with a strong acid blocks the resonance, and the unsaturated diene character prevails. Consequently pyrrole is prone to polymerization (Section 2.2.5) in the presence of strong acids.

The example of cyclopentadiene spectacularly illustrates the strong resonance tendency (i.e., the tendency to occupy a lower, more stable energy level) of pentagonal ring structures and the requirement of the aromatic sextet for resonance. It was stated in Section 2.4 that cyclopentadiene shows normally the behavior of an unsaturated diene; this is because the $-CH_2-$ group does not have free electrons. Cyclopentadiene also shows a surprising acidity, which is a rare property among hydrocarbons, except for alkynes (Section 2.2.4). That cyclopentadiene can release a proton in the presence of alkali metals is due to resonance stabilization of the free doublet of the methylene carbon:

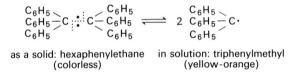

Another illustration of the stabilizing effect of resonance is the lengthening of life span of free radicals when linked to resonant systems and the actual existence of stable free radicals. We have seen in Section 3.1.2.6 that the life span of free radicals of small alkyl groups, say methyl or ethyl, is of the order of 10^{-3} seconds. However, if the three hydrogens of the methyl radical are replaced by phenyl groups, the resulting *triphenylmethyl* (or *trityl*) is a stable but chemically reactive free radical in solution:

$$C_6H_5-C \overset{C_6H_5}{\underset{C_6H_5}{\vdots}} C \overset{C_6H_5}{\underset{C_6H_5}{-}} C_6H_5 \rightleftharpoons 2 \; C_6H_5 \overset{C_6H_5}{\underset{C_6H_5}{-}} C \cdot$$

as a solid: hexaphenylethane   in solution: triphenylmethyl
(colorless)   (yellow-orange)

This stabilization of the fragments of bond rupture is due in part to the resonance of the radical whereby the lone electron is "melted into" the π cloud of the three phenyl groups:

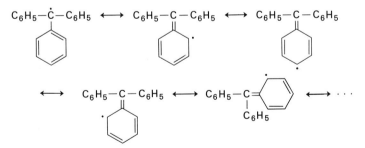

The dominant reason for the dissociation in solution of hexaphenylethane to triphenylmethyl radicals is steric hindrance, due to spatial crowding (Sections 3.2.3.4 and 3.4.3) of the six phenyl groups. This steric effect is an important participant in the stabilization of the free radicals. Triphenylmethyl has a total of 44 limit formulas. Stability of the methyl radical is increased further by substituting with conjugating groups larger than phenyl because of the increase of the number of limit formulas. Tris-biphenylmethyl $(C_6H_5-C_6H_4-)_3C\cdot$ has 496 possible limit formulas and is stable in the violet-colored radical form. Because of the resonance, the distribution of the three aryl groups around the central carbon atom in triphenylmethyl and tris-biphenylmethyl follows trigonal symmetry and the dipole moment of these compounds is zero. A great variety of such triarylmethyl radicals (known as *Gomberg radicals*) have been prepared and studied (see Suppletory Note 4).

The π-π conjugation is not limited to aliphatic conjugated chains since the electron shifts, which cause the appearance of the ionic limit formulas in aromatic or heteroaromatic ring systems, are also instances of π-π conjugation. Moreover, π-π conjugation takes place in any combination of aliphatic and aromatic structures as long as a system of alternate single and double bonds is present which can "conduct" the electron shifts. Coplanarity is another requirement for π-π transition (Section 3.2.3.4) in addition to the presence of alternate single and double bonds. Examples of π-π conjugation of mixed aliphatic-aromatic conjugated systems are:

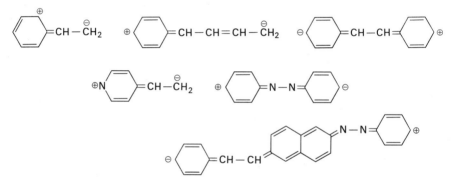

Since conjugation between different π-bonded regions of a molecule amounts to a longer over-all system, π-π conjugation results in an increase of the resonance energy over and above the sum of the resonance energies of the π-bonded regions taken separately. For example, when a phenyl group is added to one end of a linear conjugated chain the total increment of resonance energy is greater than that of the benzene ring. This excess increment, called the *force of conjugation* of the phenyl group, is due to the fact that the single bond linking the ring to the rest of the molecule acquires some degree of double bond character (Section 3.2.2.1.1):

The force of conjugation of both the phenyl and vinyl groups (for ethylene) is about 5 kcal/mole.

Nitrogen, oxygen, or sulfur can also resonate with a π-bonded system when it is not a built-in part of a heteroaromatic ring, but is linked to a conjugated carbon chain or homocyclic aromatic ring as part of a substituent group. For example:

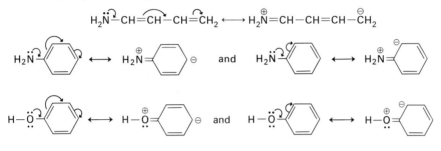

This type of electron shift is called an *n-π conjugation* or *n-π transition* (that is, occurring between the *n*onbonded free electron doublets associated with atoms such as nitrogen, oxygen, or sulfur and a π-electron system); it is also known under the alternate names of *mesomeric effect* (*M* effect) and *resonance effect* (*R* effect).

Since n-π conjugation depends on the availability of the electron doublet(s) on the donor atom, conditions which change this availability will accordingly increase or decrease resonance. For this reason the phenolate ion has a higher resonance energy (*i.e.*, is more stable) than phenol:

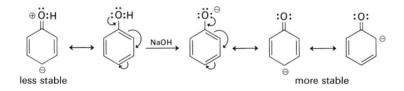

Similarly, the resonance effect of an amino group will be totally blocked by strong acids because of "freezing" the free doublet on the nitrogen:

$$H_2\ddot{N}-\text{⟨⟩} \xrightarrow{\ \text{HCl}\ } H_2\overset{\overset{H}{\ddot{N}}}{\underset{\oplus}{}}-\text{⟨⟩} \ + \ Cl^{\ominus}$$

Conversely, since in aniline the free doublet of nitrogen is pulled toward the ring due to the resonance effect, it is a much weaker base than ammonia because basicity also depends on the availability of the doublet. For this reason, N-alkyl substitution of aniline, which increases the basicity of the compound (because alkyl groups are less electronegative than hydrogen, Section 3.1.2.3), also increases the resonance effect, *i.e.*, the contribution of ionic limit formulas to the resonance hybrid:

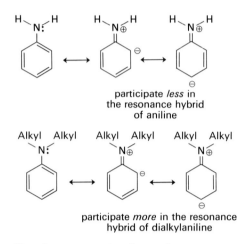

participate *less* in
the resonance hybrid
of aniline

participate *more* in the resonance
hybrid of dialkylaniline

The resonance effect is not restricted to nitrogen, oxygen, and sulfur, but may involve any atom or group having free electron doublet(s), for example:

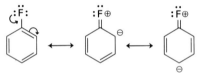

The resistance of aryl halides to hydrolysis, as compared to the relative ease of hydrolysis of alkyl halides (Section 2.1.2), can be explained as due to the strengthening of the X-aryl bond by the resonance effect. The shift of electron density back toward the ring, along the X-aryl bond, can be seen by comparing the dipole moments of alkyl and aryl halides. The dipole moments of methyl fluoride, methyl chloride, and methyl bromide are between 1.81 and 1.86 D (result of the $-I$ effect, Section 3.1.2.4), while the moments of the corresponding phenyl halides are all lower, between 1.55 and 1.57 D.

Conjugation is appreciably stronger if the electron donor atom belongs to the second period of the Periodic Table (*e.g.*, N, O, and F) than if it belongs to subsequent periods (*e.g.*, S, P, As, Cl, Br, I). This is due to the fact that conjugation establishes a π bond between the donor atom and a carbon atom, and the strength of a π bond depends on the overlapping of the bonding p orbitals (Section 3.1.2.2). Now, nitrogen, oxygen, and fluorine have the p valence electrons in $2p$ orbitals, which is the same as for carbon.

The heavier elements, however, have their p valence electrons in $3p$ and $4p$ orbitals which are considerably larger than the $2p$ orbitals. Thus, orbital overlap with the $2p$ orbitals of carbon is less effective.

It appears then that atoms, N, O, F, etc., which are withdrawing electrons by virtue of their electronegativity ($-I$ effect, Section 3.1.2.4) when linked to a saturated carbon chain, are also capable of *donating* electrons when linked to conjugated systems. In these cases the mesomeric effect overrules the inductive effect. This is called a $+M$ effect or a $+R$ effect. A number of other cases are known where the electron shift takes place in the reverse direction, from the conjugated system to the substituent which acts then as an electron *acceptor*. This is the $-M$ effect or $-R$ effect. According to a simple rule the substituents which show $+M$ effect are single-bonded groups attached to the conjugated system by way of an atom having one or more free doublets: halogens, amino, hydroxyl, and sulfhydryl groups. The substituents showing $-M$ effect are multiple-bonded groups (nitro, nitroso, nitrile, carbonyl, sulfonyl, carboxyl, and also $-CF_3$) for which resonant limit structures may be drawn, and the atom by way of which the group is attached to the conjugated system is itself involved in the resonance of the group. For example:

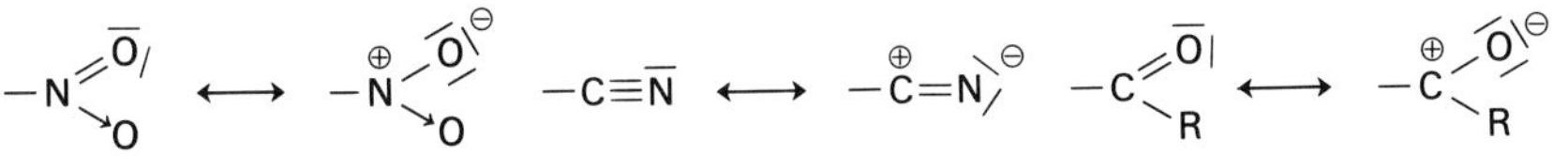

Comparative dipole moment measurements in aliphatic and aromatic compounds are the main tool used for determining the direction of the electron shift due to $+M$ or $-M$ effect. In the example which was given in Fig. 23, the nitro and carboxyl groups produce a $-M$ effect and the amino group a $+M$ effect. In p-nitrobenzene the two opposite $-M$ effects are intramolecularly compensated and cancel out; in p-aminobenzoic acid the electron shift is conducted through the ring from the amino nitrogen to the carboxyl oxygen and thus the dipole moments are additive.

A special case of the $+M$ effect is *hyperconjugation*. The π-electron cloud in the unsubstituted benzene molecule has a perfectly centro-symmetrical distribution (Figs. 19E and F, and 30). One factor in bringing about this symmetry is that all six substituents of the carbon ring, that is, all six hydrogen atoms, have the same electronegativity and so the "pull" on the π-electron cloud is the same all around. Now, if a hydrogen is replaced by a less electronegative group, e.g., by a methyl or higher alkyl, then the equilibrium is disrupted and an electron shift takes place from the substituent group toward the ring, as shown in Fig. 31. The formation of a π bond between the methyl carbon and the respective ring carbon becomes possible because of the high p orbital character of the sp^3 orbitals of the methyl carbon atom (remember that π bonds are due to the sidewise overlap of

p orbitals, Section 3.1.2.2). Since hyperconjugation involves the transfer of electron density from a σ bond toward a π-bonded system, it is also called *σ-π transition* or *σ-π conjugation*.

The asymmetry of the π-electron cloud in toluene (Fig. 31) is clearly indicated by dipole moment measurements. Thus, while the dipole moment of benzene is 0.00 D, toluene has a dipole moment of 0.37 D. Similarly acetylene, a perfectly symmetrical molecule, has a dipole moment of 0.00 D, while methylacetylene has a dipole moment of 0.75 D.

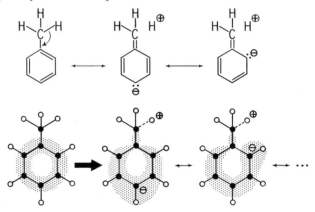

predominant π-electron distributions

Fig. 31. Shift of the π-electron distribution in toluene due to hyperconjugation.

For representing hyperconjugation, $-CH_3$ and $-CH_2-$ groups are often shown as being multiple bonded:

$$H_3\equiv C\!\!-\qquad \text{and} \qquad H_2\!\!=\!\!C$$

The resonance contribution of a methylene group by hyperconjugation is only about one half of that of a methyl group.

Hyperconjugation, although less important than the resonance effect of heteroatoms, affects many molecular properties. Because there is increased resonance due to the increased number of limit structures, the molecules are stabilized by hyperconjugation. For example, the addition of every methyl group adjacent to a double bond in a conjugated system increases the resonance energy with about 2 kcal/mole. Hyperconjugation has an especially significant effect in large aromatic systems in altering the electron distribution, and, thus, the chemical reactivity of certain bonds.[*]

[*] Increase in resonance due to hyperconjugation brings about shortening of the C—C single bond(s) involved. Recent work by M. J. S. Dewar, T. G. Taylor, and R. A. Alden suggests, however, that conjugation is not required to explain this bond shortening in certain compounds, but that this comes about because of increase of the s character of the hybrid orbitals involved in the multiple bond.

3.2.2.1 Constants Characterizing Aromatic Systems

3.2.2.1.1 Bond Order, Double Bond Character, and Bond Length. One of the consequences of the resonance concept is that in an aromatic compound any given bond which appears as a single bond in certain canonical structures will be represented as a double bond in a number of other canonical structures. Let us illustrate this with the familiar case of benzene, which in a first approximation may be represented by the two Kekulé formulas:

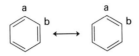

The a—b bond is a single bond in one formula and double bond in the other one. Clearly, then, the a—b bond is neither a pure single bond nor a pure double bond but an intermediate type between a pure double bond such as in ethylene and a pure single bond as in ethane. If a *bond order* (also called *bond index* or *bond number*) of 1 is assigned to C—C, a bond order of 2 to C=C, then the index of the aromatic C≐C bond in benzene is $(1 + 2)/2 = 1.50$. We say then (on the basis of the simple assumption of only two resonant limit formulas) that the aromatic C≐C bonds in benzene are exactly intermediate between C—C and C=C and have a $\frac{1}{2}$ (or 50 %) *double bond character*, which is consistent with the perfect hexagonal symmetry of the molecule. The bond index 1.50 may also be regarded as the sum of 1 for the σ bond and 0.50 for the aromatic π bond. The concepts of bond order and double bond character have been introduced by Pauling.

The double bond character of the higher aromatics may be calculated in a similar manner. Three Kekulé formulas may be written for naphthalene:

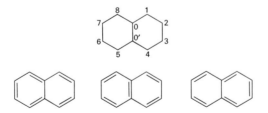

and the bonds have the following values:

Bonds	Double bond character
(0–0′)	$\frac{1}{3}$ (33.3 %)
(0–1), (0–8), (0′–4), (0′–5)	$\frac{1}{3}$ (33.3 %)
(1–2), (3–4), (5–6), (7–8)	$\frac{2}{3}$ (66.6 %)
(2–3), (6–7)	$\frac{1}{3}$ (33.3 %)

The four Kekulé formulas of anthracene:

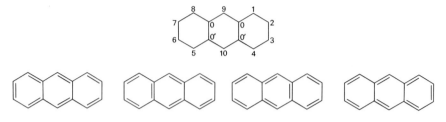

give the following values:

Bonds	Double bond character
(0–0′)	$\frac{1}{4}$ (25%)
(0–1), (0′–4), (0′–5), (0–8)	$\frac{1}{4}$ (25%)
(1–2), (3–4), (5–6), (7–8)	$\frac{3}{4}$ (75%)
(2–3), (6–7)	$\frac{1}{4}$ (25%)
(0–9), (0′–10)	$\frac{1}{2}$ (50%)

The reason for the pronounced reactivity of the mesophenanthrenic double bond becomes evident by considering the double bond character of the bonds in phenanthrene. Phenanthrene has five Kekulé-type limit formulas:

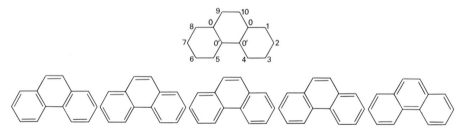

from which the double bond characters may be computed as follows:

Bonds	Double bond character	Bonds	Double bond character
(0–0′)	$\frac{2}{5}$ (40%)	(2–3), (6–7)	$\frac{2}{5}$ (40%)
(0′–0′)	$\frac{1}{5}$ (20%)	(0′–4), (0′–5)	$\frac{2}{5}$ (40%)
(0–1), (0–8)	$\frac{2}{5}$ (40%)	(0–9), (0–10)	$\frac{1}{5}$ (20%)
(1–2), (7–8)	$\frac{3}{5}$ (60%)	(9–10)	$\frac{4}{5}$ (80%)
(3–4), (5–6)	$\frac{3}{5}$ (60%)		

With the same reasoning it is possible to calculate the double bond characters of bonds in higher polycyclics.

Now, since the total bond strength of a double bond is greater than that of a single bond, and the total bond strength of a triple bond (bond order 3) is greater than that of a double bond (Section 3.1.2.2), the interatomic distances vary inversely with the bond order. This is because a greater bond strength means a greater overlapping of the atomic orbitals bringing the two atoms closer together against the internuclear repulsion. Figure 32 shows the relation between bond order and internuclear distance.

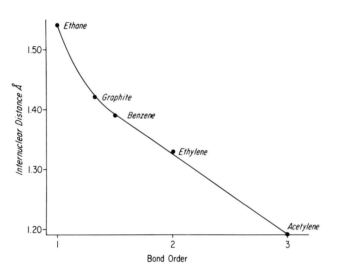

Fig. 32. Relation between bond order and internuclear distance.

3.2.2.1.2   The Mobile Bond Index and Free Valence Index of the VB and LCAO Methods. The Electric Charge Index. Bond orders based on only Kekulé formulas are obviously a crude approximation. More accurate calculations, taking into account the participation of Dewar-type canonical structures, have been carried out by the VB method. Accurate bond orders have also been calculated by the alternate LCAO method. To distinguish the bond order, as defined in the previous section, from the bond orders calculated by the VB and LCAO methods, the latter are termed *mobile bond index* (denoted as p_{ij}, where i and j stand for any adjacent atom pair). The absolute numerical value of the index of any given bond is different in the two methods because the definitions on the basis of which the calculations are carried out are different. However, *the indexes of different types of bonds give the same relative gradation in both methods.*

The mobile bond index of the VB method is a direct outgrowth of the original bond order concept. The mobile bond index is the sum of the weights of all canonical structures that represent this bond as double. To illustrate this with an example, let us take benzene, where each C==C bond is represented as double in one Kekulé formula and in one Dewar formula (Section 2.4). The weight of each Kekulé formula is 0.39 and the weight of each Dewar formula is 0.073. Thus, the mobile bond index of a bond between the adjacent carbon atoms 1 and 2 is $p_{12} = 0.39 + 0.073 = 0.463$.

Another useful molecular constant is the *free valence index* (I_i or F_i), which represents the residual affinity or fractional bonding capacity of any atom i in a molecule. According to the VB method this may be described as follows. In a simple double-bonded compound, such as in ethylene, the involvement of each π electron in bonding is total (*i.e.*, unity). In benzene, however, the involvement of any π electron in bonding is not total; a π electron on any of the carbon atoms is involved in two C==C bonds, each of which has a mobile bond index (*i.e.*, double bond character) of only 0.463. The total involvement is, therefore, 2×0.463 and the free valence index is $1 - (2 \times 0.463) = 0.073$.

The meaning of the mobile bond index in the LCAO method is somewhat more difficult to grasp in nonmathematical terms. The contribution of two π electrons to the formation of a "mobile" double bond between adjacent atoms 1 and 2 may be regarded, following Coulson, as being equal to the product $2\,C_1C_2$. This is the case for a single double bond, such as in ethylene. However, if the two π electrons are involved also in other bonds, in addition to the bond between atoms 1 and 2, then the product $2\,C_1C_2$ which represents the involvement in the 1—2 bond will be different in the different states of electron distribution. Hence the mobile bond index is the *sum* of all the $2\,C_1C_2$ products taken over all the occupied molecular orbitals. For example, in its explicit form the π electron wave function of benzene consists of six equations standing for the states of electron distribution at the six carbon atoms. In these equations the contribution of the $\psi_1, \psi_2, \psi_3, \ldots$ atomic wave functions is indicated by the coefficients $C_1, C_2, C_3, \ldots$. Now if we examine each one of these equations for the *simultaneous occurrence* of the terms ψ_1 and ψ_2 *and* indicating a *bonding state* (*i.e.*, $\psi_1 + \psi_2$) we find that only two out of the six equations satisfy this condition. In one of the two equations $C_1 = C_2 = 1/\sqrt{6}$, and in the other $C_1 = 1/(2\sqrt{3})$ and $C_2 = 1/\sqrt{3}$. Thus the mobile bond index of the bond between atoms 1 and 2 is the sum of the two $2\,C_1C_2$ products, so that $p_{12} = 2(1/\sqrt{6} \times 1/\sqrt{6}) + 2[1/(2\sqrt{3}) \times 1/\sqrt{3}] = 0.667$. Let us remember that this is the LCAO bond index of only the π component of the C==C bond.

The free valence index in the LCAO method is defined as the difference between the "maximum bonding power" (N_{max}) of an atom and the sum of the LCAO mobile bond indexes of all the bonds terminating at that atom:

$$F_i = N_{max} - \Sigma p_{ij} \tag{20}$$

where

$$N_{max} = 3 + \sqrt{3} = 4.732 \tag{21}$$

For the carbon atom the origin of the two terms which make up N_{max} may be explained as follows. An sp^2 hybridized carbon atom has three sp^2 orbitals lying in one plane and a remaining nonhybridized p orbital, the axis of which is perpendicular to the sp^2 plane (Fig. 17). Each of the sp^2 orbitals can partake in one σ bond, and to each σ bond (single bond) a bond order of 1 has been arbitrarily assigned (see previous section). The total bond order of $3\,\sigma$ bonds is consequently 3. Furthermore, following the Hultgren theorem a nonhybridized p orbital has a total overlapping power of $\sqrt{3}$ (see Section 3.1.2.2). In other words, this is the maximum contribution of a p orbital to bonding (i.e., to the $2\,C_1 C_2$ product), its maximum bonding power. Hence the sum $3 + \sqrt{3}$. For example, the LCAO free valence index of any one carbon atom of benzene is $F_i = 4.732 - [l_{C-H} + 2(l_{C-C} + 0.667)] = 0.398$, where l_{C-H} and l_{C-C} represent the bond orders of the respective σ bonds.

The *electric charge index* (q_i) gives a measure of the deviation from electric neutrality of an atom in the molecule. In the LCAO method the electron probability density in an atomic orbital ψ_i is defined as $(C_i \psi_i)^2$. The expression $1 - (C_i \psi_i)^2 = 0$ means then that deviation from unit electron charge is zero (i.e., the atom is electrically neutral). Hence, the electric charge index of an atom i in an aromatic molecule is the difference between the unit π charge and the *sum* of the squares of all the coefficients C_i of the respective atomic orbital ψ_i when involved in a *bonding* orbital, each coefficient taken *twice*. This is because in the ground state of the molecule either positive or negative deviation from electric neutrality of an atom (i.e., loss or gain of electron charge), if any, is due to involvement in bonding orbitals each of which contains *two* electrons. Expressed in another way, electric neutrality of an aromatic carbon atom means that, summing over all the bonding states, an average of one electron is present in its p orbital.

In benzene and its *unsubstituted* benzologs the *net* charge on every carbon is practically zero. This may also be expressed by saying that *every carbon atom has a unit charge*. The reason for this is that the electron migration is very small compared to the total charge, so that these shifts may be neglected. However, when odd-numbered (nonaromatic) rings, heteroatoms, or substituents are present the neutrality of charge distribution is disrupted and net electric charges appear at different atoms in the molecule. The effect of heteroatoms and methyl substituents on the charge in the *meso*-phenanthrenic region is discussed further in Section 5.1.1.6.1.

3.2.2.1.3 *Bond Types. The Vroeland–Daudel Approximation. Molecular Diagrams.* An extremely useful method, which does not require the advanced mathematical background necessary for wave mechanical calculations, has been worked out by Vroeland and Daudel* for the approximate evaluation of mobile bond and free valence indexes. The applicability of the method is, however, restricted to *conjugated molecules without substituents or heteroatoms* such as the nonsubstituted polycyclic hydrocarbons.

The method is based on the concept of *bond type* introduced by Hartmann.† The bond type of a C==C bond is defined as the number of carbon–carbon bonds adjoining to that C==C bond. The meaning of bond type may be readily understood from the formulas below, where the number at each bond represents its "type":

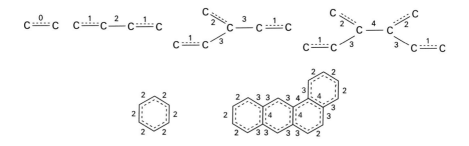

Vroeland and Daudel have shown that in a first approximation the mobile bond index of a bond is a function only of the bond type *of the adjoining bonds*. Thus each bond in a molecule may be designated by the bond types of the adjoining bonds. For example, the bond between the 1,2-carbon in butadiene will be a (2)-bond, the one between the 2,3-carbon a (1,1)-bond. In 2-vinyl-butadiene the central bond of the butadiene moiety will be designated as a (1,2,3)-bond, while in 2,3-divinylbutadiene this same bond becomes a (2,2,3,3)-bond. All the bonds of benzene have the notation (2,2). In 1,2-benzanthracene the different bonds have a variety of notations. In this manner the bond notations of conjugated hydrocarbons of any complexity may be computed.

In Table IX are given the standard mobile bond indexes calculated by Vroeland and Daudel following a modification of the VB method due to

* C. Vroeland and R. Daudel, *Bull. Soc. Chim. France* **16**, 36, 217 (1949).
† H. Hartmann, *Z. Naturforsch.* **2a**, 260, 263 (1947).

Penney. Again, as with the indexes obtained by the LCAO *versus* standard VB method, a Penney index (in terms of absolute numerical value) cannot be compared to an index calculated by the standard VB method; *only the relative gradation of indexes within one method is significant.*

Table IX

Tabulated Penney Indexes and Internuclear Distances[a]

Bond notation by types of adjoining bonds	Penney mobile bond indexes	Internuclear distances, Å	Bond notation by types of adjoining bonds	Penney mobile bond indexes	Internuclear distances, Å
(2)	0.827	1.362	(2, 3, 3)	0.493	1.423
(3)	0.873	1.353	(2, 3, 4)	0.508	1.420
(1, 1)	0.437	1.438	(2, 4, 4)	0.537	1.414
(1, 2)	0.524	1.416	(3, 3, 3)	0.537	1.414
(1, 3)	0.566	1.408	(3, 3, 4)	0.556	1.410
(2, 2)	0.612	1.398	(3, 4, 4)	0.578	1.405
(2, 3)	0.652	1.388	(2, 2, 3, 3)	0.324	1.465
(2, 4)	0.676	1.385	(2, 2, 3, 4)	0.346	1.460
(3, 3)	0.692	1.380	(2, 2, 4, 4)	0.367	1.455
(3, 4)	0.714	1.377	(2, 3, 3, 3)	0.367	1.455
(4, 4)	0.735	1.373	(2, 3, 3, 4)	0.387	1.450
(1, 2, 3)	0.367	1.455	(2, 3, 4, 4)	0.407	1.445
(1, 2, 4)	0.387	1.450	(2, 4, 4, 4)	0.428	1.440
(1, 3, 3)	0.407	1.455	(3, 3, 3, 3)	0.407	1.445
(1, 3, 4)	0.428	1.440	(3, 3, 3, 4)	0.428	1.440
(1, 4, 4)	0.440	1.436	(3, 3, 4, 4)	0.440	1.436
(2, 2, 2)	0.412	1.443	(3, 4, 4, 4)	0.469	1.430
(2, 2, 3)	0.452	1.433	(4, 4, 4, 4)	0.489	1.425
(2, 2, 4)	0.472	1.428			

[a] From P. Daudel and R. Daudel, *Biol. Med. (Paris)*, **39**, 201 (1950).

In the Vroeland–Daudel approximation the free valence indexes are calculated from the Penney mobile bond indexes using an equation identical to Eq. (20) of the LCAO method, except for the value of N_{max}:

$$F_i = 3.682 - \Sigma p_{ij} \tag{22}$$

The σ-bond skeleton of a molecule shown with its representative electronic indexes is called its *molecular diagram.* For example, the molecular diagram of 1,2-benzanthracene with the Penney mobile bond indexes and the free valence indexes calculated therefrom is:

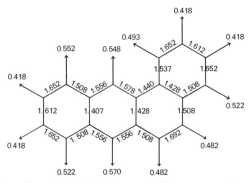

This shows that the molecular diagram allows a rapid quantitative view of the electron distribution and reactive potentialities of a molecule. In the words of Szent–Györgyi, "in the molecular diagram every atom of the ring assumes a personality, a profile, a high degree of specificity and the whole structure begins to assume that subtlety which we can expect from any structure taking part in biological reactions."

3.2.3 COLOR AND RESONANCE: SPECTRAL ABSORPTION OF MOLECULES. RESONANCE, COPLANARITY, AND STERIC HINDRANCE

3.2.3.1 Light Absorption and Transition Energy: Absorption Curves. Absorption and Color. Electromagnetic Spectrum

The study of the color of organic compounds containing double bonds is a powerful tool for gaining insight into the nature of resonance. The color of these substances is due to the interaction of visible light with their π electrons. In Fig. 28 a generalized representation of the energy levels of double-bonded systems was given. The lowest energy of the π electrons represents the ground state of the molecule (E_0). When a pure *monochromatic* light of sufficient energy hits the π electrons, their energy is raised to a higher energy level, the first excited state (E_1). A light is called "monochromatic" when all vibrations in the beam have the same frequency v, *i.e.*, pure violet, or blue, or green, etc. Now, since the energy necessary for the ⇅ → ↑↓ electronic transition (the transition energy ΔE) is obtained from the light energy, there will be a decrease of the total amount of light energy transmitted through the substance (or its solution), *i.e.*, *absorption of light* will result (Suppletory Notes 3 and 5, and Figs. 28 and 33).

It was noted above that the energy hv of a monochromatic light must be of sufficient energy to promote a transition $E_0 \rightarrow E_1$ (in other words to have $hv_{cm-1} = \Delta E/c$) for absorption to occur. Evidently then, there can be no absorption if $hv_{cm-1} < \Delta E/c$. From a purely energetic standpoint it appears surprising, however, that there is no absorption either if $hv_{cm-1} > \Delta E/c$. This apparent paradox, which will be discussed later in Section 3.2.3.3, is due to the close connection of light absorption and resonance. Because absorption occurs only at those wavelengths where hv is equal to some possible ΔE transition in the molecule, the *absorption spectrum*, which is the plot of the light absorption (in k or ε units or their logarithms) against the wavelength (in $m\mu$ or Å) or against the frequency (in v or $v_{cm^{-1}}$), is an important characteristic of an organic compound. However, the transitions between ground state and excited state sublevels 0, 1, 2, 3, 4, ... (in Fig. 28) do not appear as separate absorption lines but as one *absorption band* which is the result of the fusion of a large number of absorption lines. The absorption spectrum of a substance may, of course, show several absorption bands. In fact, a molecule may contain more than one π-bonded region and substituents producing mesomeric shifts, and these substituents, depending on their geometric relationship, may or may not conjugate with one another. Thus, the conjugation

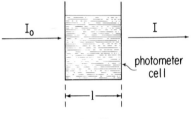

Fig. 33.

shifts of several double bonds may be cumulative (*e.g.*, in the ultraviolet spectra of polyphenyls) in which case there will be only one main absorption band. In other cases, because of branching of the "resonance pathways" (*crossed conjugation*), there may be several resonance modes resulting in the presence of several absorption bands in the spectrum.

Colorless substances have their absorption bands in the ultraviolet region. Colored substances have their main absorption band in the visible region. The color seen depends on the position of this absorption band because the visible color is complementary to the color of the absorption band. *Complementary colors* are pairs of colors which, when combined, give the effect of white. "White" light radiated by the sun contains all the pairs of complementary colors. Figure 34 shows the series of colors composing the spectrum of white light and the relationship of this series to the complementary pairing of colors. Selective absorption of a certain radiation present in white light leaves the "residual" complementary color and this imparts the sensation of color. Thus, a substance which has its absorption band in the violet appears greenish-yellow colored in white light and, vice versa, absorption in the greenish-yellow results in a violet color; all the other pairs of complementary colors except those involved in absorption and color remain unchanged. For example, chlorophyll which is green absorbs in the red, and hemoglobin which is red absorbs in the green. A substance appears

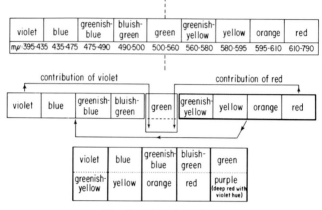

Pairs of complementary colors

Fig. 34. The pairing of complementary colors from the series of spectral colors. Green may be regarded as the "midpoint" of the spectral colors, which divides the visible spectrum in two halves. The complementary pairing of the two halves is accomplished by transposing the right half under the left half as indicated by the arrow in the figure. The complementary color of the midpoint is produced by contribution from identical positions of both halves: purple, which is the complementary color of green, contains elements of red and violet.

black in a light which corresponds to its absorption band in the visible since *this is* the light which is absorbed by the substance (black corresponds to total absorption, *i.e.*, absence of light). Thus, a substance which appears black *in white light* has a broad absorption band "engulfing" all the colors of the visible spectrum. It will be remembered, of course, that the visible and ultraviolet radiations, which are responsible for the electronic spectra that interest us here, are but a segment of the whole electromagnetic spectrum schematically shown in Fig. 35.

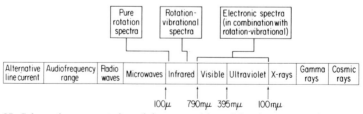

Fig. 35. Schematic representation of the composition of the electromagnetic spectrum. The frequency and energy of these ranges increases from the left toward the right. The regions of the spectrum giving rise to the different molecular absorption spectra are shown.

3.2.3.2 Definitions of Absorption Band Characteristics. Chromophores and Auxochromes

Introduction of new functional groups onto the molecular skeleton of a resonant system, or the lengthening or shortening of the conjugated system itself results almost always in the displacement of the absorption band or bands. The displacement of an absorption band toward the longer wavelengths is called a *bathochromic shift* (or *red shift*); displacement toward the shorter wavelengths is called a *hypsochromic shift* (or *blue shift*). Such shifts in the *position* of a band may or may not be accompanied by an increase or decrease of its height, *i.e.*, in its molar extinction coefficient (see Suppletory Note 5). An increase in the height of an absorption band is called a *hyperchromic effect* and a decrease is called a *hypochromic effect*.

There is a parallelism between bathochromic shift (which is the displacement of the absorption band) and *color deepening* which means change in the visible color of a compound. The order of color deepening is the succession of colors which appear to the eye as the *absorption band* is moved across the visible spectrum from the blue to the red: greenish-yellow → yellow → orange → red → purple → violet → blue → green. Greenish-yellow is the *lightest* color and green the *deepest*.

Chemical groupings which are responsible for the color of organic substances are termed *chromophores*. The groups:

$$\ce{>C=C<} \qquad \ce{-C#C-} \qquad \ce{>C=N-} \qquad \ce{-N=N-} \qquad \ce{>C=O} \qquad \ce{-N=O} \qquad \ce{-N(=O)(-O)}$$

are chromophores. Molecules which contain one or more chromophores are called *chromogens*. For example, azobenzene is a chromogen and $-N=N-$ is its chromophore. A functional group which intensifies or deepens the color of a chromogen is called an *auxochrome*. The most important auxochromes are $-OH$, $-O$-alkyl, $-NH_2$, and $-N(alkyl)_2$. For example, $-N(CH_3)_2$ is the auxochrome of the azo compound 4-dimethyl-aminoazobenzene (Section 2.4.1.2).

The auxochromes also play a second role in that, being polar groups, they enable the chromogens to "dye" materials such as wool, silk, cotton, wood, and leather. Such compounds are *organic dyes*. Chromogens alone have usually no dyeing properties, *i.e.*, they may not be indelibly absorbed and fixed to the above materials. In large molecular weight dyes $-SO_3H$ and $-COOH$ groups are often present in addition to the auxochromes. These groups are not auxochromes since they modify the visible absorption spectrum of the chromogen only very little if at all; their role is exclusively to increase the adsorbability to the fibers, the dyeing capacity of the molecules.

Although the terms chromophore, chromogen, and auxochrome permit a practical classification of organic dyes, it must be understood that they do not denote special chemical entities. The role of these groups in producing or enhancing color is only the increasing of conjugation by increasing the number of resonant limit formulas. Actually it is quite arbitrary from the standpoint of resonance theory to make a distinction between chromophores and auxochromes. For example, biphenyl is a colorless compound having an absorption band in the ultraviolet. Insertion of $-N{=}N-$ between the two phenyls produces a large bathochromic shift, and the yellow-orange colored azobenzene results. Substitution of azobenzene in the 4-position by a $-N(CH_3)_2$ group produces an additional bathochromic shift due to the mesomeric effect of the substituent. The respective main absorption bands are: biphenyl at $252\ m\mu$; azobenzene at $320\ m\mu$; 4-dimethylaminoazobenzene at $413\ m\mu$.

3.2.3.3 Rotational, Vibrational, and Electronic Spectra. π-Electron Systems as Electromagnetic Oscillators

The light absorption of organic molecules in the visible and ultraviolet regions is not exclusively due to electronic transitions. Superimposed on the absorption due to the electronic transitions proper, there is also a small contribution to absorption by the rotational and vibrational movements of the molecules.

The rotational spectra arise because of the absorption of radiant energy resulting in rotational movements of the molecule as a whole about different molecular axes. Absorption due to molecular rotations is overwhelmingly in the far infrared and in the microwave region (*microwave spectrum*).

The vibrational spectra reflect changes in the positions of the atomic nuclei relative to each other. The length of a bond is not a static value but represents the *mean distance* of the two nuclei oscillating about it at a well-defined frequency. If the bond is perturbed by a radiation of a frequency corresponding to the frequency of the oscillations of the nuclei, then radiant energy is absorbed resulting in, for example, the "stretching" of the bond. The frequency range of the radiations absorbed by chemical bonds corresponds to the near (*i.e.*, adjacent to the visible), medium, and far infrared regions (*infrared spectrum*). The infrared absorption frequency of bonds is often so little affected by other atoms in the molecule that it may be used for identification of certain chemical groupings. Groups such as

$$\ce{>C=O} \qquad \ce{>C=C<} \qquad -SO_2- \qquad -N{=}O$$

have characteristic infrared "stretching frequencies" which have been tabulated and by which the presence of these groups in molecules may be ascertained. The presence of a methylene group is indicated by an infrared absorption band due to the vibrating deformation of the valence angles of the $-CH_2-$ group ("bending frequency"). The interpretation of the infrared spectra is an important tool for the identification of functional groups in molecules.

The far infrared and microwave spectra are mostly pure rotational spectra. The near infrared vibrational spectra are, on the other hand, sometimes complicated by the superposition of the rotational spectra. Finally, the electronic spectra generally appear, as we have said above, in combination with both the rotational and the vibrational spectra. The $0, 1, 2, 3, 4, \ldots$ sublevels of the ground state and the excited state which we have seen in Fig. 28 represent discrete energy levels within these states, due precisely to the rotational and vibrational motions of the molecules. These discrete energy levels are sometimes called the "rotational-vibrational fine structure" of the electronic spectrum. In organic molecules the details of this fine structure are usually lost because of the very great number of rotational and vibrational states and the mutual overlapping and coalescence of the individual transitions into bands (Section 3.2.3.1).

The transition energy of an absorption band should then be regarded as composed truly of three energy terms:

$$\Delta E = \Delta E_{\text{electronic}} + \Delta E_{\text{vibration}} + \Delta E_{\text{rotation}} \tag{23}$$

However, the orders of magnitudes of the three energy terms are so different that the vibrational and rotational terms may be disregarded in the interpretations of the electronic spectra of conjugated systems. The energies corresponding to the 100 and 790 $m\mu$ edges of the ultraviolet plus visible segment of the spectrum (responsible for the electronic transitions) are 286 and 36 kcal/mole, respectively. On the other hand, the energy differences between the vibrational levels and between the rotational levels are only about 2–5 and 0.01–0.1 kcal/mole, respectively. One kcal/mole (which is roughly the thermal energy of molecules at room temperature) corresponds to the lowest rotation-vibration level of the ground state E_0 (sublevel 0 in Fig. 28).

There are quantitative wave mechanical procedures for the calculation of the positions of the absorption bands and their absorption coefficients in organic compounds. These are beyond the scope of this chapter. However, a qualitative concept of the light absorption of conjugated systems may be attained on the basis of the theory of Lewis and Calvin which considers π-electron systems as electromagnetic oscillators analogous to some extent to mechanical oscillating systems. The analogy between vibrating strings and π-electronic molecular oscillators is discussed in some detail in Suppletory Note 6, and some vibration modes of a vibrating string are illustrated in Fig. 36. The meaning of the force constant of harmonic oscillators is defined

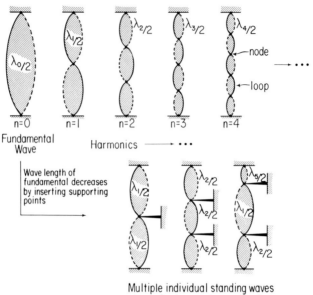

Wave length of fundamental decreases by inserting supporting points

Multiple individual standing waves at new fundamental wave lengths

Fig. 36. Vibration modes of a vibrating string.

in Suppletory Note 7 using the simple mechanical harmonic oscillator in Fig. 37; in Note 7 the frequency of oscillation is derived from the expressions of the potential and kinetic energy. Figure 38 shows the variations of the potential energy with the displacement of the oscillating mass in a mechanical harmonic oscillator, and illustrates the close analogy with the potential energy curves of electronic harmonic oscillators.

The electronic oscillations in the excited state of a straight-chain polyene, for example, in octatetraene, may be described as:

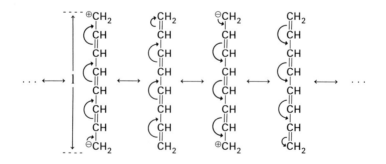

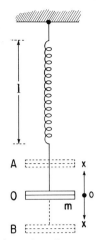

Fig. 37. Simple harmonic motion of a mass suspended from a spring.

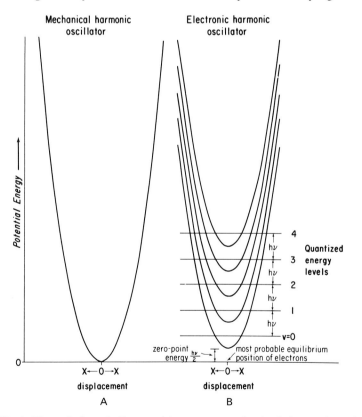

Fig. 38. A. The typical parabolic potential energy curve of a simple harmonic motion in a mechanical oscillator. The displacement x represents the displacement of the oscillating mass. B. The potential energy curves of an electronic harmonic oscillator at quantized energy levels.

where l is the total length of the conjugated chain. The oscillations corres-pond to the periodic deformations of the nonpolar π-electron pattern, i.e., to the *shifting of electron mass back and forth across the molecule.* The motion of the electrons from either extreme position toward the other extreme (the two ionic limit formulas) passes through the most probable equilibrium position (the nonpolar limit formula) having the lowest energy. Therefore, such an electronic oscillator is analogous to mechanical harmonic oscillators (see Suppletory Notes 6 and 7), and a molecular force constant (see Suppletory Note 7) may be calculated.

Consider one oscillating unit of the polyene, which is *a single double bond* segment $-CH{=}CH-$; this in the normal state of the molecule has no dipole moment. Placed in a constant electric field the displacement of the π electrons from their most probable equilibrium position produces a dipole moment. A dipole moment produced in a constant field of unit strength is defined as the polarizability α. Therefore, if μ is the moment produced in one double bond segment by a field of strength E, then the polarizability of the double bond is:

$$\alpha = \frac{\mu}{E} \tag{24}$$

Substituting the expression of the dipole moment $\mu = e \cdot x$ [this is the same as Eq. (14), but taking x for the displacement of a full electron charge $\delta = 1$] with the negative sign of the electron charge into Eq. (24), and taking into account that 2 electrons have been displaced in the double bond, we get:

$$\alpha = \frac{-2e \cdot x}{E}$$

from which the displacement of the electron pair produced by the field E is:

$$x = \frac{\alpha \cdot E}{-2e} \tag{25}$$

Since the electric charge of an electron is $-e$, the electric force acting on 2 electrons in the field is $-2e \cdot E$. During electron displacement this force is balanced by the "restoring force," *i.e.,* by the tendency of the double bond to regain the nonpolarized ground state electron distribution. Accord-ing to Hooke's law (see Suppletory Note 7) the restoring force is $k \cdot x$ where x is the displacement of the oscillating mass and k the force constant of the particular oscillating system. Thus we may write:

$$-2e \cdot E = k \cdot x \tag{26}$$

Substituting Eq. (25) for x in the above and rearranging, the force constant is obtained as:

$$k = \frac{4e^2}{\alpha} \tag{27}$$

This expression of the force constant is now substituted into Eq. (c) of Suppletory Note 7 describing the frequency of a simple harmonic oscillator:

$$v = \frac{1}{2\pi}\sqrt{\frac{k}{m}} = \frac{1}{2\pi}\sqrt{\frac{4e^2/\alpha}{2m_e}} \tag{28}$$

where the oscillating mass m becomes here $2m_e$, the resting mass of a pair of electrons. However, the *total* electron mass which oscillates in the whole molecule is $n \cdot 2m_e$, n being the number of double bonds. The frequency v of the electronic oscillations is, therefore:

$$v = \frac{1}{2\pi}\sqrt{\frac{4e^2/\alpha}{n \cdot 2m_e}} = \frac{\sqrt{2e^2/\alpha m_e}}{2\pi}\sqrt{\frac{1}{n}} \tag{29}$$

The energy of these oscillations is hv. This is the lowest energy level, the ground state. The higher energy levels of electronic oscillations can have only discrete values which are integral multiples of hv:

$$E_{pot} = v \cdot hv \tag{30}$$

where v, the quantum number of the oscillations, may be 0, 1, 2, 3, 4,... The molecular electron energy levels thus follow the quantum rule, *i.e.*, are quantized (compare to the atomic electron energy levels, Section 3.1.1.2).

The quantum number $v = 0$ would mean that there is a possible level where the potential energy would vanish. This concept had to be revised, however, because the solution of the Schrödinger equation (see Suppletory Note 8 for Section 3.1) for the potential energy function (see Suppletory Note 7) $E_{pot} = \frac{1}{2}kx^2$ gives the following expression:

$$E_{pot} = (v + \tfrac{1}{2})hv \tag{31}$$

This indicates that the electron oscillations possess a residual energy which cannot be lost even at the lowest energy state of the molecule. This energy $\frac{1}{2}hv$ (for $v = 0$), also written as $\frac{1}{2}hv_0$, is called the *zero-point energy*. Figure 38B shows the potential energy curves of an electronic harmonic oscillator at the quantized energy levels 0, 1, 2, 3, 4. These levels correspond to the displacement of the parabolic kinetic energy curves with an energy difference hv.

Now, a quantum oscillator differs from an ordinary electromagnetic oscillator in that *it does not absorb or emit energy* while being on a *stationary quantized level* (see Suppletory Note 1 for Section 3.1). Radiant energy is absorbed by an electronic oscillator only if the energy quantum hv of the radiation corresponds to the energy difference of its quantized levels so that passage from one level to another level may be possible; conversely, the energy of radiation which may be emitted corresponds to the difference of these levels. The fact that only transitions of certain energy are possible is called a *selection rule*, in this case $\Delta v = \pm 1$. The energy required to pass from say level $v = 0$ to $v = 1$ will be:

$$\Delta E = E_1 - E_0 = (1 + \tfrac{1}{2})hv - (0 + \tfrac{1}{2})hv = hv \tag{32}$$

If there is asymmetry of the oscillations, the energy of transition between quantum levels v_a and v_b becomes:

$$\Delta E = E_b - E_a = (v_b + \tfrac{1}{2})hv - (v_a + \tfrac{1}{2})hvx \tag{33}$$

where x is the *coefficient of anharmonicity* (see Suppletory Note 6). This means that when there is anharmonicity the selection rules do not hold rigorously. The deviation from the selection rules gradually decreases, however, toward the transitions taking place between pairs of higher energy levels.

The important conclusion which may be drawn from Eq. (29) is that *the frequency of the main absorption band varies inversely with the square root of the number of double bonds* (since e and m_e are constants of the electron, and α is constant for a homologous series of compounds). This may also be stated as: the frequency of the main absorption band varies inversely with the square root of the geometric length l of the conjugated chain, since $l \cong (2n - 1)l_C$ where l_C is the average bond length of the double and single bonds, and n is the number of double bonds.

The expectation that, according to this theory, the increase of the number of double bonds in a linear conjugated chain should be accompanied by a bathochromic shift of the main absorption band is dramatically substantiated by a vast body of experimental evidence. Table X gives examples of such bathochromic shifts in three different types of compounds. Despite their apparent structural dissimilarity, for all three types of compounds resonant limit formulas may be drawn which clearly show the presence of a long linear conjugated chain across the molecule, for example:

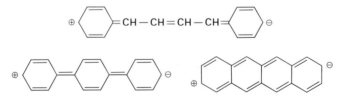

However, not only the position of the main absorption band but also the intensity of absorption is affected by resonance. In homologous series, such

Table X
Color and Absorption Maxima of Diphenyl Polyenes, Polyphenyls, and Acenes

Compound		Visible color	λ_{max}, $m\mu$
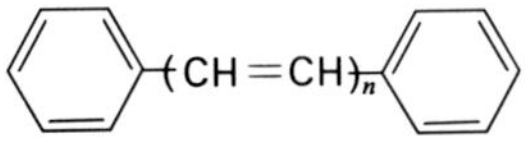 $\bigcirc$—(CH=CH)$_n$—$\bigcirc$	$n = 1$	Colorless	319
	$n = 2$	Colorless	352
	$n = 3$	Colorless	377
	$n = 4$	Greenish-yellow	404
	$n = 5$	Greenish-yellow	424
	$n = 6$	Yellow	445
	$n = 7$	Yellow	465
 $\bigcirc$		Colorless	200
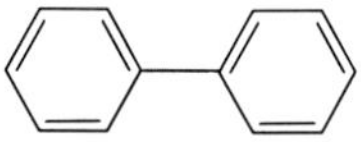 $\bigcirc$—$\bigcirc$		Colorless	252
 $\bigcirc$—$\bigcirc$—$\bigcirc$		Colorless	280
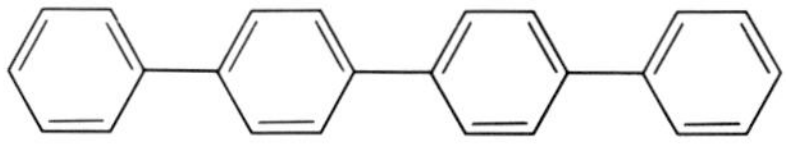 $\bigcirc$—$\bigcirc$—$\bigcirc$—$\bigcirc$		Colorless	300
 $\bigcirc$—$\bigcirc$—$\bigcirc$—$\bigcirc$—$\bigcirc$		Colorless	310
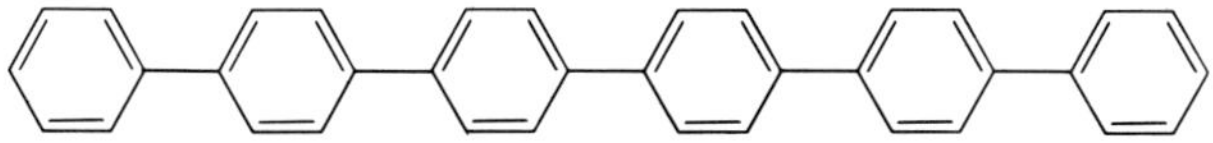 $\bigcirc$—$\bigcirc$—$\bigcirc$—$\bigcirc$—$\bigcirc$—$\bigcirc$		Colorless	318
 $\bigcirc$		Colorless	200
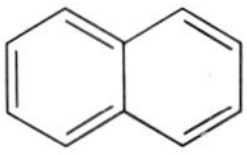 $\bigcirc\bigcirc$		Colorless	275
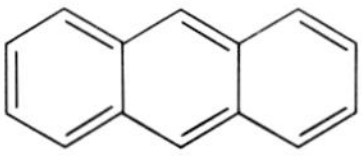 $\bigcirc\bigcirc\bigcirc$		Colorless	370
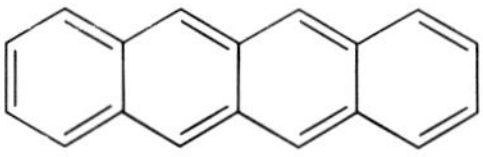 $\bigcirc\bigcirc\bigcirc\bigcirc$		Orange	460
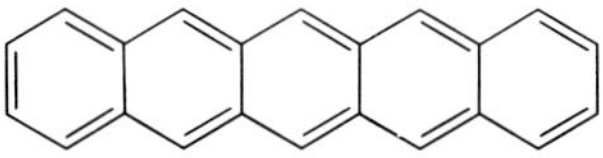 $\bigcirc\bigcirc\bigcirc\bigcirc\bigcirc$		Blue	580
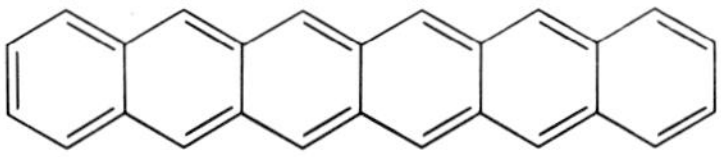 $\bigcirc\bigcirc\bigcirc\bigcirc\bigcirc\bigcirc$		Green	671

as in Table X, there is, together with the bathochromic shifts, increasing hyperchromicity paralleling the increase of the number of double bonds.

The mere length of the conjugated system is not the only parameter to be considered regarding light absorption. On reexamining the relation between auxochrome effect of certain groups and the effect of these same groups on conjugation, we should recall that in all these groups there is a strong electron donor atom, generally N or O, which is directly linked to the conjugated system. Thus the groups which produce an auxochrome effect are the very same which produce a strong mesomeric shift (Section 3.2.2). The free electron doublets of such electron donor atoms are, however, much more easily excited than electrons involved in π bonding. A $(CH_3)_2\ddot{N}-$ group has a much greater tendency to produce an electron shift than, say, a $\diagdown_{\diagup}C{=}C_{\diagdown}^{\diagup}$ group. In fact, a $(CH_3)_2\ddot{N}-$ group produces a much greater bathochromic shift of the main absorption band (i.e., a greater color deepening) and greater increase of the molar absorption coefficient than a $\diagdown_{\diagup}C{=}C_{\diagdown}^{\diagup}$ group.

The formal canonical structures cannot account for this difference in behavior of the two groups. For example, while triphenylcarbinol $(C_6H_5)_3C{-}OH$ is colorless in dilute acids, after addition of a dimethylamino group in the para position on one of the phenyls the red-colored fuchsone imonium dye salt is obtained:

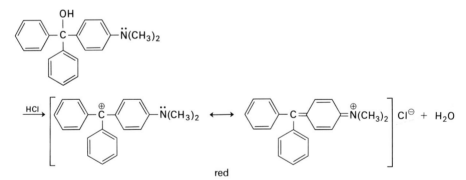

red

The crucial role of the free doublet of the nitrogen is clearly shown by the fact that *the iodomethylate of the dye*

$$[(CH_3)_3\overset{\oplus}{N}{-}C_6H_4{-}\underset{\underset{OH}{|}}{C}(C_6H_5)_2] \quad I^{\ominus}$$

does not give a colored dye salt in dilute acids because of blockage of the nitrogen doublet.

Now, replacement of the dimethylamino group by $CH_2=CH-$ causes disappearance of the red color in spite of the fact that canonical structures having similar length can be formally drawn for the cationic form:

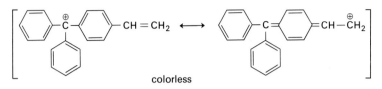

colorless

The oscillations initiated in mechanical oscillating systems (see Suppletory Notes 6 and 7) are "damped" oscillations, so that the amplitudes successively decrease and ultimately reach zero. This is because the energy invested when starting the oscillations is gradually lost because of transmission to the environment, the resistance of the air, the mechanical rigidity of the oscillating system itself, etc. To maintain a constant amplitude, small bits of energy must be periodically supplied to the system to make up for this loss. However, the oscillations can only be kept going if the supplying of these bits of energy is correctly timed. It is a common experience that the amplitude of the swings of a simple pendulum can only be maintained constant or increased if the periodicity of the added hits is *in phase* with the swings. Otherwise, the incorrectly timed energy bits will actually dampen the oscillations which will rapidly come to a standstill. *Energy can only be transferred from an energy source to an oscillating system if the oscillations of the source and the system have the same frequency and are in phase.* This rule holds for the transmission of energy between any kind of oscillating systems and provides the explanation why there is no light absorption by conjugated systems if the energy $hv_{cm^{-1}}$ of the light is greater than the energy $\Delta E/c$ of some possible electronic transition (Section 3.2.3.1). According to resonance theory the first excited state is stabilized preferentially by the ionic limit formulas (Section 3.2.2). Hence a conjugated molecule can only absorb light energy if the frequency of the radiations equals the self-frequency of those oscillations of the π-electron system which involve the ionic limit formulas. However, since the energy of quantized oscillations is hv (h being constant), this may be stated as: *for the transmission of energy between quantized oscillators there must be a matching of energy levels.*

3.2.3.4   Linear, Angular, and Branched Resonant Systems. Anti-Auxochromes. Effect of "Nonconducting" Groups in the Resonance Path. Coplanarity and Steric Hindrance

Conjugation is strongest in resonant systems where the electron shifts can proceed in a linear direction. For example, the polyenes, polyphenyls, and acenes are such *linear* resonant systems. Accordingly, the increments of bathochromic shifts, when passing from the lower to higher members in these series, are relatively large (Table X).

The strength of conjugation is considerably weaker if, because of the geometry of the molecule, the resonance shifts must follow an *angular* turn. This results in lesser bathochromic shifts (*i.e.*, lesser color deepening) than in the corresponding linear resonant systems. Thus, successive addition of benzene rings produces much less color deepening in the phenes than in the acenes (compare to Table X):

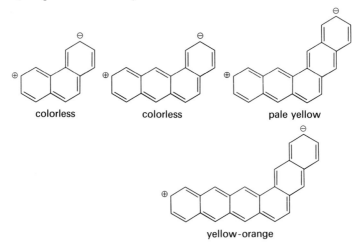

colorless	colorless	pale yellow

yellow-orange

In general, in a given type of compound the bathochromic shifts produced by the addition of further conjugating units are the most pronounced if the molecular geometry allows maximum separation in space between the ends of the conjugated system.

Branching of the pathway of the resonance shifts produces a reverse effect, a hypsochromic shift, in spite of the increase in the total number of double bonds. This is best illustrated with the triphenylmethane dyes. We have seen that the presence of *one* dimethylamino group in para position on triphenylcarbinol gives the red-colored fuchsone imonium dye salt in dilute acids (colored dye salt formation in dilute acids or bases is often termed *halochromism*):

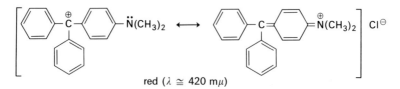

red ($\lambda \cong 420$ mμ)

Substitution by a second dimethylamino group in para position on another phenyl group gives a deep bluish-green-colored dye salt, Malachite Green, for which the following canonical structures may be written:

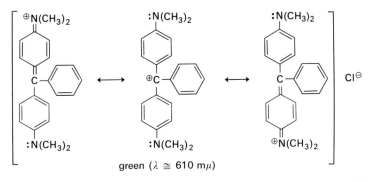

green ($\lambda \cong 610\ m\mu$)

The deepening of the color by the second auxochrome group still follows the Lewis–Calvin theory since the lengthening of the resonant system is accompanied by a bathochromic shift of the main absorption band from 420 to 610 $m\mu$. However, substitution by a third dimethylamino group gives a deep violet-colored dye salt, Crystal Violet. This represents a hypsochromic shift from 610 to 580 $m\mu$ for which the theory can seemingly not account:

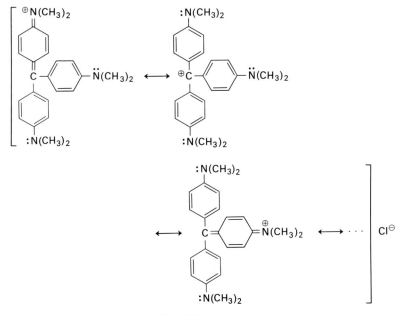

violet ($\lambda \cong 580\ m\mu$)

This hypsochromic shift is due to the fact that the linear conjugation as in Malachite Green is now regularly interrupted by the resonance contribution of the third dimethylaminophenyl group in Crystal Violet. The median carbon atom becomes, thus, the site of a *resonance node*. This is as if the uninterrupted free path of the "resonance wave" between the two dimethylamino groups (as in Malachite Green) would now be *to some degree* divided into two halves. This division of the resonance path must, however, be understood in probabilistic terms: there is no actual blockage of resonance across the central carbon atom, but the probability of the linear electron shifts directly between the two nitrogen atoms is decreased. Thus, the molecule absorbs as if its resonance path would be to some extent shortened; the absorption maximum (*i.e.*, the resonance wavelength of Crystal Violet) is an intermediate value between the absorption maximum of Malachite Green (having the maximum length of the linear resonance path) and the absorption maximum of the red fuchsone imonium dye salt (in which the resonance path is half as long as in Malachite Green). Unlike the wavelength shifts, however, the intensity of absorption (the *molar absorption coefficient*) gradually increases from the fuchsone imonium dye salt to Crystal Violet.

A very similar hypsochromic shift due to branching may be observed when comparing the two diphenylmethane dyes, Michler's hydrol blue and the golden-yellow Auramine O:

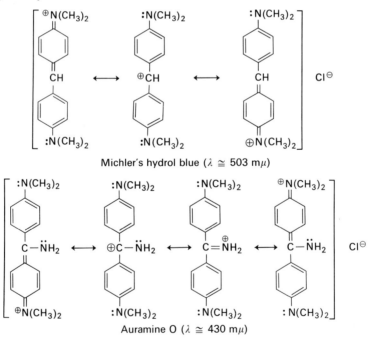

Michler's hydrol blue ($\lambda \cong 503$ mμ)

Auramine O ($\lambda \cong 430$ mμ)

This shows that the amino group linked to the central carbon atom (as in Auramine O) has a more powerful hypsochromic effect than the di-methylaminophenyl group (as in Crystal Violet). This is because in the former compound the electron donor amino nitrogen is *directly* linked to the central carbon atom. If the electron donating ability of the amino nitrogen is decreased, the hypsochromic effect of the group is abolished. Thus, *N*-acetyl Auramine O is blue just as the unbranched Michler's hydrol blue.

The wavelength of the main absorption band and the intensity of absorption are influenced, however, not only by the auxochrome electron donor group or groups linked to the *terminal end(s) of the conjugated system*, but substituents in other positions also modify the resonance. In particular, chemical groupings having a $-I$ and/or $-M$ effect can behave as *anti-auxo-chromes* because of "trapping" of the π electrons and thereby hindering the electronic oscillations along the longest resonance path. For example, the resonance involving the longest conjugated system in *p*-dimethylamino-azobenzene,

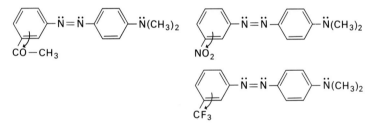

which is conveniently termed *transmolecular* or *p-p' resonance*, is considerably decreased by substitution with a hydroxyl, chloro, acetyl, nitro, or trifluoro-methyl group in the "prime" ring, because of inductive electron pull.

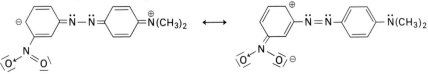

The anti-auxochrome effect of $-M$ groups may also be regarded as due to *crossed conjugation* which is similar to branching of the resonance path-ways. The mesomeric electron pull of the anti-auxochrome group corre-sponds, in fact, to a secondary resonance path which competes with the main conjugation, resulting in a partial repression of activity of the auxo-chrome group. For example:

The resultant effect of two or more groups is a function of the angle(s) formed by the resonant paths, which makes it analogous to the summation of group dipole moments (Section 3.1.2.3).

The auxochrome and anti-auxochrome effects are inversed in the halochrome anions in the sense that anti-auxochromes (such as $-OH$ which now has a $+M$ effect because in basic solution the mesomeric effect exceeds the inductive effect; Section 3.2.2) impart conjugation to the halochrome anions by introducing a new atom in the resonant path. This can be well illustrated with the case of another dye of the triphenylmethane group, the yellow Aurin:

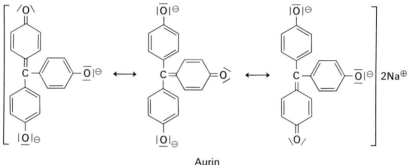

Aurin

However, apart from the inversion of the auxochrome and anti-auxochrome effect in anionic dyes, the path of conjugation in the carbon skeleton maintains its general resonance characteristics. Aurin has a branched resonant path as does the cationic Crystal Violet. Lowering of the intensity of conjugation in one of the three resonant branches in Aurin establishes a linear resonant path and results in the deepening of the color (*i.e.*, bathochromic shift) as shown by the purple-red basic form of phenolphthalein:

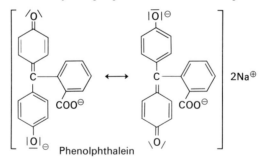

Phenolphthalein

We have seen in the previous section that within a homologous series of compounds the extent of the bathochromic shift of the main absorption band is a function of the length of the conjugated system. An expectable consequence of this is that any break in the conjugated chain (in the regular

alternation of single and double bonds) or any hindrance of the transmission of the "resonance wave" due to other factors results in an abolish-
ment of the bathochromic shift. This shows a close similarity with the
relation between length and fundamental wavelength of the oscillations in
vibrating strings (see Suppletory Note 6).

Figure 39 illustrates the insertion of insulating linkages in the oscillation
path of mechanical and molecular resonant systems. The $-CH_2-$ and
$-CH_2-CH_2-$ groups are insulating linkages because the carbon atoms
have filled octets. There is essentially no transmission of resonance shift

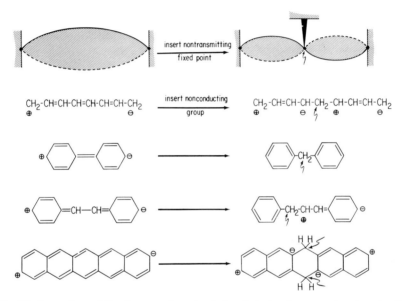

Fig. 39. An analogy of the cleavage of mechanical and electronic resonant systems by the
insertion in the oscillation path of nonconducting points or groups, respectively.

across these linkages. This amounts to a cleavage of the original resonant
systems into independent smaller resonant systems. Accordingly, the absorption spectra of the compounds containing the $-CH_2-$ groups show
absorption bands corresponding to the absorption of both resonant moieties.
For example, introduction of a $-CH_2-$ group in the center of the double-
bonded system of octatetraene, as shown in Fig. 39, divides the resonant
path into two separate butadiene systems. Thereby the absorption band of
octatetraene (at 302 mμ) is shifted to 210 mμ which is, in fact, the absorption
band of butadiene. However, because every molecule contains two absorbing
butadiene moieties, the molar absorption coefficient is roughly double
that of butadiene. Similarly, disruption of the integrity of the biphenyl

resonance path by a —CH_2— group, as in diphenylmethane, results in the disappearance of the 252 mμ biphenyl band and emergence of the typical absorption band of benzene. Introduction of a —CH_2— group in stilbene causes cleavage into separate benzenic and styrenic resonant systems. Finally, hydrogenation of pentacene affects the median ring. The transformation of the two *meso* —CH= groups into —CH_2— groups represents a division into two independent naphthalenic resonant systems. In fact, hydrogenation abolishes the dark blue color of pentacene (λ_{max} = 580 mμ), and the resulting dihydropentacene absorbs at about 280 mμ which is roughly the absorption maximum of naphthalene (λ_{max} $\cong$ 275 mμ). There is, however, the expected doubling of the intensity of absorption.

An especially interesting way to insulate resonant moieties is represented by the *m*-polyphenyls:

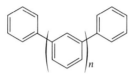

Since conjugation can occur only between the ortho-ortho or para-para positions, the two lateral benzene rings do not conjugate. The positions of the absorption maxima reflect clearly this situation since from n = 0 → 12 the change of λ_{max} is only from 252 to 253 mμ.

Coplanarity is an important requirement for conjugation between resonant moieties in a molecule. This is a consequence of the orbital geometry of the sp^2 hybridized carbon atom; for maximum overlapping of the non-hybridized p_z orbitals, *i.e.*, for maximum strength of π bonding, the planes of the individual sp^2 orbitals must lie in one plane (Section 3.1.2.2).

Consider Fig. 40 showing biphenyl (A), 2-methylbiphenyl (B), 2,2'-dimethylbiphenyl (C), and 2,6,2',6'-tetramethylbiphenyl (D), drawn proportionally to molecular dimensions. The radii of the circles centered at the ends of C—H and C—CH_3 bonds represent the *van der Waals radii* of the hydrogen atoms and of the methyl groups, respectively. The van der Waals radius represents the closest distance of approach of two atoms or groups (see further in Section 3.4.3). The boundary of the sphere corresponding to a van der Waals volume is, however, not a hard, unyielding surface but must be pictured as being somewhat elastic and compressible, since this boundary actually represents the fuzzy frontiers of the electron clouds. Figure 40 shows that there is overlapping between the van der Waals volumes of the substituents in the 2, 6, 2', and 6' positions. The overlap surface area, which is a quantitative measure of the overlapping of van der Waals volumes, indicates that crowding around the intercyclic bond increases in the following order: two *o-o'*-hydrogen pairs as in (A) < one *o-o'*-hydrogen pair plus one *o-o'*-hydrogen-and-methyl as in (B) < two *o-o'*-hydrogen-and-methyl as in (C) < two *o-o'*-methyl pairs as in (D). It is important to make a clear distinction between the overlapping of bonding atomic orbitals (Sections 3.1.2.1 and 3.1.2.2) and the overlapping of van der Waals volumes. The former is a measure of the stability of a bond, *i.e.*, the greater the overlap the greater the bond strength; the latter is a measure of the interatomic or intergroup *repulsion*. To express this differently: the potential energy of a molecule decreases with the increase of the overlap of atomic orbitals, while the

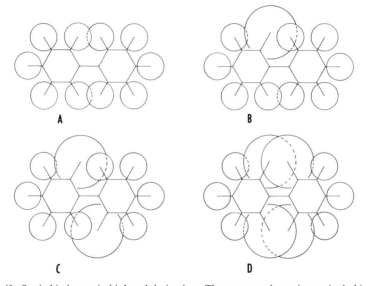

Fig. 40. Steric hindrance in biphenyl derivatives. The compounds are increasingly hindered in the following order: biphenyl (A); 2-methylbiphenyl (B); 2,2'-dimethylbiphenyl (C); 2,6,2',6'-tetramethylbiphenyl (D). The structures are represented drawn proportionally to molecular dimensions. The following parameters were used: aromatic $-C=C-$ 1.39 Å; internuclear $=C-C=$ 1.45 Å; aliphatic $\equiv C-C\equiv$ 1.54 Å; $\equiv C-H$ 1.1 Å; 1.0 Å and 2.0 Å were taken as the van der Waals radii of the hydrogen atom and the methyl group, respectively.

potential energy of a molecule increases with the increase of the overlap of van der Waals volumes, *i.e.*, with increasing crowding (see conformations of *n*-hexane in Section 2.1.3). This repulsion is due to the electric repulsion between the respective electron clouds.

The planarity of the biphenyl compounds in Fig. 40 depends, then, on the balance of two opposing forces: (a) *p-p'* Conjugation will tend to render the molecule coplanar (*i.e.*, to bring the two phenyl groups into one plane) because of the attraction of the π electrons of the two carbon atoms at the two ends of the intercyclic bond. It is this attraction, tending to produce the overlap of the p_z orbitals, which confers the double bond character to the intercyclic bond and tends to orient coplanarly the sp^2 hybrid orbital planes of the benzenic nuclei. (b) On the other hand, the interatomic or intergroup repulsion (because of van de Waals overlap) between the substituents, in ortho position relative to the intercyclic bond, will tend to render the molecule nonplanar by twisting the planes of the two phenyl groups about the intercyclic bond. We say that the crowding in the ortho position constitutes a *steric hindrance* to p-p' conjugation.

It follows from the above that conditions which increase π-electronic attraction across the intercyclic bond increase coplanarity, and *vice versa*. For example, the interplanar angle Θ of biphenyl which is $\ll 20°$ (and probably close to $0°$ in solution) at ordinary temperatures increases to $45°$ in the vapor phase; this is because at the high temperature of vaporization the energy conferred to the molecule is sufficient to "break" the intercyclic π bond, in other words, to abolish the intercyclic π-electron overlap. On the other hand, substitution at the one end of the conjugated system by an amino or dimethylamino group, or by any other group producing a mesomeric shift, increases coplanarity. The influence of a $+M$ group may be regarded, for example, as due to the displacement of the free doublet resulting in an increased electron density at the *para* carbon of the substituent-bearing ring, and this brings about an increased π-electronic attraction across the intercyclic bond.

Since the main absorption band of biphenyl at $252 \, m\mu$ is due to the contribution of the p-p', o-p', and o-o' ionic limit formulas, which involve conjugation across the intercyclic bond, the displacement in the main absorption band is a sensitive indicator of the degree of coplanarity. Figure 41 shows the gradual shift of this biphenyl band from 252 to $200 \, m\mu$ (the center of the absorption band of benzene) with the increasing crowding of the ortho positions in the four compounds A through D in Fig. 40. In compound D, because of extreme crowding, intercyclic conjugation between the two benzenic nuclei completely ceases; hence the absorption band of D is at the same position as that of benzene.

From the absorption bands the transition energies (see Suppletory Note 3), and from the latter, in turn, the resonance stabilization (Δ kcal) of the excited states, may be calculated. In these calculations account must be taken of the fact that the resonance stabilization of the ground state of biphenyl is known from calorimetric measurements to be about 5 kcal/mole greater than that of benzene, because of the force of p-p' conjugation; for similar reasons an increment of resonance stabilization of about 1 kcal/mole may be assumed for 2-methylbiphenyl (Fig. 41). The diagram shows that the resonance energy (Δ kcal) of the excited states of the biphenyl compounds (relative to the excited state of benzene) varies inversely with the extent of crowding, that is, with the loss of coplanarity. Although the exact function which connects the resonance energy of these excited states with the interplanar angle Θ is not known, a rough estimate of these angles can be made following an ingenious idea of Braude. Using the simplest function which passes through the fixed points assuming $\Theta = 0$ (for maximum resonance energy) and $\Theta = 90°$ (for minimum resonance energy):

$$\Delta \text{ kcal} = k \cdot \cos \Theta \tag{34}$$

where k is the slope of the curve. Thus, the interplanar angles of compounds B and C are estimated to be $38°$ and $60°$, respectively. Introduction of an

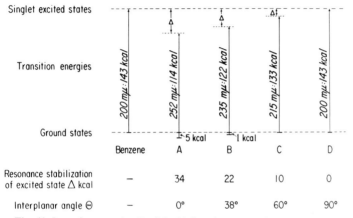

	Benzene	A	B	C	D
Singlet excited states					
Transition energies	200 mμ:143 kcal	252 mμ:114 kcal	235 mμ:122 kcal	215 mμ:133 kcal	200 mμ:143 kcal
Ground states		5 kcal	1 kcal		
Resonance stabilization of excited state Δ kcal	—	34	22	10	0
Interplanar angle Θ	—	0°	38°	60°	90°

Fig. 41. Interplanar angles Θ of the biphenyl compounds in Fig. 40 as determined from the resonance energies of the excited states using Eq. (34). These resonance energies were calculated by subtracting the respective transition energies from the transition energy of benzene. Because of greater resonance stabilization of the ground states of compounds A and B, the increments (5 and 1 kcal) have been subtracted from the respective transition energies before calculating the resonance energies of the excited states. [From E. A. Braude, *Experientia* **11**, 457 (1955).]

o-o' bridge into biphenyl, as for example in fluorene and 9,10-dihydro-phenanthrene, imposes a greater restriction on the interplanar rotation and, accordingly, there is a bathochromic shift relative to biphenyl ($\lambda = 252$ mμ):

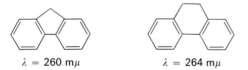

$\lambda = 260$ mμ $\lambda = 264$ mμ

A spectral characteristic which renders valuable information on steric hindrance and resonance in aromatic systems is the average force of transition, called the *oscillator strength*. The intensity of an absorption band as expressed by its highest molar absorption coefficient (*i.e.*, its *height*) is actually a very imperfect measure of the strength of the oscillations, because the *width* of the absorption band representing the total number of individual transitions which make up an absorption band (see Suppletory Note 3 and Section 3.2.3.1) is not taken into account. Thus, a more correct measure of the force of a transition is obtained by considering both the height and the width of a band, that is, the average surface area delimited by the band. The oscillator strength *f* is given by the equation:

$$f = \frac{mc^2}{\pi e^2 N}(v_2 - v_1)\varepsilon_{max} = 4.32 \times 10^{-9}(v_2 - v_1)\varepsilon_{max} \tag{35}$$

where m and e are the mass and the charge of the electron, c the velocity of light, N the Avogadro number, v_2 and v_1 the wave numbers (see Suppletory Note 1 for Section 3.1) corresponding, respectively, to the upper and lower edges of the band considered *at half intensity*, and ε_{max} the highest molar absorption coefficient of the band.

The oscillator strength is related to another interesting and useful fundamental constant, the *transition dipole moment*, through the equation

$$2.303\frac{(v_2 - v_1)\varepsilon_{max}}{v_{max}} = \frac{8\pi^3}{3hc}D^2 \tag{36}$$

Solving for the dipole moment, we get:

$$D = 0.0958\sqrt{\frac{(v_2 - v_1)\varepsilon_{max}}{v_{max}}} \tag{37}$$

where v_{max} is the wave number at ε_{max}. The transition dipole moment D is obtained in debye units.

3.2.4 RESONANCE AND THE ACIDITY OF THE CARBOXYL AND OTHER OXY-ACID GROUPS. THE BRÖNSTED AND LEWIS CONCEPTS OF ACIDITY AND BASICITY. POLAR REACTIONS. REACTION MECHANISMS

The concept of the acidity of organic compounds as described in Section 3.1.2.4, could lead to the erroneous idea that the proton-releasing tendency of the carboxyl group is due to the $-I$ effect of the keto group (which is a part of the carboxyl group). The impression, that the withdrawal by the keto group of the electron doublet toward the oxygen in the O—H bond is a *static* phenomenon, may have been strengthened further by the fact that as the carbon-bound hydrogen atom in formic acid is replaced by successively longer and longer alkyl chains (the electronegativity of which decreases with the chain length), compounds of successively lower and lower acid strength result (Section 3.1.2.4). However, if the acidity of the carboxyl group would be actually due to static electron withdrawal by the keto group, then the increment of acid strength over the acid strength of a corresponding enol should correspond only to that of an alcohol which is, *in fact*, not the case. This is illustrated by displaying the electron displacements in acetic acid and acetone, due to the $-I$ effect of the keto group:

$$
\underset{\text{CH}_3-\text{C} \rightleftharpoons \text{O}}{\overset{\overset{\text{O}}{\|} \; \overset{\text{H}}{|}}{}}
\qquad\qquad
\underset{\text{CH}_3-\text{C} \rightleftharpoons \text{CH}_2}{\overset{\overset{\text{O}}{\|} \; \overset{\text{H}}{|}}{}}
$$

Therefore, *static* electron displacement cannot account for the acidity of the carboxyl group. The acid strength of acetic acid is much greater than the acid strength of acetone.

It is the concept of resonance which provides the obvious explanation for the acid strength of the carboxyl group. The partial polarization of the C=O bond may be conceived as due to resonance between the two limit formulas:

$$
\text{>C=O} \quad \longleftrightarrow \quad \text{>}\overset{\oplus}{\text{C}}-\overline{\text{O}}|^{\ominus}
$$

The group dipole moment of the keto group (2.80 D) shows that the C=O bond is an intermediate between a pure covalent bond (0.00 D) and the theoretically calculable dipole moment assuming total polarization (5.95 D). In the carboxyl group, resonance is greatly increased because of the presence of *two* oxygen atoms. This amounts to a considerable stabilization of the carboxyl anion resulting in the release of the proton:

$$
\text{R}-\text{C}\underset{\overline{\text{O}}-\text{H}}{\overset{\overline{\text{O}}}{<}}
\quad\longleftrightarrow\quad
\left[\text{R}-\text{C}\underset{\overline{\text{O}}|^{\ominus}}{\overset{\overline{\text{O}}}{<}}
\quad\longleftrightarrow\quad
\text{R}-\text{C}\underset{\text{O}\backslash}{\overset{\text{O}}{<}}{}^{\ominus}\right] \text{H}^{\oplus}
$$

The proton release by acid groups other than carboxyl may be formulated in a similar way, for example:

$$
\text{R}-\overline{\underline{\text{S}}}-\overline{\text{O}}-\text{H} \quad\longleftrightarrow\quad \left[\text{R}-\overline{\underline{\text{S}}}-\overline{\text{O}}|^{\ominus}\right] \text{H}^{\oplus}
$$

a sulfenic acid

$$
\text{R}-\overset{..}{\text{S}}\underset{\overline{\text{O}}-\text{H}}{\overset{\text{O}}{<}}
\quad\longleftrightarrow\quad
\left[\text{R}-\overset{..}{\text{S}}\underset{\text{O}/^{\ominus}}{\overset{\text{O}}{<}}
\quad\longleftrightarrow\quad
\text{R}-\overset{..}{\text{S}}\underset{\text{O}/}{\overset{\text{O}}{<}}{}^{\ominus}\right] \text{H}^{\oplus}
$$

a sulfinic acid

$$
\underset{|\underline{\text{O}}|}{\overset{|\overline{\text{O}}|}{\text{R}-\text{S}-\overline{\text{O}}-\text{H}}}
\longleftrightarrow
\left[
\underset{|\underline{\text{O}}|}{\overset{|\overline{\text{O}}|}{\text{R}-\text{S}-\overline{\text{O}}|^{\ominus}}}
\longleftrightarrow
\underset{|\underline{\text{O}}|}{\overset{|\overline{\text{O}}|^{\ominus}}{\text{R}-\text{S}\rightarrow\overline{\text{O}}|}}
\longleftrightarrow
\underset{|\underline{\text{O}}|_{\ominus}}{\overset{|\overline{\text{O}}|}{\text{R}-\text{S}\rightarrow\overline{\text{O}}|}}
\right] \text{H}^{\oplus}
$$

a sulfonic acid

Since the stability of a structure increases with the number of resonant limit formulas, the stability of the respective anions and, thus, the proton-releasing tendency (*i.e.*, the acid strength) increases in the order: sulfenic < sulfinic < sulfonic. This example illustrates the underlying basis of the general rule that the strength of oxyacids increases with the number of coordinated oxygen atoms. It can be shown in an analogous way that the number of resonant limit structures decreases with the number of protons. Hence in a series of tetraoxyacids the acid strength decreases in the order $HClO_4$ > H_2SO_4 > H_3PO_4 > H_4SiO_4. This is, however, not the whole explanation of this order of the acid strength, since it may be noticed that the electronegativity (*i.e.*, electron-withdrawing tendency; Section 3.1.2.3) of the central atom varies in the same order as the acid strength: Cl > S > P > Si. Given identical electronegativities of the central atoms and identical oxidation numbers, the acid strengths of two acids are roughly similar. For example, a carboxylic acid and the corresponding sulfinic acid

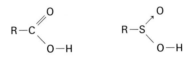

are of similar strength, because both carbon and sulfur have electronegativities of 2.5.

Some years ago acids and bases were defined in elementary chemistry as compounds which yield hydrogen and hydroxyl ions; this was known as the *Arrhenius theory* of acids and bases. Later it became clear that the theory required modification. Thus, in aqueous solutions acids (A) dissociate according to the equation:

$$HA + H_2O \rightleftharpoons H_3O^\oplus + A^\ominus$$

because just as free electrons cannot exist in solution, free, uncombined protons also cannot exist in solution. Protons always associate with undissociated water molecules to form the $H_3O^\oplus$ hydronium ions by means of onium-type coordinate bonds (Section 3.1.2.7). The dissociation of bases (B), on the other hand, may be represented as:

$$B: + H_2O \rightleftharpoons [B:H]^\oplus + OH^\ominus$$

Thus the Arrhenius theory cannot account for many acid-base reactions. In particular, it is not applicable to reactions in nonaqueous solvents in which acids and bases do not dissociate. For example, aniline may be titrated with anhydrous hydrochloric acid in benzene, in spite of the fact that hydrochloric acid is practically unionized in this solvent:

$$H:\overline{\underline{Cl}}| \; + \; C_6H_5-\ddot{N}H_2 \; \rightleftharpoons \; C_6H_5-\overset{\oplus}{N}H_3 \; |\overline{\underline{Cl}}|^\ominus$$

Reactions of this type led to a broadening of the acid-base concept by Brönsted. In the *Brönsted system* an acid is defined as any substance that can give up a proton, and a base is a compound or ion which can accept a proton. A strong acid is one which has a strong tendency to donate a proton; a strong base is one which has a strong tendency to accept a proton. Thus, in the Brönsted system an acid-base reaction amounts to the *exchange of proton*.

The Brönsted theory provides an explanation for the ionization of acids and bases in water. The ionization of acids is not a "spontaneous" phenomenon, but rather the proton is "pulled off" by water acting as a Brönsted base (*i.e.*, proton acceptor), and this results in the formation of the positively charged hydronium ions. Conversely, water can also act as a Brönsted acid. In the presence of a strong base, water donates a proton to the base and this results in the liberation of negatively charged hydroxyl ions. Thus, water (and some other hydroxylic solvents) may act either as a base or an acid depending on the relative acid or base strength of the other molecular species present; in other words it is amphiprotic (Section 3.1.2.7). The ion which remains after the proton(s) is removed from an acid is called the *conjugate base* of the acid. The molecular species formed when the proton(s) combines with a base is called a *conjugate acid*. For example, water is the conjugate base of hydronium ion, and hydronium ion is the conjugate acid of water; hydrogen chloride is the conjugate acid of chloride ion, and chloride ion is the conjugate base of hydrogen chloride; ammonia is the conjugate base of ammonium ion, and ammonium ion is the conjugate acid of ammonia.

In the Brönsted system any molecular or ionic species which can release proton(s) is an acid and, conversely, any species with an unshared electron doublet is a base. In other words, acids are not limited to cations nor bases to anions. For example, an acid may be a neutral molecule (CH_4, $CH_3 \cdot CO \cdot CH_3$, HCl, etc.), a cation (*e.g.*, $H_3SO_4^{\oplus}$, $H_3O^{\oplus}$, $NH_4^{\oplus}$, etc.), or an anion ($HSO_4^{\ominus}$, $HCO_3^{\ominus}$, etc.). Similarly, a base may be a neutral molecule [*e.g.*, NH_3, H_2O, $(C_2H_5)_2O$], an anion ($CH_3^{\ominus}$, $HO^{\ominus}$, alkyl-$O^{\ominus}$, etc.), or a cation [$Al(OH)_2^{\oplus}$, $NO^{\oplus}$, $PCl_2^{\oplus}$, etc.]. Because the Brönsted system is not limited by the old concept of the ionization of acids and bases it can account for acid-base reactions in both nonaqueous solvents and aqueous solutions.

Now, if we reexamine the typical acid-base reaction of the Brönsted system:

$$HA + :B \rightleftharpoons H:B^{\oplus} + A^{\ominus}$$

it is readily seen that *neutralization involves sharing of an electron pair* between $H^{\oplus}$ and the conjugate base :B. This constitutes the essence of the Lewis acid-base system: *a Lewis acid is an electron-pair acceptor and a Lewis base is an electron-pair donor*. The formation of a coordinate bond

(Section 3.1.2.7) is, thus, a typical neutralization reaction. For example, a typical Lewis acid, BCl_3 (in which the boron atom has an incomplete octet), can be actually titrated in chlorobenzene solution with bases such as pyridine or trimethylamine using Crystal Violet as indicator.

The bases of the Lewis system, also called *nucleophilic* (nucleus loving) *reagents* or *nucleophiles*, are largely identical with the bases of the Brönsted system, because molecules which share an electron doublet with an electron acceptor (a Lewis acid) also share it with a proton. The important nucleophilic reagents are: (a) simple inorganic anions; (b) compounds containing elements with unshared electron pairs; (c) compounds containing π electrons. Acids in the Lewis system, also called *electrophilic* (electron loving) *reagents* or *electrophiles*, are, however, of several types, for example: (a) compounds containing an incomplete octet; (b) compounds containing an octet which can be expanded; (c) simple inorganic cations; (d) compounds having $C=O$, $N=O$, $C=N$, and $C\equiv N$ bonds.

The "acid-base reactions" as defined in the Lewis system encompass the organic reactions involving the making and breaking of bonds, except the free radical reactions (Section 3.1.2.6). Because the Lewis acid-base reactions involve electron-pair donors and electron-pair acceptors and, thus, change in the distribution of the electron charge of the reactants, these reactions are also called *polar reactions*. Unlike the free radical reactions, many polar reactions are catalyzed by acids or bases and are subject to influence by polar solvents. According to Lewis, acid-base reactions are classified, either as *neutralization reactions*, or as *displacement* or *substitution reactions*. We have seen above that the formation of a coordinate bond between two molecular or ionic species represents a Lewis neutralization reaction. A displacement reaction takes place when a bond is broken and a new bond is formed because of displacement of a weaker Lewis acid (or base) by a stronger Lewis acid (or base) from its combination. The terms "electrophilic" and "nucleophilic" are often used to designate substitution reactions. Distinction is made between the *substrate* (the molecule undergoing transformation), the *leaving group* (the substituent which leaves the molecule), and the *attacking reagent* (the ionic or molecular species which becomes attached to a carbon of the substrate, replacing the leaving group). *The reaction is named following the type of the reagent.* For example:

$$CH_3-CH_2-Cl + :NH_3 \longrightarrow CH_3-CH_2-\overset{\oplus}{N}H_3 + Cl^{\ominus}$$

is a *nucleophilic substitution* reaction because it involves displacement of chloride ion by the "attacking" nucleophile, ammonia. On the other hand, the nitration of benzene:

$$\overset{\text{\raisebox{2pt}{$\downarrow$}}}{\underset{|\underline{O}|}{O=N-\bar{O}-H}} \longrightarrow \left[O=N\rightarrow\bar{O}|\right]^{\oplus} + {}^{\ominus}:\bar{O}-H$$

$$\left[O=N\rightarrow\bar{O}|\right]^{\oplus} + C_6H_5-H \longrightarrow C_6H_5-NO_2 + H^{\oplus}$$

is an *electrophilic substitution*, named from the electrophilic $NO_2^{\oplus}$ ion. It should be clearly understood that during this reaction the substrate gives rise to the nucleophile $C_6H_5:^{\ominus}$ intermediate. The three major intermediates of organic reactions are then: carbon radicals $-\overset{|}{\underset{|}{C}}\cdot$ (intermediates of free radical reactions), carbonium ions $-\overset{|}{\underset{|}{C}}^{\oplus}$ (intermediates of nucleophilic substitutions), and carbanions $-\overset{|}{\underset{|}{C}}:^{\ominus}$ (intermediates of electrophilic substitutions).

The molecular locus on the substrate, which will be the site of attack by the reagent, depends on the electron density distribution; molecular diagrams (Section 3.2.2.1.3) have been fairly successful in predicting the point of attack. While the terminology of Lewis acid-base reactions is not totally devoid of ambiguity, it is very useful for describing organic reaction mechanisms; by *reaction mechanism* is meant the pathway by which reacting molecules are transformed into new compounds.

Nucleophilic substitution reactions at a saturated carbon (sp^3), which interest us here in particular, may be of S_N1 (standing for substitution-nucleophilic-monomolecular) or S_N2 (substitution-nucleophilic-bimolecular) variety. The S_N2 mechanism describes a one-step reaction in which breaking of the bond between the substrate and the leaving group "X," and formation of the new bond between the substrate and the attacking nucleophile "NU:" occur simultaneously:

$$NU: + \overset{}{\underset{}{{>}C{-}\underline{X}|}} \longrightarrow \left[NU:{-}{-}\overset{\oplus}{\underset{|}{C}}{-}:X\right] \longrightarrow NU-C{<} + |\underline{\bar{X}}|^{\ominus}$$

transition state

Because the nucleophile and substrate are *synchronously* involved in bond breaking and bond making, the rate of the reaction depends on the concentration of both the substrate and the reagent; hence it is bimolecular. For example:

$$R-\underline{\bar{S}}|^{\ominus} + \overset{CH_3}{\underset{CH_3}{\overset{|}{\underset{}{H{\diagdown}C{-}\overset{}{\underline{Cl}}}}}} \longrightarrow \left[R-\underline{\bar{S}}:{-}{-}\overset{H\quad CH_3}{\underset{CH_3}{\overset{}{\underset{|}{C}}{}^{\oplus}{-}:\underline{Cl}|}}\right] \longrightarrow R-S-\overset{CH_3}{\underset{CH_3}{\overset{}{\underset{}{CH}}}} + |\underline{Cl}|^{\ominus}$$

The S_N1 mechanism describes, on the other hand, a two-step reaction in which the bond between the substrate and the leaving group is broken *before* the new bond is established, and the reaction proceeds by way of a free carbonium ion:

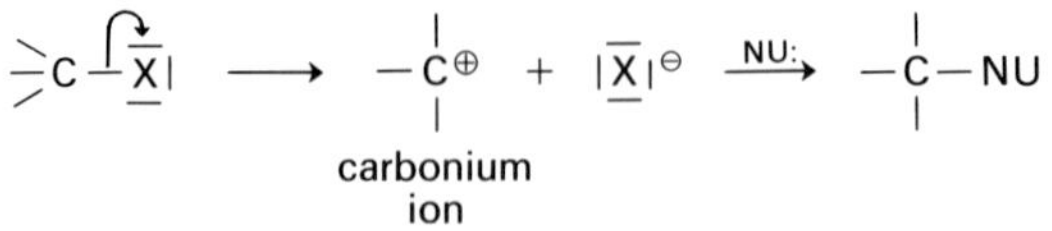

$$\ce{>C-XI -> -C^{\oplus} + IXI^{\ominus} ->[NU:] -C-NU}$$

carbonium
ion

Because the first step giving rise to the reactive carbonium ion is slow, the rate of the total reaction is determined by the concentration of the substrate only; hence it is monomolecular. For example, if the above reaction between a mercaptan and *sec*-chloropropane is carried out in a polar solvent (alcohol, dioxane, etc.), which acts as a weak Lewis base stabilizing the carbonium ion, the reaction type changes from S_N2 to S_N1:

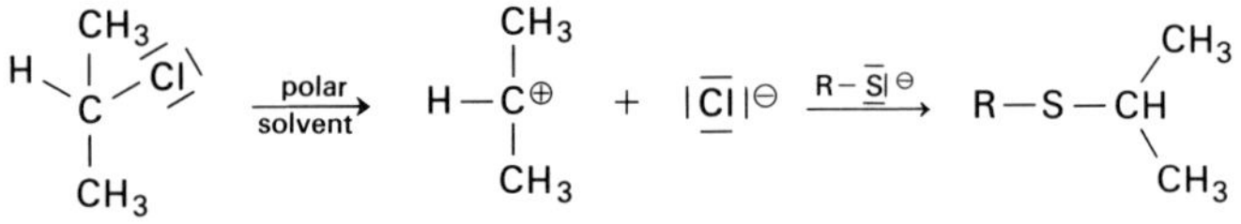

$$\ce{H-C(CH_3)(CH_3)(Cl) ->[polar][solvent] H-C^{\oplus}(CH_3)(CH_3) + ICl I^{\ominus} ->[R-S I^{\ominus}] R-S-CH(CH_3)(CH_3)}$$

Since the solvent plays an important role, the reaction now is truly pseudo-monomolecular and is also called *solvolytic displacement*. It can be readily seen that S_N1 reactions are acid catalyzed, since one acid can displace another (the carbonium ion Lewis acid) from its combination. The S_N1 or S_N2 character of a nucleophilic substitution depends on the extent of stabilization of the carbonium ion by the substituents of the attacked carbon atom. Thus, a secondary carbon (as above) constitutes an intermediate type where the molecularity of the reaction depends strongly on the experimental condition. Substitution on a primary carbon proceeds overwhelmingly through S_N2 mechanism, while substitutions on a tertiary or aryl-substituted carbon proceeds overwhelmingly through S_N1 mechanism.

SUPPLETORY NOTES FOR SECTION 3.2

NOTE 1

The bonding and antibonding orbitals represent two energy states of interacting electrons. Figure 25 shows that the energy level of the antibonding orbital is higher than the energy level of the bonding orbital at each point of the energy curves. The reason for this may be seen by examining the electron probability density in the internuclear region. In the LCAO method (Section 3.1.2.1), for example, the wave function of the antibonding orbital is the *difference* of the atomic wave functions. The antibonding orbital of the hydrogen molecule is:

$$\psi_- = C_1\psi_1 - C_2\psi_2 \tag{a}$$

from which the electron probability density is:

$$\psi_-^2 = (C_1\psi_1 - C_2\psi_2)^2 = C_1^2\psi_1^2 + C_2^2\psi_2^2 - 2C_1C_2\psi_1\psi_2 \tag{b}$$

The terms $C_1^2\psi_1^2$ and $C_2^2\psi_2^2$ are the same as in Eq. (11) indicating the fact that the electron probability densities in the two contributing atomic orbitals ψ_1 and ψ_2 are the same whether the molecular orbital is bonding or anti-bonding. However, the overlap $2C_1C_2\psi_1\psi_2$ has now a *negative sign* showing a "negative electron density" (*i.e.*, mutual electron repulsion) in *that* internuclear region where, in the bonding orbital, the overlap occurs. In other words in the antibonding molecular orbital the contributing atomic orbitals *do not overlap*. Since energy must be communicated to two overlapping orbitals to separate them, an antibonding orbital represents a higher energy state than a bonding orbital:

$$E_- = \frac{2\alpha - k\beta}{1 - S} \tag{c}$$

By comparing Eq. (c) to Eq. (12) it can be readily seen that $E_- > E_+$. In fact we have stated in connection with Eq. (12) that the unit β of the resonance integral has a negative sign. Hence the product $k\beta$ becomes positive and, furthermore, the sum of the two energy terms is now divided by a value *less* than unity.

A pair of radio-frequency resonant circuits coupled in "phase" and in "phase opposition" can serve as a useful analogy for bonding and anti-bonding orbitals. Consider the two circuits $L_1^\uparrow C_1$ and $L_2^\downarrow C_2$ shown in the upper left corner of Fig. 26, in which the arrows $\uparrow$ and $\downarrow$ represent the fact that the turns of the two coils have *opposite* directions (such as a right-handed and left-handed screw). The two circuits have the same resonance frequency $v = 1/(2\pi\sqrt{L \times C})$, that is $L_1^\uparrow \times C_1 = L_2^\downarrow \times C_2$, and they are fed by a system of high frequency voltage sources, the oscillations of which are "in phase" (*i.e.*, their wave trains coincide). Consider now the $L_1^\uparrow C_1$ circuit separately, *in the absence* of $L_2^\downarrow C_2$. If the frequency of the source is varied so as to approach and pass the resonance frequency v, the circuit energy, measured by means of a detector (composed of a sensing coil and an oscilloscope), describes a bell-shaped curve, the typical resonance curve ψ_1. An identical curve ψ_2 is obtained for $L_2^\downarrow C_2$ *when measured*, in the same way, *in the absence of* $L_1^\uparrow C_1$.

Bringing the two coils together results in "coupling" of the two circuits, meaning that the two coils will be in each other's magnetic field and the energy of one circuit can be transferred to the other. The extent of coupling, expressed by the coupling coefficient k, depends on the geometric closeness of the two coils and their respective positions.

Coupling of $L_1^\uparrow C_1$ and $L_2^\downarrow C_2$ results in the overlapping of the resonance curves ψ_1 and ψ_2, and the overlapping will be so much greater as k is greater. In measuring the resonance curve of the *coupled system* $\psi_1 + \psi_2$ the detector follows the variations of the energy of the *resultant electromagnetic field*. The plot of the source frequency against the circuit energy is the resonance curve of the coupled system, $\psi_1 + \psi_2$ (upper right corner in Fig. 26). Because of coupling $\uparrow\downarrow$ of the two coils, the electric oscillations in the two circuits are in phase, and the energies are consequently *additive* at every point of the overlap. Thus at the point of the greatest overlap the energy is $2E_0$, where E_0 is the energy of a single resonance curve at that same point [compare to the term $2C_1C_2\psi_1\psi_2$ of the bonding orbital in Eq. (11)]. The frequency corresponding to the point of the greatest overlap is the (mutual) resonance frequency v_0. The appearance of the two resonance humps is due to strong coupling, and the positions of v_1 and v_2 depend on the value of k.

Consider now the circuits $L_1^\uparrow C_1$ and $L_2^\uparrow C_2$ in the lower left corner of the figure. The arrows $\uparrow$ and $\uparrow$ represent the fact that the turns of the two coils have *identical* directions (such as either two right-handed or two left-handed screws). The resonance curves ψ_1 and ψ_2 of the two circuits, when *measured independently from each other*, are identical since they are evidently identical circuits. Moreover, they are also identical to the *individual* resonance curve of the circuit $L_2^\downarrow C_2$, since the terms being in "phase" or in "phase opposition" have meaning only relative to another circuit. *Coupling $\uparrow\uparrow$* of the two coils will result in electric oscillations in the two circuits, which oscillations are in phase *opposition*. Consequently the resultant energy of the *coupled system* is $\psi_1 + (-\psi_2) = \psi_1 - \psi_2$, meaning that the energies are *subtractive* at every point of the overlap. At the point of the greatest overlap (v_0) the energy $E_0 = 0$ and, furthermore, there is "narrowing down" of the two contributing curves as shown by the resultant energy curve in the lower right corner in the figure. Compare the above resultant energy function $\psi_1 - \psi_2$ of the coupled system to the wave function [Eq. (a)] of an anti-bonding orbital.

A radial electron probability curve such as in Fig. 10A is, in a sense, the wave mechanical embodiment of the resonance curve of an $L \times C$ radio-frequency circuit. The maximum electron wave intensity (*i.e.*, the radial electron probability at r_0) corresponds to the peak energy of the $L \times C$ circuit at the resonance frequency v. The analogy can now be readily seen. If two atoms approach each other their radial electron probabilities will be additive or subtractive in the region of the overlap, depending on whether the spins are paired (*i.e.*, "in phase") or unpaired (*i.e.*, in "phase opposition") just as the energies of the radiofrequency resonance circuits discussed above.

The resonant circuit analogy has also another usefulness because it relates complementary pairing to electromagnetic wave energy. In fact, when we pass from the Bohr atom model to the quantum mechanical interpretation of electron states, which states correspond to electron waves of different energy levels, the notion of spin quantum numbers, as specifying the sense of spinning of a particulate point-charge, loses obviously its physical meaning. In wave mechanics the electron spin appears as a mathematical property of a differential equation due to Dirac, which describes the electron states. It is, however, not too inaccurate to view the two spin states as corresponding to two possible patterns of distortions of the cloud of an electron; this can give rise to complementary↑↓ or to the repulsive↑↑ interactions between two electrons.

NOTE 2

The meaning of *resonance energy* will be illustrated using benzene as an example. For this we will calculate the *heat of formation* from the experimentally measured heat of combustion.

Benzene consists of 6 C atoms and 6 H atoms. In the normal molecular state these elements occur as a solid and a gas, respectively. The heats of atomization of solid carbon and molecular hydrogen have been measured to be 340.7 kcal/C_2 and 103.3 kcal/H_2. The energy which has to be communicated to dissociate 6 C (solid) and 3 H_2 (gas) into atomic carbon and hydrogen is, thus:

$$6\,C\,(solid) + 1022\,kcal = 6\,C\,(atomic) \qquad (a)$$

$$3\,H_2\,(gas) + 310\,kcal = 6\,H\,(atomic) \qquad (b)$$

which is a total of 1332 kcal.

On the other hand, the heat liberated during the combustion of carbon and hydrogen is:

$$C\,(solid) + O_2 = CO_2 + 94.5\,kcal \qquad (c)$$

$$H_2\,(gas) + \tfrac{1}{2}O_2 = H_2O\,(liquid) + 68.4\,kcal \qquad (d)$$

For the above 6 C (solid) and 3 H_2 (gas), by adding Eqs. (c) and (d), and multiplying, the total heat of combustion is:

$$6\,C\,(solid) + 3\,H_2\,(gas) + 7\tfrac{1}{2}O_2 = 6\,CO_2 + 3\,H_2O\,(liquid) + 772.2\,kcal$$

It is, then, 772.2 kcal energy which would have to be absorbed by the system if this reaction could be driven backwards. The energy which would be required to drive both reaction steps backwards is:

$$6\,CO_2 + 3\,H_2O \text{ (liquid)} \xrightarrow{772.2 \text{ kcal}} 6\,C \text{ (solid)} + 3\,H_2 \text{ (gas)}$$

$$+ 7\tfrac{1}{2}\,O_2 \xrightarrow{1332 \text{ kcal}} 6\,C \text{ (atomic)} + 6\,H \text{ (atomic)}$$

a total of $1332 + 772.2 = 2104.2$ kcal (Fig. 27). This is the total energy, the *enthalpy* of the system.

The combustion of benzene itself yields per mole:

$$C_6H_6 + 7\tfrac{1}{2}\,O_2 = 6\,CO_2 + 3\,H_2O \text{ (liquid)} + 789.2 \text{ kcal}$$

which is less than the total energy of the 6 C (atomic) + 6 H (atomic) initial state. The difference of the two energy levels $2104.2 - 789.2 = 1315$ kcal/ mole is the energy absorbed during the formation of benzene from its elements, that is, its *heat of formation* (Fig. 27). Note that this is the heat of formation of the *actual molecule* in which resonance "proceeds," since it is calculated by using the measured heat of combustion.

Now, if a way can be devised to determine the heat of formation of a *localized Kekulé form* of benzene (*i.e.*, the heat of formation of *cyclohexatriene*) then the resonance energy of benzene may be calculated. The resonance energy in fact represents the difference between the heat of formation of the hypothetical nonresonating cyclohexatriene and the heat of formation of benzene.

Cyclohexatriene contains 6 C—H bonds, 3 C—C bonds, and 3 C=C bonds. The heat of formation of cyclohexatriene is the sum of the heats of formation (*i.e.*, of the bond energies) of these bonds. The heat of formation and the bond energy of a bond are synonymous, since the bond energy is the energy liberated when two atoms unite to form a bond (Section 3.1.2.1). The energy of the C—H bond is obtained by calculating the heat of formation of methane from its heat of combustion by the same method which was used above for benzene; the heat of combustion of methane is 213.1 kcal/mole and the calculated heat of formation is found to be 395.2 kcal. Methane contains 4 C—H bonds, and thus the energy of a C—H bond is one fourth of 395.2, or 98.8 kcal/mole. The energy of the C—C bond and of the C=C bond is then calculated by difference from the heats of formation of ethane (6 C—H bonds and 1 C—C bond) and of ethylene (4 C—H bonds and 1 C=C bond) by subtracting 6 and 4 C—H bond energies, respectively. The heat of combustion of ethane is measured to be 370.4 kcal/mole; the calculated heat of formation is 674.4 kcal and the C—C bond energy is found to be 81.6 kcal. The heat of combustion of ethylene is measured to be 331.8 kcal/mole; the calculated heat of formation is 541.3 kcal and the C=C bond energy is found to be 146.1 kcal.

The sum of the bond energies of 6 C—H bonds, 3 C—C bonds, and 3 C=C bonds is 1276 kcal; this is then the heat of formation of cyclohexatriene. Hence, the energy of resonance of benzene is $1315 - 1276 = 39$ kcal/mole (Fig. 27). A different way of saying this is that the experimental heat of formation of benzene is 39 kcal lower than the value calculated by using bond energies. Therefore, since the energy level of benzene is closer to the final state than the energy level of cyclohexatriene, we say that benzene is "stabilized by resonance" with an increment of 39 kcal/mole.

That the aromatic C=C bond in benzene is intermediate between the saturated C—C bond and the unsaturated C=C bond is also indicated by its intermediate value of the heat of formation. The benzene molecule contains 6 C—H bonds and 6 aromatic C=C bonds. The heat of formation of the aromatic C=C bond is, therefore:

$$\frac{1315 - (6 \times 98.8)}{6} = 120.4 \text{ kcal}$$

(compare to 81.6 kcal for C—C and 146.1 kcal for C=C).

NOTE 3

Many organic molecules with multiple bonds possess in addition a *second excited state*, called the *triplet state*, which involves inversion of the spin of the two separated electrons:

The triplet state is not a possible resonant form because, for one reason, two electrons with *unpaired* spins do not correspond to a bond and because *resonance occurs only if the structures have the same number of unpaired electrons*. Because the two electrons in the triplet state have parallel spins, they may not occupy the same molecular orbital following the Pauli Exclusion Principle and, thus, an electron is raised to a higher energy antibonding state (Section 3.2.1). The rule of maximum multiplicity (Section 3.1.1.4) states that two electrons in identical but separate orbitals have less repulsion between them (lower potential energy) if they have parallel spins. Accordingly, the triplet state corresponds to a somewhat lower energy level than the singlet state.

The number of unpaired electrons N in a molecule defines its *multiplicity* (not to be confused with the "rule of maximum multiplicity") following the simple formula $N + 1$. The first excited state (which does not involve spin inversion) has no unpaired electrons and has, therefore, a multiplicity of $0 + 1 = 1$, hence the name *singlet* state meaning that the spin states of the two electrons are given by the one term [↑↓ + ↓↑]. The ground state has also "singlet character" because the multiplicity is the same in the ground state as in the first excited state. A mono-radical has one unpaired electron; its multiplicity is, therefore, $1 + 1 = 2$ and is called a *doublet* meaning that the spin states may be [↑] and [↓]. When two unpaired electrons are present in a molecule the multiplicity is $2 + 1 = 3$, hence the name *triplet* meaning that there are three spin terms [↑↑], [↓↓], and [↑↓ − ↓↑]. Stable organic biradicals may be singlets or triplets, depending on whether the two spatially distant electrons are paired or unpaired.

In certain compounds the singlet → ground state and the triplet → ground state electronic transitions are accompanied by the emission of visible radiation which has the energy corresponding to the difference of energy levels. The singlet → ground state transition is responsible for fluorescence emission, and the triplet → ground state transition for the phosphorescence emission phenomenon (Fig. 28). The reason that not all organic molecules show fluorescence is that the electronic excitation energy can be totally lost in intermolecular collision processes, and also because of the presence of small amounts of substances which are fluorescence "quenchers," etc. Fluorescence is common among aromatic polycyclic compounds. In many compounds the general shape of the fluorescence emission spectrum is the mirror image of the light absorption spectrum. This is due to the fact that there is a general relation between the absorption and the fluorescence emission processes in that the molecules are raised to the singlet state by the very energy of the absorbed radiation. However, the fluorescence emission spectrum is always at a longer wavelength (lower energy) than the absorption spectrum (*Stokes' law*), partly because there is always loss of energy in the form of heat dissipation (Fig. 28). The *energy of* the *transition* (ΔE), which represents the gain (or loss) of energy, may be calculated from an absorption (or emission) band following the relation:

$$\Delta E = h \cdot v_{cm^{-1}} \cdot c \tag{a}$$

where $v_{cm^{-1}}$ is the wave number (see Suppletory Note 1 for Section 3.1) of the band. The energy of the ground state → first excited state transition ($E_0 \rightarrow E_1$) may be calculated from the absorption band in the visible or the closest to the visible.

Both the singlet → triplet and triplet → ground state transitions involve spin inversion which is a process of low probability (is "forbidden"). Because the transitions to and from the triplet state have a low probability, it takes much longer to return from the triplet state to the ground state than from the singlet state to the ground state. Thus, the lifetime of triplet states is between 10^{-4} second to several seconds, while the lifetime of excited singlet states is 10^{-8} to 10^{-9} second. These lifetimes, which are both very high as compared to the hypothetical lifetimes of resonant limit structures (may be as low as 10^{-14} second as calculated from the resonance energy, Section 3.2.1), provide another explanation why neither the excited singlet nor the triplet states may be included as contributing resonant forms of the ground state. Because of the relative stability it is considered highly possible that triplet states of many compounds of biological importance play the role of energy carriers.

Note 4

There are two important methods for the study of free radicals. One method is based on the measurement of magnetic susceptibility. A more recent and much more sensitive and elegant method is the electron spin resonance (ESR) spectrometry.

The Gouy-Pascal balance is the most commonly used apparatus for the measurement of magnetic susceptibility. The sample, enclosed in a glass tube, is suspended on the arm of a sensitive analytical balance or a torsion balance. The suspended sample is positioned so that it is partly between the poles of a strong electromagnet (4000–10,000 gauss). The sample is equilibrated, and the field is switched on. Now, samples of ordinary organic compounds containing only *paired* electrons will be repelled by, and tend to move out from, the magnetic field. This is because the applied magnetic field induces in the filled bonding orbitals a magnetic moment opposing the direction of the field. Such compounds are called *diamagnetic*. On the other hand, an *unpaired* electron has an uncompensated permanent magnetic moment; thus, if an external field is applied, it is oriented in the direction of the field lines. Consequently, compounds having one or more unpaired electrons (*i.e.*, radicals) are attracted by an applied magnetic field (are pulled down between the poles); such compounds are said to be *paramagnetic*. The measurements of magnetic susceptibility can give, therefore, valuable information whether or not a compound contains unpaired electrons and about the number of unpaired electrons.

Because of the high concentration of free radicals required to detect changes in magnetic susceptibility, this method was not adaptable to study free radicals in samples of biological origin. For the study of free radicals in biological samples, the ESR spectrometry, which has a very much greater sensitivity, is used exclusively; free radicals have been detected in this way at concentrations as low as 10^{-8} *M*. ESR spectrometry is based on the absorption of microwave energy during the spin inversion of an unpaired electron in the magnetic field. We have seen in Suppletory Note 4 for Section 3.1 that the spin magnetic momentum of an electron can have two values only $\pm(eh/4\pi mc)$. These two values mean that when an *unpaired* electron is in a magnetic field, its spin magnetic momentum is either parallel or antiparallel to the direction of the field. If the strength of the magnetic field is varied, there comes a point where the energy of the applied field will be equal to the energy difference between the two spin magnetic momenta. At that point spin inversion occurs and electromagnetic radiation is absorbed, provided that the energy of the radiation per quantum corresponds to the energy of the spin inversion. Therefore, the energy difference between the two spin magnetic momenta is

$$\Delta E = g\beta H = h\nu$$

where g is a proportionality constant (~ 2.003), β the value of the Bohr magneton (9.27×10^{-21} ergs/gauss), H the magnetic field strength (in gauss), and ν the frequency of the microwave source.

Experimentally the sample, placed between the poles of a strong electromagnet (fields of the order of 10,000 gauss with an upper limit of 25,000 gauss have been used), is surrounded by the field coil of a klystron microwave oscillator (set to a frequency of about 28,000 megacycles) and by the sensing coil of a detector linked to a recorder or oscilloscope. Starting at low values the strength of the magnetic field is gradually increased, the frequency of the microwave being kept constant. At the point where the energy of the field equals (is "in resonance" with) the energy of electron spin transition, microwave energy is absorbed which is shown by the detector system as a characteristic signal extending over 10–50 gauss. Molecules which contain only *paired* electrons give no ESR signal.

As we have seen from the example of triphenylmethyl, because of resonance the unpaired electron may "move about freely" over the whole molecule, or, to say it more correctly, may be pictured as being present at different sites of the molecule since electrons are indistinguishable from each other. Therefore, the ESR spectrum is determined by the whole molecular structure rather than by the spin of the individual electron. However, similarly as in the case of paramagnetic susceptibility, the intensity of an ESR signal is directly proportional to the number of radicals present, *i.e.*, can be used to measure relative concentrations. In quantitative studies diphenylpicrylhydrazyl is used for calibration:

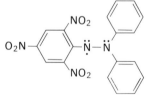

ESR spectrometry has been extensively used to study free radicals in biological oxidations, in various organic compounds exposed to radiations, in living tissues, organic complexes involving electron transfer (Section 3.3.3), and various ionic species.

NOTE 5

The light absorption capacity of a substance is measured photoelectrically. Consider Fig. 33. If I_0 is the intensity of the incident light beam and I is the intensity of the transmitted light beam (both in terms of galvanometer deflection in arbitrary unit degrees) then the light *transmittance* T in per cent is $I/I_0 \times 100$. The logarithm of the ratio I_0/I is the *optical density* or *absorbance* (E) of the medium; $E = \log I_0/I$. The absorbance is proportional to the thickness l of the medium and to the concentration c (in %) of the absorbing substance (*Beer–Lambert law*). The constant $k = [1/(l \cdot c)] \cdot \log I_0/I$ is the *extinction coefficient* (for a given wavelength). The *specific absorbance* is the extinction coefficient for unit concentration and unit thickness, $E_{1\,cm}^{1\%}$. The *molar absorption coefficient* is $\varepsilon = [1/(l \cdot m)] \cdot \log I_0/I$, where m is the molar concentration (the number of mole-grams per liter). By expressing the absorption in terms of molar absorption coefficient, the absolute absorption of different chemical substances may be compared.

NOTE 6

Consider a piano wire stretched between two fixed points (Fig. 36). If this string is plucked it vibrates with an amplitude which varies from a maximum at the center to zero at the ends. Given always identical tension of the wire, the wavelength of the standing wave of the vibration increases proportionally with the length of the wire. The longest possible wavelength of the vibration is the double of the length of the string, λ_0, because a standing wave is the result of the passage of two "wave trains" in opposite directions. The vibration of longest wavelength (or lowest frequency) of an oscillating system is called its *fundamental*. However, most oscillations are not "pure." The sound emitted by a vibrating string is composed of vibrations of more than one frequency, and this produces the characteristic quality of a sound. The fundamental vibration is of the greatest intensity, and the accompanying vibrations, the *harmonics* or *overtones*, are of much less intensity. The fundamental and the harmonics together constitute the *vibration modes* of the string. The frequencies of the harmonics ($n = 1$, $2, 3, 4, \ldots$) are the exact integral multiples of the fundamental. In producing the harmonics the string vibrates in more than one segment and this results in points of zero amplitude, called *nodes* and in points vibrating at maximum amplitude, called *loops*. All the nodes are situated along the axis of vibrations; the axis represents what is called a *nodal plane*, meaning the locus of all points along which the sum of amplitudes is zero.

Also π-electronic molecular oscillators have nodal planes. The nodal plane of a π-electron system coincides with the plane of the σ-bond frame

(Figs. 19A–F). The lobes of the p_z orbitals "above" the nodal plane are regarded as "$+$" lobes, the lobes "below" the nodal plane are the "$-$" lobes. If in a LCAO molecular wave function the wave functions of two *adjacent atoms* have different signs ($+$ and $-$), this means that in the first atom the π-electron density is highest on one side of the nodal plane, in the "$+$" lobe, and in the other it is the highest on the other side, in the "$-$" lobe. Thus, along the distance separating the two atoms the π-electron density passes through the nodal plane; we say then that there is a node in the molecular wave function. This also means that electron density is zero at one point between the two atomic nuclei, *i.e.*, that the two π electrons are in an antibonding state between these two atoms (compare Suppletory Note 1 for Section 3.2).

Damping the oscillations at one point of a string creates a vibrational asymmetry in the fundamental wave. This vibrational asymmetry results in *anharmonicity* which is when the overtones cease to be the exact integral multiples of the fundamental. The insertion of fixed supporting points along the length of the string divides the unique oscillating system into two or more shorter oscillating systems. Because vibrations are not transmitted across the fixed points, these oscillating systems are now "insulated" from each other. Each of these oscillating systems has, therefore, a distinct fundamental wavelength which depends on the length of the string in the segment (Fig. 36).

NOTE 7

The restoring *force constant* is an important characteristic of oscillating systems. The significance of this quantity is explained by using the analogy of a mass suspended on a spring. Consider the system in Fig. 37. The mass m if pulled down beyond its rest position O and released, will oscillate up and down about this position. The work stored, that is the potential energy of m, is maximum at the extreme positions A and B.

If the motion of m, from say A toward B, is analyzed it is seen that the acceleration is the greatest at the beginning of the motion. The acceleration rapidly decreases and reaches zero when m passes through O at which time, however, the velocity of m (*i.e.*, its kinetic energy) is at maximum. The velocity of m rapidly decreases beyond the O position and drops to zero at the extreme position B; the maximum kinetic energy of m at O has been transformed into maximum potential energy at B. The same takes place when m returns from B toward A, and so on. The mass m performs a simple harmonic motion (for the amplitude function of a simple harmonic motion, see Suppletory Note 7 for Section 3.1), and this is due to the fact that springs obey *Hooke's law*. A mass is said to have a simple harmonic motion about a fixed point if its acceleration toward it is proportional to the distance

from it. Hooke's law states that the force applied to cause an elastic deformation of a body is proportional to the deformation produced. Applied to the
spring this means that the force F necessary to stretch or compress the spring
increases proportionally with the displacement x from the O rest position.
However, the ratio of the force and the displacement is constant: $k = F/x$;
this is called the *force constant* of the spring. The force constant is an expression of the "springiness" of the spring, that is, of its tendency to regain
its normal resting position. This may be readily seen by rearranging this
simple equation to $F = kx$, which shows that the force necessary is not
only proportional to the displacement but also to the force constant. The
work stored as potential energy in a spring stretched or compressed by a
displacement x is the *average force* $\frac{1}{2}kx$ multiplied by the displacement:

$$E_{pot} = \tfrac{1}{2}kx^2 \tag{a}$$

Figure 38A shows the characteristic parabola of this potential energy
function.

The potential energy given in Eq. (a) is transformed into kinetic energy,
with a maximum value of $\frac{1}{2}mv^2$ at the middle of the path where the maximum
velocity attained, expressed with the angular velocity ω (see Suppletory
Note 7 for Section 3.1), is $\omega \cdot x$. Here the kinetic energy is therefore $\frac{1}{2}m\omega^2 x^2$.
Since all the kinetic energy originates from the potential energy, the two may
be set equal to one another:

$$\tfrac{1}{2}kx^2 = \tfrac{1}{2}m\omega^2 x^2 \tag{b}$$

from which $\omega^2 = k/m$. However, since the angular velocity $\omega = 2\pi/T$, the
frequency of oscillation of the system may be derived as

$$\frac{1}{T} = v = \frac{1}{2\pi}\sqrt{\frac{k}{m}} \tag{c}$$

Actually, it can be intuitively felt that the frequency of oscillations of
such a system is directly proportional to the "springiness" (*i.e.*, the force
constant) and inversely proportional to the mass (the weight). In another
way of expressing the frequency, the force constant is given as k_u (force
constant for unit length of spring) and the length l of the spring is introduced
into Eq. (c)

$$v = \frac{1}{2\pi}\sqrt{\frac{k_u}{l \cdot m}} = \frac{\sqrt{k_u/m}}{2\pi}\sqrt{\frac{1}{l}} \tag{d}$$

Keeping m constant, the frequency varies inversely with the square root of
the length of the elastic system [compare to Eq. (29)].

SELECTED READING FOR SECTIONS 3.1 AND 3.2

GENERAL

1. Brown, G. I.: "A Simple Guide to Modern Valency Theory." Wiley, New York, 1962, 174 pp.
2. Seel, F.: "Atomic Structure and Chemical Bonding," Methuen Monograph. Wiley, New York, 1963, 112 pp.
3. Jennings, J. R.: "Molecular Structure." Franklin, Englewood, New Jersey, 1965, 128 pp.
4. Wheeland, G. W.: "The Theory of Resonance." Wiley, New York, 1944, 316 pp.
5. Lewis, G. N. and Calvin, M.: The color of organic substances. *Chem. Rev.* **25**, 273–328 (1939).
6. Brode, W. R.: Color and chemical constitution. *Am. Scientist* **43**, 259–284 (1955).
7. Pullman, B.: "The Modern Theory of Molecular Structure." Dover, New York, 1962, 87 pp.
8. Szent-Györgyi, A.: "Introduction to a Submolecular Biology." Academic Press, New York, 1960, 135 pp.
9. Martin, D. F. and Martin, B. B.: "Coordination Compounds." McGraw-Hill, New York, 1964, 99 pp.
10. Murmann, R. K.: "Inorganic Complex Compounds." Reinhold. New York, 1964, 120 pp.
11. Karagounis, G.: "Introductory Organic Quantum Chemistry." Academic Press, New York, 1962, 204 pp.
12. Braude, E. A.: The labile stereochemistry of conjugated systems. *Experientia* **11**, 457–464 (1955).
13. Mislow, K.: "Introduction to Stereochemistry." Benjamin, New York, 1966, 193 pp.
14. Pauling, L.: "The Nature of the Chemical Bond." Cornell University Press, Ithaca, New York, 1960, 644 pp.
15. Ketelaar, J. A. A.: "Chemical Constitution—An Introduction to the Theory of the Chemical Bond." Elsevier, Amsterdam, 1953, 398 pp.
16. Clar, E.: "Polycyclic Hydrocarbons," Vol. I. Academic Press, New York, 1964, 488 pp.

QUANTUM MECHANICAL CALCULATIONS

A. *For refresher-study and self-study of mathematical prerequisites, in particular of matrix and vector algebra and group theory*

1. Norton, M. S.: "Finite Mathematical Systems." Webster (McGraw-Hill), New York, 1963, 64 pp.
2. Norton, M. S.: "Basic Concepts of Vectors." Webster (McGraw-Hill), New York, 1963, 64 pp.
3. Adler, I.: "The New Mathematics," John Day, New York, 1958, 187 pp.
4. Gondin, W. R., and Sohmer, B.: "Intermediate Algebra and Analytic Geometry Made Simple." Doubleday, Garden City, New York, 1959, 192 pp.
5. Sawyer, W. W.: "Prelude to Mathematics." Penguin Books, Baltimore, Maryland, 1955, 214 pp. (In particular, see sections on transformations, matrix algebra, determinants, and groups.)
6. School Mathematics Study Group: "Introduction to Matrix Algebra." Yale University Press, New Haven, Connecticut, 1961, 231 pp.
7. Searle, S. R.: "Matrix Algebra for the Biological Sciences." Wiley, New York, 1966, 296 pp.
8. Hohn, F. E.: "Elementary Matrix Algebra," Macmillan, New York, 1958, 305 pp.

9. Owen, G. E.: "Fundamentals of Scientific Mathematics." Johns Hopkins Press, Baltimore, Maryland, 1961, 274 pp.
10. Ledermann, W.: "Complex Numbers." Routledge and Kegan Paul, London, 1965, 62 pp.
11. Ayres, F.: "Theory and Problems of Matrices." Schaum, New York, 1962, 219 pp.
12. Gondin, W. R., and Sohmer, B.: "Advanced Algebra and Calculus Made Simple." Doubleday, Garden City, New York, 1959, 222 pp.
13. Carmichael, R. D.: "Introduction to the Theory of Groups of Finite Order." Ginn, Boston, 1937, 447 pp. (Reprinted by Dover, New York.)
14. Heine, V.: "Group Theory in Quantum Mechanics." Pergamon, Amsterdam, 1960, 468 pp.

B. *Setting up and solving of problems*

1. Jaffé, H. H. and Orchin, M.: "Symmetry in Chemistry." Wiley, New York, 1965, 191 pp.
2. Liberles, A.: "Introduction to Molecular-Orbital Theory." Holt, Rinehart and Winston, New York, 1966, 198 pp.
3. Roberts, J. D.: "Notes on Molecular Orbital Calculations." Benjamin, New York, 1962. 156 pp.
4. Cotton, F. A.: "Chemical Applications of Group Theory." Interscience, New York, 1963, 295 pp.
5. Streitwieser, A.: "Molecular Orbital Theory for Organic Chemists." Wiley, New York, 1962, 489 pp.
6. Coulson, C. A.: "Valence." Oxford University Press, London and New York, 1961, 404 pp.
7. Linnett, J. W.: "Wave Mechanics and Valency." Methuen, London, 1963, 184 pp.
8. Syrkin, Y. K., and Dyatkina, M. E.: "Structure of Molecules and the Chemical Bond." Dover, New York, 1964, 509 pp.
9. Daudel, R., Lefebvre, R., and Moser, C.: "Quantum Chemistry: Methods and Applications." Interscience, New York, 1960, 586 pp.
10. Pullman, A., and Pullman, B.: "Les Théories Electroniques de la Chimie Organique." Masson, Paris, 1952, 665 pp.
11. Dewar, M. J. S.: "Hyperconjugation." Ronald Press, New York, 1962, 184 pp.
12. Pullman, B., and Pullman, A.: "Quantum Biochemistry." Interscience, New York, 1963, 876 pp.
13. Löwdin, P.-O., and Pullman, B., Editors: "Molecular Orbitals in Chemistry, Physics, and Biology." Academic Press, New York, 1964, 578 pp.

STUDY OF MOLECULAR SPECTRA

1. Beaven, G. H., Johnson, E. A., Willis, H. A., and Miller, R. G. J.: "Molecular Spectroscopy." Heywood, London, 1961, 336 pp.
2. Rao, C. N. R.: "Ultra-violet and Visible Spectroscopy—Chemical Applications." Butterworths, London, 1961, 164 pp.
3. Sonnessa, A. J.: "Introduction to Molecular Spectroscopy." Reinhold, New York, 1966, 116 pp.
4. King, G. W.: "Spectroscopy and Molecular Structure." Holt, Rinehart and Winston, New York, 1964, 482 pp.
5. Bauman, R. P.: "Absorption Spectroscopy." Wiley, New York, 1962, 611 pp.

Theory of Reactions

A. *Elementary refreshers on kinetics and thermodynamics*

1. Chemical Bond Approach Project: "Chemical Systems." Webster, (McGraw-Hill), New York, 1964, 772 pp.
2. Hargreaves, G.: "Elementary Chemical Thermodynamics." Butterworths, London, 1962, 120 pp.
3. Latham, J. L.: "Elementary Reaction Kinetics." Butterworths, London, 1962, 120 pp.
4. Morris, K. B.: "Principles of Chemical Equilibrium." Reinhold, New York, 1965, 114 pp.

B. *Reaction mechanisms*

1. Vanderwerf, C. A.: "Acids, Bases, and the Chemistry of the Covalent Bond." Reinhold, New York, 1961, 117 pp.
2. Herz, W.: "The Shape of Carbon Compounds." Benjamin, New York, 1963, 152 pp.
3. White, E. H.: "Chemical Background for the Biological Sciences." Prentice-Hall, Englewood Cliffs, New Jersey, 1964, 152 pp.
4. Robinson, R.: Some intramolecular electrical effects on the course of chemical change. *Endeavour* **13**, 173–183 (1954).
5. Ingraham, L. L.: "Biochemical Mechanisms." Wiley, New York, 1962, 108 pp.
6. Gould, E. S.: "Mechanism and Structure in Organic Chemistry." Holt, Rinehart and Winston, New York, 1959, 790 pp.

3.3 Secondary Valence Forces

3.3.1 The Hydrogen Bond

3.3.1.1 The Nature of the Hydrogen Bond

A hydrogen bond consists of the linking of two electronegative atoms by a hydrogen atom. The two electronegative atoms "bridged" by the proton are called *bridgehead atoms*. The nature of this link may be described as follows. Because of the electron withdrawal by the electronegative proton-donor bridgehead atom, the covalent bond to the proton becomes *partially* polarized and the proton acquires a δ^+ charge. Thus, electrostatic attraction arises not only between the proton and its own δ^- charged bridgehead atom but between the same proton and δ^- charged atoms of neighboring molecules as well. This is illustrated with the following example:

which is usually represented as:

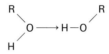

In compounds of biological interest the bridgehead atoms are usually oxygen or nitrogen; however, fluorine, chlorine, sulfur, carbon, and other elements can also form hydrogen bonds. The approximate order of hydrogen-bonding ability of different bridgehead atoms is $F > O > N \gg Cl > C \approx S$. Thus, for example, O—O and N—O hydrogen bonds are usually stronger than N—N hydrogen bonds.

Some attribute to the proton a coordination number of 2 and regard the hydrogen bond as a weak coordinate bond:

This notation represents the fact that in the equilibrium position the proton is usually much closer to one of the bridgehead atoms than to the other (for the bond lengths of hydrogen bonds see Section 3.4.2). Hydrogen bonds in which the position of the proton is symmetrical with respect to the two bridgehead atoms (e.g., as in the $[F--H--F]^{\ominus}$ ion) are rare. Because hydrogen bonding produces a lengthening (stretching) of the original covalent bond linking the proton, an important tool for studying the hydrogen bond is the infrared absorption spectrum (Section 3.2.3.3).

A position of extreme dissymmetry of the proton in the hydrogen bond would correspond to the formation of oxonium salt, such as:

$$\underset{H}{\overset{R}{\diagdown}}O\diagup \quad H-\underset{}{\overset{R}{O}}\diagup \quad \rightleftharpoons \quad \underset{H}{\overset{R}{\diagdown}}\overset{\oplus}{O}\diagup \rightarrow H \quad \overset{\ominus}{|\underline{O}}\overset{R}{\diagup}$$

However, it can be readily seen that two possibilities exist for the formation of the oxonium salt and these represent resonant limit formulas:

$$\left[\underset{H}{\overset{R}{\diagdown}}\overset{\oplus}{|O}\rightarrow H \quad \overset{\ominus}{|\underline{O}}-R\right] \longleftrightarrow \left[R-\overset{\ominus}{\underline{O}|} \quad H\leftarrow\overset{\oplus}{O}\underset{H}{\overset{R}{\diagup}}\right]$$

For this reason the strength of the hydrogen bond is regarded as due not only to electrostatic attraction but also to resonance energy.

Resonance provides an explanation for the fact that for stable hydrogen bond formation between two different molecular species in contact with one another the two bridgehead atoms must have similar affinities for the proton; this is, in fact, the situation in which proton exchange is maximal. There is, for example, no appreciable hydrogen bonding between methanol and diethyl ether; since the O—H bond in methanol has a high level of covalent character, the proton affinity of the alcoholic oxygen is much greater than the proton affinity of the ether oxygen. The proton is much more "released" in phenol; hence phenol and diethyl ether do form hydrogen-bonded molecular aggregates in 2:1 proportion (each of the two doublets of the ether oxygen unite with a phenol molecule). Finally, with very acid compounds (such as picric or hydrochloric acid) where there is total ionization of the bridgehead-H bond, there is no hydrogen bonding, but oxonium salt formation takes place exclusively (only one doublet is involved in oxonium salt formation).

We have seen in Section 3.1.2.8 that π-bonded systems can play the role of ligands in certain metal complexes. In these complexes, a portion of the π-electron cloud is "donated" to the central metal atom. Hence π-electronic systems may be regarded as Lewis bases. Consequently, a π-electron cloud may act as a bridgehead in hydrogen bonding provided that the electron density is sufficiently high. Hydrogen bonding by π-electron systems has received little attention so far.

Hydrogen bonds are generally much weaker bonds than the covalent and ionic bonds considered previously. Hydrogen bond strengths range usually between 2 and 10 kcal/mole, which is roughly one tenth of the strength of covalent bonds in carbon compounds. Because of the low bond strength, hydrogen bonds easily rupture and recombine in the normal environmental temperature range. Moreover, hydrogen bonds are very sensitive to pH changes or to the presence of metal ions which can form coordination compounds. This is because bonding depends on the lone electron pair(s) of the electronegative bridgehead atoms which act as Lewis bases. If the $H^{\oplus}$ concentration is increased or coordinating metal ions (Lewis acids) are present, the electron doublet(s) is "neutralized"; this results in the "breakage" of hydrogen bonds.

3.3.1.2 Some Structural Factors Affecting the Strength of Hydrogen Bonds

Electron displacement and resonance considerations can serve as useful guidelines for the approximation of the relative hydrogen bond strength between more complex organic groupings. Any substituent which affects the electron density on the bridgehead atoms will accordingly affect the hydrogen bond strength.

Hydrogen bonding between a primary or secondary amine and an oxygen bridgehead atom, which cannot contribute a proton, is weaker than bonding between the same amine and a proton-donor oxygen bridgehead; for example :

$$\begin{array}{c} R_1 \\ | \\ :N-H\cdots O=C \\ | \\ R_2 \end{array}\begin{array}{c} CH_3 \\ | \\ \\ | \\ CH_3 \end{array} \quad \text{is weaker than} \quad \begin{array}{c} R_1 \\ | \\ H-N:\cdots H-\overline{O}-C-CH_2-CH_3 \\ | \\ R_2 \end{array}\begin{array}{c} \\ \\ \| \\ O \end{array}$$

This is because the proton in R_1R_2NH is too tightly held by the nitrogen (*i.e.*, the base is a very weak Lewis acid) to contribute much to bonding when the other bonding partner (acetone) has no proton to share. However, when the bonding partner is propionic acid, for example, which has a strong tendency to release the proton, there is strong hydrogen bonding since nitrogen is a strong electron donor. Now, if the nitrogen in R_1R_2NH is double bonded to one of the alkyl groups, the nitrogen becomes less electronegative and has less attraction to the proton attached to it; hence :

$$\begin{array}{c} R_1 \\ \| \\ N-H\cdots O=C \\ | \\ R_2 \end{array}\begin{array}{c} CH_3 \\ | \\ \\ | \\ CH_3 \end{array} \quad \text{is stronger than} \quad \begin{array}{c} R_1 \\ | \\ :N-H\cdots O=C \\ | \\ R_2 \end{array}\begin{array}{c} CH_3 \\ | \\ \\ | \\ CH_3 \end{array}$$

The importance of electronegativity is clearly shown by the fact that the strength of hydrogen bonds which may be established by an oxygen bridgehead atom increases in the order :

$$\begin{array}{c} R_1 \\ | \\ :O: \\ | \\ R_2 \end{array} \quad < \quad \begin{array}{c} R_1 \\ | \\ C\overset{\delta+}{=}O\overset{\delta-}{} \\ | \\ R_2 \end{array} \quad < \quad \begin{array}{c} R \\ | \\ C-\overline{O}|^{\ominus} \\ \| \\ O \end{array}$$

The $-NH-$ and $-\overset{\overset{\textstyle O}{\|}}{C}-$ groups of amides or imides form stronger hydrogen bonds (with electron donors and proton donors, respectively) than the same groups in simple amines, imines, or ketones. This is because in amides and imides hydrogen bonding is enhanced by the resonance :

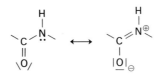

Resonance in amide groups is particularly important for explaining the hydrogen bonding in, and structural rigidity of, proteins.

The hydrogen-bonding ability of a substituent linked, on one hand, to a saturated (sp^3) carbon or, on the other hand, to an amino group having a free doublet, is especially illustrative for the role of electron density on the electron-donor bridgehead atom. For example, a nitroso group is a strong hydrogen-bonding group. Hydrogen bonding is stronger, however, with N-nitrosodialkylamines than with C-nitroso compounds. In the former there is displacement of the free doublet of the amino nitrogen toward the nitroso oxygen, and this causes an increase of electron density on the bridgehead oxygen atom. Such electron displacement cannot take place in C-nitroso compounds because of the "saturated" character of the sp^3 carbon:

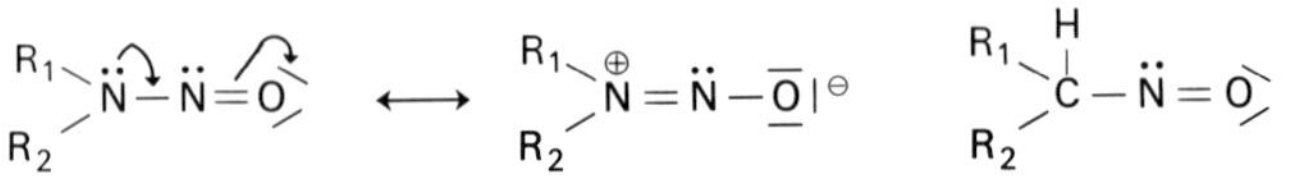

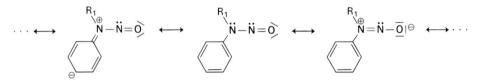

The role of the doublet is also well shown by the fact that if one of the alkyl groups in a dialkylnitrosamine is replaced by an aryl group, hydrogen bonding decreases. This is the result of the involvement of the doublet in the resonance of the aryl group, and the doublet now contributes less to the electron density of the bridgehead atom:

3.3.1.3 The Effect of Hydrogen Bonds on Some Properties of Substances

Hydrogen bonds have a profound effect in determining the physical and chemical properties of substances. The most commonly observed modifications of physical properties are: red shift in the characteristic infrared stretching frequency of the chemical groupings (e.g., C=O) involved, increase (or decrease, if intramolecular bonding occurs) of viscosity, of water solubility, and of the freezing and boiling points, and change in the heat of mixing, heat capacity, dipole moment, refractive index, etc. Hydrogen bonding can also have a marked influence on the chemical reactivity of substances; there can be a sharp increase in the dissociation of an acid if the anion is stabilized by intramolecular hydrogen bonding. *Intramolecular* hydrogen bonding often has an important effect on visible and ultraviolet light absorption. Hydrogen bonding plays a leading role in biological systems, in the maintenance of the steric conformation and polymolecular association of proteins, in the helical structure of deoxyribonucleic acids, in enzyme action, etc.

3.3.1.3.1 *Transition Temperatures, Aggregate Formation, Viscosity.* The molecular associations due to hydrogen bonding result in the abnormally high boiling points of many substances. Ammonia, water, and hydrogen fluoride have markedly higher boiling points than the compounds of homologous elements in the Periodic Table. Of these, water, for example, has a boiling point of 100°C, while the analogous sequence of substances H_2S, H_2Se, and H_2Te are gases liquefying under atmospheric pressure at $-62°C$, $-42°C$, and $0°C$; thus, if water would show normal behavior it would be a gas liquefying at about $-80°C$ at atmospheric pressure. The abnormally high boiling point is due to the fact that each molecule of water is surrounded by 4 others linked to the central molecule by hydrogen bonds (2 to the two oxygen doublets and 2 to the two protons). This tetrahedral structure is actually rigidly maintained in ice, but also persists to a large extent in the liquid state.

Similarly, alcohols, carboxylic acids, and many amines show abnormally high boiling points. For example, ethyl alcohol has a boiling point of 78°C, while its isomer, dimethyl ether, has a boiling point of $-25°C$. This is due to the fact that alcohols associate to form hydrogen-bonded polymeric chains:

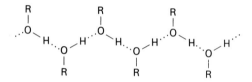

No association of this kind can take place between ether molecules.

For water, alcohols, and phenols the limit of the total number of molecules that can be held together in this way is set only by the thermal agitation at any given ambient temperature. However, in carboxylic acids, which possess also a keto group in addition to the hydroxyl group, hydrogen-bonded association is definitely restricted to dimerization; this is due to resonance of the type:

$$
\begin{array}{ccc}
& O \cdots H{-}O & \\
R{-}C\!\!\diagup\quad\diagdown C{-}R & \longleftrightarrow & R{-}C\!\!\diagup\quad\diagdown C{-}R \\
& O{-}H \cdots O &
\end{array}
$$

It is obvious from the foregoing that the elevation of the boiling point of hydrogen-bonded substances is due to *inter*molecular hydrogen bonding. *Intra*molecular hydrogen bonding has just the opposite effect on the boiling points. For example, 2-nitroresorcinol has a lower boiling point than resorcinol in spite of the fact that nitration usually brings about an elevation of the boiling point of substances. This is due to the fact that the hydrogen-bonding potentiality of the two phenolic hydroxyls is now tied up in intramolecular hydrogen bonding (which may be regarded as a form of chelation; Section 3.1.2.8):

The viscosity of hydrogen-bonded liquids is commonly higher than that of similar nonassociated compounds. This is due to the fact that the molecules passing in contact with one another form transient hydrogen-bonded associations, which is a process opposing flow (this may be simply visualized as due to the "stickiness" of the molecules passing in contact with one another). For example, alcohols have generally higher viscosities than the isomeric ethers. Polymolecular association due to hydrogen bonding is also the explanation for the high viscosity of glycols and glycerol. Viscometry can serve as a simple tool for the detection of strong hydrogen bonding between different molecular species. Figure 42 illustrates the viscosity changes in liquid mixtures of dioxane and dimethylnitrosamine (N-nitrosodimethyl-amine) with propionic acid, propionic anhydride, water, and benzene. Hydrogen bonding in the dioxane-water, dimethylnitrosamine-water, and

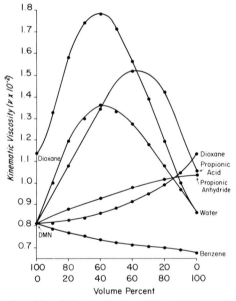

Fig. 42. Kinematic viscosities of binary mixtures of dimethylnitrosamine (DMN) with water, propionic acid, propionic anhydride, dioxane, or benzene, and of dioxane and water (at 30°C). The end points of the curves represent the viscosities of the single compounds. The proportions of the mixtures are given in volume per cent on two opposite scales on the abscissa. [From M. F. Argus, J. C. Arcos, A. Alam, and J. H. Mathison, *J. Med. Chem.* **7**, 460 (1964).]

dimethylnitrosamine-propionic acid mixtures is shown by the considerable increase of viscosity. That hydrogen bonding is responsible for the viscosity increase is shown by the fact that "elimination" of the proton as in the dimethylnitrosamine-propionic anhydride mixtures causes almost total disappearance of viscosity increase. The role of the proton is also illustrated by the absence of viscosity increase in mixtures of dimethylnitrosamine and dioxane, which are each potent in forming hydrogen bonds with proton donors. Expectedly, no interaction takes place between dimethylnitrosamine and benzene.

3.3.1.3.2   Water Solubility of Organic Compounds. Hydrogen bonding between water and the polar groups of solute molecules is the basis of the hydrosolubility of certain organic substances. For example, ethane, propane, and the higher alkanes are only slightly soluble in water, while ethanol, acetaldehyde, acetone, propanol, etc., are very soluble. Hydrogen bonding between water and the solute may be a "one-way" association (if the solute can provide only the bridgehead atom) or it may be reciprocal (if the solute is a proton donor):

Reciprocal hydrogen bonding between —OH groups of the solute and water molecules generally makes for high solubility. But in addition to the presence of hydroxyl groups per se a compound must have a relatively large ratio of total —OH group weight to nonpolar carbon chain weight in order to have a significant hydrosolubility. Thus, polyols (sugars) and polyvinyl alcohol

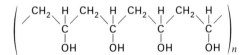

are quite soluble in water because they contain a large number of hydroxyl groups relative to the size of the carbon chain.

Shielding of the free hydroxyl group of a solute will expectedly lower the water solubility because reciprocal hydrogen bonding is reduced to "one-way" hydrogen bonding. For example, while phenol is appreciably soluble in water, the corresponding methyl ether, anisole, is practically insoluble:

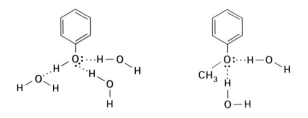

Hydrogen bonding is a major factor in the solubility of organic compounds in nonaqueous solvents as well. The solvent effect of alcohols, ketones, dioxane, dimethyl sulfoxide, etc., toward hydroxylic compounds is due to hydrogen bonding. The solvent power of alcohols is considerably enhanced by perfluorination which enhances the proton donor ability (the perfluoro alcohols actually behave as strong acids). The recently discovered hexafluoroacetone hydrate:

$$F_3C-C-CF_3$$

comes close to being a universal solvent since it dissolves easily any compound that contains receptive sites for hydrogen bond formation (*e.g.*, a variety of synthetic high polymers, and naturally occurring substances containing amide, amino, ester, alcohol, and keto groups).

3.3.1.3.3 Adsorption to Polar Surfaces. Hydrogen bonding plays a major role in the adsorption to and dyeing of cellulose fibers by cotton dyes (called also *substantive* dyes or *direct* dyes). The substantive dyes are elongated, rather narrow-shaped molecules liberally studded with hydrogen-bonding groups, and maintained rigidly coplanar by an uninterrupted conjugated system across the molecular frame. This represents a molecular geometry especially adapted for closely approaching the long, flat cellulose macromolecules packed in parallel sheets, and for bonding with the cellulose —OH groups. Expectedly, "shielding" the cellulose —OH groups by methylation or acetylation causes loss of affinity to substantive dyes.

3.3.2   THE HYDROPHOBIC BOND AND MEMBRANE PERMEABILITY. INCLUSION COMPOUNDS

3.3.2.1   Hydrophilic and Hydrophobic Groups. Surface Activity

Totally nonpolar substances, such as simple saturated carbon chains (alkanes), are only slightly soluble in water because there is no hydrogen bonding between the hydrocarbon and water molecules. Since any physico-chemical system has a tendency to occupy the lowest possible energy level, the molecules in the water phase form a tightly interwoven hydrogen-bonded network. Because energy must be contributed to rupture any chemical bond, the intermolecularly bonded water phase represents a lower energy level than that which would consist of separated, nonbonded molecules. Consequently, the hydrocarbon is "squeezed out," expelled, from the hydrogen-bonded network of the water phase and will accumulate on the surface; in other words, it is "insoluble."

Substitution of the carbon chain with a hydrogen-bonding group, say a —OH or —COOH, confers polar character to the molecule. Now, if the nonpolar carbon chain moiety is small relative to the polar group, the molecule is hydrosoluble. This means that the tendency of the polar group (polar "*head*") to establish as many hydrogen bonds as possible with water molecules overrules the tendency of the water phase to expel the nonpolar carbon chain moiety (nonpolar "*tail*"). Thus, for example, the lower members of the alcohols and fatty acids are soluble in water. As the size of the carbon chain increases, the water solubility decreases and there comes a point where the substance will be totally insoluble in water in spite of the presence of the polar group; because of the relatively large size of the hydrocarbon moiety the tendency of the water phase to expel it will predominate. However, even for the water-soluble members there remains a residual tendency of the water phase to expel the polar-nonpolar molecules, in that in a resting, undisturbed liquid the latter tend to accumulate on the surface, at the air-liquid interface, with the nonpolar tails oriented toward the air phase (Fig. 43A). This accumulation results in the *lowering of the surface tension* of the liquid. The origin and nature of surface tension is discussed in Suppletory Note 1* and schematically illustrated in Fig. 43B. Compounds which cause the lowering of the surface tension of solutions are said to be *surface active*. The lowering of the surface tension is due to the accumulation of the nonpolar tails at the phase boundary. Because the intermolecular attraction between the tails, and between tails and water, is much smaller than

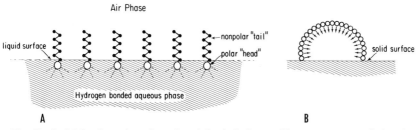

Fig. 43. A. Molecular orientation of straight-chain fatty acids at an aqueous-air interface. B. Schematic representation of the molecular basis of surface tension.

* Suppletory Notes for Section 3.3 begin on page 270.

Table XI
Hydrophilic and Hydrophobic Groups

Hydrophilic	Hydrophobic
$-SH$	$-C_nH_{2n+1}$
$-O-$	
$-C{\overset{O}{\underset{O-R}{}}}$	$-C_3H_7$
	$-C_2H_5$
$-C{\overset{O}{\underset{NH_2}{}}}$	$-CH_3$
$-NH_2$	$-CH=CH_2$
$-NR_2$	$-CCl_3$
$-\overset{}{\underset{O}{C}}-$	
$-C{\overset{O}{\underset{H}{}}}$	$-CF_3$
$-OH$	
$-C{\overset{O}{\underset{O-H}{}}}$	
$-\overset{O}{\underset{O}{S}}-O-H$	

(left axis: increasing solubility in water ↓; right axis: decreasing solubility in water ↑)

the intermolecular attraction between water molecules, there results a decrease of the surface tension. Strong surface-active agents are used as detergents. These may be anionic, cationic, or non-ionic, which defines the chemical nature of the polar head such as, $-SO_3^{\ominus}$, $-NR_3^{\oplus}$, or $-O-$, $-OH$, $-COOR$.

The polar heads which tend to remain in the aqueous phase because of hydrogen bonding are termed *hydrophilic* (water loving); the nonpolar tails are termed *hydrophobic* (water hating). Long hydrophobic tails or hydrophobic molecular regions of polar-nonpolar molecules tend to strongly adhere to each other in an aqueous phase, due to hydrophobic bonding (see next section). Because of the tendency of hydrophobic groupings to aggregate and (what amounts to the same) to penetrate into the lipid phase at aqueous-lipidic interfaces, these groupings are also termed *lipophilic* (lipid loving). Table XI gives the approximate order of hydrophilic and hydrophobic character of some functional groups commonly occurring in organic compounds.

3.3.2.2 The Nature of the Hydrophobic Bond

A hydrophobic bond represents attraction forces between nonpolar groups *in water or aqueous media*. Figure 44 illustrates the mechanism of formation of a hydrophobic bond. The nonpolar "tail" of each molecule of a polar-nonpolar compound is surrounded in aqueous solutions by a tight hydrogen-bonded "cage" of water molecules, because the tails are unable to participate in hydrogen bonding. The formation of such a water cage represents the establishment of a new liquid surface and, thus, corresponds to the raising of the energy of the system (see surface tension, Suppletory Note 1). Now, if two molecules approach each other, the tails will adhere to one another so that the carbon chains will lie alongside to achieve maximum closeness (*molecular adlineation*). Instead of two tails each being surrounded separately by a hydrogen-bonded water cage, it is now the adlineated pair of tails which is surrounded by *one* water cage. This corresponds to a lowering of energy of the system because the total liquid surface area surrounding the two tails has been reduced. The origin of the force holding the tails together is then truly *their inability to engage in hydrogen bonding*. For this reason the hydrophobic bond has also been called *anti-hydrogen bond*. Hydrophobic bonds are strong bonds because of the large number of hydrogen bonds involved in the build-up of the cage structure. Also, it can be readily seen that the hydrophobic bond strength is approximately proportional to the size of the tail and depends, furthermore, on the shape of its molecular skeleton since maximum "tail-tail" association depends on steric fit. Furthermore, tail-tail association also depends on different factors influencing hydrogen bonding between the surrounding water molecules (pH, presence of metal ions or certain organic compounds, etc.). However, the strength of hydrophobic bonds increases with the temperature up to about 60°C. For these reasons, the strength of the hydrophobic bond between given nonpolar side chains is not a fixed value, but an entire range of hydrophobic bonds of various strengths is possible. If the tail is long enough and

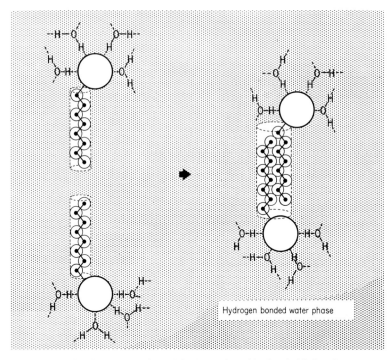

Fig. 44. A representation of the formation of hydrophobic bond.

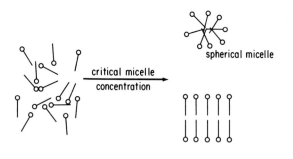

Fig. 45.

sufficiently flexible many molecules cluster together by hydrophobic bonding through their tails and form polymolecular associations (*micelles*; Fig. 45). Soap and detergent solutions commonly contain such micellar associations. However, micellar association does not occur in dilute solutions and a certain concentration must be reached for the onset of micelle formation. This concentration, called the *critical micelle concentration (CMC)* is a characteristic physical constant of surface-active agents. When a solution of a detergent reaches its CMC, surface tension is at a minimum and detergency steeply rises to a maximum.

A consequence of the ordered arrangement of water molecules around the nonpolar solute is that their movements are much more restricted even at ordinary temperatures than the movements of water molecules in the bulk phase. This stabilization of water results in an increase in the degree of hydrogen bonding between the molecules making up the cage, akin to the hydrogen bonding in ice; accordingly, the water directly surrounding hydrocarbon solutes has been termed "*iceberg*" *water*. Compounds which disrupt hydrophobic bonds are believed to behave as structure breakers by "melting" some of the iceberg water surrounding the hydrocarbon chains.

The solubilization by detergents of nonpolar fatty substances in aqueous solutions is due concurrently to hydrogen bonding and hydrophobic bonding. The detergent molecules, individually or clustered into micelles, and strongly hydrogen bonded at the polar "head" to water molecules, move about randomly in the solution due to the environmental heat energy (Brownian movement). Detergent solutions have a "solubilizing" effect on nonpolar fatty substances because molecules or clusters of molecules of the latter become attached by hydrophobic bonds to the tails or become incorporated in the centers of micelles; this results in the dispersal, in other words the emulsification, of the fatty substance in the aqueous solution.

Hydrophobic bonds play a major role in the maintenance of the three-dimensional structure of proteins and in the compounding of biological macromolecules into cell components, cells, and living tissue fabrics. Therefore, strong surface-active agents have usually a disintegrating effect on individual cells or isolated subcellular organelles of cells, because of elution of the lipid components of these and the disruption of all types of hydrophobic bonds by detergent action. Hence, surface-active agents generally possess pronounced bactericidal properties because of the ability to disrupt the bacterial cell wall and "solubilize" the cell content (*e.g.*, the well-known Zephyrol-type quaternary ammonium cationic surface-active agents). Since the ability of nonpolar tail groups to form strong hydrophobic bonds and the lowering of the surface tension of aqueous solutions by surface-active agents both depend on the size and the length of the tail, there is an approximate parallelism between surface activity and bactericidal activity in homologous series of compounds.

3.3.2.3 Inclusion Compounds

A phenomenon somewhat similar to the ordering of hydrogen-bonded water molecules about hydrocarbon solutes is the formation of *inclusion compounds*. Inclusion compounds are chemical combinations in which one component, called the *guest molecule*, fits into a cavity formed by a single or a group of several *host molecule*(s). The stability of inclusion compounds is due mainly to the fact that, akin to the "water cage" of hydrophobic bonding, the host molecule(s) form a tightly fitting bonded cage around the guest molecule. It follows that the "bonding principle" is a matter of geometric "fit" between the size and shape of the guest molecule and the size and shape of the hollow space that the host molecule(s) can form. In many cases the bonding system (*i.e.*, the distribution of valence electrons) of the two components is largely unaffected. In other types of inclusion compounds, however, there is strong electronic interaction between the host and guest molecules.

Following the shape of the cavity of the host, the inclusion compounds are classified as: (a) *Clathrates* (from the Latin word *clathratus*: enclosed by bars) in which the guest molecules fit into distinct spherical cages in the crystal lattice of host molecules; (b) *linear tubular complexes* in which the guest fits in the cylindrical space formed by a single spirally folded host molecule (if a long linear molecule) or by several host molecules bonded to each other so as to form a pipe-like arrangement; (c) *multiple canal complexes* in which the guest molecules fit into parallel tubular cavities of the crystal lattice of host molecules; (d) *layer complexes* containing "sandwich"-like alternating layers of host and guest molecules; (e) *molecular sieves* which are crystals containing interconnected networks of channels and cavities of molecular dimensions; these can "adsorb" and retain molecules which fit tightly into the molecular micropores; (f) *macromolecular insertion complexes* in which the guest fills a hollow concavity of an intricately folded macromolecule. In the following some of the main types are briefly described.

The clathrates were the first inclusion compounds, the structure of which was clearly established around 1947. In Powell's quinol clathrates the host cage is formed by regular arrangement of hydrogen-bonded hydroquinone molecules (Fig. 46A). The hexagonal rings, which constitute the frame of the cage, are the result of hydrogen bonding between hydroxyl groups so as to form "cup"-like arrangements of groups of three hydroquinone molecules as shown in Fig. 46B; this cup is the unit of the crystal lattice. Two interlocking cups (one upside down) form one cage. The hydroquinone cage

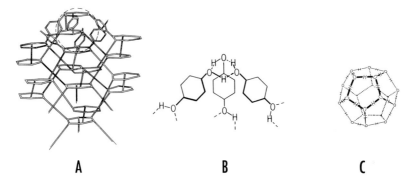

A   B   C

Fig. 46. A. Structure of hydroquinone (quinol) clathrate guest complex. The circle in the top shows one "cage." [From D. E. Palin and H. M. Powell, *J. Chem. Soc.* p. 208 (1947).] B. "Cup" of three hydroquinone molecules maintained by hydrogen bonds. C. Dodecahedron-shaped hydrogen-bonded "water-cage" of gas hydrates.

formed is roughly spherical and is about 4 Å in diameter. Hydroquinone can form clathrates with a variety of guest compounds which are chemically totally unrelated but of similar size; for example, SO_2, CO_2, CH_3-OH, $CH_2=CH_2$, HCl, H_2S, etc., and with the noble gases argon, krypton, and xenon. The chemical inertness of the latter is clear proof that clathrate formation depends on geometric fit rather than on electronic interaction between the guest and the host. Hydroquinone gas clathrates are obtained by crystallizing the quinol under pressure of the particular gas; the clathrate crystals are stable at ordinary temperature and give up the included gas only when heated or dissolved. The effect of clathration is dramatically illustrated by the fact that the amount of argon gas, which is present in a given volume of argon-hydroquinone clathrate crystals at 15°C, would have a pressure of 91 atmospheres if it were to occupy the same volume nonclathrated. The stringent steric requirements that govern the formation of the cage are shown by the facts that (a) resorcinol (in which the two —OH groups are in meta) does not form clathrates; and (b) hydroquinone can enclose formic acid and argon, but not acetic acid (too large) or helium (too small). If the guest molecule does not fill the available space tightly because it is too small, the hydrogen-bonded cage will be unstable for thermodynamic reasons; in a sense the cage would collapse and a clathrate would not be formed.

The solubility of gases and many low boiling point liquids (*e.g.*, CH_4, C_2H_4, C_3H_8, H_2S, Cl_2, noble gases) in water is also due to the formation of clathrates. Water molecules form 5-membered rings through hydrogen bonding and these rings combine to dodecahedrons leaving an internal cavity which is occupied by the host (Fig. 46C). Thus, the hydrogen-bonded water cage surrounding the tail of a polar-nonpolar compound (see Section 3.3.2.2) may be regarded as a type of "hydrate formation." The increased ordering of water molecules around hydrocarbon chains (the existence of the "iceberg" water) is decisively shown by the fact that while ordinary water freezes at 0°C, the gas hydrate of propane $C_3H_8 \cdot 17\,H_2O$, for example, freezes at $+5.8°C$. Recently, the pharmacological action of certain chemically unreactive anesthetic gases (noble gases, cyclopropane, chloroform, nitrous oxide, etc.) has been attributed to gas hydrate formation causing inhibition of the functioning of the central nervous system.

The formation of linear tubular inclusion compounds is responsible for the well-known intense blue-black color of the starch-iodine complex. In neutral and acidic solutions the starch molecule adopts a helical conformation which surrounds an adequate guest molecule. For example, in the presence of iodine, many iodine molecules are joined together to form a long, linear polyiodide chain $[---I---I---I---I---I---]$ around which the starch molecule forms a spiral wrapping (Fig. 47A). That such polyiodide

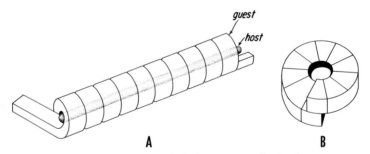

Fig. 47. A. Iodine-starch linear tubular inclusion compound; the figure represents the inclusion of a resonant polyiodide chain within the spirally folded chains of starch. B. Subunit of the cylindrical protein shell of tobacco mosaic virus.

chains exist only in inclusion compounds is due probably to two factors: (a) the space in the host molecule constrains the iodine molecules to a linear arrangement which is the most favorable geometry for resonant transitions (Section 3.2.3.4); (b) the space inside is a region of high electron density, owing to the free doublets of the great number of oxygen atoms in the glucose moieties making up the spiral; the wall of the host cavity acts therefore as an electron donor, a nucleophile, which promotes the resonance of the type:

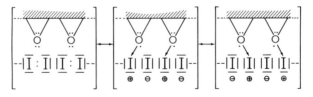

Then for the resonance of a whole polyiodide chain the following limit formulas may be written:

$$[\cdots I\overset{\ominus}{-}I\overset{\ominus}{-}I\overset{\ominus}{-}I\cdots] \longleftrightarrow [\cdots \overset{\oplus}{I} \; I-I \; \; I-I \; \; \overset{\ominus}{I}\cdots]$$

$$\longleftrightarrow [\cdots \overset{\ominus}{I} \; I-I \; \; I-I \; \; \overset{\oplus}{I}\cdots] \longleftrightarrow \cdots$$

Hence the development of the blue-black color.

Iodine forms similar deep blue-colored linear tubular inclusion compounds not only with starch, but also with polyvinyl alcohol, with the steroids, cortisone and deoxycholic acid, with benzamide, barbituric acid, benzophenone, many alkaloids, etc.; all compounds that can act as host for polyiodide chains contain electron donor groups. Other inclusion compounds of starch have been described, for instance, with higher fatty acids where the starch chain is apparently coiled around the nonpolar tail of the acid. It is not surprising then that the blue iodine reaction of starch (and of other compounds) is inhibited by the presence of straight-chain fatty acids. An interesting instance of biologically occurring linear tubular inclusion compounds is the *tobacco mosaic virus*, the infective agent of the mosaic disease of tobacco leaves. In the virus the host is a thick-walled cylindrical hollow shell built up of a spiral array of protein subunits (Fig. 47B), while the guest is a linear nucleic acid strand fitted in the cavity; the general structural make-up is identical to that of the starch-iodine complex. The infectivity resides in the guest and the only apparent role of the protein host is to chemically stabilize the included nucleic acid strand.

Straight-chain fatty acids and normal paraffins, containing more than 6 carbon atoms, can also serve as guest molecules in crystalline multiple canal inclusion compounds of urea. In these, hydrogen-bonded urea molecules are arranged in a helical hexagonal manner so as to form an inside channel about 5 Å in diameter. In the crystal lattice the channels are arranged in parallel arrays. Because of the tendency of urea to build up hydrogen-bonded shells around straight carbon chains and to form hydrogen bonds with water molecules, urea is believed to have a strong disruptive effect on hydrophobic bonds. The inclusion compounds of thiourea exhibit a very similar structure, except that because of the greater size of the sulfur than of the oxygen atom, the channel is about 7 Å in diameter. For this reason, in contrast to urea, thiourea does not complex with straight-chain compounds (which would be unstable, for the cavity would remain partly unfilled) but only with branched hydrocarbons and other bulky compounds.

Typical layer complexes are the black-colored inclusion compounds of iodine or bromine with the polycyclic aromatic hydrocarbons perylene, anthanthrene, the dibenzopyrenes, pyranthrene, ovalene, violanthrene, etc. These complexes are sandwich-type structures in which the polyiodide chain is included between pairs of coplanar hydrocarbon molecules (Fig. 48A; for the structure of the polycyclic hydrocarbons, see Sections 2.4.2.2, 5.1.1.1, and 5.1.1.2). The maximum ratio of iodine to hydrocarbon in the complex is determined by the molecular size of the hydrocarbon (Section 5.1.1.6.3). For example, the planar surface of perylene can accommodate up to three and violanthrene up to five I_2 in linear polyiodide arrangement. Similarly, graphite (Fig. 19G) forms lamellar inclusion compounds in which

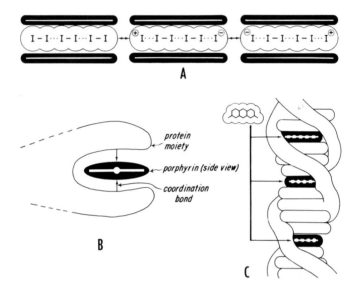

Fig. 48. A. Schematic representation of an iodine–polycyclic hydrocarbon layer complex; the figure shows a resonant polyiodide chain "sandwiched" between polycyclic hydrocarbon "plates." B. The "crevice" model of hemoglobin; the porphyrin moiety, filling a crevice in the protein portion, is connected with two ligands to the latter. C. Interaction of acridine with deoxyribonucleic acid (DNA): insertion of the acridine "plates" into the hollow concavities of the Watson–Crick DNA model. [After L. S. Lerman, *J. Cellular Comp. Physiol.* **64**, Suppl. 1, 1 (1964).]

bromine, chlorine, iodine monochloride, and bromine iodide are intercalated possibly in the same linear polyhalogenide arrangement between the poly-benzenic sheets. In all these complexes the π-electron cloud of the aromatic component plays the role of electron donor for maintaining the resonant polyhalogenide arrangement.

Many metal-aluminum silicate crystals (clays) can form inclusion compounds. The acidic montmorillonite contains interlamellar spaces between the hydrous aluminum silica layers. Montmorillonite can absorb a variety of large size aromatic amines which are intercalated between and form acid-base combinations with the layers and, accordingly, increase their spacing. Other metal-aluminum silicates, such as the synthetic zeolites, are true "molecular sieves" containing, in each crystal, literally billions of tiny cavities or cages interconnected by channels, where the size and position of the metal ions in the crystal control the effective diameter of these channels. Molecular sieves can function as carriers for a wide variety of chemical compounds; they may be "loaded," depending on the type, with guest molecules between 4 and 10 Å in maximum diameter. The guest molecules can be released by heating the loaded molecular sieve or by displacement of the chemical with another adsorbed material such as water. Zeolites also have important applications as shape-selective catalysts.

The structure of macromolecular insertion complexes has received comparatively little attention so far. Yet, this type of inclusion compound is probably of great importance in biological systems, in the catalytic activation of the substrate in many enzymatic reactions, and in the regulation of the three-dimensional structure and the function of proteins and nucleic acids by small molecules. There is strong evidence that hemoglobin has a "crevice" structure; the porphyrin ring fits into a flat crevice of the protein moiety and the central metal atom is linked to the surrounding folded polypeptide chain by two coordinate bonds, one each on opposite sides of the porphyrin frame (Fig. 48B). Other evidence indicates that the ability of certain planar polycyclic heteroaromatic compounds (acridines) to produce mutations may be related to their ability to form insertion complexes with deoxyribonucleic acid, as shown in Fig. 48C. Similar intercalation mechanisms have been proposed for the regulation of the function of the genes in the cell nucleus by hormones and by certain low molecular weight proteins (protamines).

3.3.2.4   Polarity, Partition Coefficient, and Membrane Permeation. The Ferguson Effect. The Hansch Equation

Hydrophily and lipophily are important molecular parameters which determine the penetration of biological membranes by organic compounds. As early as 1900, Meyer and Overton attempted to correlate the biological effectiveness of hypnotics and general anesthetics (called in general terms *biological depressants*) with the *partition coefficient* (ratio of concentrations) of olive oil–water phases. Traube investigated a similar correlation between the biological effectiveness of the same compounds and their ability to lower the surface tension of aqueous solutions. More recently a correlation between the bactericidal activity and surface activity of aliphatic straight-chain alcohols has been shown. The conclusions of Overton, which are still useful as rough guidelines for the prediction of permeation of plant and animal cells by organic substances, are given in Table XII.

Table XII
Rate of Penetration of Organic Substances into Plant and Animal Cells

Rate	Substance
Rapid	Monohydric alcohols, aldehydes, ketones, hydrocarbons and their mono-, di-, and tri-halogen derivatives, esters, many weak organic acids and bases
Less rapid	Dihydric alcohols and amides of monobasic acids
Slow	The trihydric alcohol glycerol, urea, thiourea
More Slow	The tetrahydric alcohol erythritol
Very slow	Hexahydric alcohols, sugars, amino acids, many neutral salts of organic acids

A concept of the permeation of biological membranes by inorganic ions and organic compounds is obtained with the aid of the *lipoid-sieve theory* proposed originally by Collander and Bärlund for the cell membrane, modified by Meyer and Teorell, and extended by Danielli, Robertson, Sjöstrand, and others to other biological membranes.

Figure 49 represents an approximation of the structure of biological lipoprotein membranes, such as the cell membrane. The core of the membrane consists of an immense array of lamellar phospholipid micelles, this lipid film being "coated" on both sides by protein molecules linked to the lipid by hydrophobic bonds, hydrogen bonds (to the polar "heads"), and weaker secondary valence attractions; in addition, each protein molecule is cemented to the neighboring protein molecules by identical secondary valence forces, and the "free" surfaces of the protein layers are covered

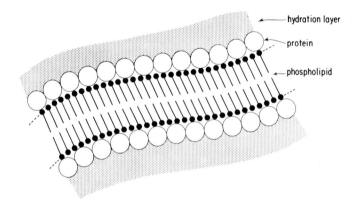

Fig. 49. Schematic representation of the structure of biological lipoprotein membranes.

by a halo of attracted water molecules (*hydration layer*). However, the membrane structure is not continuous, but is interrupted by sieve-like areas or membrane pores. These pores are holes of definite size in the membrane, and because of the composition of the membrane (phospholipids and proteins) the walls of the pores are electrically charged; the pores can be overwhelmingly anionic or cationic, or they may be amphoteric (Fig. 50).

The theory suggests that some substances penetrate membranes by passing through the lipoprotein fabric by virtue of their lipid solubility (*lipoid permeability*), while others which have low lipid solubility diffuse through the pores (*pore permeability*). In fact, many substances have a low lipid-water partition coefficient and yet show a high rate of penetration through many membranes. Another possible view is that the higher rate of penetration by less polar substances is merely a reflection of the lower charge density or lower free electron density (relative to the total surface area) of these molecules; therefore, since they are less involved in electrostatic

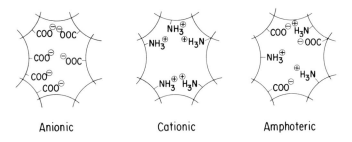

Anionic   Cationic   Amphoteric

Fig. 50. A representation of the pore types of biological membranes.

interactions with the charged walls of the membrane pores, they may pass through them relatively unhindered.

Support for this may be gathered from the investigations of Ferguson, which indicate that all changes of structure that lower water solubility (*i.e.*, polarity) in homologous series of chemically inert narcotics increase the narcotic action up to a limiting value, *regardless of whether lipid solubility is increased*. The penetration of biological membranes by these inert substances (their accumulation in the biophase running parallel with depressant action) is roughly proportional to their concentration in the aqueous phase of the medium. The general anesthetic action of noble gases (especially xenon), of diethyl ether, chloroform, cyclopropane, the local anesthetic action of ethyl bromide, and the insecticide properties of various chlorinated hydrocarbons are due to *structurally nonspecific action, to sheer accumulation* in the nerve cells, disorganizing, thereby, the respiratory and other metabolic processes and bringing the conduction of nerve impulses to a standstill. If the substance is volatile enough or sufficiently soluble in water (as is the case for the commonly used general anesthetics), it is rapidly deleted from the tissue biophase, with resumption of the blocked physiological reactions, as soon as the concentration in the surrounding medium falls. In other words, the Ferguson-type structurally nonspecific and chemically inert biological depressants act as foreign bodies at the molecular level. The narcotic or toxic effect takes place as soon as a specific fraction of the total cell or membrane volume is occupied by the foreign molecules; it follows that compounds of very different types may bring about the same biological effect. Many Ferguson-type biological depressants probably accumulate as clathrate-type hydrates (such as the noble gases; see previous section), while others which possess appreciable liposolubility may accumulate more specifically in the membranes proper.

There is a consensus nevertheless that, except perhaps for such highly inert substances as the noble gases, a favorable balance of polar and nonpolar groups is a dominant molecular characteristic for membrane permeation by most organic substances. Moreover, it is implicit in the existence of membrane pores (which have given sizes) that the molecular size and shape of the penetrating molecular species are also important factors to be considered. In some investigations on permeability the molecular size factor is introduced into the calculations as the molecular weight or the molar volume. It has to be also borne in mind that there are different kinds of biological membranes with permeability properties favoring one or another type of chemical structure. Also, the membrane permeation considered here is of the simplest type, in which expenditure of chemical energy is not required; the substances penetrating through biological membranes do so purely by way of diffusion. However, the transport of certain inorganic ions (such as $Na^{\oplus}$ and $K^{\oplus}$) and also of certain nonelectrolytes through membranes are energy-consuming processes and involve complex, still largely unknown, molecular pumping mechanisms; the functioning of these appears to depend on the activity of sulfhydryl groups in the membrane structure. Membrane transport which proceeds purely by diffusion is termed *passive transport*, while that requiring energy expenditure is termed *active transport*.

Consider now briefly the processes of pore and lipoid permeation. In pure pore permeability the molecules penetrating the membrane do not actually leave the water phase. They move by diffusion through the water-filled pores which have diameters which are large compared to the molecular size of the diffusing molecules. Since the latter do not penetrate the lipid phase of the membrane proper, the partition coefficient does not enter into the expression of permeability, and the following relationship is found to hold:

$$P\sqrt{M} = \text{constant} \tag{38}$$

Here P is the permeability of the membrane (*i.e.*, the net number of moles of solute passing through a unit area of membrane, per concentration difference expressed in moles per liter, per second), and M is the molecular weight of the diffusing species. The permeability constant characterizes here the pore size; the more permeable a membrane is, the greater the constant (depending on the case, values between about 5 and 120 have been found for biological membranes). Equation (38) clearly shows that pore permeability varies inversely with the molecular weight (*i.e.*, with the molecular size).

In lipoid permeability, on the other hand, the permeating molecules actually pass from the aqueous phase into the lipoprotein phase constituting the membrane. Thus, the molecules must be adsorbed to the lipoprotein membrane surface. This results in an increase of concentration at the membrane as compared to the concentration in the bulk phase. Since energy was expended by concentrating the solute at the membrane, the ratio of the two concentrations equals the corresponding distribution of energy, *i.e.*, the Boltzmann factor:

$$C_m/C_b = e^{-E/RT} \tag{39}$$

from which the energy of adsorption E (calories per mole) may be calculated (omitting the negative sign) as:

$$E = RT(\ln C_m - \ln C_b) \tag{40}$$

where $\ln C_m$ and $\ln C_b$ are the natural logarithms of the concentrations in the membrane and in the bulk phase (in moles per liter), T is the absolute temperature, and R is the gas constant (1.987 cal/°C). The energy of adsorption may simply be regarded as the result of hydrophobic bonding at work.

Resistance to membrane penetration by way of lipoid permeability may arise for two reasons: (a) the energy of adsorption is small; this amounts to saying that the molecules have difficulty in passing the water $\rightarrow$ lipid interface; (b) the molecules which already passed into the membrane have a tendency to remain in it, which is the same as saying that there is resistance to permeation at the lipid $\rightarrow$ water interface (at the interior surface of the membrane.) Let us consider case (b) first. Adsorbed molecules will tend to remain in the membrane if the lipid-water partition coefficient is high. Thus, the partition coefficient is a quantity which is inversely proportional with the permeability constant. Hence, for case (b) of lipoid permeability Eq. (38) becomes:

$$\frac{P\sqrt{M}}{B} = \text{constant} \tag{41}$$

where B is the partition coefficient of the substance, between *e.g.*, olive oil–water.

Examine now case (a). The success of the molecules to pass the water → lipid interface (at the exterior surface of the membrane) is indicated by the increase of concentration in the membrane relative to the concentration in the bulk phase. Increase of the ratio of these two concentrations amounts, therefore, to an increase of the permeability constant. Furthermore, the partition coefficient must be preserved in the equation, since also in this instance the passage through the lipid → water interface must be taken into account. Remembering that the ratio of the two concentrations equals the Boltzmann factor [Eq. (39)], Eq. (41) now becomes Danielli's formula:

$$\frac{P\sqrt{M} \cdot e^{2500x/RT}}{B} = \text{constant} \tag{42}$$

where 2500 is the average energy of adsorption (in calories) of one CH_2 group, and x is the number of CH or CH_2 groups, to which no polar atom is linked, in the permeating molecule.

An equation describing the relationship between partition coefficients of chemically related or homologous compounds was worked out recently by Hansch and his associates. Since the movement of a substance between "aqueous" and "organic" phases is an equilibrium process:

$$\text{substance in} \atop \text{"aqueous" phase} \quad \underset{k_z}{\overset{k_m}{\rightleftharpoons}} \quad \text{substance in} \atop \text{"organic" phase}$$

the partition coefficient B can be defined as an equilibrium constant $B = k_m/k_z$. Therefore, Hansch describes the partition coefficient of a series of substituted or homologous compounds as a function of the partition coefficient of the parent compound of the series, as patterned on the Hammett equation (see Suppletory Note 2) which relates in a similar way the electronic effects of substituents to the rates or equilibria of organic reactions. The Hansch equation states that:

$$\log\left(\frac{B_x}{B_H}\right) = k_p \cdot \pi \tag{43}$$

where B_x represents the partition coefficient of a substituted member of the series considered, B_H the partition coefficient of the parent compound, k_p is a constant dependent on the nature of the phases employed in the measurement of the B values (by definition $k_p = 1$ for n-octanol-water), and π a substituent constant, which will be called the *Hansch constant*, which represents the ability of a substituent or grouping to influence the partition coefficient. For n-octanol-water partitions, Eq. (43) may be simply written as:

$$\log B_x - \log B_H = \pi \tag{44}$$

Furthermore, for compounds which ionize in water it is more correct to take into account the dissociation constant α at the concentration of the substance in the water phase. Thus, the partition coefficient becomes, in general:

$$B = \frac{C_{octanol}}{C_{H_2O}(1 - \alpha)} \tag{45}$$

It should be noted that it is probably more correct to approximate the partition coefficient of a compound in the organic-aqueous biophases by using an octanol-water system, rather than an olive oil-water system which was the choice of the earlier investigators, since in the light of present knowledge on cell constituents, the physical properties of cellular lipids are more comparable to those of long-chain aliphatic alcohols.

The π constants are additive, so that $\log B_x$ can be estimated in a series of homologs. The additive character of π or $\log B$ is illustrated as follows:

$$\log B_{\text{2-naphthoxyacetic acid}} - \log B_{\text{phenoxyacetic acid}} = \pi_{(-CH=CH-)_2} = 1.27$$

An essentially identical value is obtained for $\pi_{(-CH=CH-)_2}$ when it is calculated from the corresponding hydrocarbons:

$$\log B_{\text{naphthalene}} - \log B_{\text{benzene}} = \pi_{(-CH=CH-)_2} = 1.24$$

The magnitude of variations of π in condensed aromatic compounds is exemplified below:

	$\log B$	$\pi_{(-CH=CH-)_2}$
Benzene	2.13 ± 0.01	
Naphthalene	3.37 ± 0.01	1.24
Anthracene	4.45 ± 0.05	1.08
Phenanthrene	4.46 ± 0.04	1.09

The following example illustrates how $\log B$ values may be calculated taking advantage of the additivity of π:

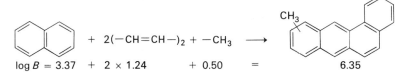

$$\log B = 3.37 \quad + \quad 2 \times 1.24 \quad\quad + 0.50 \quad\quad = \quad\quad 6.35$$

Similarly the approximate π values of longer alkyl chains may be calculated; for example, an ethyl group has $\pi = 1.00$.

The π values obtained for a given substituent from two series of compounds (e.g., phenols and 4-dimethylaminoazobenzene derivatives) differ, and the difference is proportional with the Hammett constant (σ) of the group. The π values of a given substituent in two series of compounds are related as $\pi_1 - \pi_2 = \Delta\pi = k \cdot \sigma$. Thus if the π values of a few substituents are known in both series, and also the σ constants of these substituents, then k (the slope) can be determined by plotting $\Delta\pi$ against σ.

The Hansch constant was used as an essential molecular parameter in an interesting method called $\rho\text{-}\sigma\text{-}\pi$ *analysis*. This method appears to be surprisingly successful in correlating chemical structure with biological activity in such a wide variety of biological responses as toxicity of benzoic acids to mosquito larvae, toxicity of phenyl ethyl phosphate insecticides toward houseflies, activity of substituted phenols and chloromycetin analogs against different gram-positive and gram-negative bacteria, thyroid activity of thyroxine derivatives in rodents, the plant-growth hormone activity of phenoxyacetic acids, the local anesthetic action of diethylaminoethyl benzoates in the guinea pig, and the carcinogenic activity of azo dyes and polycyclic aromatic hydrocarbons toward rats and mice.

The rate-limiting conditions for different biological responses to chemical agents may be defined in general terms as:

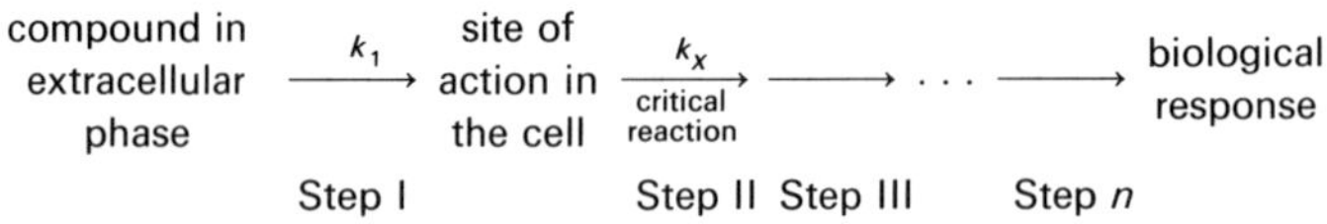

The constant k_1 indicates the rate at which a substance reaches the cellular site or sites of action (called *receptor sites*). This rate is a function of the Hansch constant and there is an optimum value for π (a π_0 value), representing the ideal lipo-hydrophilic character which assures a maximum rate for a given situation. Any increase or decrease from this optimum value, π_0, will result in a slower rate of movement of the molecule by serial adsorption-desorption processes across the many intracellular membrane boundaries through which the receptor sites are attained.

The constant k_x is the equilibrium or rate constant of the interaction of the molecule with the receptor site. Indeed, it is reasonable to assume that for many types of biologically active molecules there is one key reaction with the receptor site, which reaction is rate controlling for the elicitation of the biological response. Thus, the reactions which may occur subsequently to the critical one (Steps III to n), before the visible biological response is elicited, can be neglected in a first approximation. The rate of reaction with the receptor site is determined by the nature or chemical type of the reaction which occurs, and by the electronic characteristics (the relative chemical reactivity) of the interacting group or groups of the active molecule. Now, since the biological activity of a compound is usually compared to the activity of other substances in a given series of compounds, the constant k_x may be taken equal to the $\rho \cdot \sigma$ product of the Hammett equation (see Suppletory Note 2); this is based on the assumption that the low activity or inactivity of the parent compound of a chemical series of graded activities is due to the fact that, for the critical reaction Step II, the compound has a $\log k_x = 0$. Furthermore, since the parameter ρ is constant for a given chemical reaction type, it can be readily seen that π and σ are the major parameters which determine the relative effectiveness of members of a given series of biologically active compounds.

Assuming normal distribution of the k_1 rate constant as a function of π, that is, that the rate of movement to the receptor site decreases exponentially with the square of the difference $\pi - \pi_0$ (Fig. 51), Hansch obtained the expression:

$$\log A = -k\pi^2 + k'\pi + \rho \cdot \sigma + k'' \tag{46}$$

Here A is the activity of a particular compound in bringing about the type of biological response studied; π is determined experimentally from the partition coefficient of the particular compound and the partition coefficient of the parent compound of the series, or in some cases it may be calculated taking advantage of the additivity of π (see above); σ values may be found tabulated in the literature,[*] and for poly-substituted compounds the σ values of the individual substituents are simply summed. The "best set"

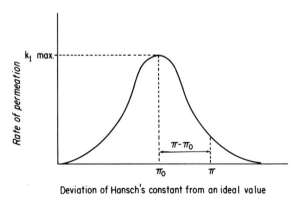

Deviation of Hansch's constant from an ideal value

Fig. 51.

[*] See, *e.g.*, H. H. Jaffé, *Chem. Rev.* **53**, 191 (1953).

of the four constants, k, k', ρ, and k'' are evaluated by the method of least squares from the known π, σ, and A values of several known members of the series studied, using the statistical procedure known as multiple regression analysis.* The activity A is often expressed in terms of the concentration necessary to bring about a constant equivalent response (e.g., LD_{50}, isotoxic concentration, ED_{50} for local anesthetic action, percentage of plant growth) obtained in an arbitrary fixed time interval. However, activity is inversely proportional to the concentration necessary to produce a given equivalent biological response, since any agent is regarded as being more active the smaller the concentration necessary to bring about the response. Thus, in such instances, $\log A$ is replaced by $\log 1/C$. Often A is expressed as *relative* activity or rank in a given series of compounds for a particular biological response; for example, the different "carcinogenicity indexes" of carcinogenic compounds are relative activities given in arbitrary scales (Section 4.3.6.2).

3.3.3 CHARGE-TRANSFER BOND

The dark blue linear tubular inclusion compounds of iodine and the black bromine or iodine-hydrocarbon complexes described in the previous section exemplify not only particular kinds of inclusion compounds, but represent also instances of a special type of secondary valence bond, called the *charge-transfer bond*. Probably the very great majority of the highly colored molecular complexes, vaguely termed in the earlier chemical literature as molecular addition complexes, are actually charge-transfer complexes. In charge-transfer there is partial transfer of *one* electron only from the donor D to a partly filled or empty orbital of the acceptor molecule A. This partial transfer can be represented in terms of resonance such as:

$$D\cdot + \cdot A \rightleftharpoons [D\cdot \ \cdot A]_t \longleftrightarrow D^{\oplus} \ :A^{\ominus}$$

where the first step corresponds to the reversible, temperature-dependent formation of a transition complex $[D\cdot\cdot A]_t$ through intermolecular resonance attraction not involving electron transfer (Section 3.3.4) and through electrostatic dipole-dipole attraction (Section 3.3.5.4); this is then followed by the actual partial electron transfer represented by the resonance transition $\longleftrightarrow$. The transferred electron resonates between the acceptor and donor, and the corresponding resonance energy is the binding force. Donors are classified as π donors or n donors according to whether the electron transferred originates from the π-electron system of the donor or is a localized

---

* C. A. Bennett, and N. L. Franklin, "Statistical Analysis in Chemistry and the Chemical Industry." Wiley, New York, 1954, p. 286.

nonbonding p electron of an atom of the donor molecule (such as the free doublets of N, O, and S). Acceptors should contain electron-attracting substituents, such as chloro, bromo, nitro, nitroso, cyano, and keto groups, atoms with unfilled orbitals, or atoms which contain octets that can be "expanded." Picric acid, trinitrobenzene, tetranitromethane, chloranil, benzoquinone, tetracyanoethylene, $AlCl_3$, $FeCl_3$, $SbCl_5$ are typical charge-transfer acceptors.

The electronic conditions which must be met for charge-transfer complex formation are then very similar to those required for coordination complex formation (Section 3.1.2.8). However, while in the latter there is electron-pair donation, in the former only one electron is transferred (see above). There are borderline cases (such as, for example, the π complexes of metals), however, where it is difficult to ascertain the true character of the newly formed molecular species. True charge-transfer may be regarded as an intermolecular one-electron bond (Sections 3.1.2.7 and 3.2.1), or it may also be regarded as resembling a Lewis acid-base reaction.

Qualitative indication of charge-transfer is sometimes provided by solubility studies. A dramatic illustration is the fact that benzene and other aromatics are appreciably soluble in liquid anhydrous HF, whereas alkanes and cycloparaffins are virtually insoluble. The solubility of benzene may be accounted for by the charge-transfer:

$$C_6H_6 + HF \longleftrightarrow [C_6H_6 \cdot H]^{\oplus} \quad |\overline{F}|^{\ominus}$$

Most common experimental evidence for charge-transfer is, however, the usual appearance of an intense, broad absorption band, characteristic of the composite system and not of either component taken separately. The charge-transfer band of many complexes is in the visible region; these are highly colored compounds. For example, the chocolate brown, purple, or black picrates of higher aromatic polycyclic hydrocarbons and the dark green aluminum trichloride complexes of many aromatics are well known. In other instances, however, charge-transfer is indicated by the appearance of a new band in the ultraviolet region. In self-complexes, where donor and acceptor molecules are the same, the charge-transfer absorption band occurs usually at higher frequencies than in heterocomplexes. Self-complexing, which results in the stacking of planar molecules like piles of coins, is believed to play a major role in holding together crystals of many planar aromatic compounds. Thus, a special feature of π complexes is that there must be a planar molecular adlineation between the partners, the donor and acceptor molecules lying parallel above and below each other. This position assures maximum contact, since the p_z orbitals from which the π electrons of the donor originate have axes *perpendicular* to the σ-bond frame (Section 3.1.2.2). In planar complexes there is a slight sidewise displacement of the molecular planes from exact superposition, which is necessary to permit maximum overlap of the p_z orbitals. Because close molecular adlineation is so important, the formation of charge-transfer complexing with planar poly-cyclic aromatic hydrocarbons is sensitive to substitution by long or bulky aliphatic chains or to other structural features which constitute a hindrance to adlineation and increase the distance between the donor and the acceptor. Conversely, the stability of the π complexes generally increases with the increase of the molecular size and with the number of methyl substituents, provided that the methyl substituent is not positioned so as to decrease coplanarity. Evidence has been accumulating in recent years that charge-transfer is an important reaction in biological systems involving aromatic and heteroaromatic ring compounds (purines, pyrimidines, flavins, aromatic amino acids, etc.). ESR spectrometry (see Suppletory Note 4 for Section 3.2), which is a unique tool for the study of free radicals and ionic species in the presence of high concentrations of other molecules, has been increasingly used in recent years for the detection of charge-transfer phenomena in biological systems.

Just as the light absorption of single molecules, the absorption of charge-transfer complexes is due to characteristic excited states. The energy content of the charge-transfer excited states may be understood from the following *hypothetical* considerations. In the process of electron transfer a single electron is removed from the donor, raised to the energy level of the acceptor molecule, and following total transfer of the electron, $D^{\oplus}A^{\ominus}$ dissociates into separate ions $D^{\oplus}$ and $A^{\ominus}$, which is also an energy-requiring process. The energy necessary to remove a single electron from the donor is its ionization potential I_P, the tendency of the acceptor to accept an electron is measured by its electron affinity E_A, and the energy which would be required to dissociate $D^{\oplus}A^{\ominus}$ into separate ions is W. Thus, the energy E (which equals $h\nu$) of a charge-transfer transition is:

$$E = h\nu = I_P - (E_A + W) \tag{47}$$

where ν is the frequency of the main absorption band. The quantities I_P and E_A may be measured experimentally or their magnitudes approximated by wave mechanical calculations. The value of W has been obtained from empirical calculation for some complexes; for donors with ionization potentials of 8–10 ev $W = 3.3$–3.8 ev. If the difference energy between the ground level I_P and the excited level $-(E_A + W)$ is small, the absorption band is in the visible; if it is large, then the absorption band will be in the ultraviolet. Similarly as for single molecules, the oscillator strength of charge-transfer complexes may be calculated using Eq. (35).

The quantities I_P and E_A are often useful because they indicate whether a particular compound will be donor or acceptor in charge-transfer with a given partner. The lower the value of I_P the more likely that the compound will act as a strong donor and the higher the E_A the more likely it will be a good acceptor. A convenient way to obtain an I_P value involves the measurement of the absorption spectrum of the charge-transfer complex formed by the compound with a given electron acceptor in solution. The calculation of I_P is carried out with the linear relation established by Foster:

$$I_P = a + b \cdot E_{CT} \tag{48}$$

where E_{CT} is the transition energy (see Section 3.2.2 and Suppletory Note 3 for Section 3.2) corresponding to the maximum absorption point of the charge-transfer band (expressed in electron volts; 1 ev = 23.06 kcal/mole), using a given acceptor. In general, the smaller the value of E_{CT} the greater the electron-donor ability of a compound. The constants, a (intercept) and b (slope), vary with the nature of the acceptor used for the evaluation of the I_P values. These constants can be readily evaluated graphically by plotting the transition energies of charge-transfer complexes between the acceptor to be used and a series of compounds with known I_P values, against these I_P values; for example, for chloranil, $a = 5.13$ ev and $b = 1.12$. The electron affinity values are more difficult to obtain. For the polycyclic aromatic hydrocarbons a rough value of E_A may be calculated from the I_P, because the molecular electronegativities of these compounds are constant:

$$\frac{I_P + E_A}{2} \approx 4.07 \pm 0.05 \text{ ev}$$

It will be recalled (Section 3.1.2.3) that the average of the ionization potential and the electron affinity is one measure of the electronegativity. The linearity of the I_P versus E_{CT} plot is particularly interesting because it seems to indicate that the dominant factor in charge-transfer is the ionization potential of the donor.

While the ionization potentials of most substances can readily be determined from the absorption spectra, the electron affinities are difficult to determine in most cases. However, by wave mechanical procedures it is possible to calculate the distribution of electronic energy levels to obtain the corresponding information. The LCAO method (see Section 3.1.2.1) yields the energy of the molecular orbitals for a *single* mobile or π electron, in the form:

$$E = \alpha + k \cdot \beta \tag{49}$$

[compare α in this equation to 2α in Eq. (13) which gives the energy of a bonding electron *pair*; in Section 3.1.2.1]. In Eq. (49) the value of β is taken to be about -55 to -60 kcal $\approx$ 2–3 ev, called the *spectroscopic* β. For the present purpose also, as in the calculation of π bond energies (Section 3.1.2.1), α is taken as the zero level of energy; this means that when $k = 0$ then $E = \alpha$. Thus, k runs parallel with the energy level; positive values of k correspond to filled (bonding) orbitals, negative values of k correspond to "empty" (antibonding) orbitals. Therefore, the lowest positive value of k which can be calculated in a molecule gives the relative value of the ionization potential of that molecule in a series of related compounds; thus the smaller the lowest positive value of k in a molecule, the greater the electron-donor capacity. Conversely, the smallest negative value of k in a molecule (which corresponds to the lowest empty molecular orbital) is a measure of the relative value of the electron affinity; the smaller the value of the smallest negative k (*i.e.*, the closer it is to zero), the greater the electron affinity of the molecule. Table XIII gives the listing of the $+k$ and $-k$ values of a series of biologically important compounds. For $+k$ (and $-k$), values of the order of 0.500 mean that the substance is a moderately effective donor (or acceptor); values about 0.200–0.100 indicate that the substance is a strong donor (or acceptor). Some exceptionally good donors have $+k$ values even lower than zero and so have a negative sign.

Table XIII

Electron Donor and Acceptor Ability of Some Biologically Important Compounds[a]

Compound	Energy of highest occupied molecular orbital $+k$	Energy of lowest empty molecular orbital $-k$
Adenine	0.486	-0.865
Guanine	0.307	-1.050
Hypoxanthine	0.402	-0.882
Xanthine (purine 7-N is NH)	0.397	-1.197
Xanthine (purine 9-N is NH)	0.442	-1.005
Uric acid	0.172	-1.194
Guanine		
1-methyl-	0.303	-1.064
9-methyl-	0.302	-1.074

Table XIII (continued)

Compound	Energy of highest occupied molecular orbital $+k$	Energy of lowest empty molecular orbital $-k$
Xanthine (purine 7-N is NH)		
1-methyl-	0.397	−1.198
3-methyl-	0.354	−1.197
9-methyl-	0.394	−1.213
Xanthine (purine 9-N is NH)		
1-methyl-	0.442	−1.009
3-methyl-	0.395	−1.009
7-methyl-	0.429	−1.041
Uric acid		
1-methyl-	0.172	−1.201
3-methyl-	0.153	−1.204
7-methyl-	0.133	−1.200
9-methyl-	0.161	−1.204
Uracil	0.597	−0.960
Thymine	0.510	−0.958
Cytosine	0.595	−0.795
5-Methylcytosine	0.530	−0.796
Barbituric acid	1.033	−1.295
Alloxan	1.033	−0.757
Phenylalanine[b]	0.908	−0.993
Tyrosine[c]	0.792	−1.000
Histidine[d]	0.660	−1.160
Tryptophan[e]	0.534	−0.863
Riboflavin[f]	0.500	−0.344
Pteridine	0.864	−0.386
2-Amino-4-hydroxypteridine	0.489	−0.650
2,4-Diaminopteridine	0.544	−0.508
2,4-Dihydroxypteridine	0.653	−0.663
Folic acid	0.526	−0.647

[a] From B. Pullman and A. Pullman, *Proc. Natl. Acad. Sci. U.S.* **44**, 1197 (1958).
[b] The π-electron system of this molecule is assumed to be that of toluene.
[c] The π-electron system of this molecule is assumed to be that of phenol.
[d] The π-electron system of this molecule is assumed to be that of imidazole.
[e] The π-electron system of this molecule is assumed to be that of indole.
[f] The π-electron system of this molecule is assumed to be that of isoalloxazine.

3.3.4 Intermolecular Resonance Attraction and Energy Transfer

The resonance excitation energy from one aromatic molecule can be transmitted to another aromatic molecule if there is a matching of energy levels (Section 3.2.3.3). This means that there is an overlapping between the fluorescence emission versus wave number profile (representing singlet excited state → ground state transitions) of the energy donor molecule and the light absorption versus wave number profile (ground state → singlet excited state transitions) of the energy acceptor molecule. For example, Fig. 52A shows the fluorescence emission spectrum of the amino acid, tryptophan (having an indole ring), and superimposed on it the light absorp-

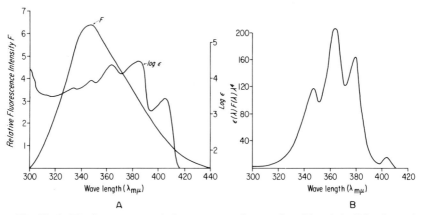

Fig. 52. A. The fluorescence emission spectrum of tryptophan (F) and the light absorption spectrum of 3,4-benzopyrene (log ε). B. The values of the $\varepsilon(\lambda) \cdot F(\lambda)\lambda^4$ overlap plotted against the wave length. [From J. B. Birks, *Nature* **190**, 232 (1961).]

tion spectrum of the polycyclic aromatic hydrocarbon, 3,4-benzopyrene. The degree of spectral overlap, called the *intermolecular resonance overlap integral* (J) is a measure of the matching of the transition energy levels and, thus, determines the rate of transfer of the π-excitation energy from the donor to the acceptor; the greater the overlap, the greater the probability of energy transfer. This integral, which is somewhat reminiscent of the expression of the oscillator strength (Section 3.2.3.4) is defined as:

$$J = \int_0^\infty \varepsilon(\bar{v})F(\bar{v})(1/\bar{v}^4)(v_2 - v_1) \tag{50}$$

where $\varepsilon(\bar{v})$ is the molar absorption coefficient of the acceptor and $F(\bar{v})$ the molar fluorescence emission coefficient of the donor at the same $\bar{v}$ median wave number of the segment considered, having the edges v_2 and v_1. Figure 52B shows the overlap spectrum of tryptophan and 3,4-benzopyrene.

In addition to the overlap integral J, the probability of energy transfer also depends on the distance R between the molecules and the average lifetime τ of the excited state [see Eqs. (51) and (52) below], and on the relative position of the two molecules. However, because of the rotations of these, the statistical average of different positions must be considered:

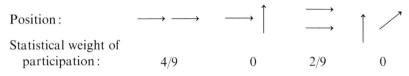

Position:

Statistical weight of
   participation: 4/9   0   2/9   0

The weights add up to two thirds, which means that only this fraction of the excitation energy may be transmitted for a given J, R, and τ.

An important consequence of the resonance transfer is that as the result of the electromagnetic coupling there is an intermolecular attraction between acceptor and donor molecules. This attraction is assumed to exist even in the resonant ground state, since, following wave mechanics, molecules in the ground state possess a zero point energy (Section 3.2.3.3). Resonance attraction is usually not large because it is not too frequent that the excitation energy levels of two molecular species are closely matched. A special example of this type of phenomenon occurs in arrays of *identical* molecules where the energy levels are perfectly matched. Very strong attraction forces can operate between identical large molecules containing π-electron systems and having large oscillator strength. This is actually shown by the high degree of poly-merization of different dyes (*e.g.*, cyanin polymers of Scheibe) in dilute solutions, in spite of the electrostatic repulsion between the constituent monomers having ionic charges. It is possible, that similarly, strong attrac-tion forces operate between large biological macromolecules or polymacro-molecular assemblies or arrays. In addition, the resonance forces between macromolecules, in which the π-electron distribution is identical, may be highly specific and possibly play a significant role in the synchronized, orderly alignment of proteins and nucleic acids during cell division.

Resonance attraction is a likely candidate to be the operating force in "long range" interactions between macromolecules, since distances of the order of 30 Å or higher are commonly found to be the characteristic inter-molecular distances through which energy transfer operates even *in small molecules*. According to Förster's theory the characteristic distance R between donor and acceptor, at which the probability of transfer and fluorescence emission without transfer are equal, is:

$$R = \left[\frac{1660}{n^2} \cdot \frac{\tau J}{\left(\dfrac{v_a + v_d}{2} \right)^2} \right]^{1/6} \times 10^{-6} \, \text{cm} \qquad (51)$$

where n is the refractive index of the solvent, τ the lifetime of the excited state, and v_a and v_d the wave number maxima of the acceptor and donor, respectively (the wave numbers corresponding to the short wavelength edge of the absorption and fluorescence emission profiles). The lifetime τ of the state of fluorescence can be calculated from the absorption of the lowest frequency electronic band (first excited state) of the donor with the formula:

$$\frac{1}{\tau} \cong 2.88 \times 10^{-9} \bar{v}^2 n^2 \varepsilon(\bar{v})(v_2 - v_1) \tag{52}$$

3.3.5 ELECTROSTATIC INTERACTIONS

Electrostatic attraction between unlike charges and repulsion between like charges are the basis of the most common type of interactions between molecules. Electrostatic forces obey Coulomb's law, hence they are also called *Coulomb forces*. Coulomb forces are operative up to distances of several angstroms between the centers of the charges. The simplest type of electrostatic interaction is between ions, which are *point charges* since the electric charge may be regarded as being concentrated in one point in the center of the particle. Electrostatic interactions between more complex charges (permanent and induced dipoles) may be understood as the summation of the individual point charge interactions.

The potential energy E between two mutually attractive charges $+e$ and $-e$ is directly proportional with their product and inversely proportional with the distance between them, $-(e^2/r)$. This term, written in the form $-e \cdot (e/r)$ makes it apparent that the potential energy may be regarded as being due to the interaction of one charge with the *field strength* e/r of the other point charge. From elementary physics, energy = force × distance; thus, the attractive force between the charges is $-(e^2/r)/r = -e^2/r^2$ which is the well-known form of Coulomb's law (see also Suppletory Note 1 for Section 3.1).

Now, in interacting molecules or particles the electric charges may be centered in more than one focus, and, furthermore, each focus may contain more than one unit charge e. The total energy of interaction is the algebraic sum of the interaction energies between pairs of charge foci, that is

$$\sum -\frac{Z_a \cdot Z_b \cdot e^2}{r_{ab}}$$

Here Z_a is the number of unit charges in one charge focus of one of the interacting partners and Z_b is the corresponding number in the other interacting partner; in the case of a simple ion pair Z_a and Z_b are the number of valences of the two ions. For an ion pair the *minimum* distance between the charge centers is the sum of the ionic radii, $r_a + r_b$.

Between the three types of electric charge distributions (ion or point charge, permanent dipole, and induced dipole) there are six possible combinations for electrostatic interaction: ion–ion, ion–dipole, dipole–dipole, ion-induced dipole, dipole-induced dipole, and two mutually induced dipoles. A synoptic tabulation of these interactions, and the order of magnitude of the interaction energy between the partners is given in Table XIV. Examples of all these combinations are known. However, no sharp distinction can be made between types, and frequently several of these interactions are involved simultaneously between molecules.

Table XIV
Synoptic Table of Electrostatic Interactions

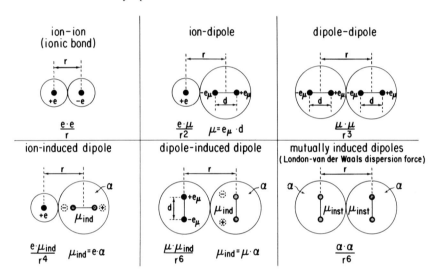

3.3.5.1   Ion–Ion Interactions

Attraction between ions represents the electrovalent or ionic bond (Sections 3.1.2.1 and 3.1.2.3), also called *salt linkage*. Ionic attraction is the basis of the energy which gives the cohesiveness to the crystals of ionic solids. Ionic attraction operates between simple ions, such as $Na^{\oplus}Cl^{\ominus}$ or $Mg^{2\oplus}2Cl^{\ominus}$, as well as between amphoteric ions; for example, the crystals of amino acids are held together by attraction between the juxtaposed amphoteric ions. As in any other type of chemical bonding, energy is released in ionic bonding; *i.e.*, this amount of energy must be contributed to pull two ions apart. Unlike the covalent bonding power of an electron, however, the ionic bonding power of electric charges is never saturated in crystals of finite size. The amount of energy released when positive and negative ions condense to form one mole of an ionic crystalline solid is called the *lattice energy* of that ionic compound.

When the interionic attraction is considered in solution, the simple Coulomb law is complicated by the fact that molecules of the solvent tend to place themselves between oppositely charged ion pairs, that is, tend to separate them. This tendency of the solvent molecules is directly proportional to the solvent's dielectric constant which is a measure of its polar character (see Suppletory Note 10 for Section 3.1). Hence, the dielectric constant ε of the solvent must be incorporated into the Coulomb formula as a multiplier of the interionic distance in the denominator. The interaction energy, per mole, is then given by:

$$E = \sum -\frac{N \cdot Z_a \cdot Z_b \cdot e^2 \times 10^{-12}}{\varepsilon \cdot r_{ab}(4.18)} \tag{53}$$

assuming that the ions approach from large distances. The energy E is obtained in kilocalories when the unit charge is given as $e = 4.8 \times 10^{-10}$ electrostatic unit, and r is in angstroms; N is the Avogadro number.

It can be seen from Eq. (53) that in solvents of high dielectric constant, the interaction energy is considerably influenced by this parameter. Pure water has a dielectric constant close to 80. However, in polyelectrolyte solutions (such as in the presence of proteins) the effective dielectric constant of water is decreased in the steric proximity (less than 15 Å) of the ionizing groups of the solute, because these groups orient the water dipoles around them. Corrected values of the dielectric constant of water, valid for $r \approx 5$–10 Å, may be obtained using the relation $\varepsilon = 6r - 11$.

3.3.5.2 Ion–Dipole and Dipole–Dipole Interactions

These interactions are responsible for the dissolution of ionic solids and polar non-ionic solids in polar solvents. For example, the dissolution of $Na^{\oplus}Cl^{\ominus}$ in water is due to the fact that the ions freed from the crystal lattice are hydrated and the energy liberated (per mole) in the hydration reaction (*hydration energy*) is greater than the lattice energy of the solid. The force holding the cluster of water molecules (*hydration layer*) around ions is due to electrostatic ion–dipole attraction:

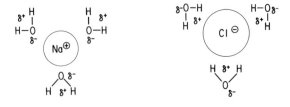

However, the hydration of some alkali metal ions may also be regarded as a coordination reaction (see Section 3.1.2.8), for example:

$$Li^{\oplus} + 4\,|\overset{H}{\underset{H}{O}}| \longrightarrow \left[\begin{array}{c} H\diagdown\;\diagup H \\ O \\ H\diagdown \quad \downarrow \quad \diagup H \\ |O \rightarrow Li \leftarrow O| \\ H \diagup \quad \uparrow \quad \diagdown H \\ O \\ H \diagup \diagdown H \end{array} \right]^{\oplus}$$

Dipole–dipole attraction explains why polar organic compounds are soluble in polar solvents. The mechanism of dissolution is essentially identical to that of ionic solids: if the *solvation energy* is greater than the energy of mutual attraction of the molecules in the crystal lattice, dissolution effectively takes place. It will be recalled that the dipole moment is the consequence of the existence of partially polarized bonds in the molecules (Section 3.1.2.3). Dipole–dipole attraction is the main force of cohesion in the crystals of polar molecules, and it plays a major role in the adsorption of various compounds to solid surfaces (*e.g.*, chromatography, heterogeneous catalysis, and also the adsorption of dyes to fibers).

Table XIV shows that the binding energy between an ion and a dipole, and between a dipole and a dipole varies inversely with the second and third power of the distance, respectively. The $1/r^2$ and $1/r^3$ terms arise as a result of carrying out the summation of the individual point charge interaction energies. In the interaction between an ion and a dipole the two partners are, on the average, positioned so as to result in attraction, since this corresponds to the lowest energy of the system. The interaction energy contains then two terms. The first term represents the attraction between the ion and the charge having the opposite sign in the dipole, and the second term represents the repulsion between the ion and the like charge in the dipole; the net attraction energy is the algebraic sum of the two terms. It may be readily seen from Table XIV that:

$$E = -\frac{e \cdot e_\mu}{r - d/2} + \frac{e \cdot e_\mu}{r + d/2} = e \cdot e_\mu \frac{-(r + d/2) + (r - d/2)}{r^2 - d^2/4} \tag{54}$$

Remembering that $e_\mu \cdot d = \mu$, the dipole moment, we get

$$-\frac{e \cdot \mu}{r^2 - d^2/4}$$

However, since the dipole is usually small as compared to the distance separating the charges, the $d^2/4$ term may be neglected and the energy of attraction appears in the form $-[(e \cdot \mu)/r^2]$.

In an analogous way the dipole–dipole interaction energy contains four terms. Two of these represent the attraction between two pairs of + and − charges. The other two terms represent the repulsion between − and −, and between + and + charges. The net attraction energy is the algebraic sum of four terms as may be seen from Table XIV:

$$E = -\frac{e_\mu^2}{r-d} - \frac{e_\mu^2}{r+d} + \frac{e_\mu^2}{r} + \frac{e_\mu^2}{r} \tag{55}$$

Carrying out the summation, the energy of attraction appears as $-2(\mu^2/r^3)$. In analogy to the field strength of an ion, the field strength of a dipole is μ/r^3.

3.3.5.3   Ion-Induced Dipole and Dipole-Induced Dipole Interactions

A nonpolar molecule with no dipole moment becomes polarized and acquires an *induced dipole moment* in the vicinity of ions or of molecules with permanent dipole moments. The polarization is due to the *dissymmetry created in the electron cloud* of the nonpolar molecule by the electric field of the ion or the dipole, so that the center of the negative charges ceases to coincide with the center of the positive charges in the nucleus. *The orientation of the charges in the induced dipole is the mirror image of the charge distribution of the inducing charge.* If the inducing charge is a positive ion, the electron cloud is pulled toward the ion and so this end will be the negative pole of the induced dipole. If the inducing charge is a permanent dipole, the induced dipole will be oriented so that the opposite charges will face each other (Table XIV). This is because the appearance of the induced dipole gives rise to electrostatic attraction between the polarized molecule, on the one hand, and the inducing ion or dipole, on the other hand, and it is this orientation of the induced dipole which results in the greatest attraction (*i.e.*, corresponds to the lowest energy of the system). There are a number of complex ions which are held together by the attractive force existing between an ion and an induced dipole. For example, in the reaction:

$$I^\ominus + I_2 \longrightarrow I_3^\ominus$$

at least part of the bonding energy is due to ion-induced dipole attraction. The adsorption of conjugated aromatic compounds to fibers is due in a large part to dipole-induced dipole interactions. Since the moment of the induced dipole depends on the length of the conjugated chain of the inducing compound, adsorption is more pronounced for longer chain compounds. For example, the adsorption of stilbene by wool (from dry solvents) is high, but that of biphenyl, which is less conjugated, is negligible. There appears to be also some evidence that dipole-induced dipole attraction is a minor contributing factor in the stability of the quinol clathrates and hydrates (Section 3.3.2.3) of the relatively unreactive noble gases.

The magnitude of the induced dipole moment μ_{ind} depends on two factors: first, on the ease by which the electron cloud dissymmetry can be brought about (i.e., the polarizability α) and, second, on the magnitude of the inducing charge since the greater the magnitude of this charge the greater is the electron displacement. Hence, the induced moment $\mu_{ind} = e \cdot \alpha$ (or $\mu \cdot \alpha$), depending on whether the inducing charge is an ion or a permanent dipole. Since the charge distribution in an induced dipole is always the mirror image of the distribution of the inducing charge, the attraction energy can be regarded in a simple way as the product of the two field strengths. Thus, the energy of the ion-induced dipole attraction is of the order of $E = (e/r)(\mu_{ind}/r^3) = (e \cdot \mu_{ind})/r^4$ [or $(e^2\alpha)/r^4$] and the energy of the dipole-induced dipole attraction is $E = (\mu/r^3)(\mu_{ind}/r^3) = (\mu \cdot \mu_{ind}/r^6)$ [or $(\mu^2\alpha/r^6)$].

3.3.5.4 Induced Dipole-Induced Dipole Interactions

The induced dipole-induced dipole interactions are the basis of the true "van der Waals forces." The concept that attractive forces exist between electrically neutral atoms or molecules was proposed first by van der Waals in connection with the two corrective constants which were introduced into the equation of state of gases. The wave mechanical theory of these forces was worked out by London. Hence they are often called London forces or London–van der Waals *dispersion forces*.

The theoretical basis of the London forces is the wave mechanical concept that electronic quantum oscillators (atomic or molecular) have a zero point energy (see Section 3.2.3.3). That is, even in the ground state and at temperatures approaching absolute zero, the electrons in atoms or molecules have an energy of motion $\frac{1}{2}h\nu_0$ which cannot be lost. This means, that while a nonpolar molecule or neutral atom does not actually have a measurable dipole moment, the instantaneous pictures of the electron cloud, if such were possible, would reveal an array of dissymmetrical charge distributions (i.e., a series of oscillating instantaneous dipoles), which on the average cancel each other so that the resulting dipole moment is zero.

Accordingly, a simplified description of the nature of the van der Waals attraction may be formulated as follows. A neutral atom or molecule (say atom 1) possesses an instantaneous dipole oscillating with a frequency ν_0 and having a dipole moment μ_1, which represents a dipole field strength of μ_1/r^3. Now, if another neutral atom or molecule (say atom 2) is brought into the field of atom 1, the latter induces in atom 2 a dipole moment $(\alpha_2 \cdot \mu_1)/r^3$, where α_2 is the polarizability of atom 2 (remembering that dipole moment = polarizability × field strength). This dipole of atom 2 has an electric field of strength:

$$\frac{\alpha_2 \cdot \mu_1}{r^3} \bigg/ r^3 = \frac{\alpha_2 \cdot \mu_1}{r^6}$$

Since atom 1 is in the dipole field of atom 2, and since the electric field of the latter changes in phase with the varying dipole μ_1 of atom 1, the energy of attraction is:

$$E \approx \mu_1 \cdot \frac{\alpha_2 \cdot \mu_1}{r^6} = \frac{\alpha_2 \cdot \mu_1^2}{r^6} \tag{56}$$

However,

$$\mu_1^2 \approx \alpha_1 \cdot \tfrac{3}{2}hv_0 \tag{57}$$

where the field strength, which is the very cause of the existence of the instantaneous dipoles, is truly the zero point energy $\tfrac{1}{2}hv_0$ (taken three times to account for the electronic oscillations along the three coordinate axes in space). Substituting Eq. (57) into Eq. (56), and taking the expression with a negative sign, since it represents attraction energy, we get:

$$E \approx -\frac{3}{2} \cdot \frac{\alpha_1 \cdot \alpha_2}{r^6} \cdot hv_0 \tag{58}$$

Since the London force is due to the mutual perturbation of charges in adjacent atoms or molecules and to the resulting attraction between instantaneous opposite dipoles oscillating in phase, the attraction between two π-electronic systems owing to intermolecular resonance (Section 3.3.4) and the attraction between two such systems owing to the London force are closely related concepts. This is because in simple π-electronic systems the induced polarization is due largely to the displacement of π electrons.

For many atoms and molecules hv_0 is of the order of magnitude of the average ionization potentials ($\sim$10–20 ev) and of the average energy of the excited states (for the relation between ionization potentials and transition energies, see Section 3.3.3). Thus, an approximation for the London force between identical molecules may be written as:

$$E \approx -\frac{3}{2} \cdot \frac{\alpha^2}{r^6} \cdot \Delta E \approx -\frac{3}{2} \cdot \frac{\alpha^2}{r^6} \cdot I_P \tag{59}$$

and between molecules of two different molecular species as:

$$E \approx -\frac{3}{2} \cdot \frac{\alpha_1 \alpha_2}{r^6} \sqrt{\Delta E_1 \cdot \Delta E_2} \approx -\frac{3}{2} \cdot \frac{\alpha_1 \alpha_2}{r^6} \cdot \frac{I_{P_1} \cdot I_{P_2}}{I_{P_1} + I_{P_2}} \tag{60}$$

We have seen (see Suppletory Note 10 for Section 3.1) that the polarizability can be calculated from the intercept (the temperature-independent component) of the total molar polarization when plotted against the reciprocal of the absolute temperature. In practice, however, α is much easier to obtain since, following Maxwell's relation, the dielectric constant ε roughly equals the square of the refractive index, n, $\varepsilon \approx n^2$. Substitution into the Clausius–Mosotti equation [Eq. (b) of Suppletory Note] yields the *molar refraction*:

$$R = \frac{n^2 - 1}{n^2 + 2} \cdot \frac{M}{d} \tag{61}$$

That light energy induces the polarization of the molecular electron cloud has been discussed in connection with the Lewis–Calvin theory of light absorption (Section 3.2.3.3). Light energy has, however, not the same polarizing effect as a constant electric field or a field of low frequency, which are utilized in the determination of dielectric constants. In fact, while the electrons can follow the very rapid variations of the electromagnetic field of visible or even ultraviolet light energy, the inertia of the total molecular mass is too great for the whole molecules to follow these rapid variations. For this reason light energy is without effect on the permanent dipoles, and the orientation polarization (see Suppletory Note 10 for Section 3.1) is zero. Therefore, Eq. (c) in this Note now becomes:

$$R = \frac{4\pi N}{3} \alpha$$

from which

$$\alpha = \frac{3}{4\pi N} R \tag{62}$$

For the calculation of the intermolecular London force between biological macromolecules, Eq. (60) may now be considerably simplified. Since the ionization potentials of most atoms of importance in proteins and nucleic acids are close to 14 ev and the polarizability can be expressed by the molar refraction, by making the appropriate substitutions Eq. (60) becomes:

$$E = \frac{38,000}{r^6} R_1 \cdot R_2 \tag{63}$$

where R_1 and R_2 are the molar refractions of the two interacting molecular species.

It is clear from Maxwell's relation that the refraction of light is in close relation with the polarizability. This is because the alternating polarization of the electron cloud by the light energy produces a decrease of its propagation velocity and because the refractive index n is precisely the ratio of the velocities of light in two media. The greater is the number of electrons in the atomic shells (*i.e.*, the heavier the atom) so much greater will be the electrical dissymmetry created by the electromagnetic field of light and, consequently, so much larger is the refractive index. Obviously then the refractive index is a measure of the polarizability. The same logic indicates that for a given substance the refractive index increases with the decreasing wavelength of the light; in fact, a shorter wavelength means a greater energy hv which produces a greater polarization, and this results in turn in a greater refractive index. The variation of n with the wavelength of light is called the *optical dispersion* of a substance. The resolution of white light into the multicolored spectrum of its monochromatic components is a well-known example of optical dispersion. The London–van der Waals force is due, as we have seen, precisely to the same phenomenon of electron cloud polarization which is also the cause of optical dispersion; hence the alternate term *dispersion force.*

It may be readily realized that *the dispersion force cannot be repulsive* but only attractive since the mutual induction of the dipoles implies necessarily that the charges are in phase. The magnitude of the dispersion force is not influenced by the temperature because the rapidity of the electronic oscillations is considerably greater than the random agitation of the molecules due to the heat energy. On the other hand, the attraction forces between the *permanent* dipoles or between the *permanent* dipoles and ions vary inversely with the heat energy $3kT$.

Dispersion forces allow only for short-range interactions because, as the equations show, they fall off very rapidly with the interatomic or intermolecular distance. The decrease is much more rapid than for interactions between permanent charges. For example, doubling the distance between two ions of unlike charges decreases by half the energy of attraction. On the other hand, the doubling of the distance of separation between induced dipoles decreases the attraction energy due to dispersion force by a factor of 2 to the sixth power, that is 64. Thus, if the distance of separation is doubled the dispersion force decreases 32 times more rapidly than the ionic attraction. Nevertheless, in spite of the weakness of the dispersion forces between individual atoms, these forces are assumed to play an important role in macromolecules and in holding together macromolecular aggregates, since the total energy of attraction between a large number of atoms can amount to the bond energy of one or more covalent bonds. This is especially so between macromolecules which have sterically complementary structures so that close molecular adlineation is possible, which decreases the distances between a large number of atoms to a minimum, allowing a maximum force of interaction. For example, dispersion forces are assumed to be operative in the interactions between antigens and their specific antibodies. The antibodies are proteins having sterically highly specific structures, which are produced by living organisms upon the encounter with various foreign proteins, bacterial toxins, and other macromolecular substances, called in general terms *antigens*. The *antibodies* are specifically tailored to combine with and so to neutralize the toxic effects of given antigens. The specificity of this interaction probably resides in the very sensitiveness of the dispersion forces to the distance of separation, so as to allow strong interactions to occur only between structures which are sterically complementary.

3.3.5.5   *Special Types of Electrostatic Interactions*

A theory of *charge fluctuation forces* specific to proteins was proposed by Kirkwood and Shumaker. At the neighborhood of the physiological pH (~ 7–7.2), proteins contain a large number of neutral and negatively charged groups, such as $-NH_2$, $-COO^\ominus$, $-O^\ominus$, which are proton acceptors, *i.e.*, bases in the Brönsted sense; to these groups protons are bound to a degree determined by the pH. Except at very low pH values the number of these basic groups generally exceeds the number of protons bound to the molecule. Therefore, there are a large number of possible patterns for the distribution of the protons among the acceptor groups. Since the energy levels of these proton distribution patterns are very close, the protons will freely fluctuate among the acceptor groups due to the Brownian motion. These fluctuations in the distribution of the mobile protons impart to the molecules fluctuating electrostatic charges. As a result of this a molecule produces an alternating electric field. If another protein molecule is present in this field its fluctuating proton distribution will be polarized so as to be in phase with the charge fluctuations in the first molecule. This results, in turn, in a mutual polarization which gives rise to an attractive force between the two molecules. The attractive force varies inversely with the square of the distance separating the molecules; this is as may be expected since, owing to the mutual polarization, the interaction amounts to the sum of attractions between a large number of paired point charges. Fluctuations of bound ions other than protons may also contribute to this intermolecular force. It may be readily conceived that the dominant charge fluctuation patterns must always be highly dependent on the three-dimensional geometry of the molecular frame and on the position of the proton-acceptor groups. Thus, it is very likely that the charge fluctuation force is an important contributor in specific interactions between proteins (and possibly between other macromolecules) which have molecular regions with identical or complementary structural patterns. The mechanism of charge fluctuation also makes allowance for the interesting possibility that the relatively distant presence of other charged macromolecules can effectively influence local interactions by reorienting the fluctuation pattern of the mobile charges.

In connection with the resonance attraction (Section 3.3.4) mention was made briefly of *long-range intermolecular forces*. Although there is no rigorous and widely accepted theory which can account as yet for the existence of such forces, there is a body of persistent experimental evidence which seems to indicate that large colloidal structures and macromolecules can recognize each other's presence at several hundreds or thousands of angstroms apart. For example, in $Fe(OH)_3$ colloidal solutions at rest, the plate-like colloidal particles arrange themselves in horizontal layers separated by layers of water of the order of 8000 Å thick. A similar phenomenon is the ordering of large rod-like particles in solution. For example, 1–2% solutions of tobacco mosaic virus separate into solution layers in which the particles are lined up in a crystalline fashion, and these layers are divided by aqueous layers as much as 500 Å thick. The pseudocrystalline regions in such ordered solutions (and also of the so-called "liquid crystals") are called *cybotactic regions*, and the phenomenon is known as *cybotaxis*. Magnetic or electric fields and the proximity of solid surfaces have an orienting influence on the cybotactic regions. An important example often cited for the possible role of long-range forces is the specific and synchronized pairing of chromosomes during cell division. In spite of these and many similar intriguing observations there remains the possibility that only the well-known short-range forces are involved, but that these bring about a chain-like propagation of cybotactic ordering extending to long distances. Nevertheless, London considered that it is possible that some yet unknown, specifically macromolecular forces exist, which may not be understood as a simple extension or sum of the short-range atomic and molecular forces, but which may depend on the properties of the molecule as a whole.

SUPPLETORY NOTES FOR SECTION 3.3

NOTE 1

The significance of surface tension may be understood as follows. Any molecule in the *inside* of a liquid drop will be under the action of attractive forces of *all* surrounding molecules. However, because these attractions are of identical force from each direction, the resulting force will be nil. Molecules *on the surface* of the drop, however, are in the vicinity of other molecules *only toward the inside* of the drop. Consequently, the molecules on the surface will be under the action of molecular forces pulling them toward the inside of the drop (Fig. 43B). Because of this tendency of the molecules to migrate into the inside of the drop, a liquid drop always tends to take up the shape of a sphere (which is the shape having the smallest possible surface area compatible with the volume). Thus, the surface of liquids has to be regarded as covered by a monomolecular elastic film. To increase the surface area of a liquid, work must be expended in order to pull molecules from the inside to the surface, against the opposing forces pulling the molecules toward the inside. The surface tension is defined as the force (in dynes; 1 dyne equals the pull of gravity on 1.019 mg) necessary to increase the surface of a liquid by 1 cm^2. Expectedly, the surface tension of strongly hydrogen-bonded liquids is high.

NOTE 2

The Hammett equation establishes a quantitative relationship between the rate or equilibrium constants of a given chemical reaction in a series of related aromatic compounds. Consider the specific rates of esterification of isopropyl alcohol by benzoyl chloride and by a series of para-substituted benzoyl chlorides:

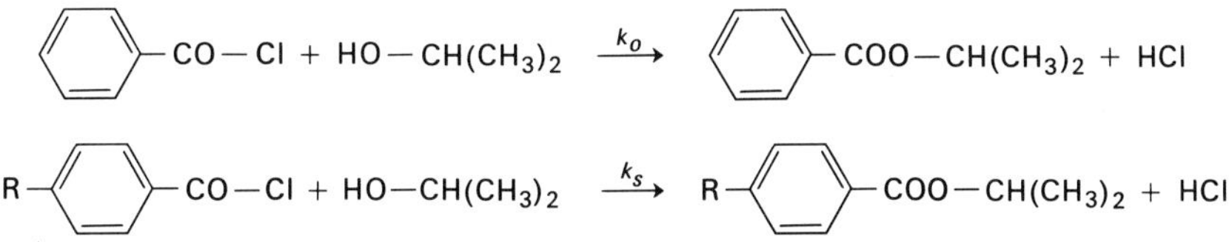

$$\text{C}_6\text{H}_5{-}CO{-}Cl + HO{-}CH(CH_3)_2 \xrightarrow{k_o} C_6H_5{-}COO{-}CH(CH_3)_2 + HCl$$

$$R{-}C_6H_4{-}CO{-}Cl + HO{-}CH(CH_3)_2 \xrightarrow{k_s} R{-}C_6H_4{-}COO{-}CH(CH_3)_2 + HCl$$

The rate constants k_o and k_s (moles of benzoate formed per second in one liter of one molar solution) may be calculated by determining the rates of liberation of HCl, by removing aliquots, cooling them rapidly, and titrating with alkali.

According to Hammett the two rate constants are related as follows:

$$\log \frac{k_s}{k_o} = \rho \cdot \sigma \tag{a}$$

which may also be written in the form:

$$\log k_s = \rho \cdot \sigma + \log k_o \tag{b}$$

The constant ρ, called the *reaction constant*, measures the sensitivity of a given reaction to ring substitution. The ionization of benzoic acid has been chosen as reference reaction for the reaction constant; for this reaction *by definition* $\rho = 1.00$. The constant σ, called the *Hammett constant* or *substituent constant*, represents the ability of substituents R to influence the reaction rate by virtue of their I or M effects (Sections 3.1.2.4 and 3.2.2). The σ values are different for substituents in para and in meta; no valid σ values can be determined for ortho substituents.

Values of σ for a large number of substituents have been determined; σ may have a positive or negative sign. In the above illustrated example, in the carbonyl group of benzoyl chloride the carbon atom normally has a partial positive charge because of the $-I$ effect of the oxygen, such as

Because of the relative electron deficiency of the carbon, benzoyl chloride is an electrophile. The reaction of isopropyl alcohol $(CH_3)_2CH-\ddot{O}-H$ (having an electron-rich oxygen) with benzoyl chloride represents then a nucleophilic attack by the alcohol oxygen upon the carbonyl carbon and $|\overline{Cl}|^\ominus$ and $H^\oplus$ are mutually displaced. Substituents (R) with positive σ values are electron acceptors (e.g., Cl, NO_2, CN). In the above example they withdraw electrons through the ring and, thus, increase the partial positive charge on the carbon. Hence, the reaction rate is greater with the substituted compound, $k_s > k_o$. Substituents (R) with negative σ values (e.g., NH_2, OH, OCH_3) are electron donors. In the above example they donate electrons in the direction of the carbonyl carbon and, hence, decrease its partial positive charge. Thus, the reaction rate of the substituted compound is lower than that of the parent compound, $k_s < k_o$.

Now, since by definition $\rho = 1.00$ for the dissociation of benzoic acid, the value of σ may be readily determined for any substituent:

$$\log \frac{K}{K_o} = \sigma \tag{c}$$

where K is the ionization constant of the substituted benzoic acid and K_o the ionization constant of the unsubstituted parent acid. The σ values, although determined with derivatives of the particular compound, benzoic acid, can be regarded henceforth as a generally valid electronic characteristic of substituent groups, indicating the ability to attract or donate electrons by the combination of the I and M effects. Once the σ values are known, the ρ constants may be determined for any type of reaction, since:

$$\rho = \frac{\log(k_s/k_o)}{\sigma} \tag{d}$$

where k_s and k_o are the rate constants for the given reaction with the substituted and the unsubstituted compound (the substituent having a known Hammett constant σ).

Equation (b) clearly indicates that for a given reaction type (therefore $\rho = $ constant) of a series of substituted compounds the reaction rates are linearly related to the σ values of the respective substituents. With some modification the Hammett equation also applies to aromatic compounds larger than benzenic.

3.4   Parameters of Molecular Geometry and Stability

3.4.1   DIMENSIONS OF ATOMS AND IONS

Except for the noble gases, the atoms of the elements do not exist singly but in covalently bonded molecular combinations. Assuming spherical atomic shapes, the size of a neutral atom is given by the *single-bond covalent radius*, also called the *atomic radius*, which is half of the internuclear distance in molecules of the element. For example, the internuclear distance in diamond is 1.54 Å and the covalent radius of carbon is 0.77 Å; the internuclear distance in Cl_2 is 1.99 Å and the covalent radius of chlorine is 0.99 Å.

The covalent radii of elements are very nearly constant and are additive (Fig. 53). For example, in the C—Cl bond the internuclear distance is the

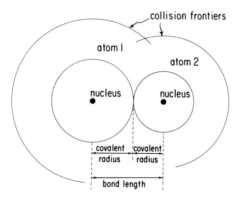

Fig. 53. Relation of the single-bond covalent radii, the van der Waals radii (collision frontiers), and the bond length.

sum of the covalent radii of carbon and of chlorine, $0.77 + 0.99 = 1.76$ Å, and this value is practically invariant for C—Cl bonds in different molecules. Thus, *the internuclear distance in a single bond is simply the sum of the covalent radii of the respective atoms.* The single-bond covalent radii (atomic radii) of a number of biologically important atoms are listed in Table XV.

Negatively or positively charged atoms (*i.e.*, ions) cannot have the same size as neutral atoms since the charge represents addition to or loss from the electron cloud. Thus, the radius of a negative ion is larger and the radius of a positive ion is smaller than the radius of the neutral atom of the element. Furthermore, the greater the charge, positive or negative, so much greater

Table XV

Atomic, Ionic, and van der Waals Radii

Element	Atomic radius, Å	Ionic radius, Å	van der Waals radius, Å
C	0.77		1.68
H	0.31		1.0–1.2
N	0.70		1.50
O	0.66	1.40 $(2^{\ominus})$	1.40
S	1.04	1.84 $(2^{\ominus})$	1.85
P	1.10		1.90
F	0.64	1.36	1.35
Cl	0.99	1.81	1.80
Br	1.14	1.95	2.00
I	1.33	2.16	2.20
Li	1.52	0.60	
Na	1.86	0.95	
K	2.31	1.33	
Mg	1.60	0.65	
Ca	1.97	0.99	
Fe	1.35	$\begin{cases} 0.75 \ (2^{\oplus}) \\ 0.60 \ (3^{\oplus}) \end{cases}$	

is the decrease or increase of the radius. For example, Table XV shows that the single-bond covalent radius of iron, 1.35 Å, decreases to 0.75 Å in $Fe^{\oplus\oplus}$ and to 0.60 Å in $Fe^{\oplus\oplus\oplus}$. The *ionic radii* determine the minimum distance between the ions of two elements (such as the ionic bond distances in crystal lattices).

From the internuclear distances of atoms having multiple bonds between them, *double-* or *triple-bond covalent radii* may be calculated (Table XVI).

Table XVI

Covalent Radii of Multiple-Bonded Atoms

Element	Atomic radius, Å
C= (aliphatic)	0.675
C⩶ (aromatic)	0.695
C≡	0.600
N= (aliphatic)	0.615
N⩶ (aromatic)	0.675
N≡	0.550
O=	0.550
O⇉	0.500
S=	0.940

The covalent radii of multiple-bonded atoms are also invariant and additive just as the single-bond covalent radii. For example, the carbon–carbon internuclear distance in an ethylenic double bond is $2 \times 0.675 = 1.35$ Å, in an acetylenic triple bond $2 \times 0.600 = 1.20$ Å, the oxygen–carbon internuclear distance in a carbonyl group is $0.675 + 0.550 = 1.23$ Å. By comparing the single-bond covalent radii and the multiple-bond covalent radii in Tables XV and XVI, it can be seen that the covalent radius decreases in the order single > double > triple bond; the decrease is 10–12% for double bonds and 20–23% for triple bonds. The decrease of the internuclear distance between multiple-bonded atoms is the logical corollary of the higher bond strength of double and triple bonds; the smaller the internuclear distance, the greater is the orbital overlap which is paralleled by the increase of bond energy (Sections 3.1.2.1, 3.1.2.2, and 3.2.2.1.1). Expectedly, the aromatic double-bond covalent radius of an atom is an intermediate value between the single-bond and aliphatic double-bond covalent radii.

3.4.2   BOND LENGTHS: THE EFFECT OF ELECTRONEGATIVITY AND OF CONJUGATION. VALENCE ANGLES. BOND ENERGIES, MECHANICAL HARDNESS, AND FLEXIBILITY

The internuclear distance between two atoms linked together is commonly called the *bond length* (Fig. 53). We have seen that the bond length can be calculated by summing the respective covalent radii. However, the additivity of these holds rigorously only when the two atoms have equal or similar electronegativities. If the bonded atoms have very different electronegativities, the measured bond length is less than the sum of the covalent radii. This "shrinkage" of the bond is due to an increment of bond strength owing to the coulombic attraction between the partial charges (which are the result of the differing electronegativities; Section 3.1.2.3). The covalent radii in Tables XV and XVI are corrected for this shrinkage, *i.e.*, the values given for the nonmetallic elements are average values in carbon compounds.

Table XVII gives the actual bond lengths and the bond energies of some homoatomic bonds. The shrinkage of the bond length is now illustrated with the following example. From the data in this table the C—F bond length is calculated as the arithmetic average of the C—C and F—F bond lengths, that is 1.48 Å. Yet, the experimentally measured lengths of C—F bonds in organic compounds range from 1.35 to 1.38 Å. Schomaker and Stevenson proposed an empirical factor correcting for the electronegativity difference. Thus, the bond length l_{A-B} between atoms A and B may be given as:

$$l_{A-B} = r_A + r_B - 0.08(X_A - X_B) \tag{64}$$

Table XVII
Bond Lengths and Bond Energies of Homoatomic
Bonds of Nonmetallic Elements

Bond	Length, Å	Energy, kcal/mole
H—H	0.74	104.2
C—C	1.54	81.6
C=C	1.35	146.1
C≡C	1.20	192.0
N—N	1.46	29.0
N=N	1.23	80.0
N≡N	1.10	170.0
O—O	1.48	35.0
O=O	1.21	96.0
S—S	2.10	50.9
S=S	1.89	54.0
P—P	2.20	51.3
F—F	1.42	36.6
Cl—Cl	1.99	57.8

where r_A and r_B are the covalent radii as computed from the homoatomic bond lengths of A—A and B—B, and X_A and X_B are the respective electronegativities. Taking into account the electronegativity difference of 1.5 between carbon and fluorine, we obtain the very satisfactory corrected value of 1.36 Å.

Another important factor causing bond shrinkage is conjugation. For example, in vinyl chloride (CH_2=CH—Cl) the C—Cl distance is only 1.69 Å, while in methyl chloride (CH_3—Cl) it is 1.78 Å. The same effect is observed in any single bond adjacent to or being part of a conjugated system. The corrected bond length of a C—C bond partaking in a conjugated system may be approximated by means of the bond order or the bond type (Sections 3.2.2.1.1 and 3.2.2.1.3).

The hydrogen bond length, which is the distance between the centers of the bridgehead atoms, varies considerably with the electronegativity of the latter. The lengths of the N—H·····N, N—H·····O, and O—H····O bonds, which are the types occurring in biological systems, are usually between 2.5 and 3.3 Å. The proton is at 0.95–1.1 Å from one bridgehead atom and at 1.4–2.2 Å from the other.

The *valence angles* or *bond angles* are the angles formed by adjacent covalent bonds. Valence angle data are necessary for the calculations of the geometric parameters (size, shape) of molecules. A listing of valence angles is given in Table XVIII. It must be remembered, however, that the valence angles are not rigid, but only reflect the most probable orientations of the

Table XVIII
Average Values of Valence Angles in Organic Compounds

Valence axes	Angle	Valence axes	Angle
C–C(C)–C		C–C(=O)–O	124°
C–C(C)–H	109°	C–C(=C)–H	120°
C–C(X)–X		C–C(=C)–C	124°
C–C(C)–C (aromatic)	120°	C=C=C	180°
C–C(=O)–C	121°	C–C≡C	180°
N–C(C)–C	109°	N–N(=N)–C	121°
N–C(C)–H	107°	N–N(=O)–O	127°
O–C(C)–C	111°	O–C(C)–H	106°
S–C(C)–C	100°	S–C(C)–H	95°

nuclei under the experimental conditions of the measurements. Certain valence angles in some molecular species can actually undergo extensive deformations without bond rupture depending on the solvent, the environmental temperature, close packing in the crystal lattice, etc. Among the strong valence bonds the σs covalent bonds and the ionic bonds have no angular dependence.

Some types of secondary valence forces also involve an optimum orientation of the partners for maximum interaction. In general, hydrogen bonds tend to be linear; this means that in a A—H····B bond there is usually little deviation (10–15°) between the A—H bond axis and the A– – – –B internuclear line. However, the hydrogen bond angle can vary over quite a wide range with but little change in energy. In some cases the deviation may be as high as 40–60° (HF and carboxylic acid dimers) or even 72° (hydrogen-bonded water "cage" of hydrates). This fact can be taken either as an indication that coulombic attraction is the main contributor in the hydrogen bond (compare to Section 3.3.1.1) or that the bridgehead atom orbitals which contribute their electrons to the proton have a high degree of s character; recall that neither coulombic attraction nor s—s bonds have angular dependence.

In hydrophobic bonding, molecular orientation or the absence of it is entirely dependent on the degree of steric complementariness of the interacting partners; during adlineation the orientation of the molecules is always such as to result in maximum bond energy. In charge-transfer between aromatic molecules, bonding is optimized by coplanar adlineation so as to achieve parallelism of the σ-bond planes.

The orders of magnitude of bond energies of the different types of valence forces are given in Table XIX. The magnitude of the bond energy does not always determine unequivocally the stability of a given bond, however. For example, while the ionic bonds are of high energy they are subject to

Table XIX
Comparative Energies of Valence Forces

Bond type	Order of magnitude, kcal/mole
Covalent bond	40–200
Ionic bond	150–250
Ion-dipole attraction	30–90
Dipole-dipole attraction	10–30
Hydrogen bond	2–10
Hydrophobic bond	max. ~ 1.2 per $-CH_2-$
Charge-transfer bond	1–20
Dispersion force	max. 0.02–1 per atom

the *ion-exchange phenomenon* in polyelectrolyte solutions; we have seen that this is the basis of the charge fluctuation force (Section 3.3.5.5). Ion exchange is due to the facts that the ionic bond strength decreases much less rapidly with the distance than does the force between two covalently bonded atoms and, furthermore, that the ionic attractive force cannot be saturated in the sense that the covalent bonding power of an atom can be. Thus, while on the average the ionic bond energy of the system remains invariant, a constant interchange of individual ionic bonds takes place.

The energies of bonds within materials generally determine their mechanical hardness. Thus, fully ionic and/or fully covalent minerals (*e.g.*, aluminum silicates, diamond) are hard. The hardness means that the bonds between the constituent atoms or ions are so strong (*i.e.*, cohesion is so great) that the material can resist, to a great extent, penetration by another material which would forcibly disrupt some of these bonds. Materials maintained by ionic or covalent bonds together with weaker bonds are, however, usually less cohesive and hard especially in a direction perpendicular to the latter bonds; to this is due the easy cleavage of particular minerals along certain crystallographic axes (*e.g.*, layered structures of graphite, mica, clay minerals). The fluidity of liquids is due to the comparatively weak intermolecular bonds (hydrogen bonds, dipole–dipole attractions). At the end of the scale, cohesion is the least in gases because of the very weak interatomic or intermolecular forces (dispersion forces).

Hard inorganic materials are, on the other hand, often brittle. Flexibility in organic compounds (*e.g.*, rubber, natural fibers, certain synthetic high polymers) results from the flexibility of the constituent individual molecular chains because of the ease of rotation about single covalent bonds and the possibility of slight but compounded distortion of a great number of valence angles. It is obvious then that cross-linking (*e.g.*, "vulcanization" of rubber by treatment with SCl_2, polymerization of ethylene to polyethylene in the presence of small quantities of certain polyenes) decreases flexibility but increases the hardness of the materials because of the establishment of new links between the polymeric chains. For the same reason cross-linking brings about drastic changes in the swelling ability of organic materials (see later in Section 3.4.4).

Molecular interactions, in particular between macromolecules, almost always involve several types of valence forces. Thus, weak covalent bonds (*e.g.*, S—S) may be reinforced or ion exchange may be minimized by several hydrogen bonds and/or hydrophobic bonds. Similarly, a charge-transfer bond may be stabilized by dispersion forces acting between a large number of atom pairs along sterically complementary molecular regions. Hydrophobic and hydrogen bonds, dipole–dipole attractions, and dispersion forces probably act concurrently for maintaining the conformations of proteins, while in nucleic acids hydrogen bonding appears to play the predominant role.

3.4.3 COLLISION RADII. STERIC HINDRANCE

The sums of the *collision radii*, also called the *van der Waals radii*, represent the closest distance of approach between the nuclei of two *nonbonded* atoms (see also Section 3.2.3.4 and Fig. 40). As two nonbonded atoms approach, the dispersion force tends to bring them closer together. However, at the onset of the overlapping of the electron clouds the interelectronic repulsion suddenly increases, upsetting the gain by the dispersion force. Orbital overlap and covalent bonding are not possible since both atoms are already bonded to other atoms, meaning that the orbitals are filled. Therefore, these distances represent the "collision frontiers" or "collision envelopes" of the atoms (Fig. 53). The van der Waals radii of some nonmetallic elements are given in Table XV. It will be noted that the collision radii of atoms of non-metals are very close to the ionic radii.

Atomic groupings such as $-CH_3$ and $-CH_2-$ in which the substituent hydrogen atoms are small as compared to the carbon may be regarded as possessing an overall collision envelope. The collision radius is 2.0 Å for both $-CH_3$ and $-CH_2-$. Similarly, since the π-electron cloud surrounding the σ-bond frame of planar aromatics is an uninterrupted envelope, an over-all collision radius may be assigned to these. The "half-thickness" of planar aromatics is 1.85 Å. The same value may be taken for the half-thickness of conjugated aliphatic chains.

It has been stated in Section 3.2.3.4 that the van der Waals radii are somewhat elastic and compressible. This accounts for the fact that when

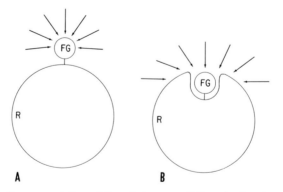

Fig. 54. Schematic representation of the relative accessibility of a functional group (FG) in sterically unhindered (A) and sterically hindered (B) conditions.

two large atoms or two large substituents (*e.g.*, —Br, —CH₃) are linked to the *same carbon atom*, the distance separating them can be appreciably smaller than the sum of the collision radii. When structures are drawn proportionally to molecular dimensions this appears as the "fusion" of the two collision envelopes.

The concept of *steric hindrance* (see also Section 3.2.3.4) is a corollary of the notions of functional group (Section 2.3) and collision frontier. The reaction rate of a functional group in a given chemical reaction sometimes shows considerable differences depending on the over-all structure of the molecule to which the functional group is linked and on the position of linking of the latter to the molecular frame. For example, in identical experimental conditions the rate of esterification of acetic acid is 80 times greater than the rate of esterification of methylisopropylacetic acid; the rate of oxime formation (Section 2.3.2.1) of cyclohexanone is 1500 times greater than the rate of oximation of 2-isopropylcyclohexanone; benzoic acid may be readily esterified while 2,6-dimethylbenzoic acid is practically refractory to esterification. Thus, while it is the functional group which determines the nature of the chemical reaction which can occur, the rate of the reaction depends to a considerable extent on the rest of the molecule. Figure 54 illustrates the fact that access to a functional group, FG, is determined by the three-dimensional architecture of the molecular frame R, and by the position of linking FG to R. In molecule A, FG is highly available for reaction, while in B the reaction is said to be *sterically hindered*. If the neighborhood of a functional group is encumbered by large substituents the molecules of any reagent can attain it only with difficulty and the reaction will be slow.

3.4.4 INCREASE OF ION SIZE DUE TO HYDRATION. BIOLOGICAL ROLES OF IONS. SWELLING OF GELS. LYOTROPIC SERIES

The phenomenon of solvation in general and hydration in particular has been succinctly introduced in Section 3.3.5.2. Ion hydration is of great importance for explaining some of the effects of ions in biological systems.

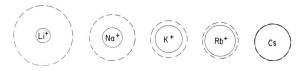

Fig. 55. Hydration shell and effective ionic size of alkali metal ions.

There is a considerable body of evidence which shows the hydration of ions. For example, from the size of the respective ions (Table XV) it would be expected that the *ionic mobility* of Li, Na, and K in an electric field would follow the order Li > Na > K; the smallest ion $Li^{\oplus}$ would move the fastest and the largest ion $K^{\oplus}$ would move the slowest. Yet, the experimentally found actual ionic mobilities follow the order K > Na > Li; moreover, the ions of the two other alkali metals, Rb and Cs, which have sizes even larger than $K^{\oplus}$, move faster than $K^{\oplus}$. This is because in aqueous solutions all these ions exist as hydrated ions, and the thickness of the hydration layer (or shell) considerably modifies the effective ionic size (Fig. 55) and, hence, the mobility.

Different investigators using different experimental procedures found, for the number of H_2O per $Li^{\oplus}$, values between 3 and 15. While it is true that the *hydration numbers* show considerable uncertainty, it remains that within any one set of experimental conditions the order of these values for the ions varies invariably in the order $Li^{\oplus} > Na^{\oplus} > K^{\oplus} > Rb^{\oplus} \geq Cs^{\oplus}$. For example, Pallmann found the following hydration numbers: $Li^{\oplus} = 10.0$, $Na^{\oplus} = 4.3$, $K^{\oplus} = 0.9$, $NH_4^{\oplus} = 0.8$, $Rb^{\oplus} = 0.5$, $Cs^{\oplus} = 0.2$. The hydration numbers point to the fact that while hydrated ions must be regarded as complex ions, the bond between the water molecules in a hydration shell, on one hand, and the ion, on the other hand, is by no means a pure coordinate bond with a well-defined stoichiometry governed by the concept of effective atomic number (Section 3.1.2.8), but has to a large extent the character of electrostatic ion–dipole attraction (Section 3.3.5.2). It is pertinent in this respect that hydrogen ion is also hydrated beyond the hydronium ion stage, which may be regarded as having a pure coordinate character. Nonetheless, the geometric requirements are the same for accommodating a maximum number of water molecules around a central ion and for accommodating ligands in a true coordination compound. Since $Li^{\oplus}$ has the smallest size and, therefore, the greatest charge density among the monovalent cations, it has the largest hydration shell. The latter decreases successively with the increase of the size of these ions, since the charge density decreases with the increase of the size. In contrast to the cations, the tendency of an anion to be hydrated increases with the ion size, and the mobilities of the halogen anions, for example, decrease as $F^{\ominus} > Cl^{\ominus} > Br^{\ominus} > I^{\ominus}$. The hydration shell of both the cations and the anions increases with the number of the charges, *i.e.*, the magnitude of the charge. For example, the hydration numbers of $Ca^{\oplus\oplus}$ and $Mg^{\oplus\oplus}$ are roughly the double of that of $Li^{\oplus}$.

It is commonplace that ions play complicated and important roles in biological systems. There are probably no biochemical reactions which are not sensitive to some extent to the *ionic environment*. Ions contribute to maintaining the proper osmotic pressure between extra- or intracellular biophases compartmented by membranes. The ionic environment modifies the three-dimensional architecture and, hence, the function of the macro-molecular polyelectrolytes, proteins and nucleic acids (Sections 8.1 and 8.2).

For example, it is well known that the change in the ion concentration and the presence or absence of particular ions have a profound effect on the activity of many enzyme systems. This is because a given type of enzyme activity requires a proper spatial distribution of the functional groups within the catalytic "active site." The proper spatial arrangement of these groups depends, in turn, on the conformation of the rest of the macromolecule, which conformation entails a unique pattern of hydrogen bonds and hydrophobic bonds, of electrostatic attractions and repulsions between functional groups, and possibly of other secondary valence forces. The ions present can exert a powerful "screening effect" between electrostatically interacting functional groups and are also known to influence hydrogen bonds and, indirectly, hydrophobic bonds. Thus, a given ionic environment, which assures the optimum activity for one enzyme or enzyme system, does not necessarily represent the optimum ionic environment for another. At the intracellular level the shifting ionic gradients represent then a channel of regulation of enzyme activities.

Ions are also important for stabilizing the structure and regulating the functions of nucleic acids. Alkaline earth metal ions are strongly bound to nucleic acids, and $Mg^{\oplus\oplus}$ and $Mn^{\oplus\oplus}$ have been shown to speed up considerably the pairing of individual deoxyribonucleic acid (DNA) strands. Bivalent cations also play a role in linking the DNA moiety to the protein moiety in certain DNA proteins. Another mechanism, involving ions, which ensures the stability of large DNA-protein aggregates is that in the cell, interstices of the macromolecular structure are "packed" with inorganic and organic ions, water molecules, metabolites, hormones, etc., these substances being in continuous interchange. This "packing" is obviously dependent on steric conditions. But what is important from the standpoint of structural stability is that, in this way, empty molecular "cavities" are avoided. These cavities would be predisposed to collapse, because of the Brownian vibratory motions of the structural segments, resulting in the deletion of conformational and functional patterns. At the same time these small molecular weight polar and/or nonpolar molecules effectively control the functions of the macromolecule and, thus, assure its integration with the cell life. Evidence is available to the effect that cellular control mechanisms are operative which regulate DNA and DNA-protein biosynthesis, and cell division, by varying the concentration gradient of inorganic ions. It is for the above reasons that when macromolecular aggregates, and especially cell organelles, are isolated from tissues they have to be maintained at temperatures much lower than the normal temperature of the tissue in the living organisms to avoid the loss of conformation (*denaturation*) or depolymerization (*i.e.*, break-up of structure). Conversely, very high unphysiological concentrations of ions also produce alterations in nucleoprotein structure and function. Clumping and bridge formation in the chromosomes are often observed in the *in vitro* culture of different tissues maintained in high salt media.

An interesting illustration of the effect of ions on macromolecular structure is given by their effect on the water uptake (swelling) of biological gels, *e.g.*, agar and gelatin. The ultramicroscopic study of the formation of these gels has shown that, when cooling the warm solutions of these substances, the hydrophilic colloidal particles approach each other and form sponge-like three-dimensional gel networks, the interstices of which are filled with water. Placed in water, these gels swell because of uptake of water due to the expansion of the interstices and breakage of a number of *points of junction* in the gel networks. Similarly rubber, polystyrene, and other nonpolar high polymers swell in benzene and other organic solvents. *The swelling of these and all other macromolecular substances and aggregates corresponds to the distancing of structural elements by the penetration of solvents or solutions into the molecular interstices.* Swelling may be unlimited or limited. In *unlimited swelling* the solvent is capable of completely solvating the macromolecular chains or colloid particles which make up the gel network; as the swelling proceeds the gel structure is gradually abolished and the substance ultimately dissolves. For example, the swelling of agar,

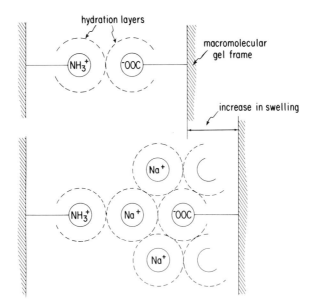

Fig. 56. A mechanism for the enhancement of the swelling of gels by cations. [Patterned after A. Frey-Wyssling, "Submicroscopic Morphology of Protoplasm and its Derivatives," p. 100, Elsevier, Amsterdam, 1948.]

methylcellulose, gelatin, natural rubber, and polystyrene in the appropriate solvents is unlimited. These substances can undergo solubilization because the points of junction in the gel network are maintained by weak secondary valence forces, such as hydrogen bonds and electrostatic attractions, and by ionic bonds which can undergo ion exchange (Section 3.4.2). However, if covalent cross-links are introduced into these substances then a number of junctions in the gel network cannot be opened, and the solvating medium is no longer capable of abolishing the gel structure. In these instances then, notwithstanding the often remarkably high solvent uptake, swelling proceeds only up to certain limiting values and the gel structure is preserved; this is the case of *limited swelling*. Thiolated gelatin and highly vulcanized rubber (containing $-S-S-$ cross-links), cross-linked polystyrene (containing a small percentage of the bifunctional divinylbenzene as copolymer), and methylcellulose cross-linked by dicarboxylic acids or epoxides can only undergo limited swelling.

The swelling of polyelectrolyte gels, such as gelatin, is strongly influenced by the pH and by the presence of ions. At the isoelectric point (*i.e.*, the pH at which the net positive and negative charge of the colloidal particles is zero) the swelling is at the minimum. The reason for this may be readily conceived on considering the scheme in Fig. 56. The upper part of this figure represents two adjacent regions of a gel frame linked to each other by the ionic bond between a $-NH_3^\oplus$ and a $-COO^\ominus$ group. Now, since ionic bonds are important participants in maintaining the cohesion of the gel at every point of the network, it is evident that maximizing the number of ionic bonds in the gel (so that there is a maximum number of paired $-NH_3^\oplus$ and $-COO^\ominus$ groups) increases the cohesion of the gel and, thus, decreases swelling.

Hofmeister studied the action of ions on the swelling of gels. Discs of gelatin (solid gel) placed in equimolar solutions of different salts show appreciable changes in the rate of swelling from one cation to another, when maintaining the same anion. In the same way the rate of swelling changes from one anion to another, when maintaining the same cation. It is found that the order in which cations enhance the swelling of gelatin at neutral pH is Li > Na > K > Rb > Cs. The order in which the anions enhance the swelling of neutral gelatin is I > Br > Cl > F. It will be noticed that these orders of the ions, called the *lyotropic series* or *Hofmeister series*, exactly parallel the order of the size of the hydrated ions (see above in this section). A mechanism by which different ions bring about differing rates of swelling can now be represented by means of the simple scheme in Fig. 56. For example, hydrated cations which enter interstices of the gel network are electrostatically ordered about the anionic $-COO^\ominus$ groups. However, because of the hydration layers of the cations, this brings about a distancing of the $-COO^\ominus$ and $-NH_3^\oplus$ groups and the weakening of the ionic bond between them, which results in greater swelling; this effect parallels the size of the hydration layer of the respective cation. According to this mechanism bivalent cations which are more strongly hydrated than monovalent cations produce a greater swelling in gelatin; for instance, $Ca^{\oplus\oplus}$ produces a much greater swelling than $K^{\oplus}$ despite the fact that nonhydrated $Ca^{\oplus\oplus}$ has a smaller ionic radius than nonhydrated $K^{\oplus}$. Similarly, the strongly hydrated $Zn^{\oplus\oplus}$ produces considerable swelling of cellulose, which swells only little in monovalent cation solutions.

The rate of swelling of biological gels (of macromolecular aggregates) depends then on the following factors: the chemical nature of the macro-molecular gel network, the pH and the ionic environment, and the temperature. Thus, when maintaining the latter three parameters constant, changes in the swelling rate indicate gross alterations in the macromolecular structure of the gel. For this reason the measurement of swelling has found some interesting applications in biology. For example, the well-known hypothesis on the nature of aging by Björksten proposes that aging consists in the gradual random cross-linking of tissue constituents by polyfunctional meta-bolites and exogenous agents; this results in loss of functionality leading to gradual senescence. One of the characteristics of senescence in mammalian organisms is the hardening and loss of connective tissue. Elden measured the swelling of isolated tendons in aging rats and found indeed an appreciably decreased swelling ability which, thus, appears to lend support to the cross-linking hypothesis of Björksten.

3.4.5 INFORMATION THEORY AND MOLECULAR STRUCTURE

3.4.5.1 Some Elements of Information Theory

Information in the quantitative sense is not a measure of knowledge conveyed, neither is it a measure of the usefulness of a message; it is a measure of the *variety* inherent in a message. "Message" in this sense is any *pattern* containing variety. It may be words of different lengths composed from letters of an alphabet, the woven pattern of an intricate lace work, the arrangement of atoms in a molecule, a two- or three-dimensional geometric figure, a graph representing the pathways of logical connections between elements of a concept, etc. The variety in all these may be quantitatively expressed as *information content*. It is possible that the information content of simple biologically active organic molecules is an important, yet almost unexplored, parameter, which governs the multiplicity of their interactions with complex macromolecular systems. In particular for the polycyclic hydrocarbons and related compounds, where a geometric relationship exists between many compounds, theoretical investigations along these lines may open new levels of understanding on the mechanism of biological action.

Consider now a simple alphabet of two letters, *a* and *b*. Depending on the number *n* of symbols used to compose messages, different numbers of messages are possible. For example, using $n = 1$, 2, and 3 symbols, the following messages can be composed:

a	b	aa	bb	aaa	bbb
		ab	ba	baa	abb
				aba	bab
				aab	bba
2 messages		4 messages		8 messages	

Similarly, it can be verified that when an alphabet of three letters is available, the total number of messages which can be composed is 3 when using one symbol per message, 9 when using two symbols, 27 when using three symbols, 81 when using four symbols, etc. It can be readily seen then that the number of messages which can be composed with the two-letter alphabet increases as 2^1, 2^2, 2^3, and the number of messages obtained with the three-letter alphabet increases as 3^1, 3^2, 3^3. Thus, when an alphabet of L symbols is available, L^n different messages *n* symbols long can be composed.

The L^n different messages represent as many available choices. The variety or information content I of the total number of possible messages is defined as the logarithm of the *available choice*:

$$I = \log L^n = n\cdot\log L \tag{65}$$

The available choice of messages, using messages 1 symbol long, is the information content, the degree of variety of the alphabet of L symbols, $I = \log L$.

In information theory it has become customary to use logarithms to the base 2 instead of common logarithms (base 10). The reason for this may be explained as follows. The *simplest alphabet* by which messages may be conveyed is a two-letter alphabet, which may be *a, b*; +, −; 1, 0; "yes," "no"; etc. The *simplest messages* which may be conveyed by such a binary alphabet are *a* or *b*, + or −, 1 or 0, "yes" or "no," etc. The number of such messages is $2^1 = 2$, where each message is 1 symbol long. The available choice in an alphabet of two symbols is therefore 2. The information required to specify one of the two symbols is called a *binary choice*. The quantity of information corresponding to one binary choice is, therefore, $I = \log 2$ $= 0.3010$. However, by using $\log_2$ instead of $\log_{10}$, we get:

$$I = \log_2 2 = 1 \tag{66}$$

In this way the quantity of information inherent in one binary choice is set to unity. Defined in this way the unit of information is called a *bit* (from the contraction of BInary digiT) or a *hartley* (designated as H). One binary choice represents, therefore, an amount of information of 1 bit or 1 hartley, the unit of information. The information, in bits, contained in any set of distinguishable elements L is:

$$I = \log_2 L \tag{67}$$

To illustrate further the meaning of information consider the following examples. How many bits of information (*i.e.*, number of random binary choices) are required to specify one particular employee among the 128 employees of an industrial firm? The first binary choice designates one of two groups of 64, the second binary choice distinguishes between two groups of 32, the third between two groups of 16, and so on up to the seventh binary choice which finally makes the choice between the two remaining individuals. Thus, in this case, using the binary alphabet "yes" and "no," seven messages (binary choices) are required to specify one particular individual among the $2^7 = 128$ possible alternatives. Since following the definition of information every binary choice represents 1 bit [Eq. (66)], the information required, which is the same as the information content of the group of 128 distinguishable elements, is 7 bits (Fig. 57). This is readily calculated using Eq. (67):

$$I = \log_2 128 = 3.322 \log_{10} 128 = 3.322 \times 2.10721 = 7 \text{ bits}$$

where 3.322 is a factor for calculating logarithms to the base 2 from common logarithms (see Suppletory Note 1*).

In a similar way, the information content of the English *alphabet* containing 26 letters is $I = \log_2 26 = 4.7$ bits. This is different from the information content of the English language which can be calculated, assuming an average word length of five letters, as $I = 5 \log_2 26 = 23.5$ bits. Such simple calculation does not, of course, account for the orthographic restrictions and redundance of the language, which exclude or favor certain combinations of letters.

An alternate way of expressing information is based on the *probability of selection* rather than availability of choice. Consider the set of distinguishable elements [a, b]. The probability of selecting any one of these two elements by random choice is $\frac{1}{2}$. If two other distinguishable elements are

---

* Suppletory Notes for Section 3.4 begin on page 294.

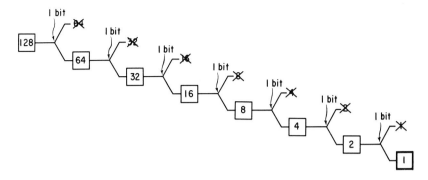

Fig. 57. Flow sheet of consecutive binary choices necessary to identify one out of 128 distinguishable elements.

added to the set, the probability of selecting any one of the elements from the new set $[a, b, c, d]$ by random choice is $\frac{1}{4}$. In the same way, the probability of selecting one element from the set $[a, b, c, d, e, f, g, h]$ is $\frac{1}{8}$, and so on. It can be easily seen that the aggregate probability w of selecting one element from these sets increases as $(\frac{1}{2})^1 = \frac{1}{2}$, $(\frac{1}{2})^2 = \frac{1}{4}$, $(\frac{1}{2})^3 = \frac{1}{8}$, etc., in general as:

$$w_i = (\tfrac{1}{2})^{z_i} \tag{68}$$

where z_i is, in these cases, some positive integer. The integer z_i represents the number of messages, in terms of random binary choice units, required for the selection of one particular element. This can be readily seen by considering that the selection of one element in the first set involves one binary choice. The selection of one element in the second set involves two consecutive binary choices; the first distinguishes between two groups containing two elements each and the second between two groups containing one element each. Selection of one element in the third set involves three consecutive binary choices, and so on.

We are now led to extend the generality of Eq. (68) by introducing fractional exponents. In fact, while $\frac{1}{2}$, $\frac{1}{4}$, $\frac{1}{8}$, $\frac{1}{16}$, etc., may be expressed as *whole* powers of $\frac{1}{2}$, fractions such as $\frac{1}{3}$, $\frac{1}{5}$, $\frac{1}{6}$, $\frac{1}{7}$, $\frac{1}{9}$, cannot be represented in this way. However, the latter can be represented as powers of $\frac{1}{2}$, by taking *fractional* values for z_i, such as $\frac{1}{3} = (\frac{1}{2})^{1.58}$, $\frac{1}{5} = (\frac{1}{2})^{2.32}$, $\frac{1}{6} = (\frac{1}{2})^{2.58}$, $\frac{1}{7} = (\frac{1}{2})^{2.81}$, $\frac{1}{9} = (\frac{1}{2})^{3.17}$. The values 1.58, 2.32, 2.58, 2.81, 3.17 represent then fractional binary choices.

By taking the $\log_2$ of Eq. (68) we get:

$$\log_2 w_i = z_i \cdot \log_2(\tfrac{1}{2}) \tag{69}$$

The multiplier $\log_2(\frac{1}{2}) = \log_2 1 - \log_2 2$. It can be shown using Eq. (a) in Suppletory Note 1 that $\log_2 1 = 0$ because $\log_{10} 1 = 0$. Since $\log_2 2 = 1$ from Eq. (66), we can see that:

$$\log_2(\tfrac{1}{2}) = -1$$

Therefore, the number of binary choices necessary to select one particular element i in the set, that is, the information content of the ith element, is:

$$z_i = -\log_2 w_i \tag{70}$$

Now, if there are m number of distinguishable elements, then the information content of the whole set is obtained by summing the information content of all the distinguishable elements, each weighted according to the probability of its occurrence. The Shannon-Wiener formula gives the information content as:

$$I = -\sum_{i=1}^{m} w_i \log_2 w_i \tag{71}$$

The calculation of the information content with this equation is illustrated by the following example. In the set $[a, a, b, c, c, c, d]$ there are a total of 7 elements. However, not all 7 elements are distinguishable. The set can be separated into four *classes* of distinguishable elements. The elements within any one class are indistinguishable

(a, a)	(b)	(c, c, c)	(d)
$i = 1$	2	3	4

These classes correspond to the distinguishable "letters" of an "alphabet." Unlike letters of an ordinary alphabet, however, the four classes here have not the same probability of occurrence. This means that in one random selection there is twice as much probability that an a and three times as much probability that a c will be taken, than there is for the selection of a b or a d. The probability of any element being chosen in one random selection is measured by the *weight* of the class in which the element belongs. The weight of a class is the number of elements in that class (n_i) divided by the number of elements in the whole set (n):

$$w_i = \frac{n_i}{n} \tag{72}$$

The weights of the four classes are $w_1 = \frac{2}{7}$, $w_2 = \frac{1}{7}$, $w_3 = \frac{3}{7}$, $w_4 = \frac{1}{7}$, respectively. By substituting into Eq. (71) we find that the information contained in the set of our example is

$$I = -\frac{2}{7}\log_2(\tfrac{2}{7}) + \frac{1}{7}\log_2(\tfrac{1}{7}) + \frac{3}{7}\log_2(\tfrac{3}{7}) + \frac{1}{7}\log_2(\tfrac{1}{7}) = 1.84 \text{ bits}$$

It can be easily shown that Eq. (71) is actually equivalent to Eq. (67). We have found, using Eq. (67), that the information content of the English alphabet is 4.7 bits. The probability of selection of each letter by random choice is $\frac{1}{26}$. Therefore, considering that there are 26 letters, we obtain the same answer using Eq. (71):

$$I = - \sum_{i=1}^{26} \tfrac{1}{26} \log_2 \tfrac{1}{26} = -[\tfrac{1}{26} \log_2(\tfrac{1}{26})] \cdot 26 = \log_2 26 = 4.7 \text{ bits}$$

Another useful parameter characterizing the variety of pattern is here defined as the average information content per element, irrespective of whether or not these elements are distinguishable. This is termed *information density* or *information efficiency* (D).

$$D = \frac{I}{n} \tag{73}$$

3.4.5.2   The Information Content of Graphs

It has been pointed out in the previous section that any pattern displaying distinguishable structural elements contains variety, and the quantitative measure of variety is information content. In the information-theoretical sense, organic molecules are not different from organized sets of letters. In the molecules, the physically different atoms or their structurally different aggregates are the "letters" of the "alphabet"; in these, the physical differences of the atoms give rise to variety in the structure (see Suppletory Note 2). Moreover, Rashevsky introduced the concept of *topological information content*, which is that physically indistinguishable structural units can also give rise to a large information content. The units, although indistinguishable physically in this case, can be different through difference of their *relations* to each other. This concept, extended further by Karreman and Trucco, is of special importance for the calculation of the information content of organic compounds. These may contain a large number of carbon atoms which often show considerable relational variety. In a first approximation the structural formulas of organic chemistry can be regarded as *graphs* representing the relations of the atoms to each other. A point in a

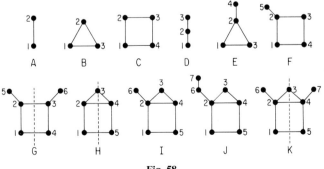

Fig. 58.

graph is called a *vertex* and a line connecting two vertices is termed an *arc*. The number of arcs terminating at a vertex is called the *degree* of the vertex.

The calculation of the information content of graphs will now be illustrated with a few simple examples taken in part from the above authors' reports (see Selected Reading). In Fig. 58A there is no way of distinguishing between the vertices 1 and 2. The information content of the graph is zero. Similarly, in B and C the vertices are indistinguishable and the information content of the two graphs is zero.

In graph D of Fig. 58 the vertices 1 and 3 are indistinguishable since both are of degree one. Vertex 2 is different, being of degree two. This graph contains, therefore, two classes of vertices, (1, 3) and (2). The probability of an element of the first class being chosen at random, *i.e.*, the weight of that class, is $\frac{2}{3}$. The probability that the element of the second class is chosen at random, the weight of the second class, is $\frac{1}{3}$. Thus, by substituting into Eq. (71), the information content of graph D is obtained as:

$$I_D = -(\tfrac{2}{3}\log_2 \tfrac{2}{3} + \tfrac{1}{3}\log_2 \tfrac{1}{3}) = 0.92 \text{ bits}$$

Now, while the graph B has zero information, connecting one more vertex to vertex 2 as shown in graph E, introduces appreciable variety into the pattern. Graph E contains three distinguishable classes of vertices (1, 3), (2), and (4). The vertices 1 and 3 are indistinguishable since both are of degree two and each is connected to one vertex of degree two and to another vertex of degree three. The weight of the three classes are $\frac{2}{4}, \frac{1}{4}$, and $\frac{1}{4}$, respectively. The information content of the graph is:

$$I_E = -(\tfrac{2}{4}\log_2 \tfrac{2}{4} + \tfrac{1}{4}\log_2 \tfrac{1}{4} + \tfrac{1}{4}\log_2 \tfrac{1}{4}) = 1.5 \text{ bits}$$

The connection of one more vertex to graph C, resulting in graph F, brings about a greater enrichment in variety than the same operation produced in transforming B into E. Graph F contains four classes of vertices, (1, 3), (2), (4), and (5) having the weights $\frac{2}{5}, \frac{1}{5}, \frac{1}{5}$, and $\frac{1}{5}$, respectively. We find for the information content $I_F = 1.92$ bits. However, adding an additional vertex to F, so as to obtain graph G, variety is reduced. This graph contains only three classes of vertices (1, 4), (2, 3), (5, 6), each class having a weight of $\frac{1}{3}$; its information content is $I_G = 1.58$ bits.

Consider now the graphs H through K. Graph H contains three distinct classes of vertices (1, 5), (2, 4), and (3). The corresponding weights are $\frac{2}{5}, \frac{2}{5}$, and $\frac{1}{5}$, and $I_H = 1.53$ bits. Calculation of the information content of graphs I and J shows that the variety of pattern gradually increases; in both these graphs each point belongs in a different class. The $I_I = 2.6$ bits and $I_J = 2.82$ bits. On the other hand, if vertex 7 is connected so as to obtain graph K, then information content is considerably reduced because now vertices 6 and 7 become indistinguishable, also 2 and 4, as well as 1 and 5. The information content is only $I_K = 1.96$ bits. It can be readily seen that *modification of the structure of a graph resulting in increase of symmetry generally tends to decrease the information content, and vice versa.* The symmetry axes of graphs G, H, and K are shown in Fig. 58. Graphs I and J have no symmetry axes. In Fig. 58 graphs B and C (which contain no information) have three and four symmetry axes, respectively, in the plane of the graph. The number of these axes is reduced to 1 in both graphs E and F.

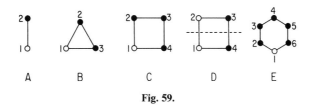

A   B   C   D   E

Fig. 59.

If some points in a graph become physically distinguishable then the information content is composed of the topological information content and the information content due to the physical differences. Thus, graph A in Fig. 59 has an information content of 1 bit because the two vertices are physically distinct. Similarly, in contrast to graphs B and C of Fig. 58, which contain no information, in Fig. 59 for graphs B and C 0.92 bits and 1.5 bits are calculated, respectively. Information in C (Fig. 59) is reduced to 1 bit by replacing the vertex ● in position 2 with a vertex ○ so as to obtain D (Fig. 59). In fact, this results in an increase of the symmetry of the graph; vertices 1 and 2 have now become indistinguishable, just as 3 and 4, so that graph D contains only two distinct classes of elements instead of three as C in Fig. 59. While a hexagonal graph with six identical vertices contains no information, the introduction of one physically distinct element, as in graph E (Fig. 59), raises the information content to 1.92 bits. This increase of the information content again parallels the decrease of the symmetry of the graph.

The organic molecules which may be the most readily studied in the information-theoretical sense are the planar polycyclic hydrocarbons and heterocyclic analogs. The structure of benzene represents a symmetrical hexagonal graph, and we have seen above that a hexagonal graph with six identical vertices contains no information; introduction of one heteroatom, such as in pyridine (corresponding to Fig. 59E), raises the information content to 1.92 bits. The number of distinguishable classes of elements rapidly increases passing from benzene to the higher benzologs. The reader may readily verify that, for example, naphthalene contains 3 classes of distinguishable elements, *i.e.,* 2 classes containing 4 elements each and

1 class containing 2 elements; anthracene contains 4 classes of distinguishable elements, *i.e.*, 3 classes containing 4 elements each and 1 class containing 2 elements. The information content generally increases considerably when passing from the acenes to the isomeric phenes. Thus, for example, the isomer of anthracene, phenanthrene, contains 7 classes of distinguishable elements, each class containing 2 elements.

For the calculation of the information content of complex graphs it can be sometimes advantageous to introduce *compound symbols*, which means taking as a basic unit for the "alphabet" several classes of indistinguishable points simultaneously. For example, although a graph composed of two hexagonal graphs contains 3 classes of distinguishable elements, (2, 3, 6, 7), (1, 4, 5, 8), and (9, 10), it may be regarded as a graph containing two vertices where each vertex represents a compound symbol of a hexagonal element.

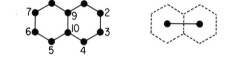

Since an aggregate probability is the product of the individual probabilities, Trucco proposed that the product of the weights of the component classes is taken as the weight of a compound symbol. However, it must be taken into consideration that the weights of the classes are increased by the fact that they are selected *together* in the random choice of the compound symbol. Therefore, the weight P_ρ of a compound symbol is obtained as:

$$P_\rho = w_a \cdot w_b \cdot w_c \cdot \ldots \cdot v_s \cdot v_t \cdot v_n \cdot \ldots (m \text{ terms}) \qquad (74)$$

where

$$v_i = 1 - w_i \quad (i = 1, 2, 3, \ldots, m) \qquad (75)$$

Trucco derives the information content I' of a compound symbol as:

$$I' = - \sum_{i=1}^{m} (w_i \cdot \log_2 w_i + v_i \cdot \log_2 v_i) \qquad (76)$$

SUPPLETORY NOTES FOR SECTION 3.4

NOTE 1

Since tables of logarithms to the base 2 are not always available it is useful to know that the logarithm to the base b of some number N may be obtained, if only logarithms to the base a are available, using the formula:

$$\log_b N = \frac{\log_a N}{\log_a b} \tag{a}$$

In particular from $\log_{10} N$ the $\log_2 N$ is obtained as:

$$\log_2 N = \frac{1}{0.30103} \cdot \log_{10} N = 3.322 \log_{10} N \tag{b}$$

NOTE 2

The information content of a pattern (for example, of a molecule or a crystal lattice) represents the opposite of randomness; randomness means that no structural details are distinguishable. Information represents negative entropy (*negentropy*) and the following formal relationship exists:

$$I = -\alpha S \tag{a}$$

The conversion factor α is obtained by considering that to specify the position of each molecule in a crystal one binary choice or 1 bit of information is required. An amount of entropy corresponding to $R \cdot \ln 2$ or 1.377 cal/$C°$/mole is removed when N bits of information are supplied per mole, and N bits per mole correspond to one bit per molecule. Therefore:

$$I \text{ (bits/molecule)} = \frac{-S \text{ (cal/}C°\text{/mole)}}{1.377} = -0.73 S \tag{b}$$

SELECTED READING FOR SECTIONS 3.3 AND 3.4

HYDROGEN BOND

1. Ferguson, L. N.: Hydrogen bonding and physical properties of substances. *J. Chem. Educ.* **33**, 267–271 (1956).
2. Huggins, M. L.: Physicochemical aspects of hydrogen bonds and their application to biology. *Am. Scientist* **50**, 485–496 (1962).
3. Orgel, L. E.: The hydrogen bond. *In* "Biophysical Science—A Study Program" (J. L. Oncley, ed.). Wiley, New York, 1959, pp. 100–102.
4. Pauling, L.: "The Nature of the Chemical Bond." Cornell University Press, Ithaca, New York, 1960. See chapter on "The Hydrogen Bond," pp. 449–504.
5. Pimentel, G. C., and McClellan, A. L.: "The Hydrogen Bond." Freeman, San Francisco, 1960, 475 pp.
6. Kamlet, M. J.: Spectral effects of hydrogen bonding in substituted anilines. *Israel J. Chem.* **1**, 428–429 (1963).
7. Argus, M. F., Arcos, J. C., Alam, A., and Mathison, J. H.: A viscometric study of hydrogen-bonding properties of carcinogenic nitrosamines and related compounds. *J. Med. Chem.* **7**, 460–465 (1964).
8. Kauzmann, W.: Some factors in the interpretation of protein denaturation (see Section III). *Advan. Protein Chem.* **14**, see especially 33–37 and 50–51 (1959).

9. Chandra, A. K., and Basu, S.: Studies on hydrogen bonds, Part I. *Trans. Faraday Soc.* **56**, 632–637 (1960).

10. Linnell, R. H., Raab, F., and Clifford, R.: Hydrogen bonding of pyridazine–water and the $n \rightarrow \pi^*$ blue shift. *J. Phys. Chem.* **68**, 1999–2002 (1964).

11. Mataga, N., and Tsuno, S.: Hydrogen bonding effect on the fluorescence of some nitrogen heterocycles. I. *Bull. Chem. Soc. Japan* **30**, 368–374 (1957).

12. Wetlaufer, D. B.: The strength of tyrosyl-carboxylate hydrogen bonds. *Compt. Rend. Trav. Lab. Carlsberg* **30**, 135–146 (1956).

HYDROPHOBIC BOND

1. Kauzmann, W.: Some factors in the interpretation of protein denaturation (see Section B). *Advan. Protein Chem.* **14**, see especially 37–47 (1959).

2. Scheraga, H. A.: Intramolecular bonds in proteins. II. Noncovalent bonds. *In* "The Proteins" (H. Neurath, ed.), Vol. I. Academic Press, New York, 1963. See Section F on "Hydrophobic Bond," especially pp. 515–530 and 584–587.

3. Némethy, G., and Scheraga, H. A.: Structure of water and hydrophobic bonding in proteins. I. A model for the thermodynamic properties of liquid water. *J. Chem. Phys.* **36**, 3382–3400 (1962); II. Model for the thermodynamic properties of aqueous solutions of hydrocarbons. *Ibid.* **36**, 3401–3417 (1962); III. The thermodynamic properties of hydrophobic bonds in proteins. *J. Phys. Chem.* **66**, 1773–1789 (1962).

4. Klotz, I. M.: Protein hydration and behavior. *Science* **128**, 815–822 (1958).

5. Wetlaufer, D. B., Malik, S. K., Stoller, L., and Coffin, R. L.: Nonpolar group participation in the denaturation of proteins by urea and guanidinium salts. Model compound studies. *J. Am. Chem. Soc.* **86**, 508–514 (1964).

6. von Hippel, P. H. and Wong, K. Y.: Neutral salts: the generality of their effects on the stability of macromolecular conformations. *Science* **145**, 577–580 (1964).

7. Wetlaufer, D. B., and Lovrien, R.: Induction of reversible structural changes in proteins by nonpolar substances. *J. Biol. Chem.* **239**, 596–603 (1964).

RELATIVE PARTITION COEFFICIENT AND BIOLOGICAL ACTIVITY. MEMBRANE PERMEABILITY

1. Albert, A.: "Selective Toxicity." Wiley, New York, 1960. See chapter on "Biological Activity Unrelated to Structure: The Ferguson Effect," p. 196.

2. Gero, A., and Reese, V. J.: Chemical model of drug action. *Science* **123**, 100 (1956).

3. Hansch, C., Maloney, P. P., and Fujita, T.: Correlation of biological activity of phenoxy-acetic acids with Hammett substituent constants and partition coefficients. *Nature* **194**, 178–180 (1962).

4. Hansch, C., Muir, R. M., Fujita, T., Maloney, P. P., Geiger, F., and Streich, M.: The correlation of biological activity of plant growth regulators and chloromycetin derivatives with Hammett constants and partition coefficients. *J. Am. Chem. Soc.* **85**, 2817–2824 (1963).

5. Hansch, C., and Fujita, T.: ρ-σ-π Analysis. A method for the correlation of biological activity and chemical structure. *J. Am. Chem. Soc.* **86**, 1616–1626 (1964).

6. Christensen, H. N.: "Biological Transport." Benjamin, New York, 1962, 133 pp.

7. Bittar, E. E.: "Cell pH." Butterworths, Washington, 1964, 129 pp.

8. Gourley, D. R. H.: Basic mechanisms of drug action. *Progr. Drug Res.* **7**, 11–57 (1964).

INCLUSION COMPOUNDS

1. Brown, J. F.: Inclusion compounds. *Sci. American* **207**, 82–90 (1962).

2. Hagan, M. M.: Clathrates: compounds in cages. *J. Chem. Educ.* **40**, 643–645 (1963).

3. Cramer, F. D.: Inclusion compounds. *Rev. Pure Appl. Chem.* **5**, 143–164 (1955).
4. Hendricks, S. B.: Base exchange of the clay mineral montmorillonite for organic cations and its dependence upon adsorption due to van der Waals forces. *J. Phys. Chem.* **45**, 65–81 (1941).
5. Lautsch, W., Bandel, W., and Broser, W.: Einschliessungs-Erscheinungen in Lösungen. *Naturforsch.* **11b**, 282–291 (1956).
6. Cramer, F.: "Einschlussverbindungen." Springer, Berlin, 1954, 115 pp.
7. Hagan, M.: "Clathrate Inclusion Compounds." Reinhold, New York, 1962, 189 pp.

CHARGE-TRANSFER BOND

1. Szent-Györgyi, A.: "Introduction to a Submolecular Biology." Academic Press, New York, 1960. See chapters on "Charge Transfer," pp. 54–65, and on "Orbital Energies," pp. 35–45.
2. Andrews, L. J.: Aromatic molecular complexes of the electron donor-acceptor type. *Chem. Rev.* **54**, 713–776 (1954).
3. McGlynn, S. P.: Energetics of molecular complexes. *Chem. Rev.* **58**, 1113–1157 (1958).
4. Pullman, B., and Pullman, A.: Electron-donor and -acceptor properties of biologically important purines, pyrimidines, pteridines, flavins, and aromatic amino acids. *Proc. Natl. Acad. Sci. U.S.* **44**, 1197–1202 (1958).
5. Slifkin, M. A.: Charge transfer interactions of proteins, amino acids and amines in polar solvents. *Spectrochim. Acta* **20**, 1543–1554 (1964).
6. Birks, J. B., and Slifkin, M. A.: π-Electronic excitation and ionization energies of condensed ring aromatic hydrocarbons. *Nature* **191**, 761–764 (1961).
7. Wentworth, W. E., Drake, G. W., Hirsch, W., and Chen, E.: Molecular charge transfer complexes. *J. Chem. Educ.* **41**, 373–379 (1964).
8. Briegleb, G.: "Elektronen-Donator-Acceptor-Komplexe." Springer, Berlin, 1961, 279 pp.
9. Mulliken, R. S., and Person, W. B.: Donor-acceptor complexes. *Ann. Rev. Phys. Chem.* **13**, 107–126 (1962).
10. Reid, C.: "Excited States in Chemistry and Biology." Butterworths, London, 1957, 215 pp.

RESONANCE ATTRACTION AND ENERGY TRANSFER

1. Memory, J. D.: Tryptophan-carcinogen resonance as a possible mechanism in carcinogenesis. *Biochim. Biophys. Acta.* **64**, 396–397 (1962).
2. Birks, J. B.: A physical theory of carcinogenesis by aromatic hydrocarbons. *Nature* **190**, 232–235 (1961).
3. Weber, G.: Fluorescence-polarization spectrum and electronic-energy transfer in tyrosine, tryptophan and related compounds. *Biochem. J.* **75**, 335–345 (1960).
4. Weber, G.: Fluorescence-polarization spectrum and electronic-energy transfer in proteins. *Biochem. J.* **75**, 345–352 (1960).
5. Förster, Th.: "Fluoreszenz Organischer Verbindungen." Vandenhoeck & Ruprecht, Göttingen, 1951. See chapter on "Aufnahme und Abgabe von Elektronenanregungs-energie," pp. 67–93.
6. Department of Biology, MIT: "Fast Fundamental Transfer Processes in Aqueous Biomolecular Systems." MIT Cambridge, Massachusetts, 1960, 56 pp.

ELECTROSTATIC ATTRACTIONS

1. Bateman, J. B.: Interatomic and intermolecular forces. *In* Höber, R.: "Physical Chemistry of Cells and Tissues." Blakiston, Philadelphia, Pennsylvania, 1945, pp. 97–114.
2. Pauling, L.: "The Nature of the Chemical Bond." Cornell University Press, Ithaca, New York, 1960. See section on "Interionic Forces and Crystal Energy," pp. 505–511.

3. Seel, F.: "Atomic Structure and Chemical Bonding." Wiley, New York, 1963. See section on "Interactions between Molecules. Dipole and Dispersion Forces. Ion Dipole Bonding," pp. 72–78.

4. Kirkwood, J. G.: The forces between protein molecules in solution: a summary. *J. Cellular Comp. Physiol.* **49**, Suppl. 1, 59–62 (1957).

5. Kirkwood, J. G.: The nature of the forces between protein molecules in solution. *In* "The Mechanism of Enzyme Action" (W. D. McElroy and B. Glass, eds.). Johns Hopkins Press, Baltimore, Maryland, 1954, pp. 4–9.

6. Kauzmann, W.: Some factors in the interpretation of protein denaturation (see Sections C and F). *Advan. Protein Chem.* **14**, see especially 47–50 and 54–56 (1959).

7. Stockmayer, W. H.: Forces between macromolecules. *In* "Biophysical Science—A Study Program" (J. L. Oncley, ed.). Wiley, New York, 1959, pp. 103–106.

8. Waugh, D. F.: Protein–protein interactions (see Section 4). *Advan. Protein Chem.* **9**, see especially 334–338 (1954).

9. Scheraga, H. A.: Intermolecular bonds in proteins. II. Noncovalent bond. *In* "The Proteins" (H. Neurath, ed.), Vol. 1. Academic Press, New York, 1963. See Section H on "Electrostatic Interactions," pp. 535–540.

10. Adamson, A. W.: "Physical Chemistry of Surfaces." Interscience, New York, 1960. See chapter on "Long Range Forces," pp. 309–323.

HYDRATION, SIZE OF ATOMS AND IONS, BOND LENGTHS, VALENCE ANGLES

1. Frey-Wyssling, A.: "Submicroscopic Morphology of Protoplasm and Its Derivatives." Elsevier, Amsterdam, 1948. See section on "Heteropolar Cohesive Bonds," pp. 98–102.

2. Höber, R.: "Physical Chemistry of Cells and Tissues." Blakiston, Philadelphia, Pennsylvania, 1945. See chapters on "The Influence of Inorganic Ions on Cell Activity" and "The Influence of Inorganic Ions on Fiber and Cell Potentials." pp. 289–325.

3. Bull, H. B.: "An Introduction to Physical Biochemistry." Davis, Philadelphia, 1964. See Chapter 3 on "Electrolytes and Water," pp. 64–83.

4. Hart, E. J.: The hydrated electron. *Science* **146**, 19–25 (1964).

5. Maccoll, A.: Bond lengths and valency angles. *Progr. in Stereochem.* **1**, 361–365 (1954).

6. Wheeland, G. W.: "The Theory of Resonance." Wiley, New York, 1944. See Appendix on "Interatomic Distances in Organic Molecules," pp. 286–296.

7. Pauling, L.: "The Nature of the Chemical Bond." Cornell University Press, Ithaca, New York, 1960, 644 pp.

8. Sutton, L. E., Editor: "Tables of Interatomic Distances and Configuration in Molecules and Ions," Special Publication No. 11. The Chemical Society, London, 1958.

9. Bondi, A.: Van der Waals volumes and radii. *J. Phys. Chem.* **68**, 441–451 (1964).

INFORMATION THEORY, TOPOLOGY, COMBINATORIAL GEOMETRY, AND MOLECULAR STRUCTURE

1. Rashevsky, N.: "Mathematical Biophysics. Physico-Mathematical Foundations of Biology," Vol. II. Dover, New York, 1960. See Chapters 28 through 35 on mapping and biology, pp. 306–422.

2. Nahikian, H. M.: "A Modern Algebra for Biologists." University of Chicago Press, Chicago, Illinois, 1964, 236 pp.

3. Quastler, H., Editor: "Essays on the Use of Information Theory in Biology." University of Illinois Press, Urbana, Illinois, 1953, 273 pp.

4. Rashevsky, N.: Life, information theory and topology. *Bull. Math. Biophys.* **17**, 229–235 (1955).

5. Karreman, G.: Topological information content and chemical reactions. *Bull. Math. Biophys.* **17**, 279–285 (1955).

6. Trucco, E.: On the information content of graphs: compound symbols; different states for each point. *Bull. Math. Biophys.* **18**, 237–253 (1956).

7. Valentinuzzi, M., and Valentinuzzi, M. E.: Information content of chemical structures and possible biological applications. *Bull. Math. Biophys.* **25**, 11–27 (1963).

8. Valentinuzzi, M., and Valentinuzzi, M. E.: Contribucion al estudio del contenido de informacion de estructuras quimicas. *Anales Soc. Cient. Arg.* **174**, 1–86 (1962).

9. Yockey, H. P., Platzman, R. L., and Quastler, H., Editors: "Symposium on Information Theory in Biology." Pergamon, New York, 1958, 418 pp.

10. Lederberg, J.: Topological mapping of organic molecules. *Proc. Natl. Acad. Sci. U.S.* **53**, 134–139 (1965).

11. Lederberg, J.: "Systematics of Organic Molecules, Graph Topology and Hamilton Circuits." Instrumentation Res. Lab. Tech. Rept. No. 1040. U.S. Natl. Aeronaut. & Space Admin. NsG 81–60. January, 1966.

12. Niggli, P.: "Les Bases de la Stéréochimie." Dunod, Paris, 1952, 266 pp. (Translated from "Grundlagen der Stereochemie." Birkhäuser, Basel, 1945.)

13. Golomb, S. W.: "Polyominoes." Scribner, New York, 1965, 182 pp.

Part II

The Nature of Tumors. Concepts and Techniques of Testing Chemical Agents for Carcinogenic Activity

4 | General Characteristics of Tumors and the Testing of Carcinogens

4.1 General Characteristics of Tumors

An outstanding investigator in cancer research has stated that one man would need 12 years to read the complete literature on cancer published in one year. The following two sections are in no sense a review of the extensive literature of the subject, but are presented as an orienting outline of the properties and characteristics of tumors in general and of chemically induced tumors in particular.

The expression "tumor" denoting a more or less circumscribed swelling, was used first by Celsus in the first century A.D. to describe the morphological manifestation of an inflammation, the other signs being rubor (redness), calor (heat), and dolor (pain). In present-day usage, the word "tumor" means a *neoplastic lesion*, seen grossly as a new *nodular tissue formation*. The advent of bacteriology and parasitology brought about the realization that a number of these "tumors" are produced by specific microbes or parasites. These "tumors" are designated by the addition of an adjective, as in *"inflammatory* tumor." Acute inflammatory processes due to streptococci and staphylococci often cause tumorlike lesions and show all the signs described centuries ago by Celsus. Chronic inflammatory lesions, called *granulomas*, are often manifested in swelling only. Inflammatory tumors are often encountered in tuberculosis, syphilis, certain forms of leprosy, mycotic (fungus) infections, or as the result of reactions to foreign bodies.

There remains, however, a considerable variety of new tissue growths which have different etiologies. These new growths, called *tumors* or *neoplasms* (sometimes termed *neoplastic tumors*) may be of physical, chemical, or viral origin. The salient point is that while in inflammatory tumors the cells mature, and proliferate only to a very limited extent, the true neoplasms are formed from abnormal cells showing various degrees of *dedifferentiation* (see Suppletory Note 1*) and which proliferate unrestrained. The growth of true neoplasms, while it may be quiescent at times, does not cease altogether but proceeds continuously, sometimes capriciously at varying rates even after the disappearance of the inducing agent. Various definitions of tumors have been given but that of Willis (1) appears to be the most satisfactory: "A tumour is an abnormal mass of tissue, the growth of which exceeds and is uncoordinated with that of the normal tissues, and persists in the same excessive manner after the cessation of the stimuli which evoked the change." A variety of tumors are partially under the physiological control of the organism, in particular are hormone dependent, at least in the initial phase of their growth. Because of the relative independence of tumors from the regulatory systems of the living body in which they are growing, tumors are regarded as *autonomous*.

Tumors may vary widely in shape, size, and color. Sometimes they form a well-defined nodule in the interior of an organ or tissue, or they rise halfway above the surface as a hemispherical projection; in other cases they are connected with the tissue of origin by a narrow pedicle. Glandular tumors often contain cavities, sometimes visible to the eye, and fluid-filled cysts. Living, healthy tumor nodules are solid, hard, and easily distinguishable, especially when they arise in soft tissues. The color of many tumor nodules is yellowish or grayish white; some tumors are dull brown, or even black, such as the melanomas. The presence of blood or its decomposition products can give tumors a brownish-orange or blackish-brown color.

A distinction is generally made between *benign* tumors and *malignant* tumors; the latter are commonly called *cancers*. Strictly speaking, the expressions benign and malignant are related to the ultimate fate of the organism carrying the tumor. Malignant tumors ultimately kill the host. Benign tumors do not do so except when they interfere with the function of a vital organ. The rate of growth, the biochemical and morphological properties of normal tissue and of benign or malignant tumors are different, and generally the characteristics of benign tumors approximate that of normal tissues.

The nomenclature and histological classification of tumors are based on the criterion of origin in or resemblance to a particular type of normal tissue. It must be borne in mind, however, that tumors arising from the same type of tissues may have quite different characteristics of growth.

The suffix -*oma* (tumor) attached to the root of the name of the tissue generally denotes benign tumors originating in or resembling that tissue: lipoma from adipous tissue, fibroma from connective tissue, chondroma from cartilaginous tissue, osteoma from bone tissue, rhabdomyoma from striated

---

* Suppletory Notes for Section 4.1 begin on page 313.

and leiomyoma from smooth muscle tissue, angioma from the cells of blood or lymph vessels, cholangioma from bile duct cells, etc. *Papilloma* denotes a benign tumor of the skin or mucous surfaces. However, in animal experiments the term *adenoma* has come to designate in general either benign or malignant tumors of glandular origin, and the term *lymphoma* designates premalignant or malignant tumors of lymphatic tissue. Similarly, the term *hepatoma* is used to designate both benign and malignant tumors of the liver originating from true hepatic (parenchymal) cells. *Myeloma* is a condition of malignant proliferation of bone marrow cells.

The term *carcinoma* designates malignant tumors which arise from cells of epithelial tissues regardless of the germ layer (see Suppletory Note 2) of origin. *Sarcoma* designates malignant tumors of mesenchymal origin (connective tissue, muscle, bone, etc.). The two terms, carcinoma and sarcoma, are used to designate malignant tumors just as the suffix -oma is used to designate benign tumors. Thus, malignant tumors of the skin (often called by a common term *epitheliomas*) are epidermoid (squamous) or basal cell carcinomas; for example, neuroepithelioma designates a malignant tumor originating from the epithelial cells of nerve tissue. Squamous cell carcinomas arise in many epithelial tissues consisting normally of squamous epithelia, or they arise in that tissue by metaplastic transformation (*e.g.*, in the lung); metaplastic transformation is the change of one sort of normal adult tissue into another. The term *adenocarcinoma* denotes a tumor of glandular origin which is unequivocally malignant. Malignant tumors of the liver are either hepatocellular carcinomas (malignant hepatomas) or cholangiocarcinomas, or in many instances combinations of both. *Teratoma* and *teratocarcinoma* denote particular types of benign and malignant tumors, respectively, which are characterized by the presence of different tissues originating in multiple germ layers (as teeth and hair which are of ectodermal, and cartilage which is of mesodermal origin) not found in the tissue where the tumor grows.

Analogous to the terminology of malignant epithelial tumors, the terms liposarcoma, chondrosarcoma, osteosarcoma, rhabdomyosarcoma, lymphosarcoma, etc., are used for mesenchymal malignant tumors. Experimentally induced subcutaneous animal tumors are often called, simply, *sarcomas* without specifying the exact tissue origin of the tumor. Sarcomas are sometimes named not according to tissue origin but according to the shape and size of the tumor cell, such as spindle cell sarcoma, fibrosarcoma, giant cell sarcoma. Some terminologies use the suffix -*blastoma* to imply that some type of malignant tumors did not arise from fully differentiated mature cells but from remaining embryonic cells from which the mature tissue originated. An *angioblastoma* (sometimes called hemangiosarcoma or hemangioendothelioma) develops from cells which in embryonal life produce blood vessels. A *lymphoblastoma* means a tumor which develops from a precursor of lymphoid cells. A *melanoma* is a usually highly malignant tumor arising from the melanin pigment-producing cells (*melanocytes*) in the skin; its color may vary from black, blue-black, dark brown to colorless (the latter is termed *amelanotic* melanoma).

Tumors can be characterized on morphological or biochemical criteria or on the rate of their growth. Morphologically, the changes characteristic for malignant tumors can be described: (*1*) on the cellular level (cytology); (*2*) on the tissue level (histology); (*3*) on the level of relation to surrounding tissue; and (*4*) on the level of their behavior in relation to the organism as a whole.

(*1*) In the discussions of carcinogenesis it is often convenient to refer to "the cancer cell." This must be regarded truly as an abstraction since there are no absolute morphological and biochemical characteristics which describe *all* tumor cells. Rather than comparing "cancer cells" to "normal cells," it is much more meaningful to compare tumor cells to cells of the particular normal tissue from which the tumor arose. If any generalization can be made, it must be grounded in such comparisons. Cancer cells tend to be larger than the cells of the corresponding normal tissue. There is a particular enlargement of the nucleus which is due to *aneuploidy* (or irregular *polyploidy*). This means that the sets of chromosomes are not homologously paired (*diploid*) or exactly twice or four times that number (*tetraploid* or *octaploid*, *i.e.*, regular polyploid), but that the different chromosomes are present in different numbers and the nucleus is, therefore, genetically unbalanced. Regular polyploidy owing to the reduplication of chromosomes without division of the nuclei (also called *monocentric mitosis*) can be brought about in some monocellular organisms by relatively mild chemical treatments (*e.g.*, chloral hydrate). Daoust (3) found that the nuclei of normal rat liver cells fall into three classes with mean volumes forming the regular geometric progression 1:2:4; these three classes correspond to diploid, tetraploid, and octaploid nuclei. The aneuploidy of the nuclei of hepatic tumors induced by feeding the carcinogen, 4-dimethylaminoazobenzene,* results in the disappearance of the three distinct nuclear classes (3). Because the enlargement of the nuclei of cancer cells tends to be greater than the enlargement of the cells themselves, the *nucleocytoplasmic ratio* of cancer cells is often greater than that of normal cells.

Cancer cell nuclei contain a greater amount of material stainable

---

* Synoptic Table listing the structural formulas of chemical carcinogens mentioned in Section 4 begins on page 464.

by basic dyes (*basophilia*), indicating an increase in nucleic acid content. Moreover, a greater number of cells are found at any given time in some phase of cell division. In a proportion of cells the division is highly abnormal, involving the thickening, breaking, "stickiness," and bridge formation of chromosomes; some of these abnormalities will be discussed in some detail in later sections. There is generally an increase of the size of the *nucleolus* (acidophilic, dense ribonucleoprotein-containing particle in the nucleus) and often the appearance of more than one nucleolus.

(2) Tumor tissue consists of atypical dedifferentiated cells and supporting *stroma* (*i.e.*, intercellular connective tissue framework). Tumors can originate in any tissue (except mature neurons of the central nervous system); cells of a tumor are originally derived from one particular kind of cell and one particular kind of tissue. In appearance and function, tumor cells usually show some resemblance to the normal parent cells, although some of their original functions are always lost; tumors can range from those consisting of cells almost indistinguishable from the normal tissue of origin to those containing cells found nowhere else in the organism. However, in the words of Rusch and LePage (4) a "tumor represents a distinct tissue entity, one tumor resembling other tumors rather than its homologous differentiated tissue. This is increasingly borne out as data accumulate for the vitamin content, the chemical make-up and the enzyme pattern of tumors." The degree of departure from the normal cells (the degree of dedifferentiation) is, generally, greater if the growth rate of the tumor is faster (*cf.* 5). Malignant tumors are sometimes so highly dedifferentiated that tumors *originating from different tissues* are often almost indistinguishable morphologically.

The growth of pathological cells is usually supported by a stroma, which carries the blood vessels nourishing the growth; often these blood vessels are poorly formed and thin walled. The blood supply can often not keep pace with the growth of the tumor tissue and, because of the inadequate supply of nutrients and insufficient rate of elimination of toxic metabolic products, this results in tissue death (*necrosis*) in some areas of the tumor. Often in rapidly growing large tumors the alive tumor tissue is but a relatively thin layer enclosing large amounts of soft, necrotic and sometimes hemorrhagic tissue.

(3) The relation to surrounding tissue is best described by comparing the manner in which a benign or a malignant tumor is related to the surrounding tissue. A benign tumor does not invade the neighboring normal tissue from which it originates but pushes it

aside and grows by expansion. Benign tumors still show to a great extent the characteristic histological pattern of their tissues of origin. Benign tumors are often encapsulated by connective tissue which clearly delimits the boundary of the tumor. A *malignant* tumor may have a slow or fast growth rate but its tendency to grow is irreversible; it infiltrates, invades, displaces, and destroys neighboring tissues. It grows by infiltration between the interstices of normal tissue, thrusting into all available tissue spaces. A special motive power, similar to ameboid movement, has been observed among cancer cells in tissue cultures, but it is not known whether this plays any part in natural tumor growth. A lytic power of tumor cells over normal cells has also been postulated. The chief sign distinguishing malignant tumors from benign tumors with regard to their relation to surrounding tissue is the *destructive character of their growth*. The line of separation between benign and malignant tumors is, however, not always so sharp as it may appear from this discussion. Growth into the adjacent tissues may be present in certain benign tumors (*e.g.*, certain fibromas or angiomas). Some epithelial tumors of the salivary gland are of the mixed type "semi-malignant" tumors (6). Truly, the term "malignancy" varies in degree, and in borderline cases may have a different meaning following the interpretation of the particular histopathologist.

(*4*) Malignant tumors often have a considerable influence on the metabolism of the whole organism even before a dissemination of the cells can be observed (rev. 7). The dissemination and growth of tumors (*metastatic tumors*) in tissues remote from the primary site is called *metastasis*. An important characteristic of malignant tumors is that they most often (but not always) metastasize, and there is frequently reoccurrence at the primary site after the removal of the *primary tumor* because of the dissemination of tumor cells due to the surgical intervention; in some instances benign tumors might also form deposits of tumor tissue in remote organs (as in endometriosis). The forming of metastasis is facilitated by the decreased adhesiveness of the cells in malignant tumors, thought to be connected with the decreased calcium content of the malignant cells (8). In metastasis individual tumor cells or small clusters of cells break off from the primary tumor, are carried away by the blood or lymph, and become lodged in distant regions of the body where they originate new, secondary tumors. The sites of metastatic localizations depend on the type and location of the primary tumor (9); certain tumors show predilection to the metastatic site, *e.g.*, metastases of thyroid carcinoma to the bone. The blood vessels and the lymphatic

system provide routes through the organism for the invading metastatic tumor cells; tumors infiltrate more often into veins, probably
because of the greater thickness of arterial wall. Metastases are found
first in lymph glands if the tumor emboli have traveled in the lymph-
atics, in the lung and liver when dissemination occurred through the
bloodstream. Curiously, metastatic localizations are relatively in-
frequent in the spleen. Metastatic tumors are often more atypical
than the primary tumor and show faster growth rate. Metastatic
tumors can, in turn, metastasize with further increase of dedifferentiation. The growth of metastases in most cases is not influenced
by the removal of the primary tumor. However, in some specific
tumors (like chorionepithelioma) metastases sometimes disappear
spontaneously after removal of the primary tumor. On the other hand,
some instances have been observed with other tumors where the
rate of growth of metastatic tumors increased upon removal of the
primary tumor.

An experimental procedure related to metastasis is the *transplantation*
of malignant tumors. In addition to the histological evidence, the ability
to metastasize and to survive transplantation are proofs of the malignancy
of a tumor. Tumors can be transplanted (grafted) into animals of the same
species, but the transplants do not always "take" (that is, survive and grow)
because defense reactions directed against the foreign proteins of the tumor
may be set up by the organism of the host. A much higher percentage of
"takes" is obtained by transplantation into animals of the same inbred
(*homozygous*) strain. However, with certain highly malignant tumors and
under special experimental conditions interstrain and even interspecies
transplantations have been successful. Malignant and also nonmalignant
tumor tissues (as well as certain normal tissues) grow well when cultured
in vitro in appropriate nutritive media under sterile conditions.

By means of tumor transplantation a number of distinct tumor lines
have been kept growing from generation to generation over many years by
transplanting from host to host. The properties of these tumor lines are
well known, and they are used extensively as standard experimental tumors
for biological and biochemical experimentation and for the testing of the
activity of potential anti-tumor agents on tumor growth; such tumor lines
are for example, the Yoshida sarcoma, Ehrlich ascites tumor, Novikoff
hepatoma. Transplantation may be carried out by inoculation of part of
the tumor tissue in saline into the new host. This requires intact cells;
damaged cells, cell filtrates, or extracts are generally ineffective. However,
recently tumors have been transferred by injection of nucleic acids extracted
from tumors (*e.g.*, 10–12). The transplanted tumor grows entirely from the

inoculated piece of tissue, the new host providing only the stroma, support, and nutriment. Extensive experiments by various workers demonstrated the relative constancy of the tumor type through a very large number of generations of transplants (*e.g.*, 13), although strain specificity seems to decrease (14).

While it is true that special types of malignancies, such as certain ascites tumors and leukemia (see below), have been transplanted successfully in mice using a single cell, usually a colony of thousands of cells is required for successful transplantation; Reinhard, Goltz, and Warner (15) have shown that the chance of survival of a transplantable mouse adenocarcinoma was proportional to the number of cells inoculated and that the latency period of tumor "take" increased as the number of injected cells decreased. Similarly, for malignant growth to become self-perpetuating a critically sized cell colony (*cancer focus*) must be attained (16); Hollomon and Fisher (17, 18) calculated that the minimum colony size is between 300 and 600 cells. Apparently, both a transplanted tumor as well as a spontaneous or experimentally induced neoplasm pass through a critical period before they become established. There is some evidence (*e.g.*, 19, 20) that individual cells or subminimal colonies possessing the potential for malignant growth may stay quiescent, nonmanifest for a long period of time (*dormant tumor cells*); there is an easy "flare-up" and beginning of irreversible malignant growth, however, under the influence of carcinogenic or growth stimuli, or a change in the hormonal balance of the host. The "dormant" nature of these cells or colonies slowly disappears if the malignant potentiality is not brought to the surface for a protracted period of time.

Benign tumors sometimes turn malignant; in fact, some regard benign tumor cells as an intermediate stage in the malignant transformation of normal cells. Various authors (*e.g.*, 6, 21) consider that the benign tumor is an inhibited stage of a potentially malignant tumor. It is generally thought that, in the course of chemical carcinogenesis, a malignant tumor is preceded by a benign growth. Much work has been done on regression of benign skin tumors (papillomas) after insufficient application of the chemical stimulus; this subject will be discussed again in Section 6.2. The classic work of Rous and his collaborators (22, 23), for instance, showed that tarring of the skin of rabbits first caused the appearance of papillomas which could regress to apparently normal skin. However, if tar (or other irritant) was applied to a papilloma over a sufficiently long period, it turned malignant. But it was evident that the papillomas or even the apparently normal skin to which they had regressed had already undergone the essential change, and the application of a mere nonspecific irritant could then precipitate the malignant state. Similarly, Mottram (24) showed that a single application of 3,4-benzopyrene to the skin caused the appearance of benign tumors; repeated applications of the carcinogen changed them into malignant tumors.

The benign or malignant tumors discussed up to this point form nodules and are called *solid tumors*. Special consideration will now be given to some types of tumors which have not a solid but a *fluid stroma*. Great interest is centered on the malignant conditions of the white blood cells, designated as "leukemias." Leukemias represent different types of disturbances of the control of leukopoiesis (production of white blood cells). Broadly speaking, the term *leukemia* (also termed *hemoblastosis*) designates *all* malignant proliferative conditions of the reticuloendothelial system (see Suppletory Note 3) and is characterized by the production of abnormal and immature circulating white blood cells (leukocytes). Lymphoid tumors with solid stroma (*lymphosarcomas*) are, in all likelihood, closely related to the true leukemias and can be differentiated only by the presence or the absence of malignant lymphocyte cells in the circulating blood; depending on which type of cells normally present in a lymph node predominate, the tumors are called *lymphocytic* or *reticulum cell sarcomas*. In the group of malignant tumors of the lymphoid tissue, *Hodgkins disease* is of quite special interest because in many respects it forms a transition between inflammatory and true neoplastic tumors. Leukemias involving every type of white blood cell can occur; however, the common types of leukemias fall into three classes: *monocytic*, *lymphocytic*, and *myeloid* leukemia. When the leukemia is due to cells from which it cannot be established with certainty whether they belong to the lymphocytic or myeloid series, the leukemia is called *blast cell leukemia*.

According to the length of survival of the host, leukemia may be *acute* or *chronic*. Sometimes the actual number of white blood cells is not raised (*aleukemic leukemia*), but the morphology of the circulating cells and of the bone marrow allows diagnosis of the condition. Acute leukemia is usually of the myeloid-monocytic type. Chronic leukemia may be (*a*) lymphocytic (or lymphoid) in which there is a high number of mature and immature lymphocytes in the blood (lymphocytes: ameboid, small white blood cells with large spherical nucleus, produced in lymphatic tissue) and widespread enlargement of the lymph nodes, liver, and spleen; (*b*) myeloid type in which there is a high count of *polymorphonuclear* leukocytes and their precursors (*e.g.* myelocytes and myeloblasts), and great enlargement of the liver and spleen. The polymorphonuclear leukocytes are a type of actively phagocytic white blood cells produced by the myeloid tissue or bone marrow, and have a size intermediate between monocytes and lymphocytes; the nucleus is constricted into a number of lobes and the cytoplasm usually contains conspicuous granulation, hence the term *granulocyte* is sometimes used. In the usual experimental animals, in which the lymphocyte is the predominant type of white blood cell, the most common leukemia is the lymphocytic type.

Special types of malignant tumors with a fluid stroma are the *ascites tumors* in experimental animals. These tumors consist of isolated individual tumor cells suspended freely in serous exudate accumulated in the peritoneal cavity (akin to a bacterial culture in a liquid medium). Most ascites tumor lines carried in transplantation have been obtained by ingenious experimental techniques from solid tumors. Klein (25) developed special techniques for systematically producing ascites tumors from solid tumors. Conversely, ascites tumors may be reconverted to solid tumors. The transplantation of ascites tumors consists of injecting intraperitoneally a small volume of the ascites fluid withdrawn from the animal into a new host of the same strain. Ascites tumors represent an elegant testing system for antitumor agents, since the effectiveness of these may be readily followed by withdrawing ascites fluid and determining the change of the cell count per unit volume. Also, using ascites tumor cells it could be demonstrated that a single cell may be sufficient to transmit a tumor in a receptive host.

While the induction of cancer in plants lies outside of the scope of this work, it should be briefly mentioned that a variety of plant tumors have also been described. The most studied of these is the *crown gall*. Crown galls are initiated by the microorganism *Agrobacterium tumefaciens*. This tumor, like animal tumors, is characterized by dedifferentiated cells and invasive growth, and it even produces metastasis-like secondary tumors in some species (26, 27). These secondary tumors are interesting because they are devoid of *A. tumefaciens*. This permitted demonstration of the truly autonomous nature of the crown gall tumor cell. Tissue of these secondary sterile tumors grows well in a medium of tissue culture which does not support the growth of normal tissue from which the tumor originated. Fragments of such cultured sterile tumor tissue, implanted into a normal host, develop into sterile tumors but are comparable histologically in every respect to tumors originated by the bacteria (28).

The ability of *A. tumefaciens* to induce crown gall is related to its production of appreciable amounts of β-indoleacetic acid, a plant growth hormone (or auxin). Nevertheless, β-indoleacetic acid alone does not induce tumor growth. Mutant strains of *A. tumefaciens*, which do not produce the auxin, do not induce tumors either. However, if the plant is treated with the hormone, simultaneously with the inoculation with the mutant microorganism, tumors will develop (29).

SUPPLETORY NOTES FOR SECTION 4.1

Note 1

This dedifferentiation means that the microscopic pattern of cells in true, neoplastic tumors often shows only little resemblance to the pattern of cells in the tissue of origin; dedifferentiated tissues are, therefore, also termed *atypical* or *anaplastic*. Cell differentiation is inherent in the embryonic development of multicellular organisms, which means that from the single fertilized egg cell there emerges, gradually, through numerous cell divisions, a variety of tissues with widely diverging microscopic morphologies and physiological functions, but in a harmonious balance, so as to finally yield the integrated macroscopic structure of the particular organism. This process of divergence into morphologically and physiologically distinguishable groups of cells (the tissues) is referred to as *cell differentiation* (2).

As the organism reaches the fully developed adult stage, differentiation attains a maximum, and further growth of the tissues eventually ceases. The ability of the cells to divide is, however, not lost and mitotic activity rapidly regains a maximum rate in the case of wound healing or other tissue repair; such limited increase in the amount of tissue by increase in the number of cells, which individually keep their usual size, is termed *hyperplasia*. For example, following removal of a small part of the epidermis or excision of a part of the liver (*partial hepatectomy*) there is a rapid increase of cell division, and the growth of *differentiated tissues* is maintained until restoration of the integrity of the tissue or organ. Then cell division subsides because the potentialities of each tissue for growth are strictly delimited by the complex and interconnected physiological control mechanisms of the organism. Unlike normal growth, however, tumor growth is autonomous of the limits set by these systemic control mechanisms. Tumor cells continue to divide without restraint and without regard for the laws which coordinate growth of tissue in the rest of the body, irrespective of the needs of the body, and in a manner distinct from such functional and useful growth as reparative or inflammatory proliferations. This results in the accumulation of large tumor masses which brings about ultimately the death of the organism.

The homeostatic control of normal tissue growth (see Sections 8.5 and 8.6) and the balanced subordination of this growth capacity for the maintenance of the organism as a whole is the very condition of the organic existence of multicellular organisms. Expectedly then, the occasional appearance of tumors, which entails the loss of regulatory restraint on some cells and dedifferentiation of the new tissue formed from these, is common to all multicellular living species, animals and plants alike.

NOTE 2

The two primary germ layers, *ectoderm* (outer layer) and *endoderm* (inner layer), are the main layers of cells which can be distinguished in the early embryonic development, immediately after gastrulation. These two germ layers give rise to the *mesoderm* (third or middle layer). During differentiation the ectoderm gives rise to the epithelial tissues covering the body, the nervous system, and the sense organs; from the cells of the endoderm develop the lining of the alimentary canal, pancreas, liver, thyroid gland, and respiratory tract; and from the cells of the mesoderm originate the connective tissue, the supporting tissues (bone, muscles, and blood and lymph vessels), the bone marrow, and the sex organs; cartilaginous tissue originates from both the ectoderm and the mesoderm. The *mesenchyme* is a somewhat more differentiated embryonic tissue originating mainly from the meso-derm; it consists of an irregular network of cells connected by branching protoplasmic processes, embedded in a jellylike matrix.

NOTE 3

The reticuloendothelial system (RES), which develops from the reticular cells of the embryonic mesenchyme (see Suppletory Note 2), is organized into two main systems: the cells of the bone marrow and the cells of the lymphatic tissue. The spleen and certain specialized cells in the liver, the fixed phagocytic cells, and the free phagocytic cells (wandering macrophages) are also part of the RES. The bone marrow cells produce the red blood cells, replacement cells of the fixed myeloid tissue, and the polymorpho-nuclear cells in the circulating blood. The cells of the lymphatic tissue produce the lymphocytes and macrophages (large phagocytic cells widely distributed in the body of vertebrates). The origin of monocytes (largest kind of white blood cells with spherical nucleus, actively phagocytic) has not been clearly established.

REFERENCES TO SECTION 4.1

1. Willis, R. A.: "Pathology of Tumours." Butterworths, London, 1960, p. 1.
2. Spratt, N. T.: "Introduction to Cell Differentiation." Reinhold, New York, 1964.
3. Daoust, R.: *Rev. Can. Biol.* **22**, 59 (1963).
4. Rusch, H. P., and LePage, G. A.: *Ann. Rev. Biochem.* **17**, 471 (1948).
5. Haddow, A.: *Nature* **154**, 194 (1944).
6. Petrov, N. N., Editor: "Cancer—A General Guide to Research and Its Treatment." Pergamon, New York, 1962, p. 8.
7. Begg. R. W.: *Advan. Cancer Res.* **5**, 1 (1958).
8. Berwick, L., and Coman, D. R.: *Cancer Res.* **22**, 982 (1962).
9. Uehlinger, E.: *Bull. Intern. Union Against Cancer* **2**, No. 2 (1964); Herbeuval, R.: *Ibid.*

10. Hidvégi, E. J., Lónai, P., Antoni, F., Unger, E., and Várterész, V.: *Neoplasma* **10**, 361 (1963).
11. Graffi, A., Gimmy, J., and Schneiders, F.: *Acta Biol. Med. Ger.* **12**, 219 (1964).
12. Cantarow, A., Williams, T. L., and Goddard, J. W.: *Nature* **205**, 1010 (1965).
13. Levine, M., and Bergmann, H.: *Am. J. Cancer* **39**, 504 (1940).
14. Little, C. C.: *Biol. Rev.* **22**, 315 (1947).
15. Reinhard, M. C., Goltz, H. L., and Warner, S. G.: *Cancer Res.* **5**, 102 (1945).
16. Berenblum, I.: *Cancer Res.* **14**, 47 (1954).
17. Hollomon, J. H., and Fisher, J. C.: *Science* **111**, 489 (1950).
18. Fisher, J. C., and Hollomon, J. H.: *Cancer* **4**, 916 (1951).
19. Hadfield, G.: *Brit. Med. J.* **2**, 607 (1954).
20. Fisher, B., and Fisher, E. R.: *Science* **130**, 918 (1959).
21. Ivy, A. C.: *Science* **106**, 455 (1947).
22. MacKenzie, I., and Rous, P.: *J. Exptl. Med.* **73**, 391 (1941).
23. Friedwald, W. F., and Rous, P.: *J. Exptl. Med.* **80**, 101, 127 (1944).
24. Mottram, J. C.: *Brit. J. Exptl. Pathol.* **26**, 1 (1945).
25. Klein, G.: *Exptl. Cell Res.* **2**, 518 (1951).
26. Braun, A. C., and Stonier, T.: Morphology and physiology of plant tumors. *In* "Protoplasmatologia. Handbuch der Protoplasmaforschung" (L. V. Heilbrunn and F. Weber, eds.), Vol. 10. Springer, Berlin, 1958, p. 1.
27. Black, L. M.: Physiology of virus-induced tumors in plants. *In* "Handbuch der Pflanzenphysiologie" (W. Ruhland, ed.), Vol. 15/2. Springer, Berlin, 1965, p. 236.
28. Braun, A. C., and Wood, H. N.: *Advan. Cancer Res.* **6**, 81 (1961).
29. Segretain, G.: *Rev. Questions Sci.* [5] **14**, 181 (1953).

4.2 Some Aspects of the Pathology of Induced Tumors

The first chemically induced tumor obtained experimentally resulted from prolonged painting of the ears of rabbits with coal tar by Yamagiwa and Ichikawa (1). Painting of the skin with a solution of a carcinogen, particularly of carcinogenic hydrocarbons, is still a common form for rapidly inducing experimental tumors. The tumors thus produced are usually squamous cell carcinomas (epitheliomas). Although the early investigators used the ears of rabbits, currently mice are mainly used for skin carcinogenesis experiments.

The normal epidermis of mice consists of two layers of small undifferentiated epithelial cells. These are the cells which show first changes after application of a carcinogen, in that they differentiate into basal and spinous cells, and thus, come to resemble the structure of the epidermis in humans. This first reaction of the skin and dermal tissue to the application of a carcinogen is nonspecific and may also occur in response to noncarcinogenic irritants. If the application of the carcinogen is repeated, necrosis in the center of the painted area and hyperplasia in the periphery develops, resulting in thickening of the epithelium. The hair follicles undergo similar changes. Inflammatory reaction is present, surrounding the necrotic area, and is grossly manifested by erythema (redness of the skin); appreciable loss of hair occurs. These changes can regress if the application of the carcinogen is terminated, or they can advance to form papillomas. These benign tumors are simply wartlike overgrowths of the epidermis topped by a conical mass of keratin. Already during the benign period there is swelling of the epithelial cells and their nuclei, and vacuolation of the cytoplasm. Depending on the animal strain used, on the solvent employed, and on the length and frequency of application of the carcinogen, the development of a benign tumor may or may not be followed by malignant transformation.

With the onset of malignancy, the number of mitoses increases, particularly of cells derived from hair follicles. Epithelial cells show invasive downgrowth into the dermis, and there is marked hyperplasia. Keratin-filled cysts often form from modified hair follicles, and the interstitial connective tissue becomes loose and edematous. The neoplastic cells show varying degrees of dedifferentiation, consisting often only of irregular polygonal cells in highly malignant skin tumors. The tumor is nurtured and supported by a stroma of fibrous connective tissue containing blood vessels. If growth is so rapid as to outstrip vascular supply, necrosis in the center of the tumor can take place. Grossly the tumor appears as a large, burgeoning, sometimes

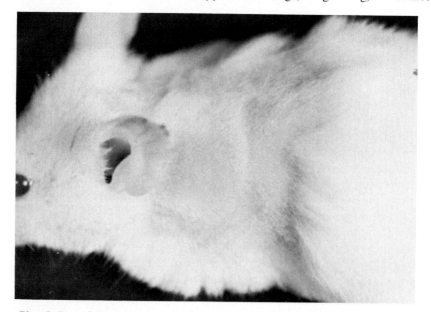

Plate I. Part of the shaved interscapular region of a normal random-bred Swiss-Webster albino mouse.

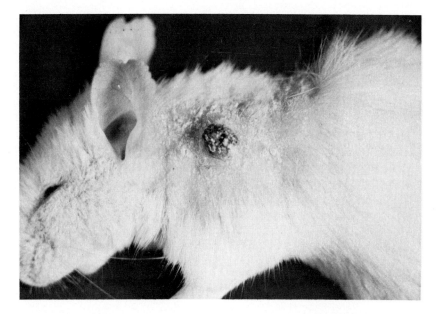

Plate II. Papilloma obtained in the same mouse (see Plate I) by depositing twice weekly on the shaved region 0.1 ml 0.3 % acetone solution of 3,4-benzopyrene for 8 weeks.

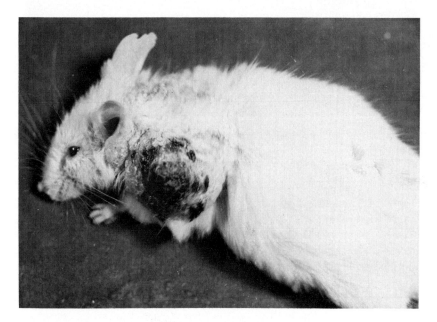

Plate III. The same mouse (see Plates I and II) after treatment for 11 weeks.

ulcerating, dark brown-gray or blackish mass. Plates I, II, III, and IV show the emergence and evolution of a skin tumor in a random-bred (*heterozygous*) Swiss-Webster albino mouse painted twice weekly, in the interscapular region, with a 0.3% acetone solution of the polycyclic hydrocarbon 3,4-benzopyrene.

An important biological process regulating the responsiveness of the mouse skin to externally applied carcinogenic hydrocarbons is the *hair growth cycle*. It is to the periodicity of hair growth that is due the wide scatter of the individual responses which may be observed in a group of mice receiving treatment with a hydrocarbon carcinogen, despite the fact that

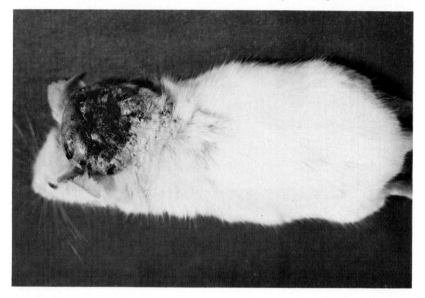

Plate IV. Malignant epithelioma in the mouse after identical 3,4-benzopyrene treatment for 17 weeks.

the group is highly homogeneous, *i.e.*, that the mice are of an inbred strain, the same sex, and approximately of the same age, and are maintained on a standard diet at identical room temperature. For example, in such a standardized group one animal may develop a papilloma after 6 weeks of treatment, while in another a papilloma may appear as late as 20 weeks or occasionally even much later. Such variations are appreciably larger than may be reasonably attributed to individual variations in susceptibility.

The finding that the growth of hair of the mouse is a cyclic phenomenon and that the periodic growth of hair is associated with marked changes in the thickness of the skin is due to Andreasen (2). He observed first that each

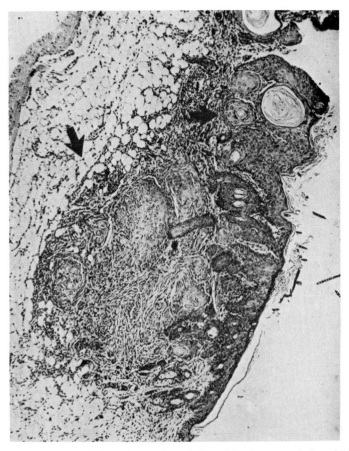

Plate V. Keratinizing epithelioma induced by painting a 0.3 % benzene solution of 3,4-benzo-pyrene on the skin of the mouse. Note keratin pearls (arrow on right) and early invasion (arrow on left).

hair cycle consists of a *growth phase* characterized by the development and growth of a new generation of hair and increasing thickness of the skin, and a *resting phase* in which the hair clubs do not grow and are anchored in the dermis of a very thin skin. Figures 60 and 61 show the parallelism between the growth of the hair (in millimeters) and the thickness of the skin (in microns) on the back of newborn "Swiss" mice, both variables plotted against the days of life.

Andreasen and Engelbreth-Holm (3), Borum (4), and Berenblum *et al.* (5) have studied the effect of hair cycle on the yield of tumors induced by the potent hydrocarbon carcinogen, 9,10-dimethyl-1,2-benzanthracene, in groups of mice. They obtained a large yield of tumors when a single dose

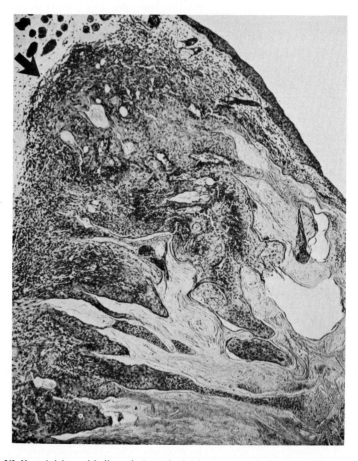

Plate VI. Keratinizing epithelioma induced by 3,4-benzopyrene in the mouse. A more advanced stage than the one shown in the previous plate. Invasion extends to the muscle layer (arrow).

of the hydrocarbon solution was deposited on the skin at the beginning of a resting phase, but a small yield of tumors when the carcinogen was applied at the beginning of the growth phase. For example, in Borum's experiments (4) in a group of 100 mice, the dorsal skins were in the growth phase in 55 mice, and in the resting phase in 45 mice, at the time of the single application of the carcinogen. At the final count of tumor-bearing mice at 3 months, none of the 55 mice but 88.7 % of the 45 mice developed papillomas.

Berenblum *et al.* (5) have demonstrated that the hair cycle influences the tumor yield by modifying the persistence of the carcinogen in the tissues.

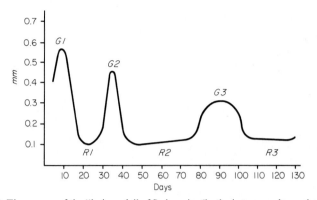

Fig. 60. Time curve of the "hair cycle" of Swiss mice (in the interscapular region), measured at intervals of 2–6 days. Distances from the surface epithelium to the roots of the hair follicles (in mm) were measured at right angles under the microscope using a calibrated micrometer eyepiece, following histological fixation, paraffin embedding, sectioning, and staining of the preparation. G represents the growth phase, 1st, 2nd, and 3rd; R represents the resting phase, 1st, 2nd, and 3rd. [From I. Berenblum, N. Haran-Ghera, and N. Trainin, *Brit. J. Cancer* **12**, 402 (1958).]

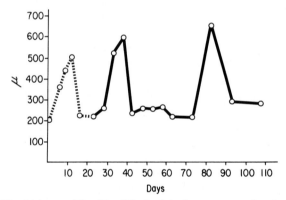

Fig. 61. The thickness of the skin of the back in the mouse as a function of the age in days. The thickness of the skin (in μ) during the first hair cycle (dotted line) is calculated from measurements of the thickness in a group of mice, and the thickness during the second and third hair cycles was obtained by using the same individual mouse (solid line). The technique of measurement was similar to that described in the legend of the previous figure. [From E. Andreasen, *Acta Pathol. Microbiol. Scand.* **32**, 157 (1953).]

In fact, the carcinogen, being a lipophilic compound, tends to accumulate in the sebaceous glands and around the roots of the hairs, while it is shed relatively rapidly from the surface of the epidermis. The hair cycle effect is, hence, due to an unduly short retention of an adequate concentration of the carcinogen when applied at the onset of the growth phase. In the latter case the carcinogen is quickly flushed out by the sebum secretion, whereas it persists for a long time when application is made at the beginning of the resting stage. A fluorescence microscopic study (5) has shown that the fluorescence of the hydrocarbon in the sebaceous glands and lower regions of the hair follicles persists about 10 times longer in the resting phase than in the growth phase. This mechanism of the hair cycle effect on the tumor yield is also supported by the marked infrequency of tumor in nonhair-bearing sites, *e.g.*, soles of the feet and hairless scars, and by the small tumor yield when a single application of the carcinogen is made on the skin of newborn mice in which the hair follicles are yet undeveloped.

A test method for carcinogens, more easily standardized than application to the surface of the skin, is the subcutaneous injection of a solution of the compound into experimental animals (most often rats). With many compounds, in particular with the carcinogenic polycyclic hydrocarbons, the tumors thus produced are sarcomas arising from fibrous tissue (fibrosarcomas, angiosarcomas, myosarcomas). Their development has been described in great detail by Orr (6), who implanted subcutaneously a solution of 20-methylcholanthrene in a wax pellet. He describes an initial inflammation, the first reaction to any irritant on or under the skin. This soon subsides. About the fifty-fifth day cells, histiocytes or lymphocytes, begin to proliferate, not in immediate proximity of the pellet, but beyond a thin zone of collagen. Later there occurs an increase in size of the proliferating cells and their nuclei, and a malignant growth is established. The resulting sarcoma consists of large, long, spindle-shaped cells with abundant cytoplasm in long processes and central, long, oval, vesicular nuclei. Multiple mitosis, bipolar or multipolar, also multinucleated giant cells and polymorphic cells are seen. The cells are in bundles, surrounded by a fine matrix of reticular fibers; there is little stroma (7).

Apart from skin tumors and subcutaneous sarcomas, tumors have been induced in many other tissues and organs by chemical compounds using various routes and means of administration. Often compounds display pronounced specificity toward a certain tissue (*target tissue*); the tissue target may be the site of application, the site of storage, or the site of metabolism of the carcinogen. For example, the azo dye 4-dimethylaminoazobenzene (butter yellow) induces a high incidence of liver tumors when fed to rats; mice are more resistant than rats to the hepatocarcinogenic action of 4-dimethylaminoazobenzene. Similarly, the administration of beryllium salts produces mainly malignant bone tumors, osteosarcomas, in various species. Many carcinogens have, on the other hand, multiple tissue targets; for example, dimethylnitrosamine produces liver, lung, and kidney tumors in rats upon feeding. Tumors in a particularly large variety of organs and tissues are obtained by using 2,7-bisacetylaminofluorene as a carcinogen. This compound, fed to rats, produces a high incidence of

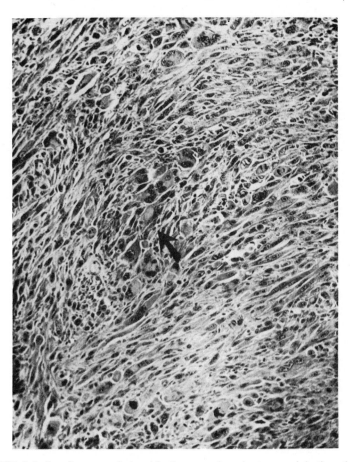

Plate VII. Spindle-cell sarcoma induced in the mouse by subcutaneous injection of 0.25 mg 20-methylcholanthrene. Note arrangement of the spindle-shaped cells and numerous multinu-cleated giant tumor cells (arrow).

primary tumors in the skin,* liver, heart, kidney, mammary gland, glandular part of the stomach, small intestine, brain, cranial nerve, ear canals, tongue, pancreas, hypophysis, the adrenal, Harderian, ceruminous, and salivary glands, and the bone marrow, and is, therefore, the most ubiquitously acting (termed multipotential) carcinogen known at present (8). Not only the carcinogenic potency of a compound, but also its specificity toward certain

* *Note added after completion of Section 4.* Reports on the production of skin tumors by *oral* administration of carcinogens have been extremely rare. The finding of Morris *et al.* (8) with respect to tumor localization in the skin following feeding 2,7-bisacetylaminofluorene was confirmed by S. W. How and K. C. Snell [*J. Natl. Cancer Inst.* **38**, 407 (1967)]. M. Gruenstein,

tissue targets and even species may undergo drastic changes by modification of the chemical structure.

Carcinogenesis in the guinea pig deserves special mention because this species is much more resistant than others to practically all carcinogens, and until recently it was believed to be totally refractory to the induction of liver tumors; this gave rise to the idea that the guinea pig is endowed with a species-specific cancer resistance, thus prompting hypotheses and experiments. However, recently it was found that the guinea pig is just as or more susceptible than rats to the induction of liver tumors by the simple compound, diethylnitrosamine (9), and also by cycasin [a naturally occurring carcinogenic glycoside (10)].

Tumors of the skin, subcutaneous tissue, lung, liver, kidney, mammary gland, and lymphatic tissue are the most commonly encountered in the study of experimental carcinogenesis. In many inbred strains of mice, adenomas of the lung occur spontaneously. In such strains the time of occurrence, and the number and size of lung tumors are affected easily by even minute quantities of carcinogen. Lung tumors often arise, in addition to local growths, after subcutaneous injection of carcinogenic hydrocarbons, and even after cutaneous application of tar (11). An extensive investigation of chemically induced lung cancer in different inbred strains of mice was undertaken by Andervont (12) and Andervont and Lorenz (13). They showed that subcutaneous injection of 1,2,5,6-dibenzanthracene into mice of a certain strain (Strain A), liable to spontaneous lung tumors, increased the number of these tumors. Lorenz and Stewart (14) who administered carcinogenic hydrocarbons orally obtained, apart from tumors in the intestinal tract, numerous pulmonary cancers, attributable to absorption of the carcinogen through the alimentary canal into the bloodstream. The quantities involved, however, must have been minute, since they could not be detected spectroscopically in lung tissue or blood. Magnus (15) ascribed earlier the production of lung tumors to aspiration of small quantities of carcinogen by the experimental animal while the substance is being administered orally. The most typical lung carcinogen is, however, ethyl carbamate, which is highly specific in certain strains of mice toward

---

D. R. Meranze, and M. B. Shimkin [*Cancer Res.* **26**, 2202 (1966)] obtained three different histological types of cutaneous tumors, including epidermoid carcinomas, in Wistar rats by intragastric instillation of high doses of 20-methylcholanthrene. A. S. Mulay and H. I. Firminger [*J. Natl. Cancer Inst.* **13**, 57 (1952)] described dermal-subcutaneous tumors in Osborne-Mendel rats which received *p*-dimethylaminobenzene-1-azo-1-naphthalene orally. Following simultaneous prolonged administration of dimethylnitrosamine and 20-methylcholanthrene to male Sprague-Dawley rats, C. Hoch-Ligeti, M. F. Argus, and J. C. Arcos [*J. Natl. Cancer Inst.* **40**, 535 (1968)] observed epidermoid carcinomas in addition to subcutaneous fibrosarcomas, and lung and liver tumors.

the tissue target, lung (16, 17); in addition to this organ, ethyl carbamate produces tumors also in other tissues in different species. More recently various nitrosamines and diazomethane were shown to be highly active toward the lung tissue. The latter compound, being a gas, is administered in inhalation; this route of administration is of particular importance for studying the effect of cigarette smoke, internal combustion engine exhaust fumes, asbestos, dust, and other particulate irritants on lung tissue, and tumorigenesis in conditions approximating that of the human environment. It is possible that in addition to the commonly incriminated lung carcinogens in the human environment (exhaust fumes and cigarette smoke) other more difficultly eliminable factors may also play a role. Thus, lung cancer in man is possibly produced by inhalation of carcinogenic tar dust. Campbell (18, 19) showed that road dust, containing 2–3% tar, causes cancer of the skin in 70% of mice and increases the incidence of lung tumors to tenfold that of the control animals. The experiments were performed by exposing mice to a cloud of dust in a respiratory chamber. Tar-free dust gave rise to a much smaller number of lung tumors and to no skin tumors.

Macroscopically, lung tumors in rodents are yellowish-grayish white, somewhat translucent hard nodules, more often starting at the periphery or surface of the lung lobules. Lung tumors belong to the class of epithelial tumors (adenomas or carcinomas). The induced tumors in the lung of mice are similar to the spontaneously occurring lung tumors. They consist of closely packed cuboidal (boxlike) or columnar cells which are arranged in glandlike fashion. The tumor cells contain a single, round or oval nucleus. The cytoplasm is acidophilic (stainable by acid dyes). Generally, only few mitotic figures can be observed. The cellular elements are arranged around sparse stroma of fibrous tissue containing only a few blood vessels. These most common alveologenic tumors have the histological appearance more of an adenoma (benign) than a carcinoma (malignant); however, metastases from these tumors have been observed. Apart from this adenomatous type of tumor, squamous cell carcinomas have been produced in the lungs of mice, rats, and guinea pigs. Vorwald (20) induced metastasizing carcinoma in the lung of rats treated with beryllium. The squamous cell tumors arise in the bronchi by squamous metaplasia of the respiratory epithelium. Lung tumors containing spindle-shaped cells were described by Campbell (19).

Most types of hepatic carcinogens have little or no carcinogenic activity in direct contact, and therefore with these compounds skin or subcutaneous tumors at the site of application are rare.* Hepatic carcinogens are active on oral administration, and the potency of some of them is greatly influenced

* *Note added after completion of Section 4.* Until recently it has been considered that the liver is the *exclusive* target tissue of 4-dimethylaminoazobenzene and its derivatives. J. A. Miller and

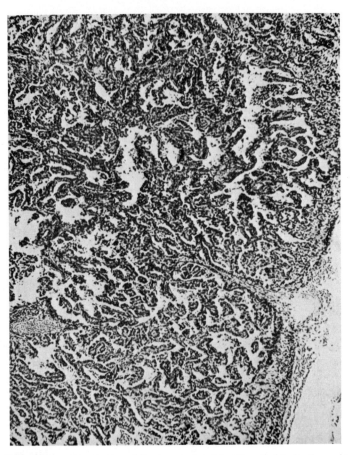

Plate VIII. Adenomatous tumor of the lung induced by 20-methylcholanthrene in strain A mouse.

E. C. Miller [*Cancer Res.* **21**, 1068 (1961)] were the first to show that 3-methoxy-4-aminoazo-benzene and its *N*-methyl and *N,N*-dimethyl derivatives have little carcinogenic activity toward the liver when fed to rats, but produce a high incidence of squamous cell carcinomas of the ear duct; the first dye also produces a low incidence of tumors of the small intestine and the mammary gland, and a scattering of tumors of the skin. These findings were confirmed by G. Fare and J. S. Howell [*Cancer Res.* **24**, 1279 (1964)], and G. Fare and J. W. Orr [*Cancer Res.* **25**, 1784 (1965)] have shown that when 3-methoxy-4-dimethylaminoazobenzene is assayed by skin "painting" in rats it produces a high incidence of multiple skin tumors; surprisingly, this compound proved to be totally ineffective when painted on the skin of mice. In an extension of these studies G. Fare [*Cancer Res.* **26**, 2406 (1966)] has found that also 4-aminoazobenzene and its *N*-methyl and *N,N*-dimethyl derivatives produce a high incidence of skin tumors when painted on the skin of rats. These reports sharply contradict the view, which pervaded the literature of chemical oncology in the last three decades, on the exclusive hepatocarcinogenic activity of aminoazo dyes.

by the composition of the diet consumed by the experimental animal. Nevertheless no hard and fast rules can be formulated. Thus, for example, the pentacyclic heteroaromatic compound, 3,4,5,6-dibenzocarbazole, can act on the skin and subcutaneously like a polycyclic aromatic carcinogen (to which class in fact it belongs), and on the liver like a typical hepatic carcinogen. Moreover, even polycyclic aromatic hydrocarbons can produce hepatomas under special experimental circumstances: Andervont and Lorenz (13) demonstrated the formation of liver tumors through intravenous injections of 1,2,5,6-dibenzanthracene, and cases of liver tumor induction by *topical* contact with carcinogenic hydrocarbons have been described (21); Klein (22) induced hepatomas in a high percentage of new-born suckling mice upon administering *per os* 20-methylcholanthrene. Liver tumors can be induced by administration of a great variety of agents, such as 2-acetyl-aminofluorene, ethionine (the *S*-ethyl analog of the natural amino acid, methionine), 4-dimethylaminostilbene, various tannins, aflatoxin, pyrrol-izidine alkaloids, to note but a few in addition to the agents mentioned above.

Next to the genesis of skin tumors, the gradual emergence of liver tumors lends itself the most readily for following grossly the course of tumorigenesis, since rats, which are preferentially used for this type of experiments, are sufficiently large and sturdy to bear repeated *exploratory laparotomies* (surgical opening of the abdominal cavity under general anesthesia, examina-tion of the abdominal organ or organs, and suturing up; Section 4.3.6.1.1). For example, during the feeding of 3'-methyl-4-dimethylaminoazobenzene the normally smooth surface of the liver takes up a slightly granular appear-ance after as little as one week. This granular appearance, which becomes gradually more pronounced with the subsequent weeks, is due to *cirrhosis* (connective tissue growth replacing liver cells which die because of the hepatotoxic effect of the compound). However, cirrhosis (or at least ex-tensive cirrhosis) does not precede liver tumorigenesis by all agents; for example, certain nitrosamines induce liver tumors with very little or apparently no cirrhosis. Nonetheless, because of the chronological (if not causal) relationship of cirrhosis and liver tumorigenesis with many chemical agents, cirrhosis is often considered as a *precancerous stage.* Paralleling the extensive observable granulation of the surface of the organ there is a notice-able gradual hardening of the normally soft liver mass. Gradually also its reddish-brown color turns paler because of obliteration of many small blood vessels by the disorderly cirrhotic replacement growth. On the other hand, there is accumulation in the liver of appreciable amounts of the dye carcino-gen which confers to it a characteristic yellow tinge. Sometimes as early as the end of the third week a few very small white spots or tiny nodules appear on the surface of the liver lobes. In most cases these represent incipient tumors which grow rapidly, often invasively, and may attain a size of as much as

1 to 4 cm by the end of the eighth to tenth week. From then on, if not by then, the tumor masses invade, engulf, and destroy the abdominal organs. The tumors produced by azo dyes seldom form macroscopically detectable metastases, although occasionally metastatic nodules may be found in the mesentary and the diaphragm. Plates IX and X show the abdominal organs of a normal Sprague-Dawley albino rat and of a hepatic tumor-bearing rat of

Plate IX. The exposed abdominal organs of a normal Sprague-Dawley albino rat. Note the size of the liver.

identical strain, respectively; the latter received in a semi-synthetic diet 3'-methyl-4-dimethylaminoazobenzene at the level of 0.06 % for 11 weeks. Plate XI shows abdominal organs of a Wistar albino rat which was administered orally in 1 ml water 0.55 mg of diethylnitrosamine daily, five times a week, for 25 weeks; note the large hepatic tumors disseminated in the liver lobes.

Induced liver tumors are usually described as arising from liver cells (hepatoma, hepatocellular carcinoma) and from the cells of the bile ducts (cholangioma, cholangiocarcinoma). An earlier detailed study of the changes occurring in the livers of rats fed with 4-dimethylaminoazobenzene was made by Orr (23), who observed the degeneration of parenchymal cells

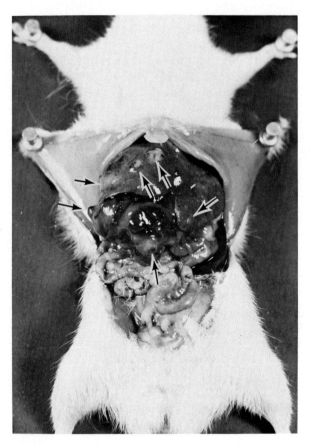

Plate X. Multiple malignant hepatomas (arrows) in a rat of the same strain, which was fed 0.06 % 3′-methyl-4-dimethylaminoazobenzene in a protein-low semi-synthetic diet for 11 weeks.

followed by a regenerative hyperplasia *prior* to tumor formation; he concluded that tumors arise during this stage of regenerative hyperplasia. A similar but more recent study on the changes occurring during feeding 3′-methyl-4-dimethylaminoazobenzene was described by Price *et al.* (24). The earliest histological alteration is the development of hyaline (jellylike glassy substance) inclusion in the cytoplasm of parenchymal cells after about

7 days of ingestion of the carcinogen. The accumulation of these inclusions is followed, in the region of their greatest concentration, by extensive necrosis and proliferation of the bile duct cells, so that the majority of the parenchymal cells which contained these inclusions were replaced by bile duct cells often arranged in a glandular pattern. In some areas bile duct cells grow to form

Plate XI. Multifocal hepatomas (arrows) in a Wistar albino rat which was administered orally 0.55 mg of diethylnitrosamine daily, five times a week, for 25 weeks. Liver viewed from below. The same rat had also a small kidney tumor (not visible here).

cord and sheetlike patterns. Around 14 days, in some cases, more than two thirds of the total parenchymal cell mass is obliterated, which explains why this period is critical for survival when feeding this carcinogen. When the proliferation of the bile duct cells has reached a maximum and the animal survived the critical period, a regression of most but not all of the bile duct cells occurs, and these are rapidly replaced in a nodular fashion by newly formed parenchymal cells resulting in a considerable distortion of the normal liver architecture. However, scattered islets of the hyperplastic ducts persist and are gradually surrounded by dense collagenous connective tissue, which is called *cholangiofibrosis*. The malignant neoplasia, regardless of their

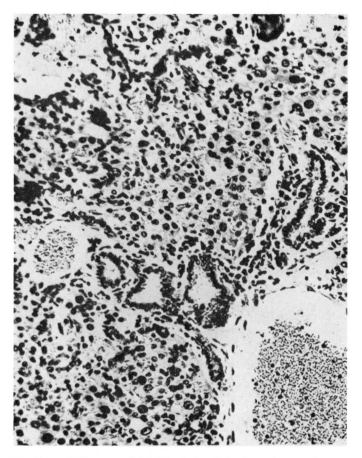

Plate XII. Liver of Wistar rat fed 0.06% 4-dimethylaminoazobenzene in a protein-low semi-synthetic diet for 4 months. Cholangioma showing typical formation of new ducts.

histological type, arise in most instances from these areas of cholangio-fibrosis and adenomatous cell pattern. True hepatoma cells resemble the parenchymal cells and are cuboidal with large, spherical, vesicular nuclei; the tumor consists of cords of such cells, surrounding blood sinuses.

Diethylstilbestrol (a synthetic estrogen having an action similar to that of the female sex hormone) is among the rare organic compounds which can induce, under specific experimental conditions, tumors of the kidney exclusively. To this effect diethylstilbestrol pellets are implanted subcutaneously under the fatty layers between the shoulder blades (through a small incision near the base of the tail using a pair of long narrow forceps) into intact male or castrated female heterozygous Syrian hamsters. Under these conditions

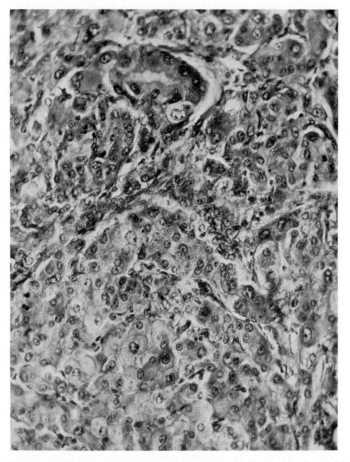

Plate XIII. Hepatocellular carcinoma in the guinea pig which received in the drinking water 1.1 mg diethylnitrosamine daily for 40 weeks.

diethylstilbestrol is a potent renal carcinogen and produces malignant, highly metastasizing, transplantable tumors in almost all treated animals. Surprisingly, while diethylstilbestrol being a synthetic estrogen is stimulating toward the endometrium (glandular epithelium lining the uterus of mammals) and mammary tissues in other rodents, the hamster does not develop mammary gland tumors due to this treatment; neither have any tumors been observed in the ureters, urinary bladder, or urethra. The hamsters develop, however, large benign adenomas of the pituitary gland. It is interesting that the male sex hormone, testosterone propionate, and also the gestation hormone, progesterone, and the adrenal hormone, deoxycorticosterone, are effective inhibitors of kidney tumor induction; consistent with this, kidney tumors with diethylstilbestrol can also be induced in noncastrated females, provided the estrogen treatment is started in a phase of the estrus cycle when progesterone secretion is low.

Kirkman (25) made a detailed study on the induction, transplantability, and histogenesis of these tumors. Macroscopically, after about 200 days of treatment, early stages of primary tumors may be seen on the surface of each kidney as slightly elevated, white, solid, subcapsular nodules. By 250 to 300 days of treatment the number of nodules has increased, and there may be marked variation in nodule size, indicating a considerable range in the length of the time required for induction of different nodules in the same kidney. After about 300 days both kidneys are considerably enlarged and have an irregular surface through which white or hemorrhagic, solid or cystic tumor masses protrude. Here and there remnants of normal kidney tissue may be seen. By this time metastases are prevalent. Sometimes free-floating nodules in the peritoneal cavity may be seen; there is invasion of the mesentary, diaphragm, peritoneum, scrotum, and the spleen. Plates XIV and XV show the kidneys of a male hamster without tumors, and the kidneys of another hamster bearing multifocal tumor nodules, following prolonged treatment with diethylstilbestrol.

Microscopically, the earliest neoplastic lesions consist of tiny clusters of tumor cells between the kidney tubules. They appear to have arisen from intertubular cellular elements as they do not show continuity nor even contact with the adjacent tubular epithelium. Alterations in the cells making up the tubules consist in variations in the size and clumping of cell nuclei and increase of the stainability of the cytoplasm by basic dyes (basophilia). These two alterations which are probably preneoplastic changes are, however, not prevented by the steroids which inhibit renal tumor induction. The small intertubular clusters expand by infiltration between the tubules; there is, however, very little actual destruction of kidney tissue. The cells in the kidney tumor are cuboidal shaped and arranged in the form of branched and connected cord and platelike patterns (somewhat reminiscent of areas of bile-duct proliferations); the cords are enclosed in a network of reticular fibers. Occasionally, in large tumors there are areas of long, spindle-shaped cells. A peculiar characteristic of the renal tumor is the frequent presence of cells bearing long ciliae facing minute cavities in the tumor. A kidney tumor growth (induced by dimethylnitrosamine) in which there is

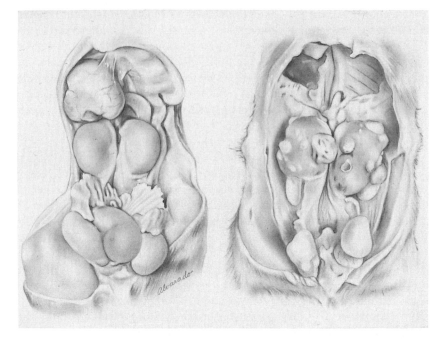

Plate XIV (left). The exposed kidneys of a normal Syrian hamster; some of the intestinal organs are removed. [Redrawn after E. S. Horning, *Endeavour* **13**, 207 (1954).]

Plate XV (right). Multifocal malignant tumors in both kidneys of a Syrian hamster following treatment with diethylstilbestrol for 250 days; diethylstilbestrol implanted subpannicularly as 20 mg pellets on the first and 150th days. [Redrawn after E. S. Horning. *Endeavour* **13**, 207 (1954).]

less clear-cut demarcation between normal and malignant tissue is illustrated in Plate XVI showing diffuse invasion of undifferentiated cells between the glomeruli.

The high incidence of urinary bladder tumors in workers exposed to 2-naphthylamine and benzidine during the manufacture of textile dyes focused interest on the chemical induction and study of tumors of the bladder. Statistical evidence showed that the incidence of bladder tumors in these factory workers is 200 times (for 2-naphthylamine) and about 60 times (for benzidine) higher than that of the general population. The disease could be reproduced experimentally by administering these compounds to animals. Bladder tumors have been obtained by feeding 2-naphthylamine to dogs (*e.g.*, 26); benzidine, as also apparently in humans, is a weaker carcinogen in the dog than 2-naphthylamine. All malignant bladder tumors are carcinomas. At the site of the tumor the bladder epithelium is thickened and

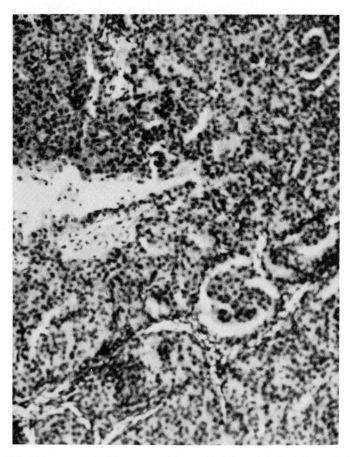

Plate XVI. Kidney tumor in Wistar rat which was administered orally 0.40 mg of dimethyl-nitrosamine daily, five times a week, for 42 weeks. Note the diffuse invasion of undifferentiated cells between the glomeruli.

keratinized, and the normal transitional epithelium changed to stratified squamous epithelium, with downgrowth of thick masses of atypical squamous cells which constitute the malignant growth (27).

An organ often affected by chemical carcinogens, particularly in susceptible inbred strains of mice, is the mammary gland. It has been suggested speculatively that mammary tissue, being subject to cyclic hormonal stimulation, has potentially greater capacity for growth than other tissue and can, therefore, be more readily precipitated into uncontrolled growth or tumor formation. No clear-cut evidence, however, has been obtained concerning this highly complex problem. In mice the emergence of "spontaneous" mammary tumors involves at least three decisive factors: hormonal stimulation, chromosomal genetic factor, and an extrachromosomal genetic factor [the Bittner milk factor (rev. 28)]. Since most mammary tumors are produced by intrinsic stimulation (*i.e.*, through sex hormones), this subject largely falls

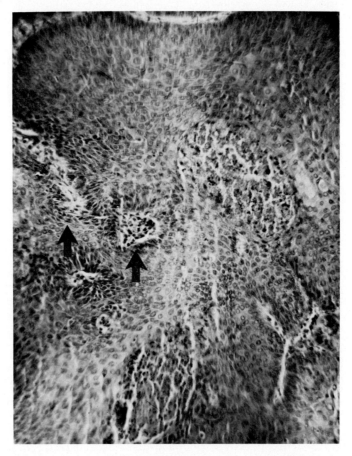

Plate XVII. Bladder tumor in a male C3H strain mouse which received 0.05 % 2-acetylaminofluorene in laboratory chow diet for 23 weeks. Note the epidermoid cell type of the carcinoma (arrows).

outside the scope of this book. A possible relation between tumors induced by hormones and by extrinsic compounds is discussed in Section 5.1.1.3.1.

Mammary tumors have been obtained repeatedly by chemical carcinogens such as 2-acetylaminofluorene, 4-aminobiphenyl, and by polycyclic hydrocarbons. The female sex hormones (estrogens) are, however, the principal mammary carcinogens, which elicit all known histological types either when applied directly to mammary tissue, or if injected at a distant site. This occurs in male and female animals with high or even low susceptibilities. As early as 1940 Cramer (29) has pointed out the important distinction between spontaneous tumor formation and cancer induced by extrinsic carcinogens (*e.g.*, 4-aminobiphenyl): estrogens are normally present in the organism whereas the extrinsic carcinogens are not. Hence, the hereditary factor, which governs individual susceptibility, is of decisive importance in spontaneous mammary tumor formation, but is not in the case of application of extrinsic carcinogens. For tumor induction by extrinsic carcinogens the hereditary factor is secondary. However, when tumors are induced by administration of estrogen, which is already present in the organism, the right hereditary factors are required in addition to the correct (exogenous supplementary) dose. By suitable inbreeding, strains of mice have been obtained with over 90% spontaneous mammary tumor incidence (Section 4.3.2.2).

The fact that mammary tumors can be induced by extrinsic chemical agents in female mice of genetically resistant strains suggests, according to Strong and Williams (30), that a normally present estrogen carries proliferation up to a certain point, at which some other agent can then "initiate the true neoplastic changes in the physiologically altered (estrogen-stimulated) mammary tissue"; this agent can be intrinsic in genetically susceptible (high spontaneous incidence) strains, or extrinsic, such as a carcinogenic hydrocarbon, in nonsusceptible strains.

As mentioned above the mammary gland is a tissue target, among other tissues, for 2-acetylaminofluorene, 4-aminobiphenyl, and certain carcinogenic polycyclic hydrocarbons (the latter produce mammary tumors, however, only in young animals) upon oral administration to rats. Mammary tumors have been obtained in mouse strains of low spontaneous mammary cancer incidence and generally in female animals. Dunning, Curtis, and Eisen (31) described the development of mammary tumors in rats after implantation of paraffin pellets containing dissolved 20-methylcholanthrene. The first, most affected part appeared to be the duct epithelium. Metaplastic change of columnar duct epithelium to squamous cell epithelium took place. Cysts lined by squamous epithelium developed from small metaplastic duct formations as a result of proliferation of the lining cells. Bonser and Orr (7) described the induction of mammary tumors in female mice of certain strains after local injection of a carcinogenic hydrocarbon. The tumors seemed to arise by intraduct proliferation of epithelium with subsequent metaplasia to give rise to squamous cell carcinoma. But "examples of adenocarcinoma composed of small well-formed acini of papilliferous and of solid polygonal-celled and tubular growths" are also cited, being similar to spontaneous or estrogen-induced mammary tumors. Possible dedifferentiation into associated spindle-celled growths is also considered. An interesting method for inducing mammary tumors is described by Orr (32). They were obtained by intranasal application of a solution of 20-methylcholanthrene in female mice of a low-incidence strain, and also in male mice after treatment with estrogen. The tumors were tubular columnar or cuboidal-celled adenocarcinoma; some dedifferentiated to spindle-celled sarcomas.

Finally, one may note that carcinogens (in moderate doses) often cause no systemic (toxic) effects in the organism or in single isolated organs; however, on prolonged administration, inhibition of body growth can be observed (see Sections 4.3.2.4 and 4.3.5). Anemia, as well as damage to liver and genital organs, has been obtained with more massive doses. Shubik and Della Porta (33) carried out pathology studies on the skin of mice painted daily with large, toxic doses of 9,10-dimethyl-1,2-benzanthracene, 3,4-benzopyrene, and 20-methylcholanthrene; with all three carcinogens they found qualitatively identical characteristic lesions in the spleen, lymph nodes, bone marrow, and the overall blood picture. In contrast to this the noncarcinogenic hydrocarbons, anthracene and fluorene, did not bring about any manifestation of toxicity.

REFERENCES TO SECTION 4.2

1. Yamagiwa, K., and Ichikawa, K.: *J. Cancer Res.* **3**, 1 (1918).
2. Andreasen, E.: *Acta Pathol. Microbiol. Scand.* **32**, 157 (1953).
3. Andreasen, E., and Engelbreth-Holm, J.: *Acta Pathol. Microbiol. Scand.* **32**, 165 (1953).
4. Borum, K.: *Acta Pathol. Microbiol. Scand.* **34**, 542 (1954).
5. Berenblum, I., Haran-Ghera, N., and Trainin, N.: *Brit. J. Cancer* **12**, 402 (1958).
6. Orr, J. W.: *J. Pathol. Bacteriol.* **49**, 157 (1939).
7. Bonser, G. M., and Orr, J. W.: *J. Pathol. Bacteriol.* **49**, 171 (1939).
8. Morris, H. P., Ray, F. E., Snell, K. C., Stewart, H. L., and Wagner, B. P.: Carcinogenicity of *N,N'*-fluorenylene-bisacetamide. *Natl. Cancer Inst. Monogr.* **5** (1961).
9. Argus, M. F., and Hoch-Ligeti, C.: *J. Natl. Cancer Inst.* **30**, 533 (1963).
10. Spatz, M.: *Federation Proc.* **23**, 1384 (1964).
11. Murphy, J. B., and Sturm, E.: *J. Exptl. Med.* **42**, 693 (1925).
12. Andervont, H. B.: *U.S. Public Health Serv. Rept.* **52**, 212, 304, 1584 (1937).
13. Andervont, H. B., and Lorenz, E.: *U.S. Public Health Serv. Rept.* **52**, 637, 1931 (1937).
14. Lorenz, E., and Stewart, H. L.: *J. Natl. Cancer Inst.* **9**, 173 (1948–49).
15. Magnus, H. A.: *J. Pathol. Bacteriol.* **49**, 21 (1939).
16. Nettleship, A., Henshaw, P. S., and Meyer, H. L.: *J. Natl. Cancer Inst.* **4**, 309, 523 (1943–44).
17. Larsen, C. D.: *J. Natl. Cancer Inst.* **8**, 99 (1947–48); **9**, 35 (1948–49).
18. Campbell, J. A.: *Brit. J. Exptl. Pathol.* **15**, 287 (1934).
19. Campbell, J. A.: *Brit. J. Exptl. Pathol.* **18**, 215 (1937).
20. Vorwald, A. J.: Pulmonary cancer in experimental exposures to beryllium. *In* "Seventh Saranac Symposium." The Saranac Laboratory, Saranac Lake, New York, 1952.
21. Shear, M. J., Stewart, H. L., and Seligman, A. M.: *J. Natl. Cancer Inst.* **1**, 291 (1940–41).
22. Klein, M.: *Cancer Res.* **19**, 1109 (1959).

23. Orr, J. W.: *J. Pathol. Bacteriol.* **50**, 393 (1940).
24. Price, J. M., Harman, J. W., Miller, E. C., and Miller, J. A.: *Cancer Res.* **12**, 192 (1952).
25. Kirkman, H.: Estrogen-induced tumors of the kidney in the Syrian hamster. *Natl. Cancer Inst. Monogr.* **1** (1959).
26. Hueper, W. C., and Wolfe, H. D.: *Am. J. Pathol.* **13**, 656 (1937).
27. Wilson, R. H., DeEds, F., and Cox, A. J.: *Cancer Res.* **1**, 595 (1941).
28. Dmochowski, L.: *Advan. Cancer Res.* **1**, 103 (1953).
29. Cramer, W.: *Am. J. Cancer* **38**, 463 (1940).
30. Strong, L. C., and Williams, W. L.: *Cancer Res.* **1**, 886 (1941).
31. Dunning, W. F., Curtis, M. R., and Eisen, M. J.: *Am. J. Cancer* **40**, 85 (1940).
32. Orr, J. W.: *J. Pathol. Bacteriol.* **55**, 483 (1943).
33. Shubik, P., and Della Porta, G.: *Arch. Pathol.* **64**, 691 (1957).

BASIC SOURCE BOOKS AND ARTICLES FOR SECTIONS 4.1 AND 4.2

1. Mayer, E.: "Introduction to Dynamic Morphology." Academic Press, New York, 1963, 546 pp.
2. Cameron, G. R.: "Pathology of the Cell." Thomas, Springfield, Illinois, 1951, 840 pp.
3. Bloom, W., and Fawcett, D. W.: "A Textbook of Histology." Saunders, Philadelphia, Pennsylvania, 1962, 720 pp.
4. Petrov, N. N., Editor: "Cancer—A General Guide to Research and Treatment." Macmillan, New York, 1962, 387 pp.
5. Smith, H. A., and Jones, T. C.: "Veterinary Pathology," 2nd ed. Chapter 7: "Neoplasia." Lea & Febiger, Philadelphia, Pennsylvania, 1961.
6. Stewart, H. L., Snell, K. C., Dunham, L. J., and Schlyen, S. M.: Transplantable and transmissible tumors of animals. *In* "Atlas of Tumor Pathology," Section XII, Fasc. 40. Armed Forces Institute of Pathology, Washington, D.C., 1959.
7. Innes, J. R. M.: Malignant diseases of domesticated animals. *In* "Cancer" (R. W. Raven, Ed.), Vol. 3. Butterworths, London, 1958.
8. Dobberstein, J., and Tamaschke, C.: Tumoren. *In* "Pathologie der Laboratoriumstiere" (P. Cohrs, R. Jaffé, and H. Meessen, eds.). Springer, Berlin, 1958.
9. Stewart, H. L.: Experimental cutaneous cancer. *In* "Physiopathology of Cancer" (F. Homburger, ed.), Chapter I. Hoeber-Harper, New York, 1959; Stewart, H. L.: Pulmonary tumors in mice. *Ibid.* Chapter II.
10. Dunn, T. B.: Morphology of mammary tumors in mice. *In* "Physiopathology of Cancer" (F. Homburger, ed.), Chapter III. Hoeber-Harper, New York, 1959.
11. Stewart, H. L., and Snell, K. C.: Histopathology of experimental tumors of the liver of the rat. *In* "Physiopathology of Cancer" (F. Homburger, ed.), Chapter IV. Hoeber-Harper, New York, 1959.
12. Ewing, J.: "Neoplastic Diseases—A Treatise on Tumors," see section on Tumors of Fowl in Chapter IX. Saunders, Philadelphia, Pennsylvania, 1940.
13. Hamperl, H., Editor: "Illustrated Tumor Nomenclature," Intern. Union Against Cancer publication. Springer, New York, 1965, 299 pp.

4.3 Testing Procedures

4.3.1 GENERAL CONSIDERATIONS ON ANIMAL ASSAYS

As we have mentioned in the "Introduction," the testing of the carcinogenic activity of chemical compounds is usually carried out in view of one or more of the following objectives: (a) to recognize the potential public health hazard that they may represent in the normal human environment or in accidental contact, so that either the material may be withdrawn from use or that effective safety measures may be instituted; (b) to determine the structure-activity relationships of a given series of carcinogens; this means that by testing the activities of compounds resulting from the systematic substitutions and other modifications of the chemical structure of a parent compound, the particular molecular geometry optimum for activity in the series may be delineated; (c) to lend support to particular biochemical or biophysical theories on the mechanism of chemical carcinogenesis.

The expectations of the early investigators, that by determining the activities of a large variety of compounds an optimum molecular geometry responsible for maximum carcinogenicity in *all* chemical series may be found, did not materialize since chemical carcinogens show the greatest possible structural diversity. Therefore, the only *truly valid* criterion of the carcinogenic activity or absence of activity of a chemical substance is whether or not it produces tumors in animal assays. This is especially important when judging the significance of test results regarding the deleteriousness of substances to man.

Unequivocal evidence for the carcinogenic activity of a certain material toward man is the actual emergence of tumors due to chronic or inadvertent exposure. Statistical data gathered from the analysis of occupational and other environmental cancer case reports (*e.g.*, skin cancer of cotton-mule-spinners; bladder cancer of dye factory workers; lung cancer of cigarette smokers, infantrymen exposed to sulfur mustard war gas in World War I, miners extracting asbestos, chromium, and beryllium ores; the liver cancer of South African Bantu Negroes due to habitual chewing of *Senecio* shrubbery leaves) are highly valuable for assessing the carcinogenic potency of chemicals toward man. The gathering of information in this manner is, however, much too slow and erratic as compared to the steadily mounting number of new applications of chemicals in the human environment. Moreover, epidemiological studies on human populations may not produce evidence before 20 years, and even then causal relationships may be difficult to establish because of the ill-defined and multiple carcinogenic influences of varying intensities and durations in the present-day man-made environment. Thus, while it is true that carcinogenic activity in animals does not categorically "prove" carcinogenic activity in humans and, conversely, that the absence of proven activity in animal tests does *not with certainty* exclude activity in man, the testing of potential carcinogens in mammalian animal species is the best approximation available. The fact remains, nonetheless, that almost all agents known to date to be carcinogenic to humans (with the possible exception of arsenic) also produce tumors in various animal species.

There are no hard and fast rules for the testing of carcinogenic activity and for the extrapolation of the results of animal assays to humans. The testing of every chemical substance (especially when a compound belongs to a previously untested structural type) is to some extent a new problem which may require a specific assay procedure. The reasonable relevance of the results of testing to humans must be accordingly assessed, each time separately, in the light of the relative evolutionary closeness of the test species and the human species and of the dietary, environmental, and socioeconomic factors in the human population.

An important consideration in selecting animal species for the evaluation of potential carcinogens is that the species should have a sufficiently short life span so that it should be practical and feasible to extend the period of testing over the greatest part of or the entire life span of the animals. Table XX gives the average and maximum life spans of some species commonly used as laboratory animals.

Table XX

Life Span of Experimental Animals[a]

	Average life span (years)	Maximum life span (years)
Mice	2	3
Rats	2	3
Hamsters	1.5	2
Guinea pigs	6	8
Rabbits	7	12
Dogs	9	15 (rarely 20–25)

[a] Owing to the courtesy of Dr. Kenneth F. Burns.

It is evident from Table XX that unless special considerations make it mandatory (such as the special susceptibility to bladder carcinogenesis by orally administered aromatic amines), testing of carcinogens on dogs is generally not practical; this species has not been widely used. The scientific disadvantage of the long life span is, furthermore, compounded by an economic one, that of the large investment in animal maintenance facilities required for testing on a statistically significant number of dogs for a sufficiently long time. For the same reasons, while the rabbit was utilized to some extent by the early investigators, it has been infrequently used as test species in recent times. If one considers the special status of the guinea pig as a test species (discussed in Section 4.2), and the comparative recentness of the introduction of the hamster as a laboratory animal, it is obvious why mice and rats have been used overwhelmingly for testing potential carcinogens. In order to take advantage of the life span of the test species, the administration or treatment should begin when the animals are young, at an age of about one tenth or a little more of the mean life span. In mice and rats this represents the period between the tenth and fifteenth week from birth; for rats, in which the early rate of growth is quite high, it is convenient to define, instead of the average age, the *weight range* of the test group (for the growth rate of test species see Section 4.3.2.4, Figs. 66A and 66B). By drawing a parallel between the average life span of 2 years for rats and mice and a human life span of 60–70 years, the (very questionable) rough approximation has been advanced in some laboratories that testing in rats and/or mice for one year corresponds to intake by humans for about 30 years.

In some testing experiments administration or treatment is extended over the entire testing period up to the sacrifice of the animals. In other experiments there is only a single administration or treatment (*e.g.*, subcutaneous injection of polycyclic hydrocarbons), or it is sometimes continued only for a limited length of time (*e.g.*, feeding of certain aminoazo dyes or nitrosamines), and this is then followed by a period of observation during which the animals are maintained under normal conditions without administration of the carcinogen. It is the conditions and the nature of the experiment and the level at which the compound is tolerated by the test animals (Section 4.3.5) that indicate the schedule to be followed or preferred. The term "testing period" usually refers to the sum of the period of administration or treatment and of the period of observation.

In the earlier literature a number of chemical substances were tested only for a few days or a few months and were found inactive (included in references 1 and 2). Negative results obtained on the basis of such short testing periods are not significant if not outright meaningless and, in fact, many an "inactive" compound retested later for longer periods proved to be carcinogenic. Also, substances regarded as innocuous may be found later to be carcinogenic by investigators using new methods of administration and uncommon species of test animals. Any testing to be meaningful at all must be conducted for a *minimum* of one year unless the substance proves to be carcinogenic earlier. As a general rule the length of the period of testing should be at least one third to one half of the average life span of each species; some investigators in the field (*e.g.*, Hueper) consider, however, that this rule should be even more stringent and that in species with an average life span of less than 5 years the total length of exposure time and subsequent observation period (if any) should be equal to the whole life span. For these reasons no chemical compound may be stated *safely* to be devoid of carcinogenic activity toward man unless it has been found inactive when tested in a variety of mammalian species and by a variety of routes of administration for a length of time corresponding to at least half of the life span of each species. Practical considerations in carrying out carcinogenicity assays on an increasing flood of potential food additives and pesticides have led, however, to some unfortunate compromises. For example, a committee of the British Government recommended that these substances should be tested for carcinogenic activity in the rat and the mouse in both oral and subcutaneous routes, and that at least 12 animals of each sex in each group should survive and be autopsied at $1\frac{1}{2}$ years (for the mouse) and 2 years (for the rat), respectively (3). While this compromise may be regarded as good under the circumstances, it is also true that the chances are rather remote of detecting the carcinogenicity of compounds of low activity (*e.g.*, inducing tumors in 5–10% of the animals) in a group of 12 or 24 animals.

Certain scientific considerations of experimental oncology may not be carried over to assess the potential innocuousness of a substance to man. For example, a compound producing tumors in only 5% of the animals in the experimental group is considered by oncologists to be a very weak carcinogen. It is obvious, however, that the same substance would be regarded as a major health hazard if it was proved to produce the same tumor incidence in a human population.

One of the main difficulties of assessing the relevance of the results of animal assays to humans is (as we have briefly mentioned in Section 4.2) that the susceptibility of different species to a given carcinogen shows usually considerable variations: a carcinogen which is highly active in one species may be totally inactive in another, and *vice versa*. The extrapolation of results to man may also be complicated by anatomical differences between species; for example, rodents have forestomachs (lined with squamous cell epithelium just as the esophagus and may, in fact, be regarded as its continuation) as well as glandular stomachs, and the occurrence of stomach tumors in rodents is almost entirely limited to the forestomach which has no counterpart in humans. The susceptibility of a species to a given carcinogen also depends on the genetic strain of the animal, sex, dietary conditions, the route of administration, and the medium (solvent), if any, which was used as "carrier substance" or "carrier vehicle" for the administration of the agent tested. Moreover, as we have seen, carcinogenic substances generally show a rather selective specificity toward certain target tissues (*e.g.*, liver, kidney, lung). For these reasons a positive result (*i.e.*, that a compound is carcinogenic in some species under certain conditions) carries much greater weight than a negative result (*i.e.*, the conclusion that it is inactive) since among the practically limitless number of combinations of experimental conditions and species there may be some in which the compound may prove to be carcinogenic. The selecting of the susceptible species for specific carcinogenicity tests and the correct mode of application is always a problem; for example, the painting of carcinogenic hydrocarbons to the skin of rats and guinea pigs or the applying of aromatic amines to the skin of mice will hardly demonstrate their activity.

There is some evidence that carcinogenic substances show *cumulative effects*. This means that the carcinogenic effect persists for a long period even after elimination of the active agent by metabolism, and so even minute doses may prove to be carcinogenic if their administration is repeated for a sufficiently long time, because the carcinogenic action of all single doses is additive (*e.g.*, 4, 5, 6). If we accept the validity (Section 4.3.6.2.3) of these findings then the conclusion must be that *no threshold dose or "safe" dose for carcinogenic substances may be set*, the more so as there may be summation of *different* carcinogenic influences present in the human environment. This view was voiced in a different form by Clayson (7) who wrote: "Ideally the slightest *real* suspicion of carcinogenicity ought to be enough to prevent a substance from being allowed into the human environment, whereas the most rigid proof ought to be insisted upon when the result is to be used as evidence on which to base further work or to support a theory of carcinogenesis. In practice the reverse is true. Precautions in handling substances add to their cost and economic factors usually weigh against the acceptance as valid of any but the most overwhelming evidence that such substances may be deleterious to man, whereas poor evidence is sometimes used to support hypotheses."

4.3.2 CHOICE OF THE TEST SPECIES. THE USE OF INBRED STRAINS. CARE AND MAINTENANCE OF THE ANIMALS. THE DIET

4.3.2.1. *Some Guidelines on Species Differences in Susceptibility to Tumor Induction*

The response to chemical tumor-inducing agents varies greatly from one species to another. Although the rabbit was the first experimental animal used to demonstrate the carcinogenic action of coal tar through the formation of skin tumors, this species is completely refractory to subcutaneous tumor induction with 3,4-benzopyrene (the first well-defined carcinogen isolated from coal tar), 1,2,5,6-dibenzanthracene, and other hydrocarbons; in general, the rabbit seems to be less responsive than mice or rats to hydrocarbon carcinogens administered subcutaneously. An exception appears to be

20-methylcholanthrene, which was found to be as active on subcutaneous injection in the cottontail rabbit as in mice or rats (8). A carcinogenic constituent of coal tar so far unknown, seems also to be more potent for rabbits than for mice, since *whole* coal tar is more active for rabbits than for mice (9). Rabbits appear to be refractory to liver tumor induction by azo compounds.

Mice and rats are the two species which are, by far, the most widely used for testing carcinogens because of their short life span, high reproductive rate, small size, and relatively high susceptibility to chemical carcinogens. The mouse skin (and also the skin of the rabbit) is very susceptible to polycyclic hydrocarbons and structurally similar carcinogens, considerably more so than the skin of the rat. On the other hand, the subcutaneous tissue of the rat is more sensitive than that of the mouse to the induction of sarcomas by subcutaneous injection of polycyclic hydrocarbons and other carcinogens; for example, the carcinogenic activity of a variety of cross-linking agents has been tested in the subcutaneous tissue of the rat. Subcutaneous sarcomas have also been produced with great ease in fowl by subcutaneous injection of hydrocarbon carcinogens. The mouse is the species of choice for lung tumor induction by urethan and its derivatives and by mustard-type alkylating agents. The mouse is also the species best suited for the study of leukemia; this condition is brought about in a small proportion of experimental animals by certain chemical carcinogens and with a high incidence by X-rays. The rat is eminently susceptible to hepatic carcinogenesis by aminoazo dyes and other compounds, and it is, therefore, the species preferentially used for studying liver tumor induction. Also the skin of this species is highly susceptible to tumor induction by topical application of certain aminoazo dyes. Tumors in rats with a multiplicity of target localizations are produced by 2-acetylaminofluorene, although mice, fowl, and cats are also susceptible.

Hamsters, cats, and guinea pigs, in this order, are increasingly more resistant than mice and rats to hydrocarbon carcinogens. The special status of the guinea pig as a test species has been mentioned in Section 4.2. Monkeys appear to be highly resistant to epithelial carcinogenesis by hydrocarbons; exhaustive tests with Rhesus monkeys have been carried out by Pfeiffer and Allen (10), who used three different carcinogens in various solvents, dosages, and methods of application over a period of 7 to 10 years. Only some proliferative hyperplastic growth of epithelium, but no tumor, was obtained.

The dog is resistant to hydrocarbon carcinogens; on the other hand, it is the choice species in which bladder tumors are induced by oral administration of 2-naphthylamine, 4-aminobiphenyl, and benzidine (1, 2). Tumors have been induced by subcutaneous injection of aromatic amines also in rats and mice, and by feeding aminoazo dyes to rats, mice, and hamsters; there are, naturally, appreciable differences of species susceptibility to particular compounds. Unlike its behavior toward polycyclic hydrocarbon carcinogens, the rat skin is quite susceptible to tumorigenesis by surface application of the aromatic amine, 2-anthramine, which produces a high incidence of malignant tumors of unusual histological types (11, 12). The mouse skin, on the other hand, is comparatively resistant to carcinogenesis by 2-anthramine. 4-Nitroquinoline N-oxide, a compound structurally related to carcinogenic aromatic amines, is highly active in producing epitheliomas on the mouse skin (13). Nitrosamine carcinogens induce tumors (mostly hepatomas) in mice, rats, hamsters, guinea pigs, dogs, rabbits, chickens, sheep, and monkeys (e.g., 14–18). Similarly, liver damage and liver tumors are induced in a wide species spectrum by aflatoxin, secreted by the common mold *Aspergillus flavus* (e.g., 19–21).

The ferret, the cavy, the European salamander or newt, the leopard frog, the alligator, and the fish have been occasionally used as test species. It is not likely, however, that they will be used for the routine testing of potential carcinogens.

Cancer in man brought about by coal tar was the basic observation which led to the development of chemical oncology. 3,4-Benzopyrene, one of the carcinogens present in coal tar (probably the most active one), has been isolated as mentioned in the "Introduction." Experimental tumor induction in humans is undesirable for obvious reasons, although a few attempts are known. Cottini and Mazzone (22) observed, as a result of surface application of 3,4-benzopyrene to 26 volunteers, a sequence of histological events and papilloma formation very similar to that occurring in the early stages of experimental tumor induction in animals; the experiment was terminated after 4 months of application of the hydrocarbon, before irreversible malignancy was established. In analogy with the situation in mice all papillomas and beginnings of infiltration regressed after 2–3 months. Data gathered from occupational cancer case records indicate that, just as in animals, the hydrocarbon-induced human tumors usually begin as papillomas, then turn malignant becoming epitheliomas. Henry (23) gives a statistical evaluation of the average latent period for the less carcinogenic shale oil and mineral oil as about 50 to 60 years, and for the more carcinogenic pitch and tar as 25 years, although the shortest latent period observed for epithelioma formation due to pitch was 10 months. For the dye intermediates, 2-naphthylamine and benzidine, which are responsible for the comparatively high incidence of bladder cancer among dye factory workers, Goldblatt (24) reckons that the usual latent period is between 11 and 16 years. Melick *et al.* (25) calculated a latent period of 5–19 years for bladder tumor induction among workmen manufacturing 4-aminobiphenyl. The hydrocarbons and aromatic amines are the carcinogenic industrial hazards known for the longest time. The list is, however, by no means exhausted as we have also seen in previous sections.

There is an increased lung cancer incidence among workers inhaling chromate dusts, and among miners of asbestos, iron, and nickel ores; also cancer of the nasal sinuses has been noted among the latter. Cancer of the bone is often found in workers exposed to the dust of beryllium compounds. The carcinogenicity of *all* these agents toward man could be verified in animal experiments with the sole exception of arsenic which appears to be a weak carcinogen to humans on the grounds of statistical evidence.

4.3.2.2   *The Use of Inbred Strains and Random-Bred Animals. Spontaneous Tumor Incidence of Inbred Strains*

By means of selective inbreeding, genetically homogeneous (homozygous) strains of the most used rodent species have been developed; individuals of an *inbred strain* are practically as similar as identical twins. While a large number of inbred strains of mice have been described, there are only a few inbred strains of rats. Owing to the efforts mainly of the Roscoe B. Jackson Memorial Laboratory, the National Cancer Institute, and a number of enterprising breeding laboratories most of these strains are commercially available in the United States. Inbred strains of guinea pigs are rare and are not commercially available.

A strain is regarded as inbred when it results from at least 20 consecutive brother-sister matings; parent-offspring mating may substitute for brother-sister mating provided that mating is always with the younger of the two parents (26). Some strains of mice have now been inbred for more than 100 generations. For developing an inbred strain the individuals which show the undesirable traits in the litters are discarded and only the individuals selected for the characteristics for which the animals are being bred are mated in each generation. For instance, if the selection is directed to obtain a strain of high spontaneous mammary tumor incidence, then the litter of only those females which develop spontaneous mammary tumors will be used for further mating in each generation. In this way the genetic traits responsible for susceptibility to spontaneous mammary tumors in females will be selected and the genetic variability of the random-bred stock is reduced to a minimum; "by this process the morphological and physiological characters which have a genetic basis become uniform and fixed within the strain" (27).

Furthermore, starting from an inbred strain, *sublines* (or *substrains*) may be selected, which are genetically different from one another and from the parent strain. Just as inbred strains of a species differ from one another and also from the random-bred "wild" variety, the sublines of an inbred strain can differ from one another. By crossing strains and sublines of definite characteristics (*e.g.*, high and low susceptibility to a certain type of tumor) further investigations can then be carried out as to the genes involved in the production of this particular type of tumor, their number, chromosome location, and other properties with which they are linked.

The advantage of inbred strains is that they show a high constancy of biological responses. The morphological and growth characteristics, the metabolic pattern, the levels of enzymes in particular tissues, for example, all vary within relatively narrow limits from one individual to another, unlike in a group of random-bred animals of the same species. Thus, the use of inbred strains in biological studies may be compared to the use of pure reagent grade chemicals in chemical experimentation. Nonetheless, as every living organism is highly responsive to changes in diet and environment, homogeneous strains no matter how rigorously selected often develop slight deviations from the original genetic stock when transferred to a breeding colony at a different location.

Some of the more often used mouse strains are: A (albino), BALB (albino), C (cinnamon), C3H (color of wild house mice), C57 black, CBA (color of wild house mice), DBA (dilute brown), SWR (inbred "Swiss" albino), NZB (obese albino). A substrain is designated by the name of the parent strain followed by a bar and the appropriate substrain symbol. The substrain symbol may consist of an abbreviation of the name of the person or laboratory maintaining it; for example, A/Jax (A strain of the Roscoe B. Jackson Memorial Laboratory), C3H/Bi (subline of Dr. J. J. Bittner). Numbers or lower case substrain symbols may indicate the number of generations at which two substrains were separated from a common strain *prior* to complete inbreeding, for example C57BR/a and C57BR/cd, or DBA/1 and DBA/2. Sometimes first generation hybrids between two inbred strains are used. Such hybrids are designated by the symbol F_1; for example, $AKD2F_1$ is the hybrid offspring of an AKR/J female ($\female$) and of a DBA/2J (represented as D2) male ($\male$). For details on nomenclature see reference (26).

The most often used inbred rat strains are the Wistar albino, Sprague-Dawley albino, Sherman albino, and Long-Evans hooded (black and white). Random-bred guinea pigs commercially available from breeding farms are the short smooth-haired and long-haired angora varieties. The commercially available random-bred hamsters are the Syrian Golden and the Chinese varieties.

Among the many biological characteristics and responses of inbred strains the most important from the standpoint of carcinogen testing is that they usually have a known incidence of spontaneously occurring tumors. Nevertheless, even for strains where the type of spontaneous tumors and their incidence are well known it is advisable in every testing experiment to carry a control group, which does not receive the potential carcinogen to be tested, but which otherwise receives the same treatment, handling, and diet as the animals in the test group. The spontaneous tumor incidence of this control group, determined at the end of the testing period, is then indicative of the actual tumor incidence of the strain under the dietary and other conditions of the experiment; this is of importance because the spontaneous tumor incidence of the strain is often obscured by the nature of the diet. The tumors which may arise in the groups which received the compounds to be tested are evaluated in the light of the tumor incidence of the control group.

The spontaneous tumor incidences of mouse strains are by far the best known. Strains may be selected which show the occurrence of cancer in only one tissue. Other inbred strains exist which develop cancer with two tissue localizations. For example, strain C3H mice are known to develop a high incidence of mammary tumors in females and liver tumors in males; both sexes of strain A mice develop spontaneous lung tumors and the breeding females also mammary tumors. However, this does not mean that the females do not have the potentiality to develop lung tumors but only that the period of latency of the spontaneous mammary tumors is much shorter than that of the lung tumors and so the animals die before the lung tumors develop. Indeed, if the mammary tumors are removed in these females, and so life is sufficiently prolonged, these animals eventually develop lung tumors. Other strains, such as the C57 black, have been selected for absence or low incidence of mammary and lung tumors. A synoptic tabulation of the spontaneous tumor incidence of some of the best-known mouse strains is given in Table XXI.

The spontaneous tumor incidence of the rat strains is much less well known. However, in general, spontaneous tumors appear to be more rare in the inbred rat strains than in the inbred mouse strains, except that old rats are known to develop a low percentage of lymphosarcomas usually originating from abdominal lymph nodes. In 1956 Davis et al. (28) reported an incidence of 48% of mammary tumors in 2-year-old rats. In examining specifically the thyroid, adrenal, pituitary, ovary, uterus, brain, and testicle, Thompson and Hunt (29) reported 40% adenomas of the thyroid, 16% adenomas of the pituitary, and 8% tumors of the adrenal gland in rats $1-2\frac{1}{2}$ years old. Paralleling the resistance of the guinea pig to carcinogenesis by many chemical agents, spontaneous tumors appear to be a rarity in this species. Lipschütz et al. (30) found in a small percentage of 4- to 6-year-old female guinea pigs tiny nodules of uterine adenocarcinoma.

It is a debated question whether random-bred stock animals or inbred strains should be used for evaluating the carcinogenic activity of hitherto untested compounds. In the writers' opinion it is more correct to test on a random-bred stock on the grounds that it is more likely that at least a few individuals will respond to the administration of an active agent in a group

Table XXI

Percentage Spontaneous Tumor Incidence in Inbred Strains of Mice[a]

Strain:	AKR ♀	AKR ♂	C3H ♀	C3H ♂	A/He ♀	A/He ♂	A/Jax ♀	A/Jax ♂	DBA/1 ♀	DBA/1 ♂	DBA/2 ♀	DBA/2 ♂	BALB/c ♀	BALB/c ♂	C57BR/cd ♀	C57BR/cd ♂	C57L/He ♀	C57L/He ♂	C57BL/6 ♀	C57BL/6 ♂
Mammary tumors	3		95		74		28		80		43		8				3			
Lung tumors		2		4	30	51	41	49	2	2	2	5	26	29						
Skin tumors			2				5			3	2				36	18	38	35	11	4
Liver tumors				21						6						14	5	7	4	3
Leukemia	85	77				3					2	4	2	2			7		6	3
Reticulum cell sarcoma										3							2	3	3	5
Kidney tumors						2		2												

[a] From a tabulation of the Roscoe B. Jackson Memorial Laboratory, prepared by E. S. Russell.

which is genetically heterogeneous. Although in some instances the percentage of animals with tumors may not be high in a random-bred group, nonetheless the emergence of tumors indicates that individuals of the species with a certain genetic make-up are responsive to the carcinogenic stimulus of the agent. A corollary of this consideration, verified by experimental observations, is that while one inbred strain may be highly responsive to an agent, the same carcinogen may fail to induce tumors in animals of another inbred strain of the same species. Conversely, if a chemical agent was found to be carcinogenic when tested in an inbred strain it will with certainty produce tumors at least in a few individuals when retested in a random-bred stock. For these reasons potential carcinogens should be first tested, if at all possible, in a random-bred stock, especially if considerations of human contact prompted the testing, remembering also that the human population is highly random-bred; negative results obtained with a compound of a hitherto untested chemical series in a highly inbred strain should be regarded with suspicion. On the other hand, for studying the structure-activity relationships of a homologous series of carcinogens, by testing the effect of various substitutions and other molecular modifications, the use of a susceptible inbred strain is much more likely to yield reliable and reproducible results than random-bred animals. Of course, the relative carcinogenicities found with a series of compounds in one inbred strain are valid only in that particular strain; testing in another inbred strain, however susceptible it may be to that series of carcinogens, may yield different relative activities.

4.3.2.3 The Care, Handling, and Identification of the Test Animals

4.3.2.3.1 *The Animal Quarters.* It must be immediately stressed that the elementary requirement to produce reliable data in any type of scientific research involving animals is to have correctly designed, efficiently run, clean animal quarters in which environmental conditions are rigidly controlled, and to have a healthy, sturdy, humanely handled animal stock; these requirements are particularly stringent for studies on chemical carcinogenesis. To carry out investigations with sick, ill-treated animals which are under environmental stress amounts to the same as working with dubious, technical-grade chemicals and dirty glassware! Unfortunately, because of the rapid expansion of biological and medical research, funds earmarked for research activities have often outrun the funds destined for the modernization of outmoded animal quarters, or for the building of new facilities. An important reason for this is a psychological one: since most of biological and medical research is supported directly or indirectly by public funds which most often necessitates specific itemized advanced budgeting, requests for newfangled, complex laboratory apparatus carry more "glamor" than requests for the modernization or building of animal facilities. Often this difficulty or temptation is compounded by an administrative hierarchy uninformed or unconvinced of the basic necessity for good animal quarters. Yet, this is one of the critical barriers to superior quality of scientific research involving animals!

A number of articles and books have appeared on the care and maintenance of small laboratory animals (*e.g.*, 31–41), and some of these are available upon request. The present section is not intended to supplement these but rather to provide some general guidelines. In this the authors have drawn upon their experience with small laboratory animals. However, "optimum animal care" encompasses a variety of possible physical arrangements and also variations in certain rules to be followed, and, consequently, readers familiar with animal work may prefer some arrangements and rules to others. Nevertheless, the present guidelines will be useful as a starting point for those who have been drawn to chemical oncology from non-biological disciplines.

Maximum vermin control (against cockroaches, flies, beetles, silverfish, bedbugs, wild or escaped rodents, etc.) is a must for animal quarters since vermin constitute vectors for transmitting diseases which can drastically influence the outcome of experiments or for epidemics which can decimate the colony. For maximum vermin control all interior walls, ceilings, and floors should be carefully sealed. If the whole construction is not smooth-surfaced concrete, all cracks should be filled with a good grade caulking compound or plaster of Paris, and the walls and ceiling double or triple coated with pastel green or yellow enamel paint. Smooth-surfaced concrete or plastic-sealed concrete is probably the best material for the floor irrespective of the rest of the construction; well-distributed drains must be provided in the floor. This arrangement is very suitable for permitting routine washing of the surfaces with detergent solution and rinsing by hosing. To assure effectiveness of these routine hygiene measures the surfaces to be cleaned should be uninterrupted as far as possible by pipes and electrical wiring, even if carefully shielded. The providing of uninterrupted surfaces is facilitated by the fact that windows are not necessary for quartering the usual laboratory rodents, mice, rats, and hamsters; these are nocturnal animals and are inactive during daylight. The electric lighting fixtures, switches, and outlets (if any) should be sealed so as not to provide breeding nests for insect vermin. A few sealed ultraviolet lamps disposed at half-height on the walls, and beamed downward, help odor control and cut down on the airborne transmission of respiratory diseases.

Although rodents in the wild occur under extremes of climates, air conditioning and filtering equipment must be incorporated in the planning of all animal facilities to provide an optimum physiological state; inbred strains are especially sensitive to extremes of temperature. The planning of air conditioning equipment *must include* provision for a *standby replacement system* to take care of emergencies of breakdown, in the summer months, especially under semi-tropical and tropical humid climates. The intake and output points of the air conditioning and circulation system must be distributed so as to *avoid exposure of the animals to draft* which would predispose them to respiratory infections. For example, if the cages used in the quarters are freely open to air circulation (such as the cages built of heavy wire and used mostly for rats, hamsters, and guinea pigs) then the air conditioner outlets bringing the air into the room should be provided with deflectors directing the air current sidewise; similar caution must be exercised when, for the conditioning of small quarters, individual window-unit air conditioners are used instead of a built-in central system. Preferentially, the air conditioner outlets should be high up in the wall or in the ceiling, and the evacuating vent low on the opposite wall. In animal quarters the simple problem of temperature conditioning is complicated by the necessity of the evacuation of ammonia vapors due to the bacterial decomposition of excreta. For example, for temperature conditioning the most uniform distribution would be accomplished by a single inlet at the floor level and several points of exhaust at the ceiling; this optimum circulation pattern for temperature conditioning is, however, quite inefficient for the evacuation of the ammonia vapors which are several times heavier than air. To prevent the introduction of dust and pathogenic bacteria into the animal quarters, discardable or washable air filters have to be incorporated into the incoming air duct; some animal facilities use electrostatic precipitators to remove solid particles.

Two factors have to be considered in planning the air conditioning system: (a) the necessity of providing the proper change of air and (b) the heat load of the animal facility which depends on the species quartered and the size of the population. Various evaluations of the U.S. National Institutes

Table XXII

Space and Air Requirements of Laboratory Rodents

Species	Weight (gm)	Average gross space required (cubic ft)	Fresh air required (cubic ft/min)	Heat radiated (BTU/animal/hr)[a]
Mouse	21	1.0	0.10	0.6
Rat	200	3.5	0.75	3.6
Guinea pig	410	6.0	1.50	5.7

[a] BTU (British Thermal Unit) = 252 cal.

of Health for mice, rats, and guinea pigs gave the average values shown in Table XXII.

In a not overcrowded animal quarter, housing a typical rodent colony, these fresh air requirements amount to changing the air of the room between 14 and 18 times per hour. This assures optimum air distribution; lingering odors and also heavy drafts are avoided. However, the discarding of the heated or cooled air in its entirety after each change is costly, and it is customary to recirculate a proportion of the used air; ideally not more than 40% should be recirculated.

In addition to temperature control, the control of relative humidity is important for reducing chronic respiratory diseases in rodents, especially rats; this puts additional demands on the conditioning system. Relative humidity should not rise above 65% or go below 20%. The best relative humidity for the commonly used laboratory animal species is about 50%; the average figures for optimum room temperatures and relative humidities are given in Table XXIII.

Table XXIII

Temperature and Humidity Optima for Laboratory Animals

Species	Optimum room temperature	Optimum relative humidity (%)
Mouse	20–22°C (68–72°F)	50–60
Rat	18–21°C (65–70°F)	45–55
Hamster	20–22°C (68–72°F)	45–50
Guinea pig	18–21°C (65–70°F)	45
Rabbit	16–18°C (60–65°F)	40–45
Dog	22°C (72°F)	45–60

In order to assure effective vermin, dust, and humidity control of the rooms actually housing the animals, the following rooms must be provided: a *separate room* equipped with washing tanks and a steam sterilizer in which the cages, cage-racks and dropping-trays collecting excreta are cleaned and sterilized, bedding changed and drinking-water bottles cleaned and filled, etc.; another room for the preparation and storage of special diets; and one in which surgical and other procedures may be carried out on the animals. These rooms should be in preference not directly adjacent to the animal rooms but attainable through connecting corridors.

4.3.2.3.2 The Housing of Animals. Selection of Cages. Selection of the type of cages and racks used depends to some extent on the species quartered and the alternative whether all animals housed will be purchased from breeding companies or that the laboratory plans to breed, totally or in part, its own animal stock. The considerations advanced here are based on the transient housing of purchased animals.*

The animal quarters must be quiet to avoid auditory stress to small rodents. Noisy species, especially dogs, should be quartered in separate rooms and devocalized; this minor surgical operation, which involves the severance of the vocal cords, assures relative quiet in the room for 4 to 5 months.

While partly or wholly wooden cages may be used for housing small rodents in other types of biological research and are preferred for the breeding of animals, such cages are definitively contraindicated for studies on chemical carcinogenesis since it is not possible to completely remove carcinogenic or cocarcinogenic contaminants from the wooden parts. These contaminants can drastically modify, for example, the biological response of the mouse skin (which is notoriously sensitive to tumorigenic influences) to potential carcinogens. Several years ago the emergence of skin tumors was reported in untreated control mice which had been housed in wooden cages painted with a lice-repellent creosote preparation. Cages and racks used must be entirely metal constructions which can hence be thoroughly detergent washed and steam sterilized. Recently, the use of disposable thin plastic boxes (with permanent metal top to which the water bottle is fastened) has been introduced for mice and small weanling rats. Metal cages and feeding pans should be well constructed and must be periodically inspected for loose wire ends or wire cloth screens which may cause lacerations in the animals leading occasionally to infected cysts, and may also cause the transfer of carcinogenic materials to lacerated parts of the animal body.

* Some breeding companies in the United States, supplying laboratory animals nationally, are:

Carworth Farms, Inc.
New City, Rockland County, New York 10956

Charles River Breeding Laboratories, Inc.
251 Ballard Vale Street, North Wilmington, Mass. 01888

Holtzman Co.
421 Holtzman Road, Madison, Wisconsin 53713

Lakeview Hamster Colony
P.O. Box 85, Newfield, New Jersey 08344

Lemberger Co.
P.O. Box 482, Oshkosh, Wisconsin 54902

Microbiological Associates
4846 Bethesda Avenue, Washington, D.C. 20014

Millerton Farms, Inc.
Millerton, New York 12546

National Laboratory Animal Co.
P.O. Box 93, Creve Coeur, Missouri 63141

Rockland Farms, Inc.
New City, Rockland County, New York 10956

Roscoe B. Jackson Memorial Laboratory
Bar Harbor, Maine 04609

A. R. Schmidt Co.
2826 Latham Drive, Madison, Wisconsin 53713

Taconic Farms, Inc.
Germantown, New York 12526

Cages constructed of galvanized steel (framework) and 3-mesh 18-gauge wire cloth (a custom-made adaption of cage type LC-26 of the Geo. H. Wahman Manufacturing Co., Baltimore, Maryland) were found in our laboratories to be very satisfactory for housing mice; these cages have metal trays (1 inch or 2.5 cm deep) serving as a removable floor, and a boxlike depression in the wire cloth screen in the top is provided for feeding pelleted dry feed (laboratory chow). The cages have front wire screen doors. A simple, efficient, and low-cost arrangement to provide drinking water is the use of an inverted 8 oz (approx. 250 ml) glass bottle with rubber stopper and a stainless steel tube bent at 120° angle; this tube is inserted through the wire mesh. A wire bottle-holder clamp or spring permits diagonal suspension of the bottle on the cage door with the stainless steel drinking tube protruding inwardly at about 2–3 inches from the cage floor; this allows easy checking of the water levels. A cage 9 × 15 × 9 inches (22 × 37 × 22 cm) size can comfortably house 10 mice. Figure 62 (to the left) shows a cage of this type,

Fig. 62. To the left is shown a cage unit for the maintenance of laboratory mice, and to the right a cage unit for hamsters, rats, or guinea pigs, both complete with drinking-water bottles and holders for the identification cards. In the mouse cage note the boxlike depression in the top provided for feeding dry laboratory chow pellets; on the cage to the right a separate external hopper (as shown) is provided for this purpose. The cage to the left houses adequately 10 mice; the cage to the right houses 4 hamsters, 2 rats, or 1 guinea pig.

complete with water bottle and identification card holder. Mice require a *bedding material* with which the floor trays are filled to level. The bedding material must be economical, soft in order to provide for adequate nesting, capable of absorbing large quantities of fluid (urine), able to bind ammonia odor, should not be edible by mice, and should withstand sterilization or be available commercially already sterilized; also, the bedding material should be easy to incinerate and should be dustless in order to avoid as much as possible complications with respiratory diseases and the general cleanliness of the animal quarters. Wood shavings (white pine alone or in preference mixed with cedar which lessens animal odor) are satisfactory as bedding substance. Recently, ground corn cobs (San-I-Cel) have been introduced as bedding material; San-I-Cel is dust-free and is also available treated with a deodorizing additive. Advantageously the cages are kept in multi-level movable stands (cage-racks) mounted on casters with ball bearings; since these mouse cages are relatively heavy it is not convenient to use racks holding more than 25–30 cages (distributed 5–6 cages per row).

For housing rats, hamsters, and guinea pigs heavy wire cages constructed by welding from 14- and 6-gauge galvanized wire are quite satisfactory (for example, Rodere Cage No. 425, available from the Bussey Products Co., Chicago, Illinois). A cage of this type (Fig. 62, to the right) $8\frac{1}{2} \times 11 \times 8\frac{1}{2}$ inches ($21 \times 28 \times 21$ cm) size can adequately house 4 adult hamsters, 2 rats, or 1 guinea pig. Racks holding 25 or 50 of these cages (in 5-cage rows) are available; the 50-cage rack is double faced and must be set away from the wall. The cages open at the top and have, on each side of the top, rims which slide into brackets attached to the underside of the shelves of the rack, so that each cage hangs suspended. All excreta and uneaten food falls through the wire floor and is collected in the dropping pans on the shelf below. These are far enough from the floor of the cages so that the animal cannot reach through the mesh to withdraw any of the material collected in the pans. The efficiency of the collection of the excreta and the general cleanliness of the rack can be further improved by placing on the top of the pans under every row of wire cages heavy waxed paper (*e.g.*, Jute Tympan treated paper or regular 40 pound waxed Kraft paper). Rolls of the paper are mounted at the level of each cage row and cleaning is accomplished by pulling out the soiled paper from beneath the cages at the side of the rack opposite to the paper rolls; this automatically pulls in clean paper from the rolls. While this system can entirely substitute for the cage pans in case of necessity, still the use of the pans and paper together assures much greater cleanliness since in this way all fecal matter rolling down from the paper will be collected in the pans and will not soil the rack. Figure 63 shows a rack capable of holding 50 cages, complete with dropping pans and paper rolls.

changes, and drafts during shipment, it is advantageous to submit rats (especially prone to respiratory infections) destined for long-term experiments to treatment with Terramycin for 1 week upon arrival; the antibiotic is administered in the drinking water at the level of 75 mg per liter. Miller *et al.* (42) used this treatment for periods of 6 consecutive days at 4–8 week intervals, for controlling respiratory infections in rat colonies during the testing of carcinogens throughout the whole span of the experiment. Guinea pigs are much more resistant to respiratory infections than rats and should not receive treatment by antibiotics (Terramycin or other) under any circumstances because this treatment often brings about intestinal obstruction, possibly by upsetting the equilibrium of the intestinal bacterial flora.

Among the small rodents used in cancer research the pure albino rats (but not the hooded or gray rats) are the tamest and most intelligent laboratory animals. With a minimum of precautions and rules, bites are easily avoided. Never frighten a rat with sudden brisk movements and never try to pick up a sleeping or resting rat suddenly. Always give time to the animal, resting unaware in its cage, to adjust to change. The rat should be picked up bodily and handled gently but firmly. Don't pick up a rat by the tail unless it is vicious and tends to bite. Fighting rats should be picked up by the *end* of the tail, swung pendulum-wise once or twice, landed on a table top and grasped instantaneously with palm of the hand over the animal's back, and thumb and index finger holding the forelegs firmly across the chin; in this way the animal cannot lower its head to bite. Use well-fitting cotton gloves (workmen's gloves) to handle vicious rats; however, it is more convenient not to use gloves for the routine care of tame rats. Avoid picking up fighting rats near the base of the tail, as a rat can climb up its own strong tail and bite.

Hamsters have a tendency to jump from the operator's hand. They should be held either by both hands, or the loose skin behind the neck should be grasped by thumb and forefinger and the hind legs held between the third and fourth finger. This last single-handed manipulation (necessary for giving injections, for example) requires some practice as the animal can literally turn around in its own loose skin. For this reason and because of their tendency to jump, hamsters should be handled low above a table top.

Mice are generally by far the most vicious among the laboratory rodents. To avoid bites the mouse is best picked up by the tail. For simple manipulations, such as shaving of the fur in the interscapular region and depositing carcinogen solutions on the skin, it is convenient to place the animal on a wire screen cage top while firmly holding the tail. In this way the animal's body will be firmly extended and strained because the animal will attempt to run forward; the mouse tends to maintain this position during treatment. For giving injections the animal is picked up from the above position by grasping firmly, with the other hand, the skin on the back all along the spine from the neck down to the tail.

Guinea pigs should be especially gently handled as they are the most easily frightened among the laboratory rodents. They very seldom bite but occasionally may scratch with their hind legs. For single-handed manipulation, guinea pigs are picked up bodily by holding them around the back at the level of the chest with one hand. When it is necessary to hold the animal for a longer period of time and assistance is available, the other hand should be placed under their hind legs to give more support.

Subcutaneous injections to rodents can be given most easily into the flank or into the abdominal wall. For giving intraperitoneal injection the needle is quickly thrust in, directed slightly downward (to avoid laceration of the liver and penetration of the intestines), at the level of the center of the abdomen. If the coat of the animal is soiled, remove the fur by shaving at the location of the intended injection. Use a new or carefully sharpened needle of correct length; a "barbed" needle will cause pain to the animals. Check that the injected solution has a pH in the physiological range. Acid or alkaline solutions cause tissue necrosis which can drastically modify the biological response.

One of the most often employed procedures to identify laboratory rodents is by ear punches or ear notches. The ear punching system utilizes a simple hole, a simple notch, and a double notch in various combinations in different areas of the two ears. The figures in the right ear give the units and the figures in the left ear the decimals of the system; using this system the animals can be numbered from 1 to 99 as shown in Fig. 65. A disadvantage of the punching system is that when rats are housed together in pairs or small colonies, the punches and notches are sometimes mutilated by fighting. Farris (38) proposed a technique of cutting small V-shaped wedges, four in each ear, using scissors or a special punch. This numbering system of the animals may be considerably extended by combining it with markings on the skin and fur with brightly colored biological stains (*e.g.,* chrysoidine yellow, fuchsine red, malachite green, trypan blue); these markings are, however, only semipermanent and have to be renewed every 4–6 weeks. Random-bred individuals of a species (hamsters, guinea pigs, rabbits) most often differ in color and color pattern of the coat, and this is used as a basis for identification as a replacement of or in combination with the ear punching or notching system.

In addition to the identification on the animal body, all cages must bear identification cards, filled in with permanent ink or ball-point pen, giving the following information: species, strain, sex, date of arrival, birth dates, experiment identification number (if any), group number, treatment, date treatment began, animal numbers, other remarks. Identification cards must be firmly inserted into the card holders which are fastened to the cages, and the cards should be replaced as soon as they begin to decay. Three separate systems are recommended to record the observations on the animals: (*a*) The *record of body weights* should be a loose-leaf notebook of ruled pages or a system of large file cards, on which vertical columns are dated and a horizontal line is provided for each animal of a group, so that the average group weight may be easily determined for any time period; this record is the depository of the results of the weekly weighings of animals (especially for rats, hamsters, and guinea pigs) as sudden changes in body weight or of the

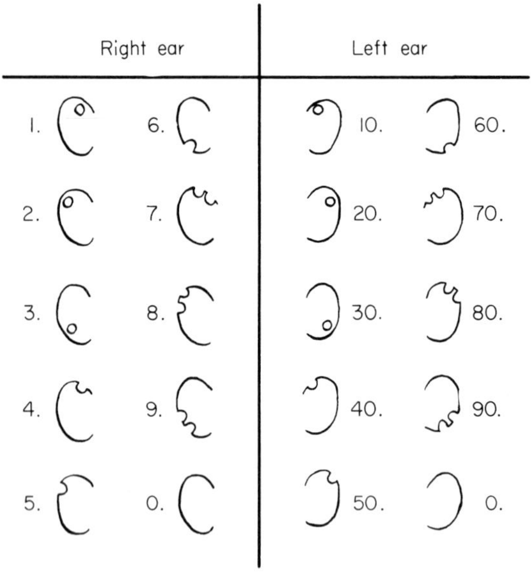

Fig. 65. System of numbering rodents (mice, rats, hamsters, guinea pigs) from 1 to 99 by ear punching.

growth rate are often informative of the emergence of internal tumors; (*b*) The *record of general observations* should consist of another notebook with pages assigned to each animal; in this should be described every other pertinent observation, disease from which the animal may have recovered, change of behavior, etc.; (*c*) The *record of autopsies* should be a loose-leaf binder containing a standard autopsy blank assigned to every animal; the method of recording autopsies and the description of the standard autopsy blank used in our laboratories is given in Section 4.3.6.1. Moreover, in addition to the three experimental records, large animal quarters should have a "key-book" by means of which different animal groups, identified by the experiment number and/or the name of the responsible investigator, can be geographically located.

The most common diseases of laboratory mice and rats, with which we will be concerned here, are the respiratory infections already mentioned above. In mice the more common type is the *infectious catarrh* of the upper respiratory tract caused by a pleuropneumonia-like organism (PPLO). In rats the more common type respiratory infection is of the lower respiratory tract, the *endemic* or *virus pneumonia.* Virus pneumonia is prevalent in all laboratory rat colonies, and it is probably safe to say that all adult rats have it in a milder or more advanced form. However, the chronic and sometimes barely detectable infection is considerably aggravated by poor ventilation, damp ammoniacal atmosphere, fluctuating room temperature, poor diet, and other stresses such as rough handling and noisy quarters. The aggravation of the disease is readily indicated in the rats by wheezing, occasional coughs and sneezing, pinkish mucus nasal discharge, and watery discharge from the eyes. On autopsy the advanced lesions in the lung lobes appear as yellow nodules with mucoid liquid or semi-solid greenish-yellow center; these nodules are surrounded by red or red-gray collapsed lung tissue. Sometimes a whole lobe may become hard and fibrous with small cavities containing pus. Guinea pigs are relatively resistant to respiratory infections if adequate vitamin C is provided and the quarters are dry.

Insecticides and fungicides should be used with caution and discretion. Animals which become infested with lice or fleas should be dusted with talc containing 0.5% rotenone, pyrethrin, or hexachlorocyclohexane (BHC), or 5% malathion (O,O-dimethyldithiophosphate of diethylmercaptosuccinate). BHC, while more toxic than rotenone or pyrethrin, has the advantage of killing the insect eggs as well, so that one application usually suffices; it has, on the other hand, a penetrating musty odor. Malathion is also effective for eliminating mange mites which burrow into the skin of mice, rats, and other animals. The use of insecticides containing DDT, lindane, and/or chlordane for the general insect control of the animal quarters is not recommended. When testing potential carcinogens on the mouse skin, which is extremely sensitive to carcinogenic influences, the use of insecticides should be avoided and a parasite-free state should be arrived at by rigidly enforcing an overall animal room hygiene, because the carcinogenic or cocarcinogenic effect of the insecticides may drastically influence the biological response.

For maintaining efficient and clean animal quarters, no matter how small, it is necessary to introduce and rigidly enforce a strict animal room routine. This means that certain operations must be carried out at fixed daily, weekly, or biweekly intervals. These operations may be divided into two groups: (a) animal maintenance and treatment, and (b) general hygiene of the animal quarters.

Animal maintenance and treatment involves that all animals must be checked for health and general behavior every morning and evening, and unusual observations (if any) recorded. The levels of drinking water (or special solution substituting for the drinking water) and of solid food (laboratory chow pellet or special diets) must be checked every evening and the containers refilled if necessary and water bottles changed; animals receiving semi-synthetic diets high in glucose are especially sensitive to lack of water. When refilling feeders (such as in Fig. 64, right) with semi-synthetic and other diets compounded in the laboratory and not compressed into pellets, old residual diet soiled with feces and urine should be discarded and the feeder cleaned. Guinea pigs also receive daily fresh greens (lettuce, cabbage, fresh grass, dandelion greens, etc.) which provide their vitamin C requirement (Section 4.3.2.4). The animals should receive the treatments (skin "painting," injections, feeding by stomach tube, etc.) required for the particular experiments at the scheduled times. Surgical gloves must be worn for the skin "painting," injecting, or administering carcinogens by stomach tube (see Section 4.3.3). Weighing and recording of the weights should be carried out on fixed days, weekly or twice weekly.

The general hygiene of the animal quarters concerns the removal of the excreta, changing the bedding, washing and refilling the water bottles, washing and sterilizing the cages, dropping pans, and racks, and washing and hosing the floor and walls of the animal quarters. The used heavy waxed paper collecting excreta on the racks described above must be pulled and removed daily. Daily duty also includes washing and refilling the set of water bottles collected the previous evening (there should be at least two complete sets to permit complete replacement) and readying them on rolling carts for rechange, and washing and hosing of the cement floor of the quarters. The bedding of mice should be changed thrice weekly. All excreta, bedding, soiled paper should be removed from the animal quarters immediately after collection in closed containers and not stored, as it will attract insect vermin. Special care must be exercised when collecting excreta, bedding, and dirt containing carcinogenic hydrocarbons and aromatic amines, or their carcinogenic metabolites; the animal caretaker performing this operation should wear heavy rubber gloves, a rubber apron, and a light surgical mask for protection. The dropping pans underlying the waxed paper on the above racks should be detergent washed and steam sterilized once weekly. All cages housing animals must be changed, detergent washed and steam sterilized every second week, and the racks (hosed if necessary) steam sterilized monthly. The washing with detergent solutions and hosing of the animal room walls should also be scheduled as a biweekly duty. It goes without saying that the diet preparation room should be kept spotlessly clean and vermin free. Dry laboratory chow pellets must be stored in *closed* bins to avoid becoming nests for insects.

All personnel extensively working with laboratory animals and exposed to contact with excreta, to bites and scratches must be protected against tetanus by yearly booster injections. The personnel carrying out treatment by carcinogenic polycyclic hydrocarbons and heteroaromatic compounds, and the equipment used, should be routinely monitored by ultraviolet light; glasses must be worn during prolonged monitoring to protect the eyes.

The maintenance of efficient and clean animal quarters requires an exacting routine. However, the importance of this work must be impressed upon and reiterated at times to all personnel involved in it. It is on the meticulous carrying out of diet preparations, treatments and administrations, and on the good physiological state of the animals which is influenced by a multitude of environmental factors, that depends the success of experiments involving sometimes a considerable total expenditure of time and material. The best and most ingenious experimental design can become futile if carried out with sick animals which received a wrong treatment or the correct treatment at wrong times. It is on the sense of responsibility of all the personnel involved that depends ultimately to a large extent the outcome and validity of many experiments in biological and medical research.

4.3.2.3.4   Some Methods of Anesthesia for Small Rodents. In certain procedures involved in the testing of carcinogens (*e.g.,* implantation of carcinogen-containing pellets subcutaneously or into the bladder; exploratory laparotomy), it is necessary to bring about anesthesia of the test animals. Different methods of anesthesia have been used of which two of the most time-tested ones will be described here.

Ether. Although ether is less than ideal, it has been preferred for mice and rats in our laboratories for a variety of reasons. For all operative procedures of short duration and to be carried out on large numbers of animals (*e.g.,* exploratory laparotomy), this is the anesthetic agent of choice. There is rapid recovery from ether anesthesia because of the fast excretion of the agent. This is a not negligible advantage when working on animals having some degree of respiratory involvement, because prolonged anesthesia favors the accumulation of mucus in the bronchi and the trachea and this can become fatal in some instances. Furthermore, in our views, ether should be used in preference on all animals having some degree of impairment of liver function. This is specifically the case when the compounds being administered are toxic and carcinogenic toward the liver. In our experience, *because of the narrow gap between the anesthetic dose and the lethal dose, safe operations under ether anesthesia require two persons; one constantly observes the rhythm of breathing and doses the ether as necessary.*

Ether anesthesia of rats may be carried out as follows. For initial anesthesia (also termed induction) the animal, already shaved as necessary for the operative procedure to be carried out, is placed on a square of several layers of porous paper generously wetted with ether and is immediately covered with a large (about 3 liters) glass bell jar. Do not place the animal in too strong an ether atmosphere which will irritate the mucous membranes, because the animal will struggle and will be difficult to anesthetize safely. The amount of ether necessary for initial anesthesia roughly parallels the size of the animal within a species; some practice will show the right amount to be employed. Because of the above-mentioned narrow gap between the anesthetic and lethal doses, the rat under the bell jar must be *constantly* under observation. Within a few seconds the gait of the animal will become uncertain, and when its movements have stopped it is *immediately* removed from under the jar, strapped to the operating platform in the position needed for the particular surgical procedure, and the maintenance ether mask applied. This ether mask is conveniently a 50-ml capacity square glass jar having a 4-mm diameter hole on one side at about 8 mm distance from the bottom; an absorbent surgical cotton pad or gauze pad (about 15 mm thick), generously wetted with ether is placed at the bottom of the jar. The mask is deposited on the operating platform (with hole upward) so as to cover about halfway the snout of the animal; air intake is assured through the wide gap between the edge of the mouth of the jar and the animal's head. By moving the mask forward or backward the distance between the cotton pad and the nostrils can be varied and thus the ether intake regulated. Additional ether can be pipetted as needed onto the cotton pad through the hole.

The initial anesthesia arrangement is also proper for the humane killing of small rodents (mice, hamsters, rats, guinea pigs). A larger amount of ether (or chloroform) is used, and the animal is maintained under the bell jar 1–2 minutes beyond the cessation of the respiration.

Long-acting anesthetics. Pentobarbital sodium has been recommended and used as a long-acting anesthetic for all commonly used small laboratory rodents when given intraperitoneally and for rabbits when given intravenously (43). Chloral hydrate administered intraperitoneally has also been extensively used (at the level of 400 mg/kg body weight) because of the very wide safety margin and relatively quick action. It appears, however, that when chloral hydrate is used as the sole anesthetic at this high dose level, a side effect which is observed some time later in occasional animals is ileitis, causing mortality from intestinal blocking (44). An agent chemically similar to chloral hydrate, tribromoethanol, has been successfully used in our laboratories by intraperitoneal administration. Tribromoethanol in amylene hydrate is commercial in the United States under the name of Avertin (Winthrop), containing 1 gm tribromoethanol and 0.5 gm amylene hydrate per milliliter; Avertin is administered intraperitoneally at the level of 1 ml/100 gm body weight of a 1.5% solution in physiological saline.

Anesthesia by a combination of intraperitoneally administered pentobarbital sodium and low doses of chloral hydrate (at which level the side effect of intestinal blocking does not occur) has been proposed for rats and guinea pigs by Valenstein (44). Table XXIV shows the dose levels of the two agents recommended by Valenstein for the 200–700 gm weight range. These figures for pentobarbital sodium are based on a 35-mg dose per kilogram body weight, with adjustment for the greater sensitivity of the lighter animals and the greater tolerance of the heavier animals. For some

Table XXIV

Anesthetic Dose of Pentobarbital Sodium and Supplementary Dose of Chloral Hydrate[a,b]

Animal wt. (gm)	Pent. sod.[c] (ml)	Chloral hydrate[d] (ml)	Animal wt. (gm)	Pent. sod. (ml)	Chloral hydrate (ml)
200	0.12	0.11	475	0.32	0.25
225	0.13	0.12	500	0.33	0.27
250	0.15	0.13	525	0.34	0.28
275	0.17	0.15	550	0.36	0.29
300	0.19	0.16	575	0.38	0.30
325	0.22	0.17	600	0.40	0.32
350	0.23	0.19	625	0.41	0.33
375	0.25	0.20	650	0.43	0.35
400	0.27	0.21	675	0.45	0.36
425	0.29	0.22	700	0.47	0.37
450	0.30	0.24			

[a] From E. S. Valenstein, *J. Exptl. Anal. Behaviour* **4**, 6 (1961).
[b] Figures are for intraperitoneal injections.
[c] Based on 60 mg/ml concentration.
[d] Based on 300 mg/ml concentration.

inbred strains these figures may require adjustment. If the animal is not sufficiently anesthetized by the pentobarbital sodium after about 20 minutes, the dose of chloral hydrate given in the table (based on 160 mg/kg) may be injected with complete safety. The operative procedure can normally begin 5 minutes after the second injection. Valenstein recommends a second injection of chloral hydrate equal to one half of the first if the animal starts to come out of the anesthesia before the operation has been completed.

4.3.2.4 Nutritional Requirements, Diet and Growth Rate

For the testing of many carcinogens, laboratory rodents are maintained on a standard diet and water, both made available *ad libitum*. For reasons of economy, or unavailability of adequate standard feed in some countries, many investigations in earlier times were carried out with animals maintained on autoclave-sterilized hospital food scrap, or on diets composed of locally available grains (rice, millet, corn, etc.) and enriched or not by minerals and other additives. This state of affairs obviously introduced great scattering in the reproducibility of many an earlier experimental work requiring a uniform dietary history of the animals during the whole life span. Therefore, most of present-day research uses a processed, protein-vitamin-mineral enriched, standardized dry feed, compressed into solid pellets of different sizes (chows of the Ralston Purina Co., diet pellets of Rockland Farms, etc.). It is important that the feed be purchased from a firm which carries out analytical control of the feed's nutritional quality and can give, upon request, precise information on the origin of the raw materials used. In fact, in some instances it may become necessary to be able to trace the origin of the raw materials in order to ascertain that the feed is free of constituents or contaminants having carcinogenic (*e.g.*, fatty constituents overheated during the manufacturing process) or hormone effects (*e.g.*, stilbestrol or certain insecticides). Moreover, the feed must be fresh and *positively* not moldy (or manufactured from moldy raw materials); indeed recent work has shown that several molds produce highly toxic and hepatocarcinogenic metabolites (*e.g.*, aflatoxin).

The most commonly used processed standard diet, the *laboratory chow*, is compounded on the average from the following ingredients (Purina): meat meal, dried skim milk, wheat germ, fish meal, liver meal, dried beet pulp, corn grits, oat middlings, soybean oil meal, dehydrated alfalfa meal, molasses, vitamin B_{12} feed supplement, riboflavin supplement, brewer's dried yeast, thiamine, niacin, vitamin A in oil, D-activated plant sterol, 0.5% phosphates, 0.5% iodized table salt, and 0.02% manganese phosphate. This typical composition of the laboratory chow may undergo slight modifications with the change of availability of certain constituents of plant origin in the different seasons. *The common laboratory chow does not provide vitamin C.* Mice and rats which do not require this vitamin do well on laboratory chow and water alone, without other diet supplement. Similar to mice and rats, dogs have no specific requirement for vitamin C. Special chow pellets compounded for the dog (in view of its essentially carnivorous nature) contain a higher percentage of animal proteins than the standard laboratory chow; however, dogs are adaptable and can be kept on standard laboratory chow.

Several stock grain diets, compounded in the laboratory, have been described by different authors. The advantage of these over pelleted chow for testing carcinogens is mainly that, being ground powder diets, they are directly adapted without further processing to the incorporation of the compounds to be assayed. To illustrate the composition of such a "home-made" stock grain diet the ingredients of one, used earlier by Miller *et al.* (45) for testing the carcinogenic activity of 2-aminofluorene derivatives in rats, is given here: ground yellow corn 68%, linseed oil meal 16%, powdered skim milk 12%, alfalfa leaf meal 2%, corn oil 0.96%, iodized table salt 0.5%, $Ca_3(PO_4)_2$ 0.5%, percomorphum liver oil (providing the vitamins A and D) 0.04%.

The diet of the guinea pig, in contrast to mice, rats, and dogs, is literally built around the requirement for vitamin C. The commercial chow diets sold in the United States under the name of *guinea pig chow* provide vitamin C. A typical pelleted guinea pig diet (Purina) is compounded from: ground wheat, ground yellow corn, dry skim milk, soybean meal, cottonseed meal, alfalfa meal, cane molasses, wheat middlings, animal fat, vitamin B_{12} supplement, riboflavin supplement, calcium pantothenate, niacin, ascorbic acid (vitamin C), vitamin A supplement, D-activated plant sterol, vitamin E supplement, calcium carbonate, low fluoride rock phosphate, iodized salt, manganese sulfate, manganous oxide, zinc oxide. In the writers' experience, however, while the use of vitamin C-containing diets is advantageous, it is not safe to rely exclusively on the vitamin C supplied in this way because feed stored for long periods of time, or even short periods in a hot and humid atmosphere, loses a considerable proportion of the vitamin C content. We recommend for guinea pigs an abundant *daily* supplement of fresh greens (lettuce, cabbage, parsley, etc.). In fact, guinea pigs may be maintained on vitamin C-devoid rabbit chow if adequate greens are provided. Vitamin C may also be supplied in the drinking water at the level of 1 gm per liter. This vitamin C solution may be stored in the refrigerator up to 24 hours; the drinking water bottles should be emptied and refilled daily.

Guinea pigs receiving fleshy greens like lettuce or green peppers can rely to a large extent on the greens for water and can restrict considerably their water intake from the water bottle of the cage. For this reason, when a carcinogen tested is water-soluble and is administered through the drinking water, the guinea pigs must get their vitamin C supply in a small volume of a concentrated solution. Guinea pigs supplied in this way should receive 3 times a week 1 ml of a 100 mg per milliliter vitamin C solution. This is administered conveniently by depositing the solution on the back of the tongue using a syringe with a 2-inch long 17-gauge blunted needle; the tip of the needle is fitted with a $\frac{3}{4}$-inch plastic tube. This is a simple technique which can be mastered in a short time.

Guinea pigs which do not get adequate amounts of vitamin C rapidly develop *scurvy*. The early gross symptoms are listlessness and irregular gait, swollen gums, and occasionally small tumorlike growths about the eyes. In an advanced stage there is considerable weight and hair loss, the animals acquire a scrawny appearance and excrete loose feces; death occurs within a few days. As mentioned above, vitamin C deficiency considerably weakens the guinea pigs' relative natural resistance to infections of the respiratory tract.

The vitamin C requirement of hamsters and rabbits has not been clearly determined. The vitamin C requirement, if any, of the hamster seems to be quite low as compared to that of the guinea pig. Hamsters do well when maintained on laboratory chow supplemented with small quantities of fresh green vegetables or root crops. It is a good practice to provide greens for rabbits maintained on a vitamin C-devoid rabbit chow.

The food consumption of the laboratory animals varies naturally with the growth rate and the average body weight attained by the adults of the species; the different species have thus widely differing quantitative requirements as shown in the following tabulation (chow consumed/animal/day):

Mouse	3–5 gm	Guinea pig	25–35 gm
Rat	12–15 gm	Rabbit	120–150 gm
Hamster	10–12 gm	Dog	300–500 gm

The normal *growth rate curve* is an important characteristic of a species. As the term indicates, this curve gives the increase of the body weight as a function of the length of life, from the time of birth until the leveling off in the adult stage. The growth rates of males and females slightly differ, with the male reaching generally a greater size and weight in all mammalian species; however, it is customary to speak about "the" growth rate of a species which represents then the median of the growth rates of the two sexes. Normal growth rate implies that the necessary nutrients are available in an amount unlimited to the particular species, that is that the dietary requirements are satisfied to the maximum; this represents, therefore, growth in optimum conditions. Figures 66A and 66B give normal growth rate curves of the mouse and hamster, and of the rat, guinea pig, and rabbit, respectively; these curves represent the growth rate of animals fed chow diets (supplemented with greens if required for the species), and maintained in optimum environmental conditions. Any adverse condition, such as the restriction of the diet in one or another essential dietary constituent, an artificially produced change in the hormonal balance of the animal, the administration of toxic or carcinogenic substances, or an environmental stress, immediately shows up as a change from the normal growth rate or weight loss. Therefore weekly or semi-weekly weighing of the animals, especially during the testing of carcinogens administered orally, is a simple

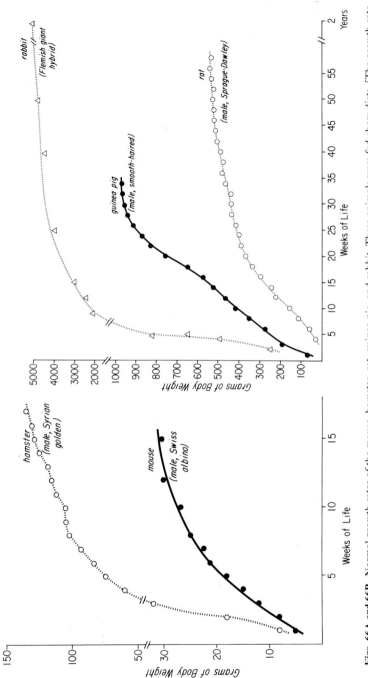

Figs. 66A and 66B. Normal growth rates of the mouse, hamster, rat, guinea pig, and rabbit. These animals were fed chow diets. [The growth rate curve of the hamster is owing to the courtesy of Dr. Kenneth F. Burns.]

but effective procedure for indicating the health of the animals and the possible toxic effect of the chemicals tested; also, sudden drastic changes in the growth rate can sometimes suggest the beginning of the emergence of tumor nodules within the animal body.

Now, the different chow diets represent *complete* regimens covering fully the dietary requirements of the particular species (together with the vitamin C providing supplement if required), and, furthermore, these diets are made available to the animals without restriction of the quantity consumed. For certain experimental purposes, however, it may become necessary to modify the diet. This modification can involve: (a) restriction of the total intake of the diet without changing the proportions of its components; this means that instead of providing chow diets *ad libitum* a fixed, weighed amount is given daily; (b) changing the proportions of the proteins, fats, and carbohydrates (that is of the constituents representing the calorie content of the diet and required for anabolic, *i.e.*, tissue-building activity, and as energy source) without restricting the total food intake, however; and (c) lowering or increasing the levels of single diet constituents, which do or do not provide part of the calorie content of the diet, but which are otherwise essential dietary components such as vitamins, inositol, choline, minerals, certain unsaturated fatty acids, and individual amino acids.

For investigations involving change in composition, the diet is usually compounded in the laboratory from commercially available components to suit the design of the particular experiment; however, many special test diets restricted in dietary components (one or another vitamin or mineral, protein, or fat) and compounded partial mixtures (salt mixtures) are now commercially available in the United States (*e.g.*, Nutritional Biochemicals Corporation, Cleveland, Ohio; General Biochemicals Inc., Chagrin Falls, Ohio). These specially compounded diets have been used mostly to study the effect of various protein, lipid, and carbohydrate dietary levels, of high or low caloric intake, or of change in vitamin, choline, and mineral levels, on the induction of tumors. In these diets unprocessed components such as natural grains are generally avoided as the composition of these may vary from batch to batch and, moreover, they may contain a wide spectrum of vitamins at levels incompatible with the particular dietary restriction desired to be brought about.

The compounded diets may be *semi-synthetic* or *synthetic*. In the semi-synthetic diets, the protein and fat-providing components are usually processed, but relatively nonpurified, natural products; for example, soybean protein or more often casein, corn oil, cottonseed oil, or olive oil. The vitamins, choline, and minerals are of synthetic origin and the carbohydrate (usually as dextrose), although of natural origin is highly purified. If the exact composition of the two natural components is known, then semi-synthetic diets may be designed in view of studying the effect on tumor induction of restricted or enhanced levels of vitamins, choline, or minerals, of high or low caloric intake provided by carbohydrates and/or lipids, or of high or low levels of total dietary proteins. Semi-synthetic diets can also be used to study the effect on tumor induction of a *high* level of a particular amino acid; for example, if the effect of a high level of tryptophan or cystine is studied then, the amino acid composition of the protein source being known, additional tryptophan or cystine is added to bring the diet up to the level desired. Obviously, semi-synthetic diets cannot be used to study the biological effect of any dietary restriction where the natural components provide high levels; for example, to study the effect of *low* levels or total absence of certain amino acids on animal growth (to determine which amino acids are essential), it is necessary to use fully synthetic diets in which the protein source is the series of synthetic, chemically pure, essential amino acids. Fully synthetic diets, while of great importance in pure nutritional investigations, are of relatively little interest for studies of chemical carcinogenesis.

Although the effect of the diet on tumor induction will be discussed in Section 7.1*, it is necessary to consider here some practical essentials of the composition and preparation of semi-synthetic diets. Liver tumor induction by many amino azo dyes, for example, is so strongly influenced by the level of riboflavin (vitamin B_2) that to study the carcinogenicity of these compounds the test animals must be maintained on a semi-synthetic diet low in riboflavin. This is due to the fact that riboflavin is a cofactor required for a liver enzyme system metabolizing azo dyes to inactive products by reductive splitting of the azo linkage (*e.g.*, 46, 47). A complete diet containing an optimal level of riboflavin gives considerable protection because it reduces the effective concentration of the carcinogen in the animal body. It is, therefore, necessary to limit the riboflavin intake to a level which represents a compromise; on one hand, it should be high enough to assure a close to normal growth rate when feeding the semi-synthetic diet without added carcinogen and, on the other hand, it should be low enough to permit rapid tumor induction when the carcinogen is added to the diet. The riboflavin levels of commercial chow diets and of natural feeds are much higher than the "compromise riboflavin level" referred to above and which is 2 mg per kilogram diet for the rat. The extent of protection provided by riboflavin is not the same for all azo dyes; there is considerable protection against hepatic carcinogenesis in the rat by the parent compound, 4-dimethyl-aminoazobenzene, but the protective effect is much less when certain derivatives, such as methyl- or fluoro-substituted in the "prime" ring, are

* Sections 5, 6, and 7 appear in Volume II; Sections 8 and 9, and the Appendices appear in Volume III.

administered (47). Because it cannot be foreseen which azo dyes are more sensitive to metabolic reductive splitting, it has become customary to test the relative carcinogenic activities of these compounds in rats, generally maintained on a standard riboflavin-low (2 mg/kg) semi-synthetic diet.

Another dietary component the level of which in certain conditions is a limiting factor of tumor induction is protein. High protein level protects (although to a much lesser extent than riboflavin) against liver carcinogenesis by 4-dimethylaminoazobenzene, and there is some evidence that it also retards tumor induction by other carcinogenic agents (2-acetylaminofluorene, carcinogenic hydrocarbons, etc.). Similarly, choline, another essential dietary constituent, is an inhibitor of ethionine-induced hepatic carcinogenesis (48), and a combination of elevated levels of choline and cystine in a semi-synthetic diet was found by György et al. (49) to retard liver tumor induction by 4-dimethylaminoazobenzene; it is true, however, that other investigators did not find a clear-cut inhibition by choline of the tumor induction by this azo dye but observed, nonetheless, a notable reduction of gross cirrhosis (e.g., 50). The type of fat used in the diet (whether corn oil, cottonseed oil, olive oil, partially hydrogenated coconut oil, etc.), while not properly a limiting factor, can also drastically influence the rate of emergence of hepatic tumors. Other components in the concentration range at which they are present in natural diets have not been found to have a limiting effect on carcinogenesis.

For all these reasons the testing not only of azo dyes but also of structurally different types of carcinogens is often carried out using in preference semi-synthetic diets in which the nature and level of each component can be strictly controlled and modified as necessary. Semi-synthetic diets are sometimes preferred when the carcinogen or potentially active compound is tested by oral administration and/or when there is the expectation that the tissue target is an internal organ, in particular the liver, or the kidney, lung, etc. On the other hand, the use of semi-synthetic diets does not present special advantage for testing the relative activities of such compounds or using such routes of administration that mainly local tumors are produced (e.g., treatment of the surface of the skin by or subcutaneous injection of polycyclic hydrocarbons).

Among mice, rats, and hamsters maintained on vitamin- and/or protein-restricted diets cannibalism and coprophagy are not uncommon; this problem is compounded by the fact that the true requirement for certain dietary components is often increased by the administration of carcinogens. Every effort must be made to avoid this scavenging, as the extra "intake" beclouds the actual dietary conditions. Cannibalism may be cut down among mice by dividing the colony into smaller groups. For rats and hamsters, which are larger animals, cannibalism can be prevented altogether by housing the animals in individual cages for certain critical periods during carcinogen administration; by the use of the welded wire cage housing described in the previous section, coprophagy can be practically eliminated among the larger rodents.

Semi-synthetic diets contain normally only the dietary essentials. For this reason it is necessary to know in particular the exact vitamin requirements of the particular species for which the diet is destined. For example, the diet of the rat, the requirements of which have been the most exhaustively studied among all laboratory animals, must contain, as essential vitamins: vitamin A, thiamine (vitamin B_1), riboflavin (vitamin B_2), pyridoxine (vitamin B_6), panthotenic acid (vitamin B_5), vitamin D, α-tocopherol (vitamin E), and probably vitamin K; as mentioned above rats do not require vitamin C. Mice and also dogs have very similar requirements except that the latter species also require nicotinamide (vitamin B_3 or PP, the pellagra-preventive factor).

To illustrate the composition of a semi-synthetic diet, a versatile test diet (51) used extensively for the assaying of azo dyes for carcinogenic activity is composed of the following ingredients (per kilogram diet): vitamin-"free" casein (hot alcohol-extracted) 180 gm, glucose monohydrate 729 gm, corn oil 50 gm, salt mixture 40 gm, choline 1 gm, vitamin A 18,500 U.S.P. units, vitamin D 310 U.S.P. units, thiamine hydrochloride 3 mg, pyridoxine hydrochloride 2.5 mg, D-panthotenic acid calcium salt 7 mg, and riboflavin 2 mg (this includes the approx. 0.10–0.15 mg riboflavin still contained in 180 gm vitamin-"free" casein after hot alcohol extraction). As a less costly vitamin A and D source, commercial halibut or cod liver or percomorphum oil concentrates of stated strength may be used instead of the pure vitamins. The amount of the vitamin A plus D concentrate added to the diet is critical in rats receiving carcinogenic azo dyes, in the sense that already 6–10 times the above recommended levels produce appreciable increase in mortality; in these rats a typical finding on autopsy is that the large intestine is filled with noneliminated hard "caked" fecal matter. Mortality due to excess vitamin A plus D (as little as 2% cod liver oil in the diet) has been observed also in rabbits (52). The originally used (53) salt mixture of the above semi-synthetic diet has the following composition: NaCl 158 gm, $CaHPO_4$ 71 gm, $MgSO_4 \cdot 7H_2O$ 96 gm, $CaCO_3$ 283 gm, ferric citrate 26 gm, KH_2PO_4 254 gm, $K_2CO_3 \cdot H_2O$ 110 gm, KI 0.76 gm, manganese acetate 0.36 gm, zinc acetate 0.36 gm, $CuSO_4 \cdot 5H_2O$ 0.28 gm. In the United States, where different salt mixtures for animal diets are commercially available, the above salt mixture may be replaced (54) for convenience by the Wesson modification (55) of the Osborne-Mendel salt mixture (Salt Mixture W, Nutritional Biochemicals Corporation, Cleveland, Ohio); in this case, since the Salt Mixture W does not contain zinc which is essential to the normal development of the rat (38), 6 mg $ZnCl_2$ must be added per kilogram diet.

Moreover, we have found, in agreement with other observations in the literature (38), that rats occasionally develop abdominal hemorrhagic tendencies; addition of as little as 0.25 mg menadione (synthetic vitamin K) per kilogram diet is sufficient to prevent this condition. No exogenous vitamin E is added; however, most natural vegetable oils contain sufficient amount of this vitamin to cover the requirement of the rat which is normally low except for females in terminal pregnancy and during lactation. (See Suppletory Note 1* for the practical preparation of the above diet.)

The exact composition of various other semi-synthetic diets, of salt mixtures, and of vitamin mixtures are described in booklets available upon request from the manufacturing firms (*e.g.*, 56, 57).

4.3.3 ROUTES AND METHODS OF ADMINISTRATION FOR TESTING CARCINOGENS

The route or method of administration is almost always critical for detecting the carcinogenic activity of a substance. For this reason, when designing an experiment for testing a potential carcinogen, the chemical properties of the substance and the possibility that it may chemically interact with constituent(s) of the carrier medium (solvent, diet components, or drinking water) and thus be inactivated, or that it may be destroyed in the gut if administered orally, before the biological effect is brought about, must be carefully considered.

The most often used routes are skin "painting," parenteral administration (*i.e.*, injection by subcutaneous, intramuscular, intraperitoneal, or intravenous route, or subcutaneous implantation), oral administration (the compound is incorporated in the diet, dissolved in the drinking water, or force-fed to the animal as a small volume of a concentrated solution or suspension), inhalation (if the compound is a gas, or may be vaporized because of its low boiling point, or can be readily transformed into an aerosol), and bladder implantation (the potential carcinogen is incorporated into a cholesterol or paraffin pellet which is then implanted into the bladder of the mouse or rat). A technique used occasionally to induce tumors of the vagina and cervix is the intravaginal instillation of solutions or suspensions of locally acting carcinogens.

4.3.3.1 Skin "Painting"

The name of this procedure is derived from the practice followed by the early investigators who applied the substance as a dilute solution in a volatile solvent to the shaved skin, actually painting it with a small brush. The use of the brush has been generally abandoned and the present practice consists in simply depositing a small, exactly known volume of a solution

* Suppletory Notes for Section 4.3 begin on page 450.

of the carcinogen (in a volatile solvent) in the center of the shaved area; the animal is kept separated and/or immobilized for a short time for gross evaporation to take place, and then replaced in its cage.

Skin painting is generally used when the substance is expected to be a locally acting carcinogen. Overwhelmingly, experiments using skin painting were carried out on mice (because of the great sensitivity of its surface epithelium, see Section 4.3.2.1) for testing polycyclic hydrocarbons and their heterocyclic analogs, despite the fact that the first demonstration of the carcinogenic activity of coal tar was made on the skin of the ears of the rabbit (58). However, skin painting has also been successfully used to produce skin tumors in mice with 4-nitroquinoline N-oxide and some of its derivatives (13, 59), diazoaminobenzene (60), and various cross-linking agents (e.g., 61–63), and skin tumors in rats with 2-anthramine (11, 12). Recently, by using skin painting, tumors of the skin have been obtained in rats with aminoazo dyes, which were long held to have exclusive tissue target specificity toward the liver (see footnote on page 325).

In the present practice, skin painting on the interscapular area (an approx. $\frac{3}{4} \times \frac{3}{4}$-inch area on an average 27-gm mouse, extending on the back of the neck between the ears and the shoulder blades) is preferred; the use of this region of the body has the advantage that the animals cannot easily lick it, which would (a) bring about a decrease of the concentration of the agent at the chosen site of application and dispersal all over the animal's nose and mouth, and (b) provide a small oral intake, which may produce tumors inside the animal body and/or influence the tumor yield on the skin by way of indirect biological mechanisms.

Before application, the mice are shaved using an electric clipper; avoid the use of a razor or chemical depilatory agents since irritation or trauma to the skin is likely to influence (generally enhance, see Section 7.6) the carcinogenic response. In many reported investigations on the testing of polycyclic hydrocarbons, these were applied as 0.3% solutions in benzene, or acetone, or ether + liquid paraffin, etc. (for the effect of the solvent on carcinogenic activity, see Section 4.3.4). A small standard volume (e.g., 0.1 ml) is deposited on the center of the shaved area using a pipette or a 1-ml syringe. The skin must be painted once, twice, or three times weekly, on fixed days at regular intervals (e.g., Mondays, Wednesdays, and Fridays). For compounds of unknown activity application must be at least twice weekly; however, no fixed rule can be formulated for the number of weekly applications, which should in principle represent a practical compromise dictated by the rate of disappearance of the substance from the skin and the toxicity level that the animals can tolerate for the length of time of the testing. To insure intimate contact of the surface epithelium with the carcinogen the hair must be repeatedly shaved whenever there is regrowth during treatment;

to distance as much as possible the time of shaving (a mild irritation) and the time of application of the carcinogen, shaving should always be done on days when the carcinogen is *not* painted. Test groups must be accompanied by a control group which should receive treatment with the solvent alone under the same conditions and following the same schedule.

4.3.3.2 *Parenteral Administration*

By their very nature the different routes of parenteral administration lend themselves much more readily to a quantitative control of the carcinogenic dose than skin painting. However, testing by any of the routes of parenteral administration does not substitute for testing by skin painting.

Subcutaneous injection is the most often used form of parenteral administration. Subcutaneous injection has been used for a wide variety of substances. For certain compounds, such as some highly reactive alkylating agents which would decompose if administered orally, it is actually the method of choice. Rats, and to a lesser extent mice, are used for testing by this route. As has been pointed out in Section 4.3.2.1 the subcutaneous connective tissue of the rat is very sensitive to carcinogenic stimuli. There is also evidence (Section 5.4) that as little irritation as imbalance of osmotic pressure in the extracellular tissue fluid, brought about by the subcutaneous injection of concentrated, hypertonic solutions of normal physiological substances (glucose or sodium chloride), can produce sarcomas in rats; for this reason Boyland (64) suggested that when water-soluble substances (physiological or not) are tested by subcutaneous route in aqueous solutions, these *should be isotonic* with the tissue. On the same ground, a conclusion of carcinogenic activity based on tumors produced by subcutaneously injected substances *at sites distant from the point of administration* carries somewhat greater weight than one based on tumors arising at the very site of injection; the same caution must be observed in interpreting data with respect to testing by intramuscular route. Nevertheless, subcutaneous injection represents a major method for carcinogen testing, and we consider that the position taken by Clayson (7) regarding the uncertainties involved is perhaps extreme. Of course, the tests must be surrounded by the necessary safeguards of careful control experiments. The animals of the control group (same strain, sex, age, and weight range) should receive injections of identical volume of the solvent alone at the same site of the body, and should be maintained for the same length of time under the same dietary and environmental conditions as the test group. At the end of the testing period the significance of the difference, if any, between the number of tumors in the test group or groups, and in the control group, must be statistically analyzed (see further in Section 4.3.6.2). This is of particular importance when the solvent is a natural fat or oil (the processing of these often involves heat treatment), which may have a low but detectable background carcinogenicity; these considerations will be treated in greater detail in Sections 4.3.4 and 4.3.6.2.

Subcutaneous injection is usually administered in the region of the upper flank. The volume injected should always take into account the size of the animal. For example, volumes up to 1.5 ml may be safely administered by subcutaneous injection into a 300-gm rat; larger volumes will cause pain and also a back-up may occur when the needle is withdrawn at the end of the injection, because of pressure of the surrounding tissues on the fluid pocket. In adult mice the volume injected should not be greater than 0.4–0.5 ml. The solvent used should not cause tissue irritation or necrosis. It has been recommended that, whenever the solubility of the substance permits, a synthetic fatty solvent should be used in order to avoid the influence of natural fats of variable and/or unknown composition on the biological response; in preference, tricaprylin is used as solvent for parenteral testing (see Section 4.3.4). However, much work has been carried out using good grade corn oil and olive oil, and the results obtained are acceptable provided that the tests were accompanied by adequate controls (see above). In the numerous experiments reported on testing polycyclic hydrocarbons and their analogs by subcutaneous route, the dose injected varies between about 0.1 and 5 mg, occasionally up to 10 mg; for testing unknown compounds of this type we recommend a dose of at least 1 mg to mice and 2 mg to rats. Testing by subcutaneous route most often involves a single injection. The animals are then kept under observation for a period of 1–2 years unless tumors become manifest earlier.

A technique of subcutaneous implantation eliminates the interference of the solvent altogether. This technique was used first by Shear (65) who subcutaneously implanted weighed quantities of crystals of polycyclic hydrocarbons (2–10 mg) moistened with glycerol. A trocar (Fig. 67) is an instrument particularly convenient for this procedure. Note on the figure that the trocar consists of a large diameter injection needle (tube) and a piston which fits snugly in it, and by means of which material deposited in the tube can be expelled through the tip. In the following is given a simple technique to load the trocar for hydrocarbon implantation. First, one drop of anhydrous thick glycerol is injected into the tube (from the side of the tip and about $\frac{1}{2}$ inch above it) by means of a syringe and a needle of appropriate diameter; then the weighed hydrocarbon (well-developed crystals are more adapted for this than microcrystalline powder) is introduced carefully, through the funnel-like ending of the tube and, finally, a second drop of glycerol is injected on the top of the hydrocarbon load. The trocar tube is then inserted subcutaneously at the selected site of the animal, the hydrocarbon load implanted by driving the piston into the tube, and the trocar withdrawn.

Alternate methods of implantation into tissues have been developed in view of different experimental goals. One method consists in the implantation of a pellet containing the carcinogen in solid solution or in mixture with a carrier substance (cholesterol, 50°–80°C melting point paraffin, wax, etc.) which is inactive or has a very low background carcinogenicity. A convenient procedure is the subcutaneous implantation in the upper flank: the respective

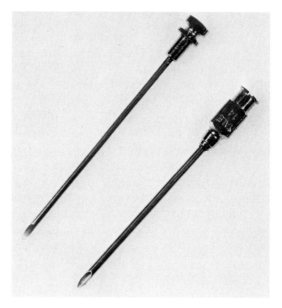

Fig. 67. Trocar (needle and piston shown separately). The one shown here is 14 gauge and 3 inches long.

region is shaved and, under light ether anesthesia (Section 4.3.2.3.4), a $\frac{1}{2} - \frac{3}{4}$-inch long incision is made in the dermis. Perpendicular to the incision, the skin is lifted and the subcutaneous tissue layers are separated so as to form a pocket about $\frac{1}{2} \times 1$ inch in size. The pellet is introduced, pushed to the far end of the pocket, the incision is closed with 1–2 stitches of surgical silk thread, and the wound is covered with medicinal collodion solution. This or similar procedures have often been used for administering polycyclic hydrocarbons. These are liposoluble, hence readily dissolved in the molten vehicle substances, and the solutions are then cooled for the preparation of the pellets; other procedures utilize mechanical mixing by triturating the carcinogen with the vehicle substance and forming the pellets cold in a tablet-making machine. Of course, when this method of implantation is used to test for carcinogenic activity, careful and adequate control experiments and statistical analysis must be carried out just as when solvents are used in other forms of parenteral administration. In particular, when the control pellets containing no carcinogen are prepared, the vehicle substance must be submitted to the same heat treatment which is employed for the preparation of the test pellets, since heat treatment may bring about chemical changes conferring some low carcinogenic activity to the vehicle substance or may increase its initial background carcinogenicity.

This method of administration has been occasionally used to produce tumors in organs or tissues other than subcutaneous connective tissue or peritoneal tissue, both of which can be reached by simple subcutaneous or intraperitoneal injection of solutions of the agents in liquid fats. Thus, brain tumors and stomach tumors have been obtained by pellet implantation. The important application of this method is, however, to determine the quantity of carcinogen absorbed by the organism during carcinogenesis. Shear and Lorenz implanted pellets of cholesterol containing, dissolved, a carcinogenic hydrocarbon in known concentration; when the tumor began to grow, the pellet was withdrawn and the amount of hydrocarbon which diffused out from the pellet and was absorbed by the organism (a very small quantity) could be found by measuring spectrophotometrically the change in concentration of the carcinogen in the pellet (66). Implantation of solutions of carcinogens in solid paraffin capsules represents a variation of the above described method. Again, another way to bring internal organs which are difficult to reach into a constant topical contact with a carcinogen over a period of time is to introduce a silk thread, previously soaked in a solution of the carcinogen, into the particular organ. In this manner tumors of the lung have been obtained with polycyclic hydrocarbons.

Intraperitoneal and intravenous administrations have been much less often used for testing of carcinogens than subcutaneous injection. There is truly no reason why the intraperitoneal route could not be extensively used for routine testing, except perhaps that the topical carcinogen concentration at the contact of the tissues is much less than in subcutaneous or intramuscular administration because the substance becomes distributed all over the total mucous epithelial surface of the peritoneal cavity and of the abdominal organs. Intravenous injection, however, presents some practical difficulties. Thus, it is an evident requirement that the solvent in which the substance is dissolved should not interact with the blood to produce hemolysis (disruption of the red blood cells) and clotting, and this puts a limitation on the substances which can be tested in this manner. Furthermore, intravenous injection into small animals (injection is often into the tail vein) is a comparatively more delicate procedure than other forms of parenteral administration, and the total amount of carcinogen which can be introduced in this way is small. Nonetheless, intravenous administration is of value to investigate the direct systemic effects of rather locally acting carcinogens. For example, Andervont and Lorenz (67) observed rapid induction of lung tumors in a high percentage of mice following intravenous injection of a stable emulsion of 1,2,5,6-dibenzanthracene in horse serum into mice.

4.3.3.3 Oral Administration

For testing by oral administration the substance can be incorporated in the diet, dissolved in the drinking water, or force-fed to the animals by a simple device called a *stomach tube* as a small volume of a solution or suspension. It is largely the chemical properties of the substance which determine the choice between the three methods, but also the nature of the experiment has to be considered and to some extent the availability of time since daily administration to a large animal colony by stomach tube is a time-consuming procedure.

Oral administration can only be used if (a) the substance is not decomposed in the stomach and/or the small intestine in the process of digestion, and (b) it is absorbed from the intestines, *i.e.*, will not simply pass through the intestinal tract and be overwhelmingly excreted with the feces. For incorporation into the diet the substance must not interact chemically with any of the components of the diet, must be resistant to prolonged exposure to air, light, and low levels of humidity and, moreover, must not be volatile. Administration through the drinking water is contraindicated if the substance is hydrolyzed upon extended standing in aqueous medium and is sensitive to air and light; the latter considerations do not apply, however, as rigorously when the substance is administered in aqueous solution by stomach tube, since solutions of substances which hydrolyze at a very slow rate may be made up freshly each time just before administration. Obviously, for chemicals which have a generally high chemical reactivity, such as most alkylating or acylating agents, testing by oral administration is generally contraindicated.

Incorporation in the diet or drinking water is employed mainly if either the compound must be administered in large quantity and for an extended period of time to induce tumors (*e.g.*, ethionine, acetamide, dioxane, azo dyes, aromatic amines), or when because of the high toxicity of the compound it can be given only at very low levels, but administration must be continued for a comparatively long time (as many nitrosamines). Incorporation in the diet or drinking water is not practical if tumors can be induced by single oral administration. For example, tumors of the stomach and esophagus have been induced by a single oral administration of the potent alkylating agent N-nitroso-N-methylurethan; for the administration of the single dose the stomach tube (described below) is a highly convenient device (68).

Depending on the solubility properties and heat stability of the compound to be tested, it is compounded into the diet either as a glucose triturate or by dissolving it in the main fat of the diet. It is customary to dissolve azo dyes in the corn oil component of the diet (see Suppletory Note 1) by mild heating; hydrocarbons and other lipid-soluble compounds should also be introduced into the diet in this manner if administration is by way of the diet. However, certain practical considerations (such as personnel safety in the animal quarters and the difficulty of thoroughly eliminating traces of the hydrocarbon from the mixing drum) indicate that direct oral administration by stomach tube is preferable. Other carcinogens such as most of the aromatic amines and difficultly soluble substances are compounded into the diet as glucose triturates. For this the weighed carcinogen is finely ground and intimately mixed with a small amount of glucose monohydrate (5–15 gm/kg diet), and it is this mixture or triturate which is compounded into the diet. In the case of a semi-synthetic diet normally containing glucose (e.g., the one described in Suppletory Note 1), the glucose used for the triturate can be a portion of the glucose component of the diet. In grain diets or other stock diets, this glucose becomes an additional dietary component and, hence, to the control diet containing no carcinogen the same amount of glucose must be added. A simple way of testing (by way of the diet) carcinogens, which do not require the carefully controlled dietary conditions provided by semi-synthetic diets, is to pass the commercial chow pellets through a feed mill and incorporate into the ground chow the compound to be assayed either as a concentrated corn-oil solution or, in preference, as a glucose triturate; depending on the case, the ground chow diet may or may not be enriched by other dietary supplements (54).

As already indicated above, the use of the stomach tube is preferable to incorporation in the diet if a single or limited number of oral administrations have to be made. The use of the stomach tube is also advantageous if the compound to be tested orally is available only in a limited quantity or difficult to come by and, consequently, all wastage of material has to be avoided. Administration by stomach tube is also recommended if the amount ingested has to be known accurately.

Water-soluble compounds are administered by force-feeding as aqueous solutions. Liposoluble agents (polycyclic hydrocarbons, azo dyes, etc.) may be administered as corn oil solutions or as aqueous suspensions. Except for special applications, requiring a single or at most 3 – 4 administrations, the routine use of corn oil is not recommended because of the extra fat intake. For prolonged routine administrations aqueous suspensions, stabilized by a colloid protector substance, should be used. Such a suspension of a polycyclic hydrocarbon, azo dye, or aromatic amine may be prepared by introducing the weighed substance, dissolved in a volatile solvent (e.g., acetone, ethyl acetate), into the appropriate volume of an aqueous 1–2% methylcellulose (Methocel) solution and then removing the solvent with a stream of nitrogen and mild heating.

Figure 68 shows a stomach tube (designed for force-feeding rats over 150 gm size) fitted on a syringe. The volume of solution which can be conveniently force-fed to rats is 1–1.5 ml. Mice and guinea pigs can also be force-fed using slightly different physical arrangements, adapted to the average size of the respective species. Mice can be conveniently force-fed using the following arrangement: 5-ml syringe with a 20-gauge $2\frac{1}{2}$ inch long

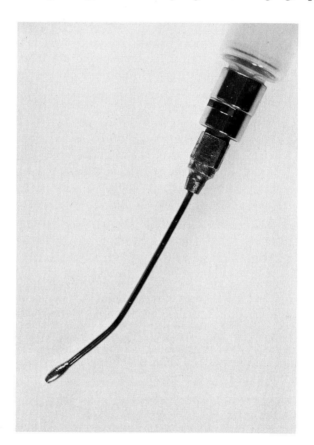

Fig. 68. A stomach tube (or feeding tube) fitted onto a 5-ml capacity "Luer-lok" tip syringe. The stcmach tube shown here, which is adapted for feeding rats over 150 gm size, is prepared from a 17-gauge, 3-inch long, stainless steel hypodermic needle, bent to a 30-degree angle $\frac{3}{4}$ inch from the tip. The tip is made appropriately blunt by filing down the slanted edge perpendicularly, and surrounding the last 6 mm with a small ball of solder which is then shaped and finished for smoothness.

needle; the tip of the needle is tightly fitted with a soft plastic tube $2\frac{1}{4}$ inch long of which a $\frac{3}{4}$-inch portion is pulled on the needle. The volume which can be conveniently force-fed to mice is about $\frac{1}{2}$ ml. The arrangement proposed by Machella and Griffith (cited in reference 38) for rats was found in our laboratories particularly convenient for force-feeding guinea pigs. This consists of a No. 8 French rubber tube catheter with a depressed eye. The length of catheter necessary to intubate the stomach depends on the size of the animal. The catheter is securely fitted on the tip of a 5 to 10-ml syringe. An average volume which can be force-fed to guinea pigs is 3 ml.

The technique of force-feeding by stomach tube, while it requires some practice, can be readily learned. An adaptation to rats is as follows. Using the left hand the rat is grasped, with the palm of the hand across the upper back, and held gently but firmly in vertical position. The rat's right front leg is immobilized by pushing it upward with the thumb; the left front leg is immobilized either by holding it between the index finger and the third finger, or by pressing it downward under the four fingers folded around the chest of the animal. The syringe fitted with the stomach tube is held in the middle between the thumb and the last three fingers of the right hand, and the piston is operated with the index finger. The blunt end of the stomach tube is slipped into the side of the rat's mouth and, always keeping it over the tongue and against the palate, it is gently eased down the throat. Figure 69 gives a schematic representation of the correct position for introducing the stomach tube into the animal. As the blunt end of the tube is passed down the esophagus a slight resistance will be felt; the stomach tube is gently eased down the esophagus until the metal base of the tube (where the feeder tube adapts to the syringe) almost touches the animal's teeth. The desired volume is now slowly released from the syringe and the tube is gently withdrawn. If the rat is not too small and if the solution is introduced slowly, escape

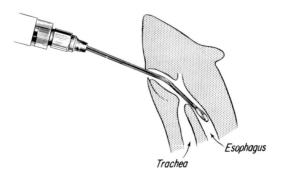

Esophagus

Trachea

Fig. 69. Schematic representation showing the correct introduction of the stomach tube into the rat with respect to the positions of the trachea and the esophagus.

and return of the fluid from the animal's stomach is rare. Routine stomach feeding of a larger group of rats requires not only practice but also patience on the part of the operator as well as on the part of the rats. Beginners should practice on relaxed rats used to handling. Correctly carried out stomach feeding is painless. Therefore, never brutalize the animals because struggling rats simply manifest their rebellion against an incorrect and painful procedure.

4.3.3.4 Inhalation

The interest of this testing procedure lies in the fact that lung tumors in man are in many instances traceable to the inhalation of carcinogens. In humans inhalation of carcinogens may be due to voluntary intake (such as tobacco smoke) or to chronic involuntary exposure to a heavily polluted general atmosphere or specific atmospheres at industrial sites. Physically, atmospheric carcinogens may appear as gases, vapors, aerosols (mist, fog, smoke), and dusts.

Many early attempts to produce lung tumors by direct exposure to the suspected carcinogen have failed. However, it is now recognized that the critical requirement for testing aerosols and dusts is that the droplet or particle size be well below an average diameter of 4 μ and for small rodents below 1 μ. Larger particles are readily arrested in the upper respiratory tract and, moreover, cannot penetrate the bronchi and fine bronchioli (69). A likely cause of the early failures was, therefore, that the particles arrested in the trachea were moved up into the pharynx (posterior part of the oral and nasal cavity) by the sweeping movements of the ciliae of the tracheal epithelium. For the same reason it is necessary to prevent the coalescence or aggregation of the particles during testing; admixture of $CaCO_3$ dust was found effective to prevent clumping of metal and metallic compound dusts (70).

Inhalation is the obvious methodological choice for testing the potential carcinogenic activity of gases. For example, the carcinogenicity of the heavy yellow gas, diazomethane, was demonstrated by Schoental by placing mice or rats in a desiccator, repeatedly for short periods of time (1–2 minutes), together with 1-ml doses of an ether solution containing 2–3 mg of diazomethane; a small percentage of the animals developed tumors and precancerous lesions of the lung after a period of time following treatment, while the control animals inhaling ether only did not develop tumors (68). For the testing of fumes, dusts, and low-boiling-point liquids (as vapors), special chambers have been devised (e.g., 70, 71; rev. 69) into which the dispersed material is introduced by controlled air stream. The exposure chamber has to be operated at a somewhat lower atmospheric pressure than the laboratories in order to prevent escape of the carcinogenic material.

Such arrangements have also been used to test the carcinogenic activity of highly toxic gases such as nickel tetracarbonyl (71). Low-boiling-point liquids (carbon tetrachloride and other chlorinated hydrocarbons, nitro-olefins, etc.) and also mineral oils may be tested in inhalation by dispersing the substances with nebulizers producing a vapor or fog in the chamber. Oil fumes can be generated by controlled slow delivery of oil drops upon overheated surfaces, and dusts are produced from solids (*e.g.*, DDT, hexa-chlorocyclohexane) by using commercial dust feeders. Special testing devices have been built (72–74) to provide intermittent or rhythmic exposure to special materials such as cigarette smoke and internal combustion engine exhausts.

More quantitative but less physiological variants of the inhalation method are the direct instillation and insufflation of the carcinogenic material into the trachea using devices similar to the stomach tube described in the previous section. A considerable simplification of the intratracheal administration, applicable to a variety of carcinogens, is due to Howell (75) who instilled with a pipette into the nostrils of rats an olive oil solution of the potent carcinogen, 9,10-dimethyl-1,2-benzanthracene; immediately following instil-lation the rats are held vertically for a couple of minutes to facilitate the descent of the solution into the bronchi and to prevent seeping of the oil from the nostrils.

4.3.3.5   Bladder Implantation

The implantation into the bladder of pellets containing potential carcino-gens, which may be regarded as a special type of parenteral administration, was first utilized by Maisin and Picard (76). The technique was further developed and standardized by Jull (77); later modification by Boyland and Watson (78, 79) brought the method to an elegant simplicity. By means of this technique the sensitivity of the bladder epithelium to tumorigenic stimuli* can be put to routine use for testing potential carcinogens. The technique in its original and modified forms has been used very effectively

---

* *Note added after completion of Section 4.* The results of D. B. Clayson and J. A. S. Springle [*Brit. J. Cancer* **20**, 564 (1966)] and G. T. Bryan and P. D. Springberg [*Cancer Res.* **26**, 105 (1966)] have thrown some doubt on the reliability of testing by the bladder implantation technique, at least for compounds of low potency. These authors found that the physical presence of the pellet is a necessary factor in the development of tumors, suggesting that it acts as a promotor by inducing mitosis in the bladder epithelium. That the mere physical presence of a pellet represents a mild carcinogenic and/or cocarcinogenic influence owing probably to the trauma (see Section 7.6) is also indicated by the finding of C. S. Weil, C. P. Carpenter, and H. F. Smyth [*Arch. Environ. Health* **11**, 569 (1965); *Ind. Med. Surg.* **35**, 561 (1966)] that the bladder tumors obtained by diethylene glycol feeding are actually due to the mechanical irritation by the calcium oxalate bladder stones formed.

to study the induction of bladder tumors mainly in mice but also in rats (*e.g.*, 79–81).

Operating on mice, Jull (77) describes the technique as follows: "Under ether anesthesia the bladder was exposed by a small incision through the skin and the abdominal wall about 1 cm above the urethral opening. The bladder was drawn out of the abdomen and supported on a small pad of gauze; an incision was then made through the dome of the bladder and the edges held apart by small metal retractors. The pellet was inserted by an assistant with forceps, and the incision in the bladder wall closed by a continuous suture of Gauge O silk thread using a Carrel's arterial curved needle. The suture passed through all the layers of the bladder wall, and the edges were drawn together so that the two epithelial surfaces were bound closely to one another; thus a continuous epithelial layer only and no muscle nor connective tissue was exposed to the direct action of the carcinogen in the pellet. The abdominal wall and skin were closed separately by sutures of cotton or thick silk.

"The operative mortality was negligible, but a number of animals died within a few weeks of the operation due to the pellets blocking the urethra. Some of the animals showed signs of infection of the urogenital tract, confirmed by examining (for the presence of bacteria) smears of the urine. This infection was palliated but not obviated by penicillin treatment."

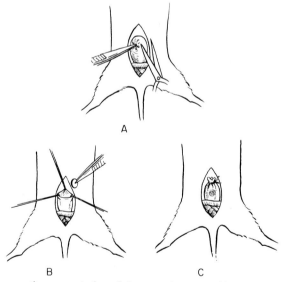

A

B   C

Fig. 70. Diagrammatic representation of the operative stages (A, B, and C) of bladder implantation in the mouse. [Redrawn after M. J. Allen, E. Boyland, C. E. Dukes, E. S. Horning, and J. G. Watson, *Brit. J. Cancer* **11**, 212 (1957).]

In the modified technique of Boyland and Watson (78, 79), using stock mice anesthetized with a mixture of 90% ether and 10% ethanol, "The abdominal wall was wetted with ethanol and an incision made with scissors to give access to the bladder. The apex of the bladder was held in forceps and a 3 mm incision made in the fundus with scissors [Fig. 70A]. The pellet, held in straight forceps, was then inserted into the bladder while the lumen was held open with 3 pairs of forceps [Fig. 70B]. The suture was then held together with forceps and ligated close to the forceps with a single fine silk ligature [*i.e.*, the incision is tied off by means of a single loop of thread instead of sewing as in the original technique by Jull; Fig. 70C]. The abdominal wall was closed by sewing in two layers using a figure-of-eight stitch." Boyland and Watson (78) state that by this method the operation is quicker and the risk of leakage of urine during the postoperative period is reduced. (For some additional details of surgery on small rodents see the technique of exploratory laparotomy, Section 4.3.6.1.1).

The pellets used by Jull (77) and by Bonser *et al.* (80) were made of 56° or 80°C melting point solid paraffin in which the carcinogen or potential carcinogen was dissolved or suspended in the molten state, at the level of 2%, 15–20%, or 30%; from the molten mixture rounded pellets of 10 – 20 mg weight were prepared by dropping the molten material from a pipette on a cold glass surface and then molding them into shape with a warm scalpel. The pellets used by Boyland and Watson (78) and by Allen *et al.* (79) were of 8–12 mg weight and contained a standard 20% of the test compound. The carrier substance was either 56°C melting point paraffin which was molten for incorporation of the test compound, or cholesterol into which the test compound was mixed by triturating together at room temperature; the pellets were pressed in a tablet-making machine. While in the investigations cited here solid paraffin and cholesterol have been favored as "inert" vehicle substances, actually a wide variety of substances can be used. Some considerations on which the selection of the vehicle substance is based are discussed in Section 4.3.4.

When the technique of bladder implantation on mice is used, all surviving animals are sacrificed (see Sections 4.3.2.3.4 and 4.3.6.1.2) at a fixed time of 40 or 52 weeks because of the very rapid autolytic changes which would take place in the bladder epithelium following unexpected death; for the same reason any mouse should be sacrificed earlier upon appearance of poor health or morbidity. To avoid wrinkling of the epithelium which would make microscopic examination difficult, immediately after sacrifice and opening of the abdomen, the urine should be removed and the bladder distended by filling it, using a syringe with needle, with Bouin's fixative (77, 79); it is convenient to carry out this procedure *in situ* (for fixation of tissues and composition of Bouin's fluid, see Suppletory Note 3). The sufficiently fixed bladder is then removed, bisected in the sagittal plane, and the interior surface is examined under a hand lens or dissecting microscope; in this way macroscopically visible tumors can be readily detected (79, 80). The two halves of the bladder will be stored in fixative for further processing in view of histopathological examination (Section 4.3.6.1.3).

The necessity of carrying, along with the test groups, an adequate control group is especially acute for testing by bladder implantation because of the particular sensitivity of the bladder epithelium to carcinogenic stimuli. Paraffin or cholesterol with or without heat treatment generally possesses some low background carcinogenicity (Section 4.3.3.2). The control group must receive, therefore, implants of pellets prepared in the identical way but containing no carcinogen. Similarly, the significance, if any, between the number of tumors in the control group and the different test groups must be analyzed statistically (see further in Section 4.3.6.2). Other considerations on the validity and significance of testing by bladder implantation have been discussed by Clayson (7).

4.3.4 INFLUENCE OF THE CHEMICAL VEHICLE OF ADMINISTRATION ON CARCINOGENIC ACTIVITY: THE SOLVENT EFFECTS

From the discussion of the different routes and modes of administration in Section 4.3.3 the reader is already familiar with the fact that the solvent or other chemical vehicle, in which the carcinogen is dissolved or suspended for administration, has often a determining influence on the course of carcinogenesis. The solvents used generally for skin painting, such as acetone, ether, benzene, do not affect much the course of carcinogenesis because of their rapid evaporation. However, ether because of its high volatility is not usually used alone but rather in mixture with liquid paraffin (*e.g.*, 82) which itself has frequently a low carcinogenic activity, and the background carcinogenicity of the mixture solvent is likely to influence (by enhancing or inhibiting) tumor induction by polycyclic hydrocarbons. It has been shown, furthermore, that when benzene is used as a solvent, skin tumors induced by 3,4-benzopyrene or 20-methylcholanthrene begin to appear somewhat later than when acetone or ether is used instead (83, 84). Crabtree has demonstrated that the delaying effect of benzene as well as of a number of other compounds is due to their property of being excreted in covalent combination with sulfur-containing amino acids, in the form of mercapturates (*e.g.*, 85; rev. 86) (see also Section 5.1.1.5). The tumor-delaying action of benzene is comparatively slight among the compounds excreted as mercapturates. For discussion of the inhibition of carcinogenesis by mercapturate-forming agents see Section 6.2.2.

Among the heavy nonvolatile solvents refined mineral oil has been recommended by Berenblum and Shubik (87) for experiments involving skin painting where a constant concentration of the carcinogen at the site of application is desirable, despite the fact that mineral oils cause retardation of carcinogenesis by 20-methylcholanthrene (88) and by 1,2,5,6-dibenzanthracene (89). Another heavy solvent for polycyclic hydrocarbons which has been experimented with is anhydrous lanolin (sheep sebum); Simpson and Cramer (90) noted the complete or almost complete suppression of the carcinogenic activity of 20-methylcholanthrene when applied to the skin of the mouse in this solvent. On the other hand, dissolved in human sebum, 20-methylcholanthrene produces a high incidence of skin tumors in mice (91). The reason for this peculiar difference, which is not known and has not been specifically investigated, is perhaps the particularly high level of phospholipids in lanolin. The inhibition of hydrocarbon-induced tumorigenesis by phospholipids has, in fact, been demonstrated in investigations on the effect of solvents on subcutaneously injected hydrocarbons (see below in this section). In the writers' views the use of nonvolatile solvents for skin painting is in general strongly contraindicated since, owing to the rubbing of the animal against its cage mates, to the cage walls and bedding material, the entire dose of solution will not remain at the original site of application but will tend to be smeared to other points on the animal's body; this renders the quantitative aspect of the testing highly questionable.

Unlike the volatile solvents commonly employed for skin painting, the solvents and solid vehicles used in the parenteral methods of administration have very often a major influence on the course of carcinogenesis. The solvents or vehicles used for parenteral administration may increase or decrease the potency of an agent. For example, a solvent can bring about a decrease of carcinogenic activity by increasing the rate of diffusion and transport of the agent from the site of administration and the rate of its excretion from the animal body. The solvent may change the carcinogen, for instance, by influencing the rate of oxidation of the agent prior to or during the process of carcinogenesis. The solvent may influence the tissue itself before or during tumor formation so that it will react differently toward the carcinogen. If one considers, therefore, the large number of compounds capable of enhancing or inhibiting the action of carcinogens and, on the other hand, the largely unknown composition of natural fats (such as corn oil, cottonseed oil, olive oil, arachis oil, sesame oil, lard, cholesterol, solid paraffin, used as solvent vehicles of natural origin), it becomes evident that these extraneous influences have to be eliminated from the testing methods or at least their influence on tumorigenesis accurately assessed. A truly quantitative approach to carcinogenesis necessarily requires a solvent which will not interfere with the biological effects caused by the substance under test.

water may diffuse out of the cholesterol pellets and are excreted from the bladder too rapidly to bring about neoplastic alterations of the bladder epithelium; too rapid diffusion may also result in the appearance of systemic toxic effects or necrosis of the tissues in contact, precisely because of the too high concentrations attained. For example, 2-amino-1-naphthol, which is notably carcinogenic when implanted in the mouse bladder in paraffin pellets (80, 105), is practically inactive when applied as the hydrochloride in cholesterol pellets (79).

Effects reminiscent of the "solvent effects" are also observed in oral administration. For example, György *et al.* (106) observed that the carcinogenic azo dye, 4-dimethylaminoazobenzene undergoes oxidative destruction in diets containing high levels of linoleic acid. Other normal or special dietary constituents possibly affect azo dye-induced hepatic tumor induction by influencing the rate of absorption from the intestinal tract and/or the rate of excretion of the carcinogen from the animal body. Thus, when rats receiving *o*-aminoazotoluene were fed high levels of lecithin, the production of liver tumors was accelerated (107). On the other hand, Miller *et al.* (108) found that addition to the diet of 0.25 % of either of two synthetic detergents strongly inhibited hepatocarcinogenesis due to 4-dimethyl-aminoazobenzene. Moreover the chemical nature, the type of fat in the diet, and the dietary level of the fat have also a marked effect on the rate of tumor induction, and this "fat effect" is distinct from the contribution of the fat to the caloric value of the diet (high caloric intake is known to accelerate the induction of tumors by different agents). These effects will be discussed in some detail in Section 7.1 on "The Effect of Diet on Tumor Induction."

4.3.5 PURITY OF THE TEST SUBSTANCES. THE PRELIMINARY ASSAY. THE DOSING SCHEDULE. DESIGNING OF TESTING EXPERIMENTS

For studying the structure-activity relationships of a given class of carcinogens, or when the testing of a substance is carried out to clarify some particular point in biochemical considerations on mechanism, the test substance(s) used should be the highest purity attainable. To ascertain the absence of highly carcinogenic impurities is especially important when the testing turns out a borderline result of, say, the appearance of tumors in 5–10 % of the animals. In such a case, although the melting or boiling point of the substance may be perfectly correct and/or the highest attainable, it is preferable to verify the purity again by column chromatography and the ultraviolet and/or infrared spectrum (if reference spectra are available). The recently introduced *zone melting* procedure is claimed to yield solid substances of higher purity than column chromatography.

If, on the other hand, the testing is prompted by public health considerations in order to determine the safety or otherwise, of pesticides, food additives, cosmetics, and industrially used technical grade substances, then it is preferable to use the commercial product so that the testing may bring out the carcinogenicity due possibly to impurities present in the original product as it is actually used. For the reasons pointed out earlier in Sections 4.3.3.3 and 4.3.4, the solutions used for administration or treatment should be freshly prepared, and compounded diets containing carcinogens should not be used beyond a reasonable length of time.

Before assaying any hitherto untested compound for carcinogenic activity, it is necessary to determine the approximate maximum level at which it can be tolerated by the test species for the duration of long-term administration. In fact, the closer the test dose is to the maximum tolerable level, the more likely it is that the carcinogenicity of a potential carcinogen will be detected. Some instances have been observed, however, where beyond a given high dose which induces tumors in a maximum number of animals, further increase of the dose results in the decrease in the percentage of tumor bearers (e.g., 109, 110). A similar phenomenon found in radiation-induced tumorigenesis has been interpreted that the too high dose destroys the partially altered precancerous cells in the target tissue from which the tumors would have originated (111). The implication for chemical carcinogenesis may be that the actually found tumors are the end results of two opposing actions, the cytotoxicity and the carcinogenic activity of the agent (112). That the highest tolerated level will sometimes give less than maximal response has also been interpreted as due to inhibition of growth of the host and possibly also of the induced tumor (113). For this reason then, theoretically at least, testing should be carried out at two or more dose levels. However, except when special circumstances warrant it, this consideration is usually disregarded for practical reasons in the routine assaying of potential carcinogens.

It is useful to know the 50% lethal dose (LD_{50}) of the compound, which can often be found in literature tabulations, in order to gain some concept of the order of magnitude of the dose, i.e., whether the acute toxicity of the compound is tolerated at 1 gm, 100 mg, 10 mg, or 1 mg level per kilogram body weight. The LD_{50} is, however, directly useful only if the compound is administered in one dose. If, on the other hand, the agent is administered at intervals during the experiment, then the chronic toxicity due to cumulative effects comes into play.

For practical purposes, therefore, most often an arbitrary dosing schedule (i.e., concentration or dose level, and frequency of administration) is chosen, which schedule is based on some possible structural similarity of the agent with previously tested known carcinogens and/or on a reasonable conservative extrapolation of the LD_{50} to chronic toxicity. This dosing schedule, using the route of administration appropriate for the compound, is then initiated on a small preliminary group; let us say, for example, that the compound is administered orally, by stomach tube, to a group of 6–10 male Sprague-Dawley rats weighing initially between 180 and 230 gm. The preliminary group must be under thorough observation and weighed daily. If the growth rate of the animals becomes stationary or there is an outright drastic decline of the body weight (or some animals die), then the dose is cut down to half either by doubling the intervals of administration or by reducing the level of administration. On the other hand, if the animals show a practically normal growth rate after say 10–12 days of administration, then the dose should be doubled. Thus, by trial and error, by progressively decreasing or increasing the dose, the correct maximum dosing schedule is approximated which still allows a normal or close to normal growth rate and apparent good health of the test animals for *at least* 5–6 weeks.

Some authors recommend (in reference 7) that the preliminary group be continued to be fed according to the final, correct dosing schedule and an additional subgroup of animals be started so that the total number of animals on which the testing is carried out should amount to an *acceptably large group size* (see below in this section). While this procedure is more economical in terms of the number of animals used for the testing, one disadvantage can be that during the maintenance of the preliminary group on low doses, in some instances metabolic adaptive mechanisms come into play which may make the over-all response somewhat different than when the animals receive the correct dosing schedule from the very onset of administration. Thus, it is preferable to sacrifice (see Sections 4.3.2.3.4 and 4.3.6.1.2) the preliminary group before beginning the long-term carcinogenicity testing with new animals, or, without including them in the final total, the preliminary group may be continued on the final dosage schedule and observed; acute weight loss or toxic symptoms in this advance group will alert the investigator to decrease or temporarily discontinue the administration of the test compound to the larger group when they approach the time interval at which the symptoms were noted in the preliminary group.

Table XXV gives a selection of dosing schedules used in the administration of some known types of carcinogens. Let us take now as an example the consideration of a preliminary dosing schedule for the yet untested S-ethylcysteine, the lower homolog of the carcinogenic amino acid, ethionine:

$$HOOC-\underset{\underset{NH_2}{|}}{CH}-CH_2-S-C_2H_5 \qquad HOOC-\underset{\underset{NH_2}{|}}{CH}-CH_2-CH_2-S-C_2H_5$$

S-ethylcysteine ethionine

The testing of S-ethylcysteine would be of interest since its activity or inactivity may yield further insight on the mechanism of action of ethionine. The latter was tested (Table XXV) and found hepatocarcinogenic when fed to rats, mixed in the diet at the level of 19 millimoles per kilogram. In view of the close structural similarity of the two compounds it is probably a fair assumption that the same dosing schedule would be correct for S-ethyl-cysteine.

As is evident from Table XXV, a dosing schedule is, of course, valid only for the species in which it was determined. Moreover, the correct dosing schedule (*i.e.*, the maximum tolerable chronic dose) may also change with the strain and sex, but especially with the age of the animals; weanling and young animals are usually more sensitive. For this reason it is important for comparative purposes and for the sake of reproducibility, in a laboratory carrying out quantitative studies on carcinogenesis, to adopt a standard initial age or weight range at which testing experiments are initiated; for example, in the writers' laboratories 180–230 gm has been adopted as the standard initial weight range for rats when studying azo dye carcinogens.

In the search for determining the correct minimum requirements for testing potential carcinogens of new structural types, the number of animals making up the test groups has been a much debated question. The important point is that the population should be large enough to make statistical evaluation possible. A number of investigators consider that at least 25 animals *of each sex* should be used (*e.g.*, 114, 115). However, for studies on the structure-activity relationships within a given well-known class of carcinogens (*e.g.*, azo dyes) testing has occasionally been carried out using only one sex and with smaller groups (*e.g.*, 51,110). The necessity for using groups of both sexes when testing new compounds is the consequence of the fact that in some species males may have a higher percentage of certain types of spontaneous tumors than females or *vice-versa* (Section 4.3.2.2). Similarly, males or females are susceptible to different degrees to certain tumor localizations in chemical carcinogenesis; for example, 2-acetylamino-fluorene and 4-dimethylaminobiphenyl produce in females predominantly mammary tumors while in males they produce predominantly liver tumors. The considerable differences in the susceptibility of the two sexes to carcinogenesis by polycyclic aromatic carcinogens have been pointed out recently (116). Obviously, when testing is carried out on a group of a single sex (see above) it is important to use strains in which the spontaneous tumor incidence will not "cover" the carcinogenic activity of the test substance. For example, because of the high percentage of spontaneous mammary tumors in the females, C3H and DBA mice (see Table XXI) are not proper strains for studying mammary tumor induction by chemical carcinogens.

Table XXV

Dosing Schedules Used in the Administration of Some Known Types of Carcinogens

Type of carcinogen	Dose and vehicle	Route and frequency	Species
Polycyclic hydrocarbons and heteroaromatic compounds	0.1 ml 0.3–0.4 % in solvent 0.5–2 mg (occasionally up to 10 mg in oil or by trocar)	Skin painting 2 × weekly Single subcutaneous administration	Mice Mice, rats
4-Aminobiphenyl and 2-acetyl-aminofluorene; derivatives and related compounds	1.62 millimoles/kg diet	Mixed in the diet	Rats
2-Acetylaminofluorene	0.1 ml 0.5 % in acetone	Skin painting 2 × weekly	Rats
	300 mg/day for 50 days	Mixed in the diet	Dogs
2-Naphthylamine	160 mg/kg diet	Mixed in the diet	Mice
2-Anthramine	1 % in acetone, starting 0.02 ml and gradually increasing to 0.3 ml at 300 days	Skin painting 2 × weekly	Rats
Amino azo dyes	2.40 millimoles/kg diet (occasionally 2.00 or 2.67 millimoles/kg)	Mixed in the diet	Rats
o-Aminoazotoluene	10–200 mg by trocar	3–10 repeated subcutaneous implantations	Mice
4-Dimethylaminostilbene and derivatives	0.22 millimoles/kg diet	Mixed in the diet	Rats
	1 or 5 mg/week in oil	8–10 repeated subcutaneous injections	Mice, rats
Trypan Blue	1 ml 1 % aqueous solution	Subcutaneous injection every 2nd week	Rats
Estrone	50–200 μg/week in oil	Weekly subcutaneous injections	Mice, rats
Methyl bis(β-chloroethyl)amine hydrochloride and related nitrogen mustards	0.10–0.25 mg in 0.25 ml water	4–8 repeated subcutaneous injections	Mice
Ethyl carbamate and derivatives	0.15–0.75 % 0.10 %	Mixed in the diet In the drinking water	Mice Mice
	1 mg/week in water	13 weekly intraperitoneal injections	Rats
Dialkylnitrosamines	5.4 μmoles/day in water	Stomach tube	Rats
Ethionine	19 millimoles/kg diet	Mixed in the diet	Rats
Carbon tetrachloride	0.1 ml of 40 % solution in oil	Stomach tube 2 × weekly	Mice
Dioxane	1 %	In the drinking water	Rats
Tannic acid	1–2 % aqueous solution	Subcutaneous injection every 5 days	Rats
Acetamide	2–5 %	Mixed in the diet	Rats

The importance of carrying adequate control groups has been emphasized already in Section 4.3.3. The size of the control groups should be *at least* as large as the size of the test groups. Ideally a testing experiment should include one *negative control* group and one *positive control* group. The negative controls should receive the same diet as the animals of the test group and, in the case of parenteral administration, should be subjected to the administration of the solvent or other vehicle substance. In the views of Della Porta (115) the negative control group should be 4 times as large as the individual test groups. The positive controls should be administered a reference carcinogen under conditions otherwise identical with those of the negative controls and the test groups; this reference carcinogen is usually selected on the basis of its structural similarity with the substance(s) tested. The importance of this control group is to make apparent any possible resistance of the animals to carcinogenesis, due to the particular strain used or to the dietary or other conditions of the experiment. In this way the activity of the test compounds may be expressed relative to the activity of the reference carcinogen; for example, new amino azo dyes are usually tested for hepato-carcinogenicity in conjunction with a 4-dimethylaminoazobenzene positive control group and their relative activities expressed accordingly (see Section 4.3.6.2.4).

4.3.5.1   Testing for Tumor Initiatory Activity

In order to bring to light the carcinogenicity of agents of only marginal activity, the concept and method of testing for *tumor initiatory activity* has been developed. Application of a *subthreshold* dose (Section 4.3.6.2.3) of, say, 3,4-benzopyrene to the skin of mice will lead, at most, to the appearance of a few transitory papillomas. However, if the same skin area is treated subsequently—repeatedly and over a period of time—with an appropriate second agent, a great number of permanent papillomas and epitheliomas will appear. The 3,4-benzopyrene applied first (in this example) is an *initiator*. The second agent, which would not produce tumors had it been applied without the initiator, is termed a *promotor*. The initiation transforms a number of cells in the skin into "dormant" tumor cells (Section 4.1) with latent potentialities for malignant growth. Promotion stimulates these cells to divide and develop into macroscopically visible tumors. Except for the possibility of being promoted into tumors, there is no known way of detecting the presence of dormant tumor cells. Initiation and promotion will be discussed in relation to the two-stage hypothesis of carcinogenesis, in Section 6.2.3.

3,4-Benzopyrene used in the above example is a *"complete"* carcinogen. This means that if it is applied *in excess* of the threshold level for an appropriate length of time, it will produce a number of tumors without subsequent applications of a promotor. On the other hand, an *"incomplete"* carcinogen even at high levels (and a complete but marginally active carcinogen under certain circumstances) will not induce tumors without promotion.

The most frequently used promotor is croton oil which is extracted from the seeds of *Croton tiglium* Lin. A disadvantage of using croton oil is that, being a natural product, its promoting activity may vary considerably from batch to batch. Other potent promotors are phenol, certain long-chain aliphatic and aliphatic-aromatic hydrocarbons and fatty acids, citrus oils, and a variety of surface-active agents known as the "Spans" and "Tweens." The Spans are esters of long-chain fatty acids with the remaining free primary hydroxyl group of the sorbitol (C_6) cyclic anhydride, sorbitan. Span 20 is the monoauryl ester; Span 60, the monostearyl ester; and Span 80, the mono-oleyl ester. Tween 20, Tween 60, and Tween 80 are derived from the respective Spans by linking (via ether linkage) polyoxyethylene chains of variable length to the three vicinal tertiary hydroxyl groups on the cyclic carbon skeleton. The Tweens used in tumor initiation studies contain between 5 and 100 total ethyleneoxide units. The Spans are lipophilic, while in the Tweens, hydrosolubility increases with the number of ethylene oxide units. All these promotors have been used on the skin of the mouse. There is some evidence that the promoting action of croton oil is specific to the mouse skin and that tumorigenesis is not promoted on the skin of the rat, hamster, and rabbit.

Consider now a hypothetical experiment of actual testing for tumor initiatory activity. The polycyclic hydrocarbon, 1,2,3,4-dibenzanthracene has been repeatedly found inactive; however, results of one early assay suggest that this compound may manifest trace activity under certain conditions (ref. 1, p. 238). An experimental design for testing would be as follows. Groups of fifteen male and fifteen female mice will receive on the shaved skin of the interscapular region, three times weekly, 0.2 ml of 0.3% acetone solution of the hydrocarbon for fifteen weeks. Identical control groups are treated with the solvent alone. After fifteen weeks, the mice, test and control groups alike, are changed to twice-weekly applications of croton oil (0.2 ml, 0.5% in acetone), and the treatment is continued for 20 weeks. The surviving mice are observed for another 16–20 weeks for the final tumor count (if any). It must be stressed that careful control experiments and statistical analysis of the test data relative to the controls are of especially great importance in the tumor initiatory tests. *In fact*, while ideally promotors are not carcinogenic, in reality most, if not all promotors (in particular the frequently used croton oil) have marginal to weak carcinogenic activity.*

* *Note added after completion of Section 4.* Similar procedures were designed to test for the tumor initiatory activity of various cross-linking anti-cancer agents, narcotics, fungicides, and herbicides [*e.g.,* F. J. C. Roe, *Cancer Res.* **17**, 64 (1957); C. E. Searle, *ibid.* **26**, 12 (1966)]. Agents which are carcinogenic toward other target tissues in the mouse, but not toward the skin, can

4.3.6   The Evaluation of Carcinogenic Activity

4.3.6.1   Examination of the Animals During Testing. Guidelines for Autopsy. Fixation of Tissue Samples. Transplantability of Tumors as Evidence for Malignancy

During the entire period of testing, that is during the period of actual administration and during a subsequent period (if any) of observation, the animals must be regularly examined for the presence of tumors. Except for the examination for skin tumors and certain abdominal tumors, for which some specific procedures are described below, it is difficult to give well-defined guidelines for this general examination of the animals. Circumspection and a keenly receptive attitude are important ingredients of any observation in descriptive biology. The investigator must be observant of any swelling, induration, or nodularity in the region of subcutaneous injection or implantation; he must be aware that subcutaneous and especially mammary tumors also arise following oral administration of various substances. Change in the gait and general behavior of the animal may be indicative of lesions affecting the sense of equilibrium either peripheral, in the ear, or in the central nervous system. For example, following feeding 2-acetylamino-fluorene, the beginning of the emergence of ear duct tumors is often signaled by a one-sided gait (the animal leaning to one or the other side) because the sense of equilibrium of the animal is affected by the tumor exerting a pressure or invading the labyrinth. Any special observation is recorded in the "Record of General Observations" (Section 4.3.2.3.3). In addition to that, the emergence of tumors is also recorded in the "Record of Autopsies" (Section 4.3.2.3.3) irrespective of whether the animal is sacrificed and autopsied at that time, or is kept alive. The former is most often the case for sizable abdominal tumors, the latter is generally the case following the appearance of readily observable tumors such as those of the skin, subcutaneous tissue, mammary gland, ear duct, etc.

4.3.6.1.1   Antemortem Examination for Skin and Abdominal Tumors. Exploratory Laparotomy. In skin painting experiments the treated body region of the animals is examined twice or thrice weekly (usually *prior* to

---

act as initiators. Thus, urethan applied to the skin [I. Berenblum and N. Haran-Ghera, *Brit. J. Cancer* **11**, 77 (1957)] and dietary 2-acetylaminofluorene [A. C. Ritchie and U. Saffiotti, *Cancer Res.* **15**, 84 (1955)] were found to initiate skin tumors, in the mouse, in conjunction with locally applied croton oil. However, 2-acetylaminofluorene applied to the skin is devoid of initiating activity [M. H. Salaman and F. J. C. Roe, *Brit. J. Cancer* **7**, 472 (1953)]. Promotor activity has also been observed in tissues other than skin. For example, following a single dose of 3,4-benzopyrene given by stomach tube, lime oil (which is also a promotor in skin) administered in the same way greatly increases the incidence of benign and malignant tumors of the forestomach in mice [W. E. H. Peirce, *Nature* **189**, 497 (1961)].

each treatment). Customarily some arbitrary standards are adopted for the beginning of a skin tumor. For example, in our laboratories a papilloma (1 mm minimum diameter) has to persist for 2 weeks to be considered as a true tumor, but it is recorded as appearing on the date it was first noted. The progression or rate of growth of skin tumors (as well as of subcutaneous sarcomas) is conveniently followed, if desired, by measuring the diameter or dimensions of the tumor with a caliper rule.

The *most reliable way* to ascertain the time of emergence of abdominal tumors is by performing periodic exploratory laparotomies on the animals. Palpation of the abdominal region (between the thumb and the four fingers) can give indications suggestive of the presence of already large abdominal tumors. It must be emphatically stressed that the impressions gathered by palpation, however definitive they may appear to be, can *by no means* be construed as evidence for the presence of tumors (which must always be ascertained by direct observation in exploratory laparotomy) but rather as a signal as to when the performance of the laparotomy is warranted, if the intervention was not planned to be carried out at repeated regular intervals. Moreover, in the authors' experience the rat is probably the only frequently used laboratory animal in which palpation may yield some more or less reliable suggestive indication; the bulkiness and large fatty deposits in adult guinea pigs, for example, render palpation an illusory procedure. The palpation should always be gentle because undue pressure on advanced abdominal tumors carries with it the risk of hemorrhage and of losing the animal at a time when it may not be intended.

Exploratory laparotomy has been routinely carried out in the testing of amino azo dyes on rats (*e.g.*, 51, 110). The routine use of this surgical procedure is made possible by the fact that even the inbred strains of rats (and also of mice) usually used in the laboratory are practically refractory to infection, so that the operation can be performed disregarding aseptic conditions. The only truly important requirement is that the surgery should be technically correct, *i.e.*, that laceration of internal structures and thus dangerous hemorrhaging should be carefully avoided, all sutures should be solid and distributed close enough so that no herniation will occur, and that no hair or fatty tissue should be sewn between the edges of the wound in order to allow rapid and good healing. Some general principles of surgery of the rat and certain surgical techniques have been described by Ingle and Griffith (in reference 38); most of these can be adapted with little modification to mice.

In the following text the technique of exploratory laparotomy on rats as performed in our laboratories is presented. The rat is placed under ether anesthesia (see Section 4.3.2.3.4) before being secured to the operating platform. An inexpensive but very convenient operative platform is a $\frac{3}{4}$-inch thick, 8×10-inch size enamel-painted pine wood board, fitted on each side with 3 hooks at about $3\frac{1}{2}$ inches apart. The board is covered with 4 layers of paper towels and the animal fastened to it by heavy rubber bands looped about the feet and over the hooks. The hair is removed from the abdominal surface (an about $1\frac{1}{2} \times 2\frac{3}{4}$ inch area) first with an electric clipper, and then the area is thoroughly depilated using a 25–30% aqueous sodium sulfide solution. This solution is applied to the surface with a thick swab or with a cotton ball handled by means of forceps. When the hairy surface turns yellowish the preparation and dissolved hair are *immediately* wiped off, and the surface is thoroughly cleansed with cotton balls dipped in water and then wiped with 95% aqueous alcohol; avoid letting the sodium sulfide solution too long in contact with the skin as it will cause burns. The incision is made starting at the center of the abdominal region or below (depending on the extent of exploration desired), along the abdominal midline. The incision is initiated by first lifting both the skin and the abdominal muscle at the desired starting point by means of mouse-tooth forceps, then a small cut penetrating through the skin and muscle into the abdominal cavity is made with scissors, perpendicular to the abdominal midline. The blunt end of $5\frac{1}{2}$ inch (blunt and sharp point) operating scissors is now inserted into the cut and, always lifting the edge of the wound, the incision is extended along the abdominal midline up to the sternum. Hemostats are not necessary for this intervention. Bleeding from the edges of the wound is very small if the incision follows narrowly the abdominal midline. Sidewise deviation from this midline may result, however, in the severance of larger veins and these may require ligation to avoid excessive loss of blood and/or obliteration of visibility in the operative field. Small metal retractors are then inserted and, by fastening them by rubber bands to the central hooks on both sides of the board, the edges of the wound are pulled apart so as to expose the abdominal organs.

The abdominal organs are now thoroughly examined for the presence of tumors. For this the fingers and a carefully fire-polished thick glass spatula are used; the latter is a convenient tool for moving the intestines about, lifting the lobes of the liver, exploring the outer surface of the stomach, etc., without laceration of the tissues and danger of hemorrhage. During the examination the abdominal organs are kept moist by wetting at times with physiological saline. If sizable tumor(s) (*e.g.*, of the liver, kidney, stomach, or small intestine) is found, the animal is sacrificed, while under the anesthesia, by puncturing the diaphragm; death will occur within a few minutes and the animal is then subjected to a complete autopsy as described later in this section. On the other hand, if no tumors are found or if an apparent tumor or nodular formation may be too small or undefined for clear-cut macroscopic diagnosis, then the animal is kept alive and the administration of the test substance and/or the observation of the animal continued.

The incisions of the abdominal muscle and of the skin are closed separately. The edges of the abdominal muscle are approximated with individual stitches, $\frac{1}{8} - \frac{1}{4}$ inch apart, using $4 - 0$ surgical silk thread and No. 4 taper-point half-circle fine intestinal needle. The edges of the skin are approximated with a continuous running suture using $5 - 0$ surgical silk or single filament nylon thread and a 2-inch long taper point straight needle; make certain that the terminal knot of the running suture is tight. The wound is covered with medicinal collodion solution. The animal is kept warm (wrapped in a towel or placed under a lamp) until recovery and then returned to its cage. Provide water abundantly as water intake is notably higher during the postoperative period. Normally, complete healing takes place in about 10 days. If the animal is in good health, exploratory laparotomy may be repeated every 3–4 weeks and a maximum of about 4–6 times during testing. To assure good healing, excessive scar tissue should be removed before approximating the edges of the incision in these subsequent operations. In our experience it is not necessary to remove the dermal suture after healing, and actually the animal removes most of it once the wound is healed.

4.3.6.1.2 Sacrifice and Postmortem Examination. At the termination of the testing period all animals participating in the experiment are killed. A humane and simple procedure for the sacrifice of small rodents has been described in Section 4.3.2.3.4 in connection with the method of ether anesthesia. The production of embolism by the intravenous injection of 3–10 ml of air or the intravenous or intracardiac injection of 10 ml chloroform or formalin are rapid and humane ways to bring about death in rabbits and dogs; dogs should be administered, intravenously or mixed in food, a large dose of pentobarbital, prior to the production of embolism.

It is of utmost importance that the animals should be autopsied before autolysis occurs, in order to avoid the loss of much of the details of microscopic tissue structure on which the histopathological examination is based. It is for this reason that the animal room routine (Section 4.3.2.3.3) includes inspection of the animals twice daily and that exploratory laparotomies are usually carried out at regular intervals. To obtain the maximum information from the experiment the animals must be autopsied *immediately* after death and the tissue samples taken. For the same reason, all animals bearing large and/or ulcerated tumors and showing signs of morbidity should be killed as they may die before the next inspection.

Autopsy of the experimental animals is an important task since it is mostly there that final evidence is collected on the biological effect(s) of the compound tested. Consequently it is of great import that the person performing the *postmortem* examination should be skilled in the technique of dissection and that he should be thoroughly familiar with the anatomy of the normal, untreated individuals of the species at hand. The review of these is beyond the scope of this book, and readers who are newcomers to biological sciences or unfamiliar with these are referred to elementary texts on techniques and anatomical descriptions of the laboratory animal species (*e.g.*, 38, 117, 118). For such readers it is also advisable to acquire the necessary skill by performing practice dissections under the supervision of a qualified biologist. Below, a suggested sequence of *postmortem* examination, generally adequate for carcinogen testing, is given; however, it must be recalled again that no formal schedule can substitute for circumspection and the observance of details. A stereoscopic microscope, $20\times$ and $40\times$ magnification, is useful for the close examination of small organs and tissue samples.

1. The total skin and subcutaneous area and skeletal muscles are carefully palpated for evidence of nodularity, with particular attention to the mammary region and the region of the throat (in view of the possibility of mammary, thyroid, and salivary gland tumors). At any region where nodularity is found, the hair is removed by electric clippers, skin and subcutaneous tissue dissected away, and the suspected tumor and adjacent tissues removed for preservation.

2. The peritoneum is opened. The entire small intestine is removed, rinsed in physiological saline and passed between the thumb and the forefinger in order to identify (as a hard nodule) any small lymphatic tumor which may have originated from the Peyer's patches (small lymph nodes distributed at intervals along the small intestine). The large intestine, cecum, testicles or uterus and ovaries, and the bladder are examined. (Special technique for examining the bladder is given in Section 4.3.3.5). The iliac node is identified and examined for enlargement (carefully avoid lacerating the adjacent blood vessels which would cause hemorrhage and obliterate visibility). Now the following organs are removed from the abdominal cavity, rinsed in physiological saline and examined in minutia: the liver as a whole (with gall bladder if any), spleen, the two kidneys with adrenals, and the stomach. The stomach is opened flat by cutting along the greater curvature, the contents emptied, the stomach rinsed in saline, and the internal surface examined for evidence of tumors (note that parasites embedded in the stomach wall may cause nodular formations). The kidneys are bisected longitudinally and the cross sections examined. The adrenals and spleen are inspected, dissected if necessary, and their enlargement (if any) relative to the average normal size is recorded. The surface of the liver lobes is carefully screened for the presence of any clear-cut tumor, small white spot, or tiny nodule. If no surface changes are noted, all lobes are cut in about 5-mm large strips and the cross-sections of these examined for possible small nodules inside of the tissue mass.

3. The diaphragm and rib cage are dissected away. The thymus gland and the heart are examined. The lung is removed as a whole, rinsed in saline, and examined in detail in the same manner as was carried out for the liver (lung tumors sometimes begin in the inside of the lobes rather than on the surface).

4. The nose, mouth, tongue, and the external ear and the area around it are inspected. The interior of the skull is then opened. The following describes the dissection of the skull of the rat. First, the animal is decapitated by severing the neck between the base of the skull and the first cervical vertebra. The skin is stripped off and the top of the skull removed at the level of the eyes as follows. The head is held solidly with a mouse-tooth forceps inserted in the eye sockets. Using $7\frac{1}{2}$-inch Liston bone-cutting forceps, initial cuts are made in the skull in both lateral directions beginning at the *foramen magnum* (the orifice through which the spinal cord passes to make connection with the brain stem in the skull). Then, $6\frac{1}{2}$-inch standard operating scissors (sharp and blunt points) are used to extend the incisions in the skull in both lateral directions to the eyes, and the bone between the eyes is then severed with the bone-cutting forceps. The top of the skull can be lifted off and the brain is then available intact for examination. The pituitary gland (hypophysis) is in the bony recesses of the floor of the skull beneath the brain.

Preparation of blood smears (see Suppletory Note 2) is not always part of a routine schedule of final evaluation. Blood smears must be included, however, and prepared *before* sacrificing the animals if there is suspicion that the compound tested is leukemogenic, if the histopathology of animals killed earlier indicates leukemia, or if in animals examined earlier during serial autopsies great enlargements of the spleen, lymph glands, and occasionally of the liver are observed, and/or outright lymphoid tumors are found.

4.3.6.1.3 Sampling and Fixation of Tissues. All observations made during *postmortem* examination are introduced in the Record of Autopsies (Section 4.3.2.3.3). Also, tumors, suspected tumors, all questionable tissue samples collected for the histopathological examination, and the preparation of blood smears (if any) are recorded there. Figure 73 illustrates a general-purpose autopsy record form.

For preservation the tissue samples must be "fixed." The action of fixatives may be compared to the action of tanning agents. They penetrate the tissues, stop autolysis by inactivating all enzymes, and generally halt all further deterioration by causing extensive cross-linking. A variety of fixative solutions are in use. Whatever fixative is used, however, it is important that the tissues be correctly sampled. This means that the tissue sample should

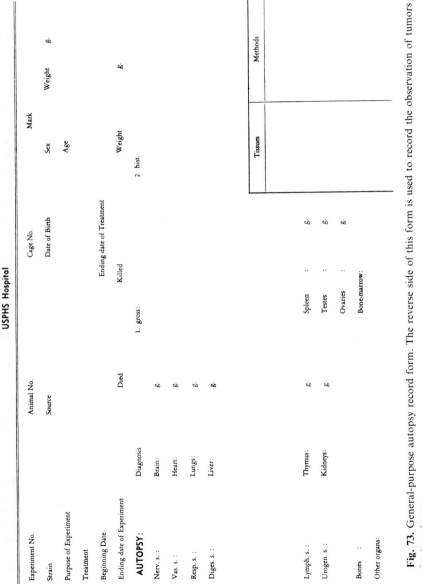

Fig. 73. General-purpose autopsy record form. The reverse side of this form is used to record the observation of tumors prior to autopsy.

be (*a*) not too large so that it may be thoroughly penetrated and fixed by the fixative; (*b*) not too small which may make further processing of the tissue and preparation of the microscope slides, in the histology laboratory, awkward; (*c*) a piece cut away from the bulk of the organ or tissue using a *sharp* scalpel or razor blade; do not use scissors or a blunt scalpel because compression of the tissue may mangle some of the tissue fine structure; (*d*) selected from the bulk of the tissue so that it will yield maximum information to the histopathologist. In order to allow good penetration of the fixative the thickness of the tissue sample (*i.e.*, the smallest of its three dimensions) should be at most 10 mm. On the other hand, it is unnecessarily awkward to carry through histological processing samples, the overall size of which is smaller than about 5 × 5 × 5 mm except when the size of an organ makes small sample-size unavoidable (*e.g.*, adrenals, hypophysis, lymph nodes). Because an important characteristic of malignant tissues is their invasiveness, a well-selected tumor sample always includes some adjacent normal tissue so that the pathologist can evaluate the invasiveness of the tumor in the borderline region. Tumor nodules of 5-mm diameter or smaller may be fixed as a whole, together with surrounding normal tissue. Larger nodules should not be fixed as one piece but should be dissected and an appropriate size tissue sample, which includes part of the tumor and some adjacent normal tissue, fixed. (For the technique of fixing and handling the bladder see Section 4.3.3.5.)

The freshly cut tissue samples are rinsed in physiological saline in order to remove all hair and blood from the surface, and are placed in the selected fixative (see Suppletory Note 3) in screw-cap glass jars large enough to hold a volume of fixative at least 10 times the volume of the total tissue to be fixed. The label on the jar should carry the following information: number of the experiment, number of the animal, date of autopsy, fixative, number of tissue samples in the jar. In addition, it is useful to duplicate this information, *with pencil*, on a small strip of white pasteboard; this strip (which will follow the sample through histological processing) is placed in the fixative together with the sample(s). The fixing of the tissue is most often the last step of experimental procedure carried out by the chemical oncologist. At this point the histopathologist takes over to evaluate the precancerous or other tissue changes (if any) brought about by the administration of the test compound and to determine the cellular type(s) of the tumor(s) produced.

It is evident that complete autopsy of all animals and histopathological examination of the tissue samples are mandatory at the termination of testing of any hitherto untested compound, since even small molecular modifications may produce important shifts in tumor localization. Similarly, both these examinations must be carried out if the purpose of the experiment is to confirm earlier results, on the ground that the earlier investigators may have missed certain tumor localizations. On the other hand, there are special experimental circumstances in which complete autopsy and even histopathological examination may be omitted and *postmortem* examination is restricted to one particular tissue or organ. For example, 3,4-benzopyrene and 3'-methyl-4-dimethylaminoazobenzene are powerful carcinogens toward the skin of the mouse (applied in skin painting) and toward the liver of the rat (administered orally), respectively. That the nodules, having the macroscopic appearance of tumors, which arise in the respective target tissues as a result of treatment with or administration of these compounds represent effectively benign or malignant tumors by histopathological criteria, has been demonstrated beyond any reasonable doubt in a great number of experiments. Say, then, that we want to study the percentage of tumor bearers (specifically skin and liver tumors) in groups of animals as a function of the length of administration or total dose received. Since in these particular cases it is justified to identify a "tumor" by macroscopic criteria, and since no distinction between benign and malignant tumors is intended, histopathological examination of the tumors may be omitted.

4.3.6.1.4 Tumor Transplantation. It has been briefly mentioned in Section 4.1 that transplantability of a tumor into another animal of the same strain is an evidence of its malignancy. For this reason tumor transplantation is often carried out not so much to establish new tumor lines but rather to demonstrate more solidly the malignancy of certain induced or spontaneous tumors. Tumor implants "take" best if implanted in a region of the body which has a good blood supply (*e.g.*, subaxillary, inguinal). Given identical regions of implantation, the percentage of "takes" in a group of animals, the rapidity of "takes" *i.e.*, the length of latency period required for the implant to begin to grow, as well as the rate of growth of the transplanted tumor once growth has begun, are all parameters of the malignancy of the parent tumor.

The technique of transplantation is very simple. The original tumor is removed, rapidly dissected, and the solid, nonnecrotic tumor tissue is collected in physiological saline or Ringer solution. In the early times a small piece of tumor tissue was cut and implanted subcutaneously; the surgical technique used for this is identical to the one used to implant carcinogen pellets (Section 4.3.3.2), except for the position of implantation. Implantation of small tissue pieces becomes even simpler with the use of the trocar. Another, more quantitative variant consists in passing a known amount of tumor tissue through a hand tissue press and suspending the collected mash in a given volume of physiological saline or Ringer solution; a small known volume of the suspension is injected using a syringe and large bore needle.

4.3.6.2 Parameters of Carcinogenic Activity: Latent Period and Tumor Incidence. Statistical Analysis of Results. Dose-Response Relationships and Threshold Dose. The Grading of Carcinogenic Activity

Comparison of the carcinogenic activities of a large number of compounds under various conditions was required for gaining insight into the relationships between chemical structure and carcinogenicity in the various classes of carcinogens. The early investigators of chemical oncology, studying mainly the carcinogenic polycyclic hydrocarbons and amino azo dyes, were content with simple classification either as active or inactive compounds. Soon, however, it became desirable to put the testing procedures on standardized bases in order to express quantitatively and then interpret carcinogenic activity. For this it became necessary to define parameters of the different testing techniques and to isolate quantitative aspects of the process of emergence of macroscopically visible tumors.

4.3.6.2.1 Latent Period and Tumor Incidence: Definitions. In comparing the potencies of carcinogens, two criteria have been used, singly or combined, to distinguish between their relative strength. The *latent period* is the length of time (expressed in days, weeks, or months) which elapses between the beginning of the application of the carcinogen and the appearance of the *first* tumor in the test group; the latent period is valid only for a given dosage because, at least within certain limits, the former is inversely proportional to the latter. Some authors use the *median latent period*, which is the central value in the ordered set of latent periods for the individual animals. Again, other investigators prefer to use the *mean latent period*, which is the arithmetic average of the individual latent periods.

The *tumor incidence*, which term has already been used in some previous sections, is now formally defined as the proportion of animals bearing tumors out of the whole number of animals treated with a given dosage and which survived the treatment. This number of surviving animals is the *effective group*. Some investigators consider that the effective group is the number of animals which survived until the appearance of the first tumor in the group. Others regard as the effective group the number of animals surviving to the length of time corresponding to the median or mean latent period. In the authors' views the effective group should be defined as the number of tumor-bearing animals which died or were killed before or at the termination of the experiment plus the number of animals having no tumors and surviving to the very end of the experiment. It is not correct to include in the effective group tumor-free animals which did not survive up to the termination of the experiment, for the obvious reason that they may have developed tumors had they survived to the end of the experiment (119). Some investigators also consider the *multiplicity of tumors*, i.e., the number of tumor nodules which may be distinguished in the target tissue(s) of each animal; this parameter is, however, more of a suggestive than of a truly quantitative value because of the frequent difficulty in distinguishing separate tumor nodules in advanced stages of carcinogenesis.

Numerically the tumor incidence may be expressed as a simple ratio; for example, 5/16 means 5 tumor-bearing animals (often in this representation the animals bearing both malignant *and* benign tumors are included) in an effective group of 16. Sometimes the malignant and benign tumor bearers are shown separately; for example, $^{12+2}/_{21}$ means 12 animals bearing malignant tumors and 2 other animals bearing benign tumors (only) in an effective group of 21. Often, for the purpose of plotting, the tumor incidence is expressed as a percentage by performing the division given in the ratio and multiplying by a hundred. It is evident that the tumor incidence depends on how the effective group is defined. The inclusion, in this group, of the animals which did not survive to the end of the experiment and bore no tumors will give misleadingly low estimates.

4.3.6.2.2 Statistical Analysis of Results. It is most important for evaluating the validity of the results of carcinogen-testing experiments to carry out statistical analysis of the data. The requirement for statistical analysis is exemplified by two typical situations: (*a*) the necessity to ascertain that the tumor incidence(s) of the test group(s) is not due to chance distribution of spontaneous tumors inherent to the strain; (*b*) the demonstration whether a certain treatment concomitant with the administration of a carcinogen does or does not modify the average latent period.

It must be clearly borne in mind that, as it was seen in the previous sections dealing with animal care, diet, routes of administration, etc., the intrinsic reliability of the data depends on the design of the experiment and a multitude of conditions which must be correctly selected and rigidly standardized. Statistical analysis does not "improve" the data, but it does show whether the result produced in the test group by the treatment is different from the result in the control group, and to what extent the difference of the two results can be ascribed to random distribution. Statistical significance, or the absence of it, certainly does not have a bearing on the numerical meaning of the data. For example, a tumor incidence of 5/25 in test group "A" has the same statistical significance ($p = 0.025$) relative to a control group tumor incidence of 0/25 as a 6/100 incidence in test group "B" compared to a control group tumor incidence of 0/100 (Table I in reference 64). However, this does not change the fact that the tumor incidence is 20% in test group "A" and 6% in test group "B." All that the probability value indicates is that while there is a 2.5% probability that the tumor incidence of 20% in the group of 25 may be ascribed to chance, a tumor incidence as low as

6% has the same probability of being a truly significant result *if* the test and control group sizes are raised to 100. This means then that in order to reduce the element of chance, sufficiently large groups of animals must be used if a test compound is expected to have a low carcinogenic activity. The problem is further compounded if the strain used has a well-detectable spontaneous tumor incidence in the target tissue of the test compound. These considerations show the requirement for carefully planning the necessary minimum group sizes in view of increasing the chances for a statistically significant result. The intent of the present section is exclusively to give a simple working knowledge of some statistical techniques for the evaluation of the data. For the theoretical bases of these the reader is referred to standard reference works (*e.g.*, 120–123).

Testing the Significance of Tumor Incidence Data. This may be carried out by the *"exact" method* or by the approximation well known as the χ^2 (*chi square*) *test*. Consider, for example, the induction of lung tumors in mice by the oral administration of ethyl carbamate at the dietary level of 0.15%, reported by Jaffé (124); the mice used were of a special inbred strain, bred in the laboratory and prone to spontaneous lung tumors. After 75 days of testing Jaffé found a tumor incidence of 3/57 among the controls and 44/75 in the test group. The question is to what extent is the tumor incidence found in the test group attributable to the random distribution of tumors, because of the proneness of the strain to spontaneous tumors, and not to the administration of ethyl carbamate. The 3 tumor-bearing and 54 tumor-free animals among the controls, and the 44 tumor-bearing and 31 tumor-free animals in the test are the *frequencies* of the two categories ("tumor-bearing" and "tumor-free") in the two groups. These frequencies are written up, for convenience, in the form of a 2 × 2 contingency table (Table XXVI).

Table XXVI
A Typical 2 × 2 Contingency Table

	Control group	Test group	Totals
Number of mice with tumors	3	44	47
Number of mice without tumors	54	31	85
Totals	57	75	132

According to the *exact method*, the probability of the occurrence of this particular distribution of frequencies is given by the ratio of factorials:

$$p_1 = \frac{47! \, 85! \, 75! \, 57!}{132!} \cdot \frac{1}{3! \, 44! \, 54! \, 31!} = 0.2164 \times 10^{-10}$$

However. there are other possible distributions of the observed individual frequencies, which distributions have increasingly smaller probabilities of occurrence as they show apparent larger and larger effects due to the carcinogen. These distributions are obtained by reducing, unit by unit, the frequency of tumors in the control group to zero and every time adjusting the other frequencies so that the marginal totals in these new contingency tables will not change. The first new contingency table would then be, by reducing the frequency of tumors in the control group to 2:

	Control group	Test group	Totals
Number of mice with tumors	2	45	47
Number of mice without tumors	55	30	85
Totals	57	75	132

The probability of occurrence of this distribution is correspondingly lower:

$$p_2 = \frac{47!\,85!\,75!\,57!}{132!} \cdot \frac{1}{2!\,45!\,55!\,30!} = 0.0081 \times 10^{-10}$$

Similarly, new contingency tables are then set up for control group tumor frequencies 1 and 0, and the probabilities p_3 and p_4 of these distributions calculated. The probability of true difference between the control and test group is given by the sum of these probabilities.

$$p = \sum_{i=0}^{4} p_i = \frac{47!\,85!\,75!\,57!}{132!} \left[\frac{1}{3!\,44!\,54!\,31!} + \frac{1}{2!\,45!\,55!\,30!} \right.$$

$$\left. + \frac{1}{1!\,46!\,56!\,29!} + \frac{1}{0!\,47!\,57!\,28!} \right] = 0.2247 \times 10^{-10}$$

The calculations involved, which are very laborious, can be considerably reduced by working with the logarithms of factorials which can be found tabulated (*e.g.,* 125).

The general form of a 2 × 2 contingency table may be written as shown in Table XXVII.

Table XXVII

General Form of 2 × 2 Contingency Tables

	Control group	Test group	Totals
Response (tumor)	S_c	S_t	$S_c + S_t$
No response (no tumor)	$N_c - S_c$	$N_t - S_t$	$(N_c - S_c) + (N_t - S_t)$
Totals	N_c	N_t	$N_c + N_t$

In this table S_c and S_t are the numbers of animals showing the biological response in the control group and the test group, respectively, and N_c and N_t are the total numbers of animals in these two groups. The general solution formula for probability following the "*exact*" *method* is accordingly:

$$p = \frac{(S_c + S_t)! \, [(N_c - S_c) + (N_t - S_t)]! \, N_t! \, N_c!}{(N_c + N_t)!} \left[\frac{1}{S_c! \, S_t! \, (N_c - S_c)! \, (N_t - S_t)!} \right.$$

$$+ \frac{1}{(S_c - 1)! \, (S_t + 1)! \, (N_c - S_c + 1)! \, (N_t - S_t - 1)!}$$

$$+ \frac{1}{(S_c - 2)! \, (S_t + 2)! \, (N_c - S_c + 2)! \, (N_t - S_t - 2)!} + \cdots$$

$$\left. + \frac{1}{(S_c - S_c)! \, (S_t + S_c)! \, N_c! \, (N_t - S_t - S_c)!} \right] \tag{77}$$

The general solution formula of the χ^2 *test* and the solution of the particular example outlined in Table XXVI are as follows:

$$\chi^2 = \frac{(N_c + N_t) \left[|S_c(N_t - S_t) - S_t(N_c - S_c)| - \dfrac{N_c + N_t}{2} \right]^2}{N_c \cdot N_t \cdot [(N_c - S_c) + (N_t - S_t)] \cdot (S_c + S_t)} \tag{78}$$

$$\chi^2 = \frac{132[|3(31) - 54(44)| - 66]^2}{(57)(75)(85)(47)} \approx 38$$

Here, the first term in the numerator is the total number of mice. This is multiplied by the squared difference of the cross-products of the observed individual frequencies (within the brackets and within the bars, and always taken with a positive sign) from which difference is subtracted the half of the total number of mice before squaring; this last term is known as the *Yates correction for continuity*. The denominator is the product of the four marginal totals of the contingency table. The probability corresponding to the calculated χ^2 value is then taken from a χ^2 distribution table from the row corresponding to 1 "degree of freedom." Any 2×2 table has *degrees of freedom* equal to 1; this means that one independent comparison has been made between the control and test group distributions. A rapid approximation of the probability can be made by remembering that for 1 degree of freedom $p < 0.01$ for $\chi^2 > 6.64$, $p < 0.05$ for $\chi^2 > 3.84$, and $p > 0.1$ for $\chi^2 < 2.71$. For the above example one finds from the distribution table that for $\chi^2 \approx 38$, $p \ll 0.001$; Fisher's "exact" test has given the probability value of 0.2247×10^{-10}. Therefore, the probability that the difference between the control and test group tumor incidences is due to chance is infinitely low, *i.e.*, the significance of the result is beyond any possible doubt by any criterion.

Most often, results of biological investigations are considered to be significant if $p \approx 0.05$ or less. However, even a result having $0.10 < p < 0.20$ cannot be totally disregarded as being not significant at all because there still is an 80–90% probability that it is not due to chance. The final criterion, of how high a probability should be regarded as still acceptable for considering a result as statistically significant, depends on how seriously the test result may be attributed to the administration or treatment. In other words, the probability value is not an absolutely rigid criterion and the meaning attached to this value by the investigator must also depend on logical inferences drawn from the results of similar experiments (this reflects the modern "Bayesian" view of statistics, stressing that in order to evaluate the true *meaning* of a probability value it should be weighted by "intuitive" considerations based on the total framework of reference; "classical" statistics regards probability levels as immutable criteria). This can best be illustrated by an example. Consider that the testing of a new compound in a group of 24 animals yielded a tumor incidence result, the significance of which, relative to the findings in a control group of 30 animals, was found to be $p \approx 0.20$. Taking this p at its face value the compound should not be regarded as a carcinogen. However, past reports in the literature described the testing of a total of 120 compounds of the same structural type and about 70 of them were found to be carcinogenic to various degrees. This fact suggests then that there is a good likelihood that a new compound of the same class would be found to be carcinogenic. Therefore, the $p \approx 0.20$ value obtained with the substance tested could be due to its very weak carcinogenic activity, which was compounded by the small number of animals used in the testing. This dictates the course of action, that the testing should be repeated with a much greater number of animals.

The Yates correction may, in principle, be omitted from Eq. (78) if the total number of observations, i.e., the number of animals is "sufficiently high," as in the example in Table XXVI. The omission of this correction is, however, not generally considered to be acceptable for the notably smaller group sizes used most often in carcinogen-testing experiments. For this reason, because the χ^2 method with the Yates correction tends to give slightly higher probability values while still being based on a mathematical approximation, it is probably preferable to use the "exact" method. In principle, Fisher's "exact" test should be used in any case when any of the four individual frequencies is less than 5.

Advance Evaluation of the Group Size. If it becomes necessary to repeat an experiment with larger groups, the number of animals to be used in both the control and the test group can be evaluated in advance. The new group size depends on how stringently the probability value is set: the smaller the desired p value the greater the size of the groups that will have to be used. It must again be stressed that the repetition of an experiment using larger groups simply increases the chance of finding the difference with a greater statistical significance, and is carried out with the assumption that the previous difference showing a low significance may have been due to the overlapping of the tumor distributions because of the small sample sizes.

Consider an experiment showing a control group tumor incidence of 2/10 or 20% and a test group tumor incidence of 6/10 or 60%, for which the χ^2 test gives $0.10 < p < 0.20$. The question is how large should the groups used in a new testing experiment be, if $p \approx 0.05$ is desired, assuming that the same tumor incidences will be found at the end of the new experiment. The approximate number of animals to be used in the new experiment in the control group *and* in the test group is given by the formula:

$$
N = \frac{\chi^2 \left(S_c + \dfrac{N_c \cdot S_t}{N_t} \right)\left(2N_c - \dfrac{S_c}{2} + \dfrac{N_c \cdot S_t}{2N_t} \right)}{\left(\dfrac{N_c \cdot S_t}{N_t} - S_c \right)^2}
\tag{79}
$$

For the above example $S_c = 2$, $S_t = 6$, and $N_c = N_t = 10$; $\chi^2 = 3.84$ for the desired $p \approx 0.05$. Solution of Eq. (79) for these values gives $N = 30.7 \approx 30$. Decimals should always be disregarded because, being derived from Eq. (78) without the Yates correction, Eq. (79) gives slightly higher values for N than the minimum required for the particular χ^2 to which it is set. The new control group and the new test group should *each* contain 30 animals.

The group size, with somewhat closer approximation, can also be evaluated from tables giving the " 'Exact' Confidence Limits for p" (e.g., in reference

125). Such tables give the confidence limits of the true long-run proportions (see Suppletory Note 4) P_x corresponding to observed sample proportions p_x (expressed as per cent: $100p_x$), for different confidence levels (most often 95% and 99%), and grouped according to increasing sample sizes N. For determining the minimum sample sizes at which two sample proportions, say p_a and p_b, will yield the desired or greater probability for true difference, the table of " 'Exact' Confidence Limits for p" is scanned for that smallest value of N, where (under the appropriate confidence level heading) the higher limit of the lower proportion and the lower limit of the higher proportion do not overlap.

Let us examine again the example calculated with Eq. (79). In this example the proportions of the control and test samples were $100p_c = 20\%$ and $100p_t = 60\%$, and the original sample sizes were $N = 10$ for both. One finds, indeed, upon consulting this table that for $N = 10$ and at 95% confidence level the confidence limits of the corresponding true long-run proportions are $2.52 < P_{20} < 55.61$ and $26.24 < P_{60} < 87.84$. Since $55.61 \gg 26.24$ there is a strong overlapping of the distributions with the observed proportions at this sample size, which is also indicated by the fact that for the probability of true difference $0.10 < p < 0.20$ was found. Now, for finding N_{min} for $p \approx 0.05$, the table is scanned and the confidence limits of 20% and 60% are evaluated for increasing values of N. Since the confidence limits are tabulated only for $p_x = x/N$ where x and N are whole numbers, in most instances the "exact" confidence limits for the particular proportions (here 20% and 60%) must be evaluated by interpolation; linear interpolation, while not exactly correct, gives a reasonably good approximation. The minimum sample size (to be used for both control and test group) is found to be 28 since this is the lowest value of N where there is no overlapping of the adjacent confidence limits of the two corresponding long-run proportions: $P_{20} < 39.33$ and $39.91 < P_{60}$. Calculation by Eq. (79) yielded $N = 30$ for the minimum group size, which is unnecessarily high according to the table of " 'Exact' Confidence Limits," since the respective confidence limits do not overlap ($P_{20} < 38.57$ and $40.60 < P_{60}$).

Significance of the Difference of Mean Latent Periods: The t Test. It is sometimes found that two agents induce tumors with similar or identical incidence in groups of comparable sizes but that there is an apparent difference in the time of appearance of the tumors in the two groups. In other instances it may become necessary to ascertain whether a treatment expected to hasten or delay tumor induction does or does not actually produce a significant change in the latent period. This requires a statistical technique devised for testing the significance of the difference of two means. Consider two groups of experimental animals having the number of tumors (*i.e.*, number of observations) N_1 and N_2 which arose with mean latent periods $\bar{X}_1$ and $\bar{X}_2$. For each group, the *standard deviation of the mean latent period* is obtained with the formula:

$$S \approx \sqrt{\frac{\Sigma(X - \bar{X})^2}{N}} \tag{80}$$

that is by squaring the differences between the mean latent period $\bar{X}$ and the individual latent periods X of that group, dividing the sum of the squares by the number of tumors in the group, and then taking the square root. If the number of independent observations, the number of *degrees of freedom* ($= N_1 + N_2 - 2$), is greater than 60 then the *standard error of the difference of the means* is

$$S_D = \sqrt{S_1^2 + S_2^2} \tag{81}$$

If the degrees of freedom are less than 60 then a *common variance* is calculated as

$$S_{1,2}^2 = \frac{\Sigma(X_1^2) - \bar{X}_1\Sigma(X_1) + \Sigma(X_2^2) - \bar{X}_2\Sigma(X_2)}{N_1 + N_2 - 2} \tag{82}$$

and

$$S_D = \sqrt{\frac{S_{1,2}^2}{N_1} + \frac{S_{1,2}^2}{N_2}} \tag{83}$$

The relevant test statistic, known as Student's t, is obtained by dividing the difference of the two means by the standard error S_D of the difference:

$$t = \frac{\bar{X}_1 - \bar{X}_2}{S_D} \tag{84}$$

The probability for the difference between the two means having been obtained by chance is taken from a t distribution table from the row corresponding to the number of degrees of freedom of the test. For the group sizes usually employed in testing, the probability can be roughly approximated by remembering that for $p \approx 0.01$ $t > 2.60$, for $p \approx 0.05$ $t > 2.00$, and for $p \approx 0.10$ $t > 1.65$. For example, one finds for two populations of latent periods, having degrees of freedom equal 37, $t = 2.026$. The corresponding probability from a t distribution table $p \approx 0.05$. This means that the extent of overlap between the distributions of the two populations is $\sim 5\%$, i.e., there is a 5% probability that the difference of the two means is due to random distribution.

4.3.6.2.3 Dose-Response Relationships and Threshold Dose. Latent period and tumor incidence are not the sole variables of carcinogenic activity. The dose range within which these two variables change as a function of the total dose administered is a third parameter of carcinogenic potency. Hence, much effort has been oriented toward the determination of dose-response curves for various carcinogens in different species and strains, both as regards the latent period and tumor incidence.

Dose-response curves can yield information on (a) the *minimum effective dose* or *threshold dose* which is the smallest dose producing a statistically significant rise in the tumor incidence and/or decrease of the latent period relative to the control level; (b) the TD_{50}, also termed ED_{50} (standing for "50% tumor dose" and "50% effective dose"), which is the dose required to bring about 50% tumor incidence; (c) the *maximum effective dose*, the lowest dose producing tumors in 100% of the animals; it was noted, however, in Section 4.3.5 that with some carcinogens there is a decrease of the tumor incidence beyond this dose; (d) the *specific induction time* (abbreviated as t_{50}), which is the time required for the emergence of tumors in 50% of a group of animals receiving a TD_{50} dose; (e) some aspects of the nature and mechanism of tumor induction.

One of the earliest reports establishing the dose dependence of the carcinogenic response is due to Andervont (126) who noted the decrease of the latent period when doses of 0.8 mg of 1,2,5,6-dibenzanthracene were injected to mice once, twice, or three times. However, while a great amount of work has been carried out subsequently on dose-response relationships, the number of reports which have a truly quantitative significance is limited. This is because for establishing small differences in response (as tumor incidence or latent period) between several close dose levels in a statistically significant way, much larger group sizes are needed than to answer the simple question whether or not a compound is carcinogenic at a relatively high dose level.

Probably the first deliberate attempts to explore the graded dose-response of a carcinogen are due to Lettinga and to Dobrovolskaia-Zavadskaia. Lettinga (127) determined the tumor incidence resulting from the injection of 1,2,5,6-dibenzanthracene into mice at dosages ranging from 0.005 to 5.0 mg. each dose being divided into five fortnightly injections administered in filtered lard; Lettinga concluded that 0.5 mg is the maximum effective dose for this hydrocarbon. Dobrovolskaia-Zavadskaia (128) tried to find the minimum effective dose of this same hydrocarbon and for this reason the dose range she explored (single injections in olive oil) represents only a small fraction of the total significant range; from her data the minimum effective dose of 1,2,5,6-dibenzanthracene in mice is 0.0025 mg. Dose-response studies of a high degree of standardization are due to Leiter and Shear (97). They used strain A mice, tricaprylin as solvent for injection, and 3,4-benzopyrene as the carcinogen, and considered a large number of experiments at a few definite dose levels to be more valuable than single experiments at many different levels; a summary of their data is given in Table XXVIII. At these marginal doses Leiter and Shear found a clear-cut difference in susceptibility due to sex: males show a higher tumor incidence than females. At comparatively high doses, however, this distinction vanishes: both males and females show the same tumor incidence. The authors also noted that, when marginal doses are used, minor changes in the experimental conditions show comparatively more important modification of the carcinogenic response.

Solid quantitative grounding to the treatment of carcinogenesis data was given by Bryan and Shimkin. These authors introduced the use of biostatistical procedures in this field and applied them (129, 130) to the results of Lettinga (127), Dobrovolskaia-Zavadskaia (128), Shimkin and Andervont (131), and to their own data (130) obtained with 3,4-benzopyrene, 20-methylcholanthrene, and 1,2,5,6-dibenzanthracene. Suppletory Note 5 and Figures 74 and 75 summarize some basic biostatistical concepts. The sigmoid dose-response curves obtained by Bryan and Shimkin (130) with these three hydrocarbons are given in Fig. 76. Plotted in probits the same curves appear as the linear relationships shown in Fig. 77, which obey the typical probit regression equation [Eq. (a) in Suppletory Note 5]. While the linear probit regression lines allow a much more accurate evaluation of the TD_{50}, the sigmoid curves have the advantage of permitting a better visualization of the practical dose limits within which the percentage response may be used for quantitative studies.

Linear relationships are also obtained if the latent period is plotted against the dose. These curves have, however, negative slopes since the latent periods decrease with the increase of the dose (Fig. 78). Accordingly, the equation describing the latent period dose-response curve has the form:

$$L_{month} = a' - b'(X - \bar{X}) \qquad (85)$$

Using this equation the dose corresponding to the mean latent period may be calculated. The tumor incidence and latent period dose-response curves may be combined advantageously (Fig. 79) in order to accurately determine the specific induction time (see beginning of this section). Bryan and Shimkin consider that the time necessary for tumor induction has, in this case, a special significance in that it measures the rate of action of a particular biological unit (or dose) of a given substance for which they propose the term *carcinogenic unit* (129). A summary of the results computed from the dose-response curves of Bryan and Shimkin (130) is given in Table XXIX.

A highly standardized study of the latent period dose-response relationship of 3,4-benzopyrene and 20-methylcholanthrene in producing epithelial tumors in C3H mice was carried out by Horton and Denman (132) and

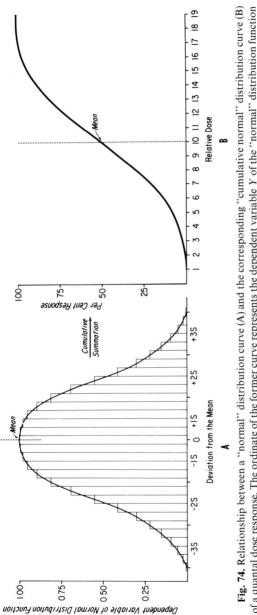

Fig. 74. Relationship between a "normal" distribution curve (A) and the corresponding "cumulative normal" distribution curve (B) of a quantal dose response. The ordinate of the former curve represents the dependent variable Y of the "normal" distribution function $Y = [1/S(2\pi)^{1/2}] \cdot \exp\{-\frac{1}{2}[(X - \mu)^2/S]\}$, where S is the standard deviation and μ is the mean of the distribution. The ordinate of the "cumulative normal" curve represents the cumulative sum of the probability rectangles enclosed by the "normal" curve, plotted against a linear abscissa scale. The ordinate 50% on the "cumulative normal" curve corresponds to the mean of the "normal" curve.

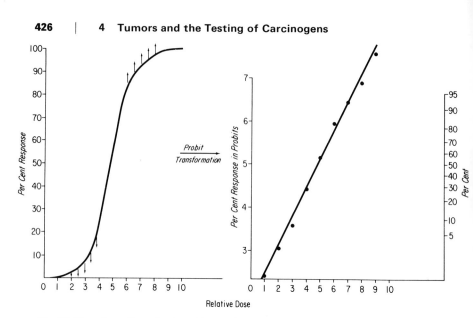

Relative Dose

Fig. 75. Transformation of a sigmoid curve into a straight line by plotting on probit paper.

Horton *et al.* (133). They used an ingenious method to determine the actual carcinogen concentration per unit area of the skin. The hydrocarbons were applied in the solvents, benzene or *sec*-amylbenzene, to the interscapular region, and the exact contact area was determined by tracing the spot under ultraviolet light. The value of the dosage per "unit area" [c in Eq. (86)] is calculated by dividing the actual percent concentration of the carcinogen in the

Table XXVIII

Average Subcutaneous Tumor Incidence in Mice with Different Dose Levels of 3,4-Benzopyrene[a]

3,4-Benzopyrene injected (mg)	Number of mice[b]	Percent			
		At 4 months	At 6 months	At 9 months	At 12 months
0.2	120	34	57	67	68
0.1	194	19	56	65	65
0.08[c]	50	32	52	54	56
0.065	270	5	32	43	45
0.05	121	6	25	36	38

[a] From J. Leiter and M. J. Shear, *J. Natl. Cancer Inst.* **3**, 455 (1942–43).
[b] Mice equally divided between the sexes.
[c] A single experiment was performed at this dose level.

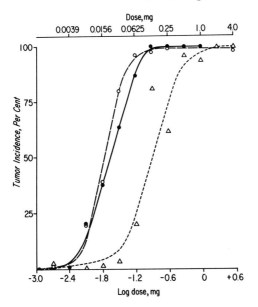

Fig. 76. Sigmoid dose-response curves of the incidence of subcutaneous tumors in relationship to dose of carcinogen. ─●──●─: 20-methylcholanthrene. ─○ ── ○ ─: 1,2,5,6-dibenzanthracene. ─ ─ △ ─ ─ ─ △ ─ ─: 3,4-benzopyrene. The hydrocarbon doses in solution in 0.25 ml tricaprylin were injected into strain C3H mice. [From W. R. Bryan and M. B. Shimkin, *J. Natl. Cancer Inst.* **3**, 503 (1942– 43).]

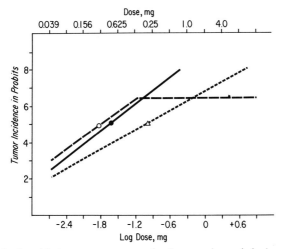

Fig. 77. Weighted probit dose-response curves for three carcinogenic hydrocarbons showing their relative positions on an absolute dose scale. ─●─: 20-methylcholanthrene. ── ○ ──: 1,2,5,6-dibenzanthracene. ─ ─ ─ △ ─ ─ ─: 3,4-benzopyrene. [From W. R. Bryan and M. B. Shimkin, *J. Natl. Cancer Inst.* **3**, 503 (1942– 43).]

solvent with the relative "spreading coefficient" of the solvent. In this study Horton and his associates investigated the accelerating properties on skin carcinogenesis of different solvents which were found to spread to different degrees on the mouse skin. The *sec*-amylbenzene was selected as reference solvent, and a "spreading coefficient" equal to 1 was assigned to it. The greater the spread (for a standard volume) the smaller is the dosage per "unit area"; this calculation follows from the definition of the "unit area" by Horton *et al.* as that area covered by 100 mg of a solution of which the relative spread equals 1.

From their experiments Horton *et al.* derived hyperbolic relationships for estimating the mean latent period (also termed by them "tumor-free life")

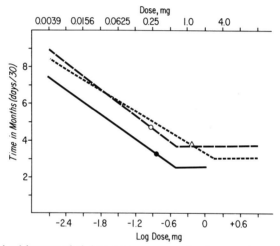

Fig. 78. Weighted latent period dose-response curves for three carcinogenic hydrocarbons showing their respective positions on an absolute dose scale. —●—: 20-methylcholanthrene. — —○— —: 1,2,5,6-dibenzanthracene. --- △ ---: 3,4-benzopyrene. [From W. R. Bryan and M. B. Shimkin, *J. Natl. Cancer Inst.* **3**, 503 (1942–43).]

expected for any given solution if no accelerating contribution is made by the solvent to the effective potency. These relationships have the form:

$$L = \frac{k_1}{f \cdot c + k_2} + k_3 \tag{86}$$

where f is the number of applications per week, c the above-mentioned dosage per "unit area," and k_1, k_2, and k_3 are characteristic constants. For 3,4-benzopyrene $k_1 = 6$, $k_2 = 0.1$, $k_3 = 20$, and for 20-methylcholanthrene $k_1 = 13$, $k_2 = 0.2$, $k_3 = 7$, using *sec*-amylbenzene as solvent. The two latent period dose-response curves corresponding to these two equations are given in Fig. 80. Similar results obtained later by Poel (134) and by Wynder *et al.*

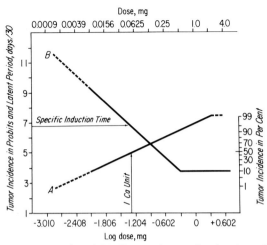

Fig. 79. Dose-response curve for 1,2,5,6-dibenzanthracene in mice. A: probit response curve. B: latent period response curve. [From W. R. Bryan and M. B. Shimkin, *J. Natl. Cancer Inst.* **1**, 807 (1940–41).]

(135) with 3,4-benzopyrene confirm that the forms of the hyperbolic function and of the corresponding curve are essentially correct. However, expectedly, the values of the k constants undergo notable changes under different experimental conditions. This was shown by the fact that using benzene for solvent, Horton and Denman (132) obtained with 3,4-benzopyrene $k_1 = 8$, $k_2 = 0.1$, and $k_3 = 3$ in the same strain of mice.

In most reports in the literature on hydrocarbon-induced epithelial carcinogenesis the relationship between tumor incidence and dose is markedly less regular than the relationship between latent period and dose. This irregularity is possibly due to the lack of standardization of the application technique, since the only truly meaningful expression of the dose is,

Table XXIX

Dose-Response Parameters of Polycyclic Hydrocarbons

	1,2,5,6-Dibenzanthracene	3,4-Benzopyrene	20-Methyl-cholanthrene
Latent period (mo):	3.72	3.02	2.48
Specific induction time (mo):	6.79	5.23	5.14
$TD_5{}^a$(mg):	0.003	0.012	0.0045
TD_{50} (mg):	0.016	0.101	0.021
$TD_{95}{}^b$(mg):	0.084	0.875	0.096

[a] Approximates the minimum effective dose.
[b] Approximates the maximum effective dose.

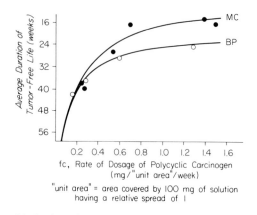

Fig. 80. The rate of induction of papillomas in C3H mice by repeated application of 20-methylcholanthrene (MC) and 3,4-benzopyrene (BP) in *sec*-amylbenzene. [From A. W. Horton, D. T. Denman, and R. P. Trosset, *Cancer Res.* **17**, 758 (1957).]

evidently, the dose deposited per *unit area* of the skin. The reports of Horton and his co-workers are, therefore, of special value also from the methodological standpoint, since they are the first investigators to take into account the spread of deposited solutions on the skin. Moreover, in skin tumorigenesis the latent period-dose plot tends to be, in general, less affected than the tumor incidence-dose plot by small changes in topical concentration. For these reasons no study of the dose-response relationships of epithelial tumorigenesis, comparable in completeness and accuracy to the classical reports of Bryan and Shimkin on subcutaneous tumor induction (129, 130), has appeared as yet. Furthermore, the *periodicity* of application inherent in the usual technique of skin tumor induction introduces some difficulties in the unequivocal interpretation of the tumor incidence data.

The effect of increasingly *discontinuous application* on the rate of tumor induction was studied by Cramer and Stowell (136). These investigators painted 20-methylcholanthrene in 0.1-mg single doses to the skin of random-bred Swiss mice, at 2 weekly intervals in one group, at 3 weekly intervals in the second group, and at 4 weekly intervals in the third group. Application was continued until 100% tumor incidence was reached in all three groups. Their results show that the total amount of 20-methylcholanthrene administered until 100% tumor incidence was attained was the highest in the group painted every 2 weeks (group C), lower in the group painted every 3 weeks (group D), and the lowest in the group painted every 4 weeks (group E). From these results the conclusion was drawn that the *total* dose of carcinogen necessary to bring about 100% tumor incidence varies inversely with the length of the interval between paintings.

If the finding of Cramer and Stowell is taken at face value, it represents a surprising and interesting result. Closer analysis of the data indicates, however, that this finding may be more apparent than real, and it may simply be an example of misinterpretation of the notion of "maximum effective dose." The data reveal that the total dose was 1.7 mg in group C, 1.1 mg in group D, and 0.9 mg in group E. Knowing the magnitude of the standard single doses (0.1 mg) and the respective frequencies of application, one computes that the time required to attain 100% tumor incidence was essentially identical in all three groups (34 weeks in group C, 33 weeks in group D, and 36 weeks in group E); similarly, identical values for the periods of time necessary to induce tumors in 50% of the animals in the three groups were found (23, 24, and 24 weeks, respectively). In other words, identical tumor incidence levels were attained after identical lengths of administration in all three groups. The inescapable conclusion must then be that all three total doses (1.7, 1.1, and 0.9 mg) operate on a plateau beyond the saturation threshold (i.e., the maximum effective dose) of a sigmoid dose-response curve. Thus, a final total dose of 0.9 mg is already sufficient to induce tumors in 50% of the animals in 24 weeks or in 100% of the animals in an average of 34 weeks. The increase of the total dose to either 1.1 or 1.7 mg is not large enough to produce any noticeable decrease in these latent periods and can, evidently, not raise the tumor incidence beyond the saturation point of 100%. Therefore, any increase of the total dose beyond 0.9 mg is trivial and represents simply an unnecessary excess. It is, moreover, possible that the 0.9-mg dose is already beyond the maximum effective dose, so that further lengthening of the intervals between paintings would have probably produced (up to a certain point) a further apparent "decrease" in the total dose. The cited paper by Cramer and Stowell did show, on the other hand, that a more substantial increase of the total dose, to 4.2 mg, reduced the latent period for attaining 100% tumor incidence to 26 weeks, and the latent period for attaining 50% tumor incidence to 17 weeks.

The fact that discrete small carcinogenic doses are additive, provided the intervals between the individual application are not long enough for "recovery" (i.e., cell repair) to take place, has been clearly demonstrated by Wynder et al. (135). These investigators painted 0.005% solution of 3,4-benzo-pyrene in acetone on the skin of random-bred Swiss mice by applying it with a No. 5 camel's-hair brush in lengthwise direction to the middle line of the back (interscapular region). The dose delivered in this manner by a single brush stroke is of the order of 5 µg. Wynder et al. found that the optimum rate of tumor formation is dependent upon the total amount of 3,4-benzopyrene solution applied and, what amounts to the same, upon the frequency with which the applications are made. For 1, 2, 3, and 5 weekly applications the papilloma incidences were after 12 months 10%, 60%, 85%, and 90% in the respective groups. If the tumor incidences in these groups, and the tumor incidences in other groups (to which administration followed various intermittent schedules), were plotted against the respective total dose received, a typical sigmoid dose-response curve was obtained (135) showing that the tumor incidence depends uniquely on the total dose and not on the length of the interval or schedule of administration. If one plots the above sigmoid curve in probits the TD_5, TD_{50}, and TD_{95} of 3,4-benzo-pyrene are found to be 0.025, 0.51, and 0.98 mg, respectively, toward the skin of random-bred Swiss mice under these experimental conditions. From the plot of the median latent period against the total dose received $t_{50} \approx 9.7$ months.

Mice and possibly rats are, however, not the only species in which the dose response of hydrocarbon carcinogenesis can be studied. For example, the subcutaneous tissue of the hamster also displays a dose-dependent response to carcinogenic hydrocarbons. An interesting feature of subcutaneous tumorigenesis in this species is that the frequency of metastatic tumors is also related to the dose administered.

Probably the first attempt to extend investigations on dose-response relationships to carcinogens other than polycyclic hydrocarbons is due to Andervont and Edwards (137). These authors found that the direct relationship between dose and tumor incidence also holds good for the azo compound, o-aminoazotoluene, and they found that the threshold dose of this compound when tested by subcutaneous injection in mice is approximately 10 mg. When administered by this route, this compound produces fibrosarcomas at the site of injection, and also causes lung and blood-vessel tumors. The laws governing the response of different strains of animals, and the principle of inheritance of tissue susceptibility to tumor formation, seem to apply to azo compounds and other carcinogenic agents as well as to hydrocarbon carcinogens. There are susceptible strains of mice (e.g., strain C), resistant strains (DBA), and strains resistant specifically to lung-tumor induction by o-aminoazotoluene (C3H).

Unlike tumor induction by subcutaneously administered o-aminoazotoluene, the production of liver tumors by the azo compounds derived from 4-dimethylaminoazobenzene is strongly influenced by the diet (see Sections 4.3.2.4 and 7.1). For this reason the study of the dose response of hepatic tumor induction by the latter compounds had to await the commercial availability of standard diet components and the standardization of all phases of the hepatocarcinogenesis assay procedure. However, once all these conditions were brought to a common denominator, feeding experiments became just as amenable to quantitative study as injection or painting experiments. Thus, Fig. 81 shows the typical sigmoid dose-response curves of 4-dimethylaminoazobenzene (5) and its highly active 3'-methyl derivative (138), obtained under similar experimental conditions. The TD_{50} values computed from the probit plots of these data are 530 and 220 mg, respectively.

The determination of minimum effective doses (usually taken as the TD_5) and the entire concept of "threshold dose" received much scrutiny in recent years in connection with studies of the dose-response relationships of various structural types of chemical carcinogens (and also of tumor-inducing high-energy radiations). The reason for this is the strong relevance of these studies to the human environment. The question is whether or not there exists a permissible or "safe" subthreshold dose, or rate of intake, of carcinogenic chemicals (and of high-energy r' 'ations). Is it possible, in other words, to set acceptable or "safe" levels for weak or marginal carcinogens for

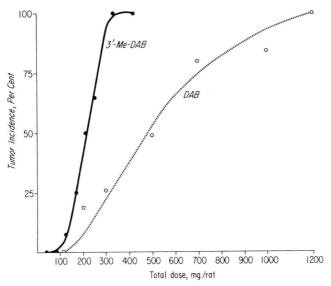

Fig. 81. Dose-response curve of 4-dimethylaminoazobenzene (DAB) given at a daily dose of 5 mg, and of 3'-methyl-4-dimethylaminoazobenzene (3'-Me-DAB), given at a daily dose of 6 mg. [Plotted after the data of H. Druckrey, D. Schmähl, W. Dischler, and A. Schildbach, *Naturwissenschaften* **49**, 217 (1962) for DAB, and of J. C. Arcos, G. W. Griffith, and R. W. Cunningham, *J. Biophys. Biochem. Cytol.* **7**, 49 (1960) for 3'-Me-DAB.]

incorporation as additives into foods and cosmetics, for consumption as drugs, for use as pesticides and in the treatment of textiles and food packaging materials, etc., or for presence in the atmosphere and water as the cumulative result of pollution by industrial plants and automobiles? The same problem exists, evidently, when deciding just what constitutes a "safe" level for radiations, *e.g.*, "background" radioactivity of the atmosphere.

No matter how high or how low the "safe" subthreshold dose of a carcinogen is set, however, the inescapable fact must be faced that unlike in animal assays where experimental conditions are rigidly set and controlled, in the human environment there are a great number of various carcinogenic influences (see also Section 4.3.1) which are mutually antagonistic at best and synergistic at worst. Therefore, even if the existence of true subthreshold levels is demonstrated for *some* carcinogens under laboratory conditions, extrapolation of the significance of such findings to humans living in the normal human environment is not truly meaningful. The multiplicity of environmental carcinogens is, furthermore, compounded by the possibility that for some types of agents, at least, even very small carcinogenic effects are cumulative (Section 4.3.1). The latter possibility has considerable ramifications in the establishment of correct legal standards for protection against industrial hazards and for the realistic appraisal of insurance risks. An analysis, based on statistical considerations, of the concept of threshold dose made by Mantel and Bryan (139) and by Mantel (140) concluded that the carcinogenic hazard never disappears but becomes gradually smaller with diminishing dose. They suggest that a more practical approach is then not to attempt to determine the threshold level of a carcinogen, but rather to determine some arbitrarily safe (1/100,000,000) level. These authors qualify their recommendation by the recognition that such arbitrary "safe" levels can become unsafe when certain noncarcinogenic compounds are present which enhance the potency of carcinogens; the same holds, as has been pointed out above, when two or more carcinogens present at subthreshold levels act synergistically.

Certain circumstances may arise, however, where the use, for a limited length of time, of substances having marginal or low carcinogenic activity is deemed as an acceptable and *quasi*-necessary risk in order to avoid other hazards which would occur with a high probability and within a short period of time. A typical example is the use of the potent tuberculostatic drug, isonicotinic acid hydrazide. This compound, which is one of the most effective agents for the treatment of tuberculosis in humans, has been shown to produce a low incidence of adenomatous lung tumors, leukemia, and reticulosis in mice (Section 5.2.1.2). So far, this compound has been found inactive to produce neoplastic changes in species other than mice. However, another hydrazine derivative, N-isopropyl-α-(2-methylhydrazino)-p-toluamide hydrochloride, is highly active in producing pulmonary tumors and leukemia in mice and mammary tumors in rats; hydrazine sulfate itself and other derivatives of hydrazine have also been shown to possess weak to moderate carcinogenic activity in a certain strain of mice (Section 5.2.1.2). One case of adenomatous hyperplasia of the bronchial epithelium has been reported in a patient treated with isonicotinic acid hydrazide. For all these reasons some investigators consider that there is a very small but finite probability that isonicotinic acid hydrazide may have a marginal or very low carcinogenicity in humans. However, if the risks are weighed, for example, between arresting a galloping tuberculosis which may be fatal within a few weeks and a very small probability of exposing the patient to lung cancer in perhaps 20 or 30 years, because of the use of this drug, there can be no doubt which course of action should be taken. Similarly, a number of agents used in the chemotherapy of leukemia and solid tumors (see Appendix I) have demonstrated carcinogenic activity in experimental animal species; here again the important short-term gains outweigh by far the risk involved.

It is highly debatable, however, whether it is wise to apply similar considerations to gains in agricultural production, food storage, and other consumer-oriented technological processes, in view of the widespread, repeated and long-term effects of these in the human environment. The regulations of the United States Food and Drug Administration prescribe, in principle, "zero tolerance" for any agent which has a reliably demonstrated carcinogenic activity. Zero tolerance means that such products cannot be used as drugs or as additives or adjuvants in foods and cosmetic products, for man and domestic animals. However, just what constitutes "reliably demonstrated carcinogenic activity" depends to some extent on the criteria set. It is evident that because of the rapid increase in world population it is necessary to insure a high yield of the agricultural production and this, in turn, implies the chemical control of plant diseases and insects; for the same reason it is essential to insure a high level of storage stability of the products and protection against pests. Unfortunately, very little is known of the cumulative long-term effects (carcinogenic, genetic, and other) to human populations of many of the chemical agents used in these processes. The right or wise decision for allowing or barring certain additives or adjuvants from consumer usage is, therefore, not an easy one and must be viewed within the much wider context of just how far can the ecological niche of the human race be broadened. Common sense dictates within this framework that if an adjuvant or additive, deemed of marginal safety, serves exclusively to improve the appearance or consumer appeal of a product, the decision of allowing or barring it should be taken on the basis of stringent criteria.

The scientific value of determining minimum effective doses of carcinogens under set laboratory conditions lies in the fact that maximum dosages often obscure side effects and influences, such as the varying tissue and strain response. Furthermore, when testing is carried out with very large doses, the effect of concomitantly administered substances, which may enhance or inhibit the carcinogenic response, may be completely suppressed. Hence, it became necessary to refine the testing procedures by using minimum doses instead of the overwhelmingly large doses (destined to give maximum tumor incidence and shortest obtainable latent period), so that the subtle effect of concomitantly administered substances in modifying carcinogenesis may be detected.

Pertinent to the problem of threshold dose are the investigations of Druckrey and his associates (rev. 5) who proposed that the effects of all single doses of carcinogens are irreversible and, hence, cumulative during the entire life span. According to them the appearance of tumors is, therefore, essentially a function of the entire dose received (expressed as TD_{50}). They found that, when tumors are induced by continuous dosing, the TD_{50} is not a constant value but is directly proportional to the magnitude of the daily dose: the smaller the daily dose the smaller the TD_{50} and *vice versa*. However, while a constant 50% tumor incidence can be attained with different TD_{50} dosages (which depend on the magnitude of the daily dose), the corresponding t_{50} values are not constant but vary inversely with the magnitude of the TD_{50} values. This is shown by the results of the induction of ear duct tumors in rats by feeding 4-dimethylaminostilbene (5, 141). Figure 82 presents the probit dose-response curves of this process when administering the carcinogen at different daily rates. It may be seen that the TD_{50} decreases with the decrease of the daily dose. Now, if these TD_{50}

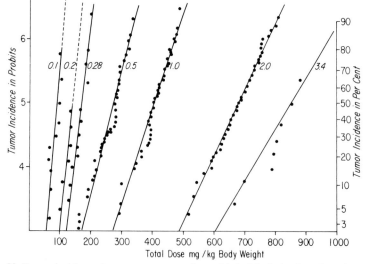

Fig. 82. Tumor incidence dose-response curve (in probits) of the induction of ear duct tumors by 4-dimethylaminostilbene, at different rates of administration. The numbers 0.1 to 3.4 adjacent to the curves represent daily doses (in mg/kg of rat body weight) administered to the different groups of rats. [From H. Druckrey, D. Schmähl, W. Dischler, and A. Schildbach, *Naturwissenschaften* **49**, 217 (1962); and H. Druckrey, *in* "Carcinogenesis—Mechanisms of Action," Ciba Foundation Symposium. Little, Brown, Boston, Massachusetts, 1959, p. 110.]

values and the corresponding t_{50} values in (days) are plotted against the daily dose in a log-log scale, the linear relationships shown in Fig. 83 are obtained.

From the TD_{50} curve Druckrey and his co-workers (5) derived an interesting relationship between daily dose and time of administration. The straight line graph of TD_{50} *versus* daily dose obeys the simple linear function:

$$\log TD_{50} = 0.67 \log d + \log K \tag{87}$$

where 0.67 is the slope of the line and $\log K$ is its intercept (not shown in the figure). Taking the antilog, we get:

$$TD_{50} = d^{0.67} \cdot K \tag{88}$$

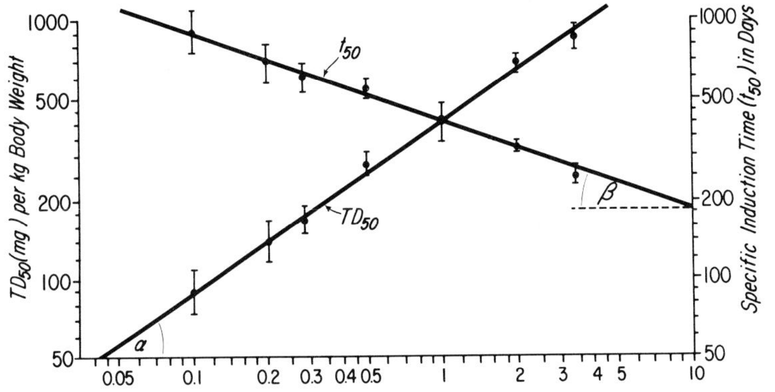

Fig. 83. Linear dependence of the 50% tumor dose (TD_{50}) and of the specific induction time (t_{50}) on the magnitude of the daily dose of 4-dimethylaminostilbene during the induction of ear duct tumors in rats (in logarithmic scales). The slope of the TD_{50} curve $\tan \alpha = 0.67$; the slope of the t_{50} curve $\tan (90° - \beta) = \cot \beta = 3$. [From H. Druckrey, D. Schmähl, W. Dischler, and A. Schildbach, *Naturwissenschaften* **49**, 217 (1962).]

However, since the daily dose is constant for every group, the TD_{50} of any group represents the product of the respective daily dose and the corresponding t_{50} (in days), that is:

$$TD_{50} = d \cdot t_{50} \tag{89}$$

Substituting this expression of the TD_{50} into Eq. (88):

$$d \cdot t_{50} = d^{0.67} \cdot K \tag{90}$$

Dividing by $d^{0.67}$, and cubing the equation, we get:

$$d \cdot t_{50}^3 = K^3 = \text{const.} \tag{91}$$

where the exponent of t_{50} represents the slope of the t_{50} *versus* daily dose curve (Fig. 83). Equation (91) may be stated as: for a given tumor incidence (*e.g.*, 50%) the product of the daily dose and the specific induction time is constant. From their own results and from data of other workers Druckrey *et al.* (5) concluded that the exponent of t_{50} is a characteristic of the particular carcinogen, and its value is generally between 2 and 3.

Equation (91), *if* its validity is confirmed by reliable experiments for other carcinogens, has important significance in that it suggests that even extremely small doses may induce tumors in an adequately long period of time. On the other hand, Eq. (91) also appears to have the interesting implication that while theoretically the concept of a "threshold dose" must be excluded, *practically* the daily dose may be set so low that the corresponding induction time falls far beyond the life span of the animal.

In these investigations of Druckrey and his associates with 4-dimethyl-aminostilbene, the time of appearance of ear duct tumors, on which the above-discussed relationship is based, can be detected by direct visual observation with reasonable accuracy. Unfortunately, other work of Druckrey and his co-workers carried out to demonstrate the validity of this

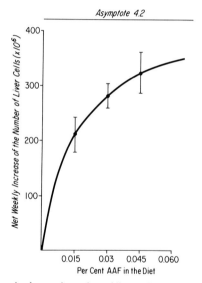

Fig. 84. Rate of increase in the total number of liver cells plotted against the relative dietary dose of 2-acetylaminofluorene (AAF); the experimental points with their standard deviations are shown. The rates represent the slopes of the linear plots of the total number of liver cells *versus* the time of administration of the respective dietary levels of AAF. The line is the theoretical curve representing the function $Y = 4.2/(1 + 1/X)$, where the asymptote 4.2 was evaluated from a linear plot of the same data, obtained by plotting $1/Y$ against $1/X$. [From A. K. Laird and A. D. Barton, *J. Natl. Cancer Inst.* **27**, 827 (1961).]

relationship to the production of liver tumors by 4-dimethylaminoazo-benzene in rats (142) and by diethylnitrosamine in rats (143) and mice (144) is not conclusive for the following reasons. In the investigations with 4-dimethylaminoazobenzene it is stated (142) that the progression of tumorigenesis was ascertained by direct observation of the livers of only a *very few* animals sacrificed at time intervals from each group; the report does not state how the time of emergence of tumor(s) in the other animals was detected. In the investigations with diethylnitrosamine in rats (143) the time of emergence of tumors was determined by *palpation*, and the total dose received by the individual animals and the length of the induction period were assessed on the basis of the time of tumor emergence thus determined. In Section 4.3.6.1.1, where the value of palpation was discussed, it was pointed out that impressions gathered by palpation cannot be regarded as experimental evidence for the presence of tumor(s). In the work of Schmähl and Thomas (144) on the induction of hepatic tumors in mice the total dose of carcinogen absorbed by the mice which revealed a tumor at autopsy was determined on the basis of the daily intake of diethylnitrosamine up to the time of occurrence of "spontaneous" death. However, careful reading of the report indicates that while some animals died actually as a result of the progression of the malignancy, other mice with very small tumor nodules died as a result of hemorrhage caused by palpation.

The work by Laird and Barton (145) constitutes one of the few reports on dose-response relationships of cellular events in the precancerous period. They found that the precancerous period in the livers of rats fed 2-acetylaminofluorene is divisible into two phases. During the first 4–8 weeks no significant change in the total number of liver cells occurs; thereafter the total number of liver cells increases at a constant rate. They have used an ingenious technique for counting the liver cells: the weight of the excised whole liver is recorded, a carefully weighed small portion of it is homogenized in an adequate medium (*e.g.*, 0.15 M KCl or 0.25 M sucrose solution) and a small known aliquot of the homogenate is mixed in a 1:40 dilution with 3% acetic acid containing a nuclear stain; the stained nuclei contained in a small aliquot of this mixture are then counted under the microscope and, thus, the number of cells in the whole liver may be calculated. Laird and Barton found that when the above rate of cell proliferation is plotted against the relative dose of the carcinogen, the curve shown in Fig. 84 is obtained describing a first-order chemical reaction. The cell proliferation rapidly comes to a standstill if the administration of the carcinogen is discontinued. Laird and Barton suggest that this preneoplastic cell proliferation is a form of compensatory hyperplasia resulting from the inactivation of a regulatory cell constituent, accomplished through its first-order chemical reaction with the carcinogen.

4.3.6.2.4 The Grading of Carcinogenic Potency. In order to compare the carcinogenic potency of polycyclic hydrocarbons, Fieser (146) first used a roughly quantitative estimate of the rapidity of action of such compounds, *i.e.*, the time required for tumor production in 50% of the animals receiving subcutaneously 5–10 mg of the different compounds. Later, Fieser (147) found it more accurate to consider the tumor incidence and the time factor separately. One suggested index was the "maximum effective dosage," the

Table XXX

Comparison of the Action of Three Carcinogenic Hydrocarbons Applied in Amounts at or above the Estimated Maximum Effective Dose to Various Tissues of Mice and Rats of Intermediate Susceptibilities[a,b]

| | Averaged latent periods, weeks | | | | |
| | Mice | | | Rats | |
Hydrocarbon	Subcut. tissue	Peri-toneum	Skin	Subcut. tissue	Peri-toneum
1,2,5,6-Dibenzanthracene	**23.5**	—	**30.4**	**30.7**	40.1
3,4-Benzopyrene	**15.3**	18.3	**19.1**	**18.7**	—
20-Methylcholanthrene	**13.0**	14.1	**18.0**	**22.6**	—

[a] From L. F. Fieser, *Am. J. Cancer* **34**, 37 (1938).
[b] Boldface numbers are weighted averages of data from several laboratories.

lowest dose yielding tumors in 100% of the animals. Table XXX shows another method of comparison where Fieser (147) summarized the results of numerous investigators by averaging the latent periods found for each hydrocarbon by the different authors. Based on this table the order of potency for mice (skin and subcutaneous tumors) is 20-methylcholanthrene > 3,4-benzopyrene > 1,2,5,6-dibenzanthracene; for rats (subcutaneous tumors) the order of potency is 3,4-benzopyrene > 20-methylcholanthrene ≧ 1,2,5,6-dibenzanthracene. Fieser (148) characterized some of the more commonly used polycyclic hydrocarbon carcinogens as follows:

1,2,5,6-Dibenzanthracene	Slowly acting carcinogen
9,10-Dimethyl-1,2-benzanthracene	Rapidly acting skin carcinogen
10-Methyl-1,2-benzanthracene	Rapidly acting producer of subcutaneous tumors
20-Methylcholanthrene	Rapidly acting all-round carcinogen
3,4-Benzopyrene	Powerful all-round carcinogen

That the order of carcinogenic activities of the three hydrocarbons tabulated in Table XXX varies according to the tissue which is affected was also the finding of Andervont and Shimkin (149). These investigators tested a number of carcinogens by skin painting, subcutaneous injection, and intravenous administration. They showed that there exists no relation between the susceptibilities of different tissues to carcinogenesis. Testing in mice, Andervont and Shimkin confirmed Fieser's order of carcinogenic activities in skin and subcutaneous tissue; however, for the induction of lung tumors (by intravenous injection) they found the order to be 1,2,5,6-dibenzanthracene > 20-methylcholanthrene > 3,4-benzopyrene.

The studies of Fieser and of Andervont and Shimkin are but representative examples of a number of published reports which show that certain tissues are more susceptible than others to the local or systemic action of polycyclic aromatic carcinogens. Compounds which display a highly selective target specificity (*e.g.*, ethionine toward the liver) represent extreme cases of this situation. This repeatedly illustrates the fact discussed in earlier sections that, in principle, carcinogenicity is a relative property and must be defined with respect to the animal species and the exact conditions of the testing. However, because carcinogenic potency and, frequently, target specificity may undergo drastic changes as a result of molecular modifications, it has become to some extent customary in discussions of structure-activity relationships and/or mechanism of action to speak about "carcinogenic activity," a "carcinogenic compound," a "strong carcinogen," etc., *in abstracto*, without reference to the species or the conditions of testing; this means that the agent in question has been found to be a carcinogen (a weak, moderate, or strong one) in *some* species and under *some* conditions of testing (*e.g.*, 150). Therefore, when using such terms in this sense, the limitation of their meaning and accuracy must be clearly borne in mind.

The early attempts to quantitatively express carcinogenic activity were marred by the uncertainties about the correct criteria to be employed and the relative unsophistication of the testing techniques. Nevertheless, some highly standardized recent retesting of polycyclic hydrocarbons indicates that many of the earlier data may be accepted as good orientation values.

The idea of comparing carcinogenic activities by the median latent period was recently revived by Eckardt (151) who proposed the following formula:

$$\text{Potency Number} = \frac{10{,}000}{\text{Time elapsed to appearance of tumors in 50\% of animals (days)}} \tag{92}$$

where the time elapsed is evaluated from the time (on abscissa) *versus* tumor incidence (on ordinate) curve plotted in probits.

Another method, based on the median latent period, for the grading of carcinogenic potency was suggested by Berenblum (152). He proposed the formula:

$$G = 16 - 16.5 \, (\log W) \tag{93}$$

and for very weak carcinogens:

$$G = 16 - 16.5 \, (\log 2w) \tag{94}$$

Here G is the grade of activity, W the time in weeks for 50% of the surviving animals to develop tumors, and w the time in weeks to develop the first tumor; the second equation is based on the assumption, justified by Berenblum by an extrapolation of experimental data, that the latent period is roughly half of the time W. One should remember, however, that grading of carcinogens in this way gives "greater semblance of accuracy than is justified" (153), considering the lack of standardization of experimental technique in the early testing procedures.

The gradation of carcinogenicities used the most extensively, mainly for carcinogens applied by skin painting or subcutaneous injection, is based on the "Carcinogenicity Index" of Iball (154). This index represents a simple combination of the tumor incidence and latent period data:

$$\text{Carcinogenicity Index} = \frac{\text{Tumor incidence (\%)}}{\text{Latent period (days)}} \times 100 \tag{95}$$

The greater the tumor incidence and the shorter the latent period the greater is this index, and *vice versa*. Iball's index expresses therefore the intuitive idea that a carcinogen is "strong" or "potent" if it produces tumors in a large proportion of the animals in a short period of time and, conversely, it is "weak" if it induces tumors in only a small percentage of the animals and is slow acting. For a number of polycyclic carcinogens Iball calculated the indexes given in Table XXXI from the tumor incidence and latent period data of tumorigenesis in mice. Because carcinogenic activity in the quantitative sense is only meaningful with respect to the particular test species and strain, target tissue, vehicle, route of administration, diet, etc., in recent testing experiments both the "epithelioma index" (by skin painting) and the "sarcoma index" (by subcutaneous injection) are often determined (*e.g.*, 155). A more generalized expression of carcinogenicity may then be given by averaging the two into an epithelioma (and papilloma) + sarcoma index (112).

A not immediately apparent shortcoming of all these numerical indexes based on the tumor incidence, latent period, and the time necessary to develop tumors in 50% of the animals is the underlying assumption that testing has been carried out with the maximum effective dose (see previous section).

Table XXXI

Carcinogenic Compounds Arranged in Descending Order of Potency in Inducing Epithelial Tumors by Skin Painting of Stock Mice[a]

Compound	Number of animals alive when first tumor appeared	Number of tumors	Per cent tumors A	Papilloma	Epithelioma	Average latent period (days) B	Index A/B × 100
9,10-Dimethyl-1,2-benzanthracene	20	13	65	6	7	43	151
20-Methylcholanthrene	18	18	100	1	17	99	101
3,4-Benzopyrene	9	7	78	2	5	109	80
Cholanthrene	49	28	57	5	23	112	51
5,6-Cyclopenteno-1,2-benzanthracene	14	13	93	1	12	194	48
2-Methyl-3,4-benzophenanthrene	16	12	75	5	7	155	48
10-Methyl-1,2-benzanthracene	18	12	67	2	10	147	45
5,6-Dimethyl-1,2-benzanthracene	19	16	84	0	16	220	38
6-Isopropyl-1,2-benzanthracene	15	11	74	1	10	204	36
3,4,5,6-Dibenzocarbazole	19	9	48	4	5	143	33
3,4,8,9-Dibenzopyrene	17	10	59	0	10	205	29
5-Methyl-1,2-benzanthracene	8	7	88	2	5	317	28
5-Ethyl-1,2-benzanthracene	9	7	78	2	5	285	27
1,2,5,6-Dibenzanthracene	65	41	63	8	33	239	26
3,4-Benzophenanthrene	18	12	67	5	7	387	17
1,2,5,6-Dibenzocarbazole	9	4	45	1	3	263	17
5-Propyl-1,2-benzanthracene	20	6	30	3	3	192	16
3,4,5,6-Dibenzacridine	28	11	39	2	9	357	11
3'-Methyl-1,2,5,6-dibenzanthracene	25	7	28	1	6	325	9
1,2,5,6-Dibenzacridine	25	6	24	2	4	350	7

[a] J. Iball, *Am. J. Cancer* **35**, 188 (1939).

Now, while it is true that probably all the polycyclic carcinogens have been tested with dose levels which are likely to be well beyond the maximum effective dose, it must also be remembered that for at least some carcinogens the tumor incidence decreases *beyond* this dose (Section 4.3.5). Theoretically, then, it would be important that an index be determined with *exactly* the maximum effective dose. Hence, for truly quantitative evaluation, testing should be carried out with a series of graded doses and that index accepted which corresponds to the maximum effective dose. Only for a very few polycyclic carcinogens are data available from which carcinogenicity indexes may be calculated on the basis of such stringent criteria. Therefore, while the indexes are important because they allow correlation of chemical and physical parameters of the molecule with carcinogenic activity, they should be used with due reservation and considered at best as semi-quantitative values.

The hepatocarcinogenic potencies of amino azo dyes derived from 4-dimethylaminoazobenzene (DAB) are often expressed by a "rough index of relative activities" proposed by Miller and Miller (47). It has been mentioned in Section 4.3.5 that the test groups of amino azo dyes are usually accompanied by a positive control group receiving the parent compound, DAB. All compounds are fed at equimolar dose levels (usually 2.40 mM) to one inbred strain and one sex of rats (Sprague-Dawley males). By assigning an arbitrary relative potency of 6 to DAB, the relative activities of the compounds are assessed by the formula:

$$\text{Relative activity} = \frac{6 \times \text{Months DAB feeding} \times \% \text{tumor incidence with test compound}}{\text{Months of feeding test compound} \times \% \text{tumor incidence with DAB}} \quad (96)$$

The arbitrary potency of 6 was assigned to DAB because when DAB and 3'-methyl-DAB (the most potent compound of the series known at the time the formula was devised) are fed at identical levels and for identical lengths of time, the tumor incidence obtained with the latter is roughly twice that obtained with the former. Thus, by assigning an activity of 6 to DAB the relative carcinogenic activities of the different dyes are obtained on a scale of rough indexes varying from 0 to 12; in recent years, however, new hepatocarcinogenic dyes were found with activities as high as 200.

4.3.7 RAPID SCREENING TESTS

A number of attempts have been made in recent years to devise rapid screening tests for potential carcinogens. The need for such tests has arisen because of the great number of new applications of well-known or new substances in connection with humans or simply because of the increasing environmental exposure to new chemicals. While animal tests performed on a large scale give a final answer (with the reservations discussed in Section 4.3.1) to the question whether or not a compound is carcinogenic in some species, the fact remains that when the assaying of a large number of compounds is required (such as when testing pharmaceuticals, food additives, pesticides), the carrying out of the tests with all the adequate safeguards for a sufficiently long time is difficult and requires a large outlay of animal quarters and trained personnel. None of the rapid screening tests proposed to date is, however, specific enough or applicable to all carcinogens, to be usable with a reliability anywhere comparable to the animal tests. Nonetheless, these rapid tests are of interest as they are based on and demonstrate some short-term morphological and biochemical effects of carcinogens. Moreover, they may indicate a trend which may prove to be successful in the future, possibly by combining the results of *several types* of rapid screening tests. Some of the better known rapid screening tests are discussed below.

1. The tetrazolium reduction test of Iversen. This method (156, 157) measures the initial increase in formazan deposition in hairless mouse epidermis after a single application of the potential carcinogen. Formazan is the red, water-insoluble reduction product of triphenyltetrazolium chloride, a colorless water-soluble salt acting as electron acceptor:

$$\left[C_6H_5-C \underset{N=N}{\overset{N-N}{<}} \overset{C_6H_5}{\underset{\oplus^{\diagdown}C_6H_5}{}} \right] Cl^{\ominus} + 2H^{\oplus} + 2e^{\ominus} \longrightarrow C_6H_5-C \underset{N=N-C_6H_5}{\overset{N-NH-C_6H_5}{<}} + HCl$$

triphenyltetrazolium   formazan

If tissues are incubated in a solution of triphenyltetrazolium, the activity of energy-generating processes in the cells reduces it to formazan. The amount of formazan deposited per milligram dry weight of tissue is measured photometrically after extraction with acetone. The detailed mechanism of the tetrazolium reaction is not known. It appears, however, that it reflects the functional state of the mitochondrial particles (see Sections 8.3 and 8.4). If the cells have not been heavily damaged by the carcinogen there exists an approximate inverse correlation between formazan deposition and respiratory rate of the skin; thus, after a single application of 20-methylcholanthrene, the initial period of increased formazan deposition is paralleled by a significant reduction of respiration (157). This observation recalls the work of Lovelock *et al.* (158) who found that many tri- and tetracyclic aromatic hydrocarbons have high electron affinity, and they suggested that carcinogens function as electron traps so that the transfer of electrons in normal respiration is impaired. Similarly, Allison and Lightbown (159) found that cellular respiration (*i.e.*, mitochondrial electron transport) is inhibited by active fractions of the natural cocarcinogen, croton oil. Table XXXII shows the results of an experimental series of tetrazolium reduction tests; according

Table XXXII

Correlation of Tetrazolium Index and Carcinogenic Potency[a]

Compound	Number of mice	Tetrazolium Index	Carcinogenic potency toward the skin of mice
1,2-Benzanthracene	16	0.682	–
Pyrene	16	0.754	–
d-Limonene	16	0.770	–
1-Stearyl-2,3-polyoxyethylene monoglyceride	16	0.825	–
Naphthalene	16	0.827	–
3-Methyl-1,2-benzanthracene	16	0.838	–
Oil of turpentine	16	0.848	–
2-Methyl-tricycloquinazoline[b]	—	0.874	–
Fluoranthene	16	0.880	–
Cholesterol	16	0.881	–
Phenanthrene	16	0.897	–
Urethan	32	0.908	–
Anthracene	16	0.909	–
1,2,6,7-Dibenzanthracene	32	0.970	–
1,2,3,4-Dibenzanthracene	32	1.010	–
β-Propiolactone	16	1.265	+
4-Nitroquinoline *N*-oxide	16	1.307	+
Tricycloquinazoline[b]	—	1.310	+
3-Methyl-tricycloquinazoline[b]	—	1.310	+
Croton oil	16	1.337	+
9,10-Dimethyl-1,2-benzanthracene	16	1.405	+
3,4-Benzopyrene	16	1.408	+
3-Methylcholanthrene	16	1.410	+
1,2,5,6-Dibenzanthracene	16	1.634	+

[a] From O. H. Iversen, *Nat. Cancer Inst. Monogr. No.* **10**, 633 (1963).
[b] These values have been taken from O. H. Iversen, *Nature* **198**, 400 (1963).

to Iversen (157), values below 1.0 in the "tetrazolium index" should indicate a substance without carcinogenic potency, values between 1.0 and 1.2 indicate a "doubtful result," and values of 1.2 and above indicate a substance with carcinogenic activity.

2. The photodynamic toxicity test on the protozoa Paramecium caudatum.
This test is carried out following the procedure of Epstein (160–162). The
phenomenon of photodynamic toxicity (meaning the toxicity effect due to
the combination of light energy and a chemical sensitizer) was demonstrated
first by Lewis (163) who described chromosome defects and cell death in chick
embryo cell cultures incubated in the dark with 3,4-benzopyrene or 1,2,5,6-
dibenzanthracene *prior* to exposure to light. Subsequently, a number of
investigators described photosensitization phenomena in a variety of *in vivo*
and *in vitro* systems.

When a culture of the *Paramecium* is incubated in the dark with a suspension of 3,4-benzopyrene and then irradiated with long wave ($360 \, m\mu$) ultraviolet light there results death of the monocellular organism, preceded by a
progressive decrease of the cellular motility, and "blebbing" of the external
membrane (*i.e.*, formation of blisterlike translucent bulges); the time of
exposure to the radiation necessary to bring about cell death is inversely
proportional with the concentration of the hydrocarbon in the medium of
incubation (160). Photodynamic activity is measured as the reciprocal of the
concentration (in $\mu g/ml$) producing 90% lethality (LT_{90}) in 30 minutes.

The photodynamic toxicity is due to a sensitized photooxidation, as it is
oxygen dependent and is inhibited by antioxidants such as butylhydroxy-
anisole and α-tocopherol; protection is also provided by the nonionic
detergent, polyoxyethylene sorbitan monostearate (known as Tween 60) and
by tryptophan (160). Studies on the mechanism of photodynamic activity of
polycyclic compounds appear to indicate that charge-transfer complex
formation plays no particular role in this biological effect (164), and the
inhibition of the photodynamic toxicity by tryptophan (160) is highly suggestive that complexing by resonance attraction is involved (*cf.* Section 3.3.4).
The hydrocarbons possibly act as photosensitizing catalysts for the production of free radical species from the many suitable sources in the cellular
environment. However, it must also be considered that the four tests used
to assay for charge-transfer formation, that is complexing with iodine,
chloranil, trinitrobenzene, and acridine (164), may not necessarily determine charge-transfer interaction, or the absence of it, with macromolecular
intracellular components. Moreover, as we have discussed in Section 3.3.3
not all charge-transfer complexing is accompanied by a visible color change.
Another possibility is that in photodynamic toxicity the polycyclic compounds function as oxygen-transfer catalysts, so that the problem of the
binding to intracellular components is not really germane to the mechanism
of photodynamic action. In fact, it has been known for some time that
various polycyclic hydrocarbons may be readily photooxidized in polar
solvents (*e.g.*, CS_2) to form endoperoxides from which molecular oxygen
and the polycyclic compounds may be regenerated upon gentle heating, in

some cases with a yield approaching the quantitative (rev. 165). An extensively studied classical example is the photooxidation of the hydrocarbon, rubrene, and the release of oxygen from the photooxide formed:

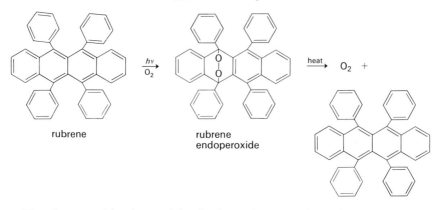

rubrene

rubrene
endoperoxide

O_2 +

The photosensitization and death of even large grazing animals (especially of individual animals having low pigmentation) due to the ingestion of plants, such as St. John's wort (*Hypericum perforatum* L., Hypericaceae), buckwheat (*Fagopyrum esculentum* L.), flax (gen. *Linum*), and redroot (*Lachnanthes tinctoria* L.), containing photosensitizing substances have been known for some time. The exact chemical structure of many of these photosensitizing substances has not been elucidated. The active agent in *Hypericum perforatum* is hypericin, a highly photooxidizable derivative of *meso*-naphthodianthrene (also called bisanthene). Hypericin, administered orally or parenterally to animals maintained in the light, brings about languor and death; 1 mg kills an 85-gm rat exposed to light, but no such effect is observed when the animal is kept in darkness. It is recognized that this disease is essentially of a photochemical nature, since the symptoms appear only in the light; moreover, nonpigmented animals present the symptoms with great acuity.

High photodynamic activity in *P. caudatum* is limited to polycyclic compounds with four or five fused rings; the inactivity of larger compounds (carcinogenic or not) is not explicable by insolubility alone and may be due in part to a low level of cellular uptake (162). Another example of the difficulties in correlating the photodynamic and carcinogenic activities is that loss of molecular coplanarity causes considerable decrease of the photodynamic toxicity in many compounds which are potent carcinogens [*e.g.*, 9,10-dimethyl-1,2-benzanthracene and the 3,4-benzophenanthrenes (162)]; also, high photodynamic activity was found in acenes and other linear polycyclics which are patent examples of noncarcinogenic compounds. These exemplify the reasons why, while compounds with high photodynamic activity have 4 times greater odds of being carcinogenic than compounds with low activity [as shown by the statistical technique of "relative odds" (166)], the photodynamic assay cannot identify a particular polycyclic compound as being carcinogenic or noncarcinogenic (162).

3. *Tests based on cell proliferation.* These tests are based on evaluation of the thickening of the mouse skin epithelium (167, 168) and on the increase of the number of epithelial cells in the newt, *Triton cristatus* or *T. vulgaris* (169, 170). Arffmann (171, 172) applied and developed further the latter test proposed by Neukomm. The newt test is based on the effect of carcinogenic polycyclic hydrocarbons and some other carcinogens on the tail region of the skin, which is particularly capable of regeneration. A very shallow subcutaneous injection is made on the side of the tail with the solution of the carcinogen (0.02–0.05 ml), and the needle is withdrawn during injection so that a small blisterlike pocket of the solution is formed. After about one week an epithelial reaction may be observed: the epidermis thickens, and begins to invade the dermis, piercing the pigmented layer. During the following 2 weeks the epithelial downgrowth widens and affects not only the subcutaneous tissue but also the superficial muscle layers, and this is followed by ulceration on the surface. However, the proliferating epithelium shows no sign of dedifferentiation, the cells, the nuclei, and the mitoses appear normal. Beginning about the fortieth day the epithelial infiltration regresses and there is gradually restoration of a nearly normal skin architecture. The correspondence between the results in newts and the carcinogenicities in mammals was found to be reasonably good in a limited series of polycyclic hydrocarbons: the potent polycyclic hydrocarbons, 3,4-benzopyrene, 1,2,5,6-dibenzanthracene, and 9,10-dimethyl-1,2-benzanthracene bring about typical positive reactions showing epithelial hyperplasia with infiltrating downgrowth between about the tenth and eighteenth days; the weakly active hydrocarbons chrysene and 1,2-benzanthracene produce a weak to moderate epithelial reaction; the inactive hydrocarbons, anthracene, phenanthrene, and triphenylene produced no reaction. No correlation was found with 1,2,4-trimethylphenanthrene, a weak carcinogen, nor with 3′,6-dimethyl-1,2-benzanthracene, an inactive hydrocarbon: the former produced no reaction, while the latter showed a strong positive response. The correspondence is even less good with nitrogen-containing heteroaromatic polycyclics and azo dyes. Moderate epithelial reaction was observed with the potent carcinogens, diethylnitrosamine and *N*-nitroso-*N*-methylurethan.

A variant of the newt test is the *skin hyperplasia test* proposed by Guérin (173), which is based on the concurrent evaluation of the two phenomena in the mouse skin: increase in thickness of the epithelium and increase in the number of epithelial cells. The thickening of the epithelium due to carcinogenic hydrocarbon treatment is due only in part to an increase in the number of cells; there is also cellular *hypertrophy* (increase in the size of the cells) which is concomitant with the swelling (174) and the increase of water content (175) of the skin tissue.

4. *The sebaceous gland suppression test.* This test (176–178) based on the disappearance of the sebaceous glands in a certain phase of histological changes (see Section 4.2) following application of certain types of carcinogenic substances, such as 20-methylcholanthrene, catalytically cracked petroleum oils and cigarette smoke condensates. Actually, the number of remaining sebaceous glands per square centimeter is inversely related to the relative carcinogenic potency of the materials. The noncarcinogenic hydrocarbons, pyrene, phenanthrene, and fluoranthene do not bring about the suppression of the sebaceous glands. However, the study by Bock and Mund (178) showed that the sebaceous gland suppression is not a reliable criterion for carcinogenic activity; for example, the potent carcinogen 7,9-dimethyl-benz[c]acridine (also known as 6,10-dimethyl-1,2-benzacridine) has only a slight suppressor activity, while colchicine which is not a carcinogen is moderately active. The sebaceous gland suppression test also failed with several highly carcinogenic aromatic amines and azo dyes. Moreover, the density of the sebaceous gland per unit skin surface is strongly dependent on the nutritional status of the animal. Thus, Argyris showed that there is extensive loss of sebaceous glands in mice maintained on a thiamine (vitamin B_1)-deficient diet for about 2 weeks (179). Clearly then the sebaceous gland test has no practical value for testing purposes.

In addition to the 4 examples discussed, a number of other approaches have been attempted to devise a rapid screening test for carcinogenic substances, such as the acridine test of Szent-Györgyi, inhibitory or growth supporting activity in mutants of the fungus *Neurospora crassa*, effects on tissue culture, production of chromosome damage, the embryonic tissue implant test. None of the tests is, however, specific to carcinogens of various types.

SUPPLETORY NOTES TO SECTION 4.3

NOTE 1

In the following is given a practical procedure for compounding the casein-dextrose based semi-synthetic diet (51, 54). Because of the difficulty of properly weighing, dispersing, and distributing dietary components to be added in milligram or gram amounts to large batches, various "mixes" are prepared. *Choline mix:* 80 gm choline chloride is intimately triturated and gradually mixed with 920 gm glucose monohydrate. *Vitamin mix:* 0.6 gm thiamine hydrochloride, 0.5 gm pyridoxine hydrochloride, 1.4 gm

D-pantothenic acid calcium salt, and 40 mg menadione are finely ground, and, gradually, while constantly mixing, 1000 gm glucose monohydrate is added. *Flavin mix:* 0.38 gm riboflavin is finely ground and gradually mixed as above with 1000 gm glucose monohydrate. *Vitamin A and D oil-mix:* For example, using a commercial halibut liver oil concentrate containing 60,000 U.S.P. units of vitamin A and 1000 U.S.P. units of vitamin D per gram ("Haliver Oil plain," Parke, Davis and Co.), 40 gm Haliver Oil is mixed with 610 gm corn oil. *Zinc mix:* 1.77 gm $ZnCl_2$ is finely ground and gradually triturated into 298 gm glucose monohydrate. Mixes should be stored in dark containers in the cold.

It is convenient to prepare 8-kg batches of the semi-synthetic diet. The use of a hand- or motor-actuated stainless steel mixing drum (with inside fins to assure intimate mixing) is recommended for thorough homogenization of such large batches. The use of a closed drum is also a consideration for personnel safety when compounding carcinogenic substances into the diet; a light respirator or well-adjusted surgical mask and protective clothing must be worn on all occasions when carcinogen-containing diets are prepared. An 8-kg batch is compounded from the following: 5650 gm glucose monohydrate (in the United States utilize "Cerelose" used in the baking industry), 1440 gm "Vitamin Free" casein and 320 gm Salt Mixture W (both available from the Nutritional Biochemicals Corp., Cleveland, Ohio), 360 gm corn oil, 100 gm choline mix, 40 gm vitamin mix, 40.8 gm flavin mix, 40 gm vitamin A and D oil-mix, 8 gm zinc mix. Half of the glucose is placed in the mixing drum. The other half and all the other components are mixed first manually, separately in a large dishpan, and this mixture is then introduced into the mixing drum. For intimate dispersion and homogenization rotate for at least 15 minutes. The diet should always be fresh; do not use diets kept at room temperature for over 2–3 weeks, and discard all moldy stocks. It goes without saying that the mixing drum must be thoroughly detergent cleaned and rinsed with acetone after mixing a carcinogen-containing diet.

NOTE 2

The end of the tail of the animal (mouse or rat) is thoroughly cleaned with water and 70% alcohol, and dried. The tip of the tail is cut off and a small drop of blood is squeezed out and deposited on a carefully cleaned microscope slide (slide A) at about $\frac{3}{4}$ inch from one end, on the midline. The end edge of a second slide (slide B) is placed against the surface of slide A across the deposited drop of blood; the two slides are held so that they will form a 30–40 degree angle. Because of capillary action the blood fills the angle between the two slides along the end edge of slide B. Now slide B, the "spreader slide," is pushed lengthwise along slide A always maintaining contact between the two slides and the angle of 30–40 degrees. The blood will follow and spread out as a film covering the surface of slide A. Some practice will permit obtaining a thin and even film or, as it is usually called, smear.

The film is allowed to dry in the air, and fixed and stained with Wright's stain. This staining solution, which is a methylene blue-eosin combination dissolved in methyl alcohol, is laborious to prepare and may be purchased from any clinical laboratory supply house. First, two straight lines about 1 inch apart are drawn with heavy wax pencil, across the middle of the slide, perpendicular to the lengthwise axis of the slide; these marks will confine the stain to the desired area in order to obtain a neat slide. The film in the confined area is covered with the staining fluid by depositing a counted small number of drops with a dropper (use sufficient amount of stain to avoid rapid drying). After 1 minute an equal number of drops of a pH 6.4 buffer (6.63 gm KH_2PO_4 + 3.20 gm K_2HPO_4 in 1 liter water) is deposited in the confined area on the top of the stain. The diluted stain is gently blown around for even distribution over the confined area. After exactly 4 minutes the slide is *flooded* with water while the stain *is still on* and washed for a total of 30 seconds or until the thinner regions of the film become pink or yellow. If the staining is too strong the film is partially decolorized for from 1 to 5 seconds in a solution made from 0.5 ml acetone plus 5 ml methyl alcohol in 200–300 ml water. The slide is rinsed with water and dried (*e.g.*, by waving it high above a flame). The slide is mounted in balsam for preservation: a drop of Canada balsam is placed in the center of the stained area, then a clean microscope coverglass is placed upon the drop and pressed down very gently until the balsam spreads out to the edges of the coverglass. In a few days the balsam will become hard and the slide can be permanently labeled and stored.

NOTE 3

Selection of the appropriate fixative from among the different fixatives in use is not arbitrary but depends on the tissue to be fixed, on the nature of the cytological constituent to be shown, and on the stain to be applied subsequent to fixing. There are, however, a number of fixatives which give a good overall morphologic picture, and examples of them are given below. Certain fixatives are appropriate for storing the fixed tissues in them. Others may render the tissues too brittle for further processing if contact is excessively prolonged; from these the tissues must be removed after fixing if they are not processed at once, and they must then be stored in 80% alcohol.

Neutral formalin fixative
Commercial formalin (35–40%)	100 ml
Physiological saline	900 ml

The solution is stored over marble chips to keep it neutral. This solution will fix average tissue samples in 24–48 hours. The tissues may remain in the formalin fixative for weeks or months without notable alteration. It is nonetheless preferable for prolonged storage to transfer the fixed tissues into alcohol. For this the fixative is decanted and aqueous ethanol 50% and 70% consecutively (each one for one day) is added to the tissues; the 70% is then replaced by 80% ethanol in which the tissues are maintained.

Mossman's fixative
Ethanol 95%	100 ml
Commercial formalin (35–40%)	100 ml
Glacial acetic acid	50 ml
Water to bring total volume to	1 liter

Some pathologists recommend that the tissues be transferred into 80% ethanol after about 3 days. However, in the authors' laboratories tissues were stored in this fixative for as long as 1 year without notable deterioration. Mossman's fixative appears to be very satisfactory for general morphology.

Bouin's fixative
Mix freshly for use:
Picric acid, saturated aqueous solution (about 10 gm in 750 ml)	75 ml
Commercial formalin (35–40%)	25 ml
Glacial acetic acid	5 ml

The tissues are fixed in Bouin's fixative for 16–24 hours, and then the excess picric acid is extracted during gradual transfer into 80% ethanol in view of further processing or for storage. The samples are first transferred into 50% aqueous ethanol for 1 day and extraction is repeated in a new 50% ethanol solution for another day. This is followed by extraction for 2 days in 70% ethanol (changed after 1 day) and finally the tissues are transferred into 80 % ethanol. Practically all the extractible picric acid should be removed by these serial alcohol extractions before the tissues are given for histopathology. Bouin's fixative brings out well the nuclear morphology.

NOTE 4

For a qualitative understanding of the meaning of confidence limits of population proportions, the notion of *true long-run proportion*, symbolized as P_x, must be understood. Suppose that there is a very large number of small marbles in a bag, say a hundred thousand, which may be regarded as infinitely large from the standpoint of practical counting. This *total population* (or *universe*) of the marbles is believed to contain a proportion of 0.2 (or 20 %) of black marbles. For the verification of this proportion the simplest would be to count and examine every marble in the total population which, of course, is not practical in view of the very large number of marbles. This difficulty is then circumvented by *randomly* drawing a sample small enough to be counted, say 50, and determining the proportion on that sample; one may find 15 black marbles out of 50, or a *sample proportion* of 0.30. The sample is then returned to the total population, the marbles well randomized by mixing, and the sampling and determination of the proportion repeated. If the whole process is repeated a great number of times it is observed that the proportion found is not constant but varies randomly between two limits, roughly between about 0.04 and 0.40. Using a larger sample, say 100, to carry out the determination in the same way, the proportions are found to be distributed between about 0.10 and 0.30. By further increasing the size of the sample the limits of the proportions continue to narrow: to about 0.14 to 0.26 for a sample of 300, to 0.16 to 0.24 for a sample of 600, to 0.17 to 0.23 for a sample of 1000, etc. This narrowing down of the limits will continue as the sample sizes approach the size of the total population, and one would be able to verify the actual true long-run proportion of 0.20 by examining one by one all the 100,000 marbles of the total population. Therefore, the greater the sample size the more closely the experimentally observed proportion of the sample will approximate the true long-run proportion.

Now, suppose that for every sample size the proportions have been determined say x number of times. One finds that the percentage of occurrence of the true proportion of 0.20 among the x number of determinations increases with the sample size. Obviously, the true proportion of 0.20 will be found 100 % of the time, that is with a probability of 100 %, if the sample size equals the total population, and this probability will decrease with the decrease of the sample size because of the spread of the observed sample proportions between larger and larger limits. If all the proportions observed with all the samples are plotted against the percentage probability of their occurrence (proportions on the abscissa and probability on the ordinate), the frontier of the "cloud" of points obtained delineates a typical bell-shaped curve, called the "*normal*" *probability distribution curve*. Because of the random sampling and the nature of the plot, the totality of the points, representing the proportions obtainable with all the possible randomly drawn samples of that particular total population, are homogeneously distributed under the curve.

For evaluating the uncertainty, due to random sampling, the concept of *confidence limit* has been developed. If the terminal "tails" on both sides of the distribution curve are "cut off" so that the removed portion corresponds to a total of 5% (or $\alpha = 0.05$) of the total surface underlying the curve, then 95% of all the points corresponding to proportions obtainable with samples of that population is within the remaining area. Therefore, if any random sample is drawn from that population, it can be assumed without examination, with a *confidence level* of $100(1 - \alpha) = 95\%$, that the proportions obtainable with that sample will lie within the "95% area." Sometimes the confidence level is given so that it corresponds to α on *each* side of the curve, that is as $100(1 - 2\alpha)$. The "cutting off" of the two "tails" also narrowed down, however, the maximum spread of the sample proportions. The two new limits of the spread are called the *confidence limits*. This, therefore, is equivalent to saying that proportions obtained with any sample of that population will lie within these limits at least 95% of the time. If the confidence limit is set to $100(1 - 2\alpha)$, this means that there is $100(1 - \alpha)$ percentage probability that any obtainable proportion will not be beyond the confidence limit on *either* side of the curve.

In many instances, determination of the true long-run proportion in a total population of objects is not feasible for practical reasons, or it may be outright impossible because the total population tends to be infinitely large. For example, the tumor incidence of a group of animals in a given experimental situation represents a sample proportion. To determine the true long-run proportion (*i.e.*, the tumor incidence with absolute accuracy) an infinitely large animal population would be required. This illustrates the point that the larger the group size the more accurately is the true tumor incidence approximated. However, while the true long-run proportion cannot be determined for many types of populations, the confidence limits of proportions can be calculated for set values of α using the binomial distribution, and these confidence limits are found tabulated for different sample sizes. Such tabulations are extremely useful for predicting the overlap of two proportion distributions, or the absence of overlap, for different sample sizes.

NOTE 5

The induction of tumors is the type of biological response designated as an "all-or-none" or *quantal* response, because all animals fall into either of the two categories "tumor bearing" or "tumor free." Such *group* responses are expressed as percentage of the total number of subjects (in this case the tumor incidence), which is plotted against the dose administered. The curves obtained are S-shaped (or sigmoid), and they show (*a*) a range of doses from zero on in which all animals are tumor free (subthreshold doses), (*b*) a range of doses in which 100% of the animals are tumor bearing (supra-optimal doses), and (*c*) an intermediate range in the neighborhood of 50% in which the percentage response rises steeply with the dose. Such curves are called *"cumulative normal" distribution curves*, which means that they are integrated normal distribution curves. Figure 74 shows the relation between the "normal" (curve A) and "cumulative normal" (curve B) distribution curves. The latter curve is obtained by cumulative summation of the rectangular probability areas under the former curve, from left to right, and by plotting the area sums thus obtained as ordinates against a linear abscissa scale.

For determining the ED_{50} value of an "all-or-none" type biological response, the sigmoid dose-response curve is first transformed into a linear relationship by the *probit transformation*. The reason for this is that for accurately establishing a sigmoid curve, the responses to a great number of concentrations would have to be determined. By transforming the dose response into a linear relationship, however, the curve which is now a straight line may be established with great accuracy using only a small number of points. The probit transformation is essentially the inverse of the process followed for "reshaping" a "normal" into a "cumulative normal" curve. The percentage responses are converted into equivalent "normal" deviations and the number 5.0 is added to each of these (in this way negative values owing to negative deviations are avoided). The plotting of the percentage on probit scale amounts to a stretching of the "cumulative" curve: on the left from the 50% value the curve is "pulled down" and on the right it is "pulled up" so as to transform it into a straight line (Fig. 75). For the actual practical plotting of percentages in probits against the dose (mg) or against the log dose, a special graph paper called *probit paper* is used (the ordinate of this is appropriately scaled). A simpler way is to evaluate the probits from percentage-probit tabulations (*e.g.*, in 125), and then plot the probits against dose or log dose on regular millimetric graph paper. The probits obtained directly from the experimental percentage values are the *empirical probits*, and the linear curve which may be drawn through these points is the *provisional probit regression line*, from which the ED_{50} may be graphically evaluated. For a more accurate determination of the ED_{50}, parameters of the *weighted probit regression line* must be calculated (120). If the regression line is straight or nearly straight (*i.e.*, the distribution is "normal"), there is *linear regression*, and the curve follows the equation:

$$Y_{probit} = a + b(X - \overline{X}) \tag{a}$$

where a and b (which is the slope of the line) are *regression coefficients*, X is the dose for a given value of Y, and $\overline{X}$ is the mean of the doses used in establishing the dose-response curve. The equation may be rearranged and solved for X when $Y = 5.0$ so as to give the ED_{50}. Of course, if the equation has been established with the logarithms of doses then X is obtained as log X and must be converted afterward into actual concentrations.

REFERENCES TO SECTION 4.3

1. Hartwell, J. L.: Survey of compounds which have been tested for carcinogenic activity. *U.S. Public Health Serv. Publ. No.* **149** (1951).
2. Shubik, P., and Hartwell, J. L.: Survey of compounds which have been tested for carcinogenic activity. *U.S. Public Health Serv. Publ. No.* **149**, Suppl. I (1957).
3. Goulding, R., and Lake, W. F.: *Monthly Bull. Min. Health Lab. Serv.* **19**, 108 (1960).
4. Druckrey, H., and Küpfmüller, K.: "Dosis und Wirkung." Cantor, Aulendorf, Württemberg, 1949.
5. Druckrey, H., Schmähl, D., Dischler, W., and Schildbach, A.: *Naturwissenschaften* **49**, 217 (1962).
6. Druckrey, H.: Quantitative Aspects in Chemical Carcinogenesis. *In* "Potential Carcinogenic Hazards from Drugs" (R. Truhaut, ed.), *UICC Monograph* Ser. 7, 60 (1967).
7. Clayson, D. B.: "Chemical Carcinogenesis." Little, Brown, Boston, Massachusetts, 1962.
8. Syverton, J. T., Berry, J. P., and Dascomb, H. E.: *Cancer Res.* **2**, 436 (1942).
9. Berenblum, I., and Schoental, R.: *Brit. J. Cancer* **1**, 157 (1947).
10. Pfeiffer, C. A., and Allen, E.: *Cancer Res.* **8**, 97 (1948).
11. Bielschowsky, F.: *Brit. J. Exptl. Pathol.* **27**, 54 (1946).
12. Lennox, B.: *Brit. J. Cancer* **9**, 631 (1955).
13. Nakahara, W., Fukuoka, F., and Sugimura, T.: *Gann* **48**, 124 (1957).
14. Argus, M. F., and Hoch-Ligeti, C.: *J. Natl. Cancer Inst.* **27**, 695 (1961); **30**, 533 (1963).
15. Takayama, S., and Oota, K.: *Gann* **54**, 465 (1963).
16. Herold, K. M., and Dunham, L. J.: *Cancer Res.* **23**, 773 (1963).
17. Schmähl, D., Thomas, C., and Scheld, G.: *Naturwissenschaften* **51**, 466 (1964).
18. Rapp, H. J., Carleton, J. H., Crisler, C., and Nadel, E. M.: *J. Natl. Cancer Inst.* **34**, 453 (1965).
19. Butler, W. H., and Barnes, J. M.: *Brit. J. Cancer* **17**, 699 (1964).
20. Carnaghan, R. B. A.: *Proc. Roy. Soc. Med.* **57**, 414 (1964).
21. Carnaghan, R. B. A., and Crawford, M.: *Brit. Vet. J.* **120**, 201 (1964).
22. Cottini, G. B., and Mazzone, G. B.: *Am. J. Cancer* **37**, 186 (1939).
23. Henry, S. A.: Occupational cutaneous cancer attributable to certain chemicals in industry. *In* "Chemical Carcinogenesis" (A. Haddow, ed.). *Brit. Med. Bull.* **4**, 389 (1947).
24. Goldblatt, M. W.: Occupational cancer of the bladder. *In* "Chemical Carcinogenesis" (A. Haddow, ed.). *Brit. Med. Bull.* **4**, 405 (1947).
25. Melick, W. F., Escue, H. M., Naryka, J. J., Mexera, R. A., and Wheeler, E. P.: *J. Urol.* **74**, 760 (1955).

26. Committee on Standardized Genetic Nomenclature for Mice: "Standardized Nomenclature for Inbred Strains of Mice, Second Listing," *Cancer Res.* **20**, 145 (1960).
27. Little, C. C.: *Biol. Rev.* **22**, 315 (1947).
28. Davis, R. K., Stevenson, G. T., and Busch, K. A.: *Cancer Res.* **16**, 194 (1956).
29. Thompson, S. W., and Hunt, R. D.: *Ann. N.Y. Acad. Sci.* **108**, 832 (1963).
30. Lipschütz, A., Iglesias, R., Rojas, G., and Gerisola, H.: *Brit. J. Cancer* **13**, 486 (1959).
31. Lane-Petter, W., Editor: "Animals for Research: Principles of Breeding and Management." Academic Press, New York, 1963.
32. "Purina Laboratory Manual" on the care and feeding of laboratory animals; available upon request. "Manual for Laboratory Animal Care," accompanied by a 35-mm strip film, correspondence course on animal care, available for a nominal fee. Ralston Purina Co., Checkerboard Square, St. Louis, Missouri 63199.
33. Snell, G. D., Editor: "Biology of the Laboratory Mouse," 2nd ed. McGraw-Hill, New York, 1966.
34. Warden, A. N., and Lane-Petter, W.: "The UFAW Handbook on the Care and Management of Laboratory Animals." The Universities Federation for Animal Welfare, 7A Lamb's Conduit Passage, London, W.C.1, 1957.
35. "Basic Care of Experimental Animals." Animal Welfare Institute, 22 East 17th Street, New York 3, New York, 1965.
36. "A Practical Guide on the Care of Laboratory Animals." Rockland Farms, New City, Rockland County, New York 10956, or A. E. Staley Manufacturing Co., Decatur, Illinois, 1958.
37. Grimson, K. S.: The dog in medical research. *U.S. Public Health Serv. Publ. No.* **312** (1961).
38. Farris, E. J., and Griffith, J. Q., Editors: "The Rat in Laboratory Investigation." Hafner, New York, 1963.
39. Inst. Lab. Animal Resources, Natl. Acad. Sci. Res. Council: "Guide for Laboratory Animal Facilities and Care," *U.S. Public Health Serv. Publ. No.* **1024** (1965).
40. Gay, W. I., Editor: "Methods of Animal Experimentation," 2 vols. Academic Press, New York, 1965.
41. Periodical publications on current topics of animal care, appearing at irregular intervals: *Charles River Dig.*, published by the Charles River Breeding Laboratories, 251 Ballard Vale St., N. Wilmington, Massachusetts 01888; *Lab. Animal Dig.*, published by the Ralston Purina Co., Checkerboard Square, St. Louis, Missouri 63199.
42. Miller, E. C., Miller, J. A., and Hartmann, H. A.: *Cancer Res.* **21**, 815 (1961).
43. Croft, P. G.: "An Introduction to the Anesthesia of Laboratory Animals." The Universities Federation for Animal Welfare, 7A Lamb's Conduit Passage, London W.C.1, 1958.
44. Valenstein, E. S.: *J. Exptl. Anal. Behaviour* **4**, 6 (1961).
45. Miller, J. A., Sandin, R. B., Miller, E. C., and Rusch, H. P.: *Cancer Res.* **15**, 188 (1955).
46. Kensler, C. J., Sugiura, K., Young, N. F., Halter, C. R., and Rhoads, C. P.: *Science* **93**, 308 (1941).
47. Miller, J. A., and Miller, E. C.: *Advan. Cancer Res.* **1**, 339 (1953).
48. Farber, E., and Ichinose, H.: *Cancer Res.* **10**, 1209 (1958).
49. György, P., Poling, E. C., and Goldblatt, H.: *Proc. Soc. Exptl. Biol. Med.* **47**, 41 (1941).
50. White, J., and Edwards, J. E.: *J. Natl. Cancer Inst.* **3**, 43 (1942–43).
51. Miller, J. A., Miller, E. C., and Finger, G. C.: *Cancer Res.* **17**, 387 (1957).
52. Goettsch, M., and Pappenheimer, A. M.: *J. Exptl. Med.* **54**, 145 (1931).
53. Miller, E. C., MacDonald, J. C., and Miller, J. A.: *Cancer Res.* **15**, 320 (1955).
54. Arcos, J. C., Gosch, H. H., and Zickafoose, D.: *J. Biophys. Biochem. Cytol.* **10**, 23 (1961).
55. Wesson, L. G.: *Science* **75**, 339 (1932).

56. "Diets Manual—Biological Test Materials, Diets, Salt Mixtures." Nutritional Biochemicals Corporation, 21010 Miles Avenue, Cleveland 28, Ohio, 1967.
57. "Biological Test Diets for Experimental Animals." General Biochemicals Inc., 15 Laboratory Park, Chagrin Falls, Ohio.
58. Yamagiwa, K., and Ichikawa, K., *Tokyo Igakkai Zassi* **15**, 295 (1915); *J. Cancer Res.* **3**, 1 (1918).
59. Nakahara, W., Fukuoka, F., and Sakai, S.: *Gann* **49**, 33 (1958).
60. Kirby, A. H. M.: *Cancer Res.* **7**, 263 (1947); *Brit. J. Cancer* **2**, 291 (1948).
61. Roe, F. J. C., and Glendenning, O.N.: *Brit. J. Cancer* **10**, 357 (1956).
62. Salaman, M. H., and Roe, F. J. C.: *Brit. J. Cancer* **10**, 363 (1956).
63. Hendry, J. A., Homer, R. F., Rose, F. L., and Walpole, A. L.: *Brit. J. Pharmacol.* **6**, 235 (1951).
64. Boyland, E.: The biological examination of carcinogenic substances. In "Causation of Cancer" (E. Boyland, ed.). *Brit. Med. Bull.* **14**, 93 (1958).
65. Shear, M. J.: *Am. J. Cancer.* **26**, 322 (1936).
66. Shear, M. J., and Lorenz, E.: *Am. J. Cancer* **36**, 201 (1939).
67. Andervont, H. B., and Lorenz, E.: *Public Health Repts. (U.S.)* **52**, 637 (1937).
68. Schoental, R.: *Nature* **188**, 420 (1960); *Acta Unio Intern. Cancrum* **19**, 680 (1963).
69. Hueper, W. C.: *Arzneimittel-Forsch.* **14**, 814 (1964).
70. Hueper, W. C., and Payne, W.: *Arch. Environ. Health* **5**, 445 (1962); **6**, 484 (1963); *Arch. Pathol.* **74**, 89 (1962).
71. Sundermann, F. W., Donnelly, A. J., West, B., and Kincaid, J. F.: *Arch. Ind. Health* **20**, 36 (1959).
72. Kotin, P., and Falk, H. L.: *Advan. Cancer Res.* **7**, 475 (1963).
73. Wynder, E. L., and Hoffmann, D.: *Cancer* **12**, 1079 (1959); *Deut. Med. Wochschr.* **88**, 623 (1963).
74. Dontenwill, W.: *Arzneimittel-Forsch.* **14**, 774 (1964).
75. Howell, J. S.: *Brit. J. Cancer* **15**, 263 (1961); **16**, 101 (1962).
76. Maisin, J., and Picard, E.: *Compt. Rend. Soc. Biol.* **91**, 799 (1924).
77. Jull, J. W.: *Brit. J. Cancer* **5**, 328 (1951).
78. Boyland, E., and Watson, G.: *Nature* **177**, 837 (1956).
79. Allen, M. J., Boyland, E., Dukes, C. E., Horning, E. S., and Watson, J. G.: *Brit. J. Cancer* **11**, 212 (1957).
80. Bonser, G. M., Clayson, D. B., Jull, J. W., and Pyrah, L. N.: *Brit. J. Cancer* **6**, 412 (1952).
81. Bonser, G. M., Clayson, D. B., and Jull, J. W.: Some aspects of the experimental induction of tumours of the bladder. In "Causation of Cancer" (E. Boyland, ed.). *Brit. Med. Bull.* **14**, 146 (1958).
82. Crabtree, H. G.: *Cancer Res.* **1**, 34 (1941).
83. Crabtree, H. G.: *J. Pathol. Bacteriol.* **1**, 39 (1941); **51**, 299 (1940).
84. Stowell, R. E., and Cramer, W.: *Cancer Res.* **2**, 193 (1942).
85. Crabtree, H. G.: *Cancer Res.* **4**, 688 (1944); **5**, 346 (1945); **6**, 553 (1946).
86. Crabtree, H. G.: Anti-carcinogenesis. In "Chemical Carcinogenesis" (A. Haddow, ed.). *Brit. Med. Bull.* **4**, 345 (1947).
87. Berenblum, I., and Shubik, P.: *Brit. J. Cancer* **1**, 379, 383 (1947).
88. Rusch, H. P., Baumann, C. A., and Kline, B. E.: *Proc. Soc. Exptl. Biol. Med.* **42**, 508 (1939).
89. Twort, J. M., and Twort, C. C.: *Am. J. Cancer* **35**, 80 (1939).
90. Simpson, W. L., and Cramer, W.: *Cancer Res.* **3**, 515 (1943); **5**, 5 (1945).
91. Plaut, A., and Sobel, H.: *Cancer Res.* **9**, 294 (1949).
92. Burrows, H., Hieger, I., and Kennaway, E. L.: *J. Pathol. Bacteriol.* **43**, 419 (1936).
93. Andervont, H. B.: *Public Health Repts. (U.S.)* **49**, 620 (1934).

94. Weil-Malherbe, H., and Dickens, F.: *Cancer Res.* **6**, 171 (1946).
95. Dickens, F.: The influence of the solvent on the carcinogenic response. *In* "Chemical Carcinogenesis" (A. Haddow, ed.). *Brit. Med. Bull.* **4**, 348 (1947).
96. Shimkin, M. B., and Andervont, H. B.: *Public Health Repts.* (*U.S.*) **55**, 537 (1940).
97. Leiter, J., and Shear, M. J.: *J. Natl. Cancer Inst.* **3**, 455 (1942–43).
98. Peacock, P. R., and Beck, S.: *Brit. J. Exptl. Pathol.* **19**, 315 (1938).
99. Dickens, F., and Weil-Malherbe, H.: *Cancer Res.* **2**, 560 (1942).
100. Mueller, G. C., Miller, J. A., and Rusch, H. P.: *Cancer Res.* **5**, 401 (1945).
101. Strait, L. A., Hrenoff, M. K., and DeOme, K. B.: *Cancer Res.* **8**, 231 (1948).
102. Brock, N., Druckrey, H., and Hamperl, H.: *Arch. Exptl. Pathol. Pharmakol.* **189**, 709 (1938).
103. Weil-Malherbe, H.: *Biochem. J.* **40**, 351, 363 (1946).
104. Weil-Malherbe, H.: *Ann. Rept. Brit. Emp. Cancer Campaign* **23**, 99 (1946); *Brit. J. Cancer* **1**, 423 (1947).
105. Bonser, G. M., Bradshaw, L., Clayson, D. B., and Jull, J. W.: *Brit. J. Cancer* **10**, 531 (1956).
106. György, P., Tomarelli, R., Ostergard, R. P., and Brown, J. B.: *J. Exptl. Med.* **76**, 413 (1942).
107. Amano, S., and Tomita, T.: *Gann* **31**, 86, 94 (1937).
108. Miller, J. A., Kline, B. E., and Rusch, H. P.: *Cancer Res.* **6**, 674 (1946).
109. Terracini, B., Shubik, P., and Della Porta, G.: *Cancer Res.* **20**, 1538 (1960).
110. Arcos, J. C., and Simon, J.: *Arzneimittel-Forsch.* **12**, 270 (1962).
111. Reif, A. E.: *Nature* **190**, 415 (1961).
112. Arcos, J. C., and Arcos, M.: *Progr. Drug Res.* **4**, 407 (1962).
113. Homburger, F., and Tregier, A.: *Progr. Exptl. Tumor Res.* **1**, 311 (1960).
114. Truhaut, R.: *Arch. Environ. Health* **7**, 351 (1963).
115. Della Porta, G.: *Excerpta Med. Intern. Congr. Ser. 75* **3**, 29 (1964).
116. Buu-Hoi, N. P., *Cancer Res.* **24**, 1511 (1964).
117. Elementary dissection techniques and compilations of anatomical charts: Berman, W.: "How to Dissect—Exploring with Probe and Scalpel." Sentinel Books, New York, 1961; Stuart, R. R.: "The Anatomy of the White Rat." Denoyer-Geppert, Chicago, Illinois, 1947, available from The Lemberger Co., biological supply house, P.O. Box 482, Oshkosh, Wisconsin, 54902; H. G. Q. Rowett: "Dissection Guides," III: "The Rat" (with notes on the mouse), IV: "The Rabbit." Holt, Rinehart & Winston, New York, 1957.
118. Cook, M. J.: "The Anatomy of the Laboratory Mouse." Academic Press, New York, 1965.
119. Argus, M. F., Kane, J. F., Sakuntala, M., and Ray, F. E.: *Radiation Res.* **16**, 37 (1962).
120. Burn, J. H., Finney, D. J., and Goodwin, L. G.: "Biological Standardization." Oxford University Press, London and New York, 1952.
121. Dixon, W. J., and Massey, F. J.: "Introduction to Statistical Analysis." McGraw-Hill, New York, 1957.
122. Fisher, R. A.: "Statistical Methods for Research Workers." Oliver & Boyd, Edinburgh and London, 1950.
123. Eisenhart, C., Hastay, M. W., and Wallis, W. A., Editors: "Selected Techniques of Statistical Analysis." McGraw-Hill, New York, 1947.
124. Jaffé, W. G.: *Cancer Res.* **7**, 529 (1947).
125. Diem, K., Editor: "Documenta Geigy—Scientific Tables." Geigy Chemical Corporation, Ardsley, New York, 1962.
126. Andervont, H. B.: *Public Health Repts.* (*U.S.*) **50**, 1211 (1935).
127. Lettinga, T. W.: "De carcinogene wurking van kleine doses 1,2,5,6-dibenzanthraceen." Academisch Proefschrift (Dissertation), Van Gorcum and Co., Amsterdam, 1937.
128. Dobrovolskaia-Zavadskaia, N.: *Compt. Rend. Soc. Biol.* **129**, 1055 (1938).

129. Bryan, W. R., and Shimkin, M. B.: *J. Natl. Cancer Inst.* **1**, 807 (1940–41).
130. Bryan, W. R., and Shimkin, M. B.: *J. Natl. Cancer Inst.* **3**, 503 (1942–43).
131. Shimkin, M. B., and Andervont, H. B.: *J. Natl. Cancer Inst.* **1**, 57 (1940–41).
132. Horton, A. W., and Denman, D. T.: *Cancer Res.* **15**, 701 (1955).
133. Horton, A. W., Denman, D. T., and Trosset, R. P.: *Cancer Res.* **17**, 758 (1957).
134. Poel, W. E.: *J. Natl. Cancer Inst.* **22**, 21 (1959).
135. Wynder, E. L., Spranger, J. W., and Fark, M. M.: *Cancer* **13**, 106 (1960).
136. Cramer, W., and Stowell, R. E.: *Cancer Res.* **3**, 668 (1943).
137. Andervont, H. B., and Edwards, J. E.: *J. Natl. Cancer Inst.* **3**, 355 (1942–43).
138. Arcos, J. C., Griffith, G. W., and Cunningham, R. W.: *J. Biophys. Biochem. Cytol.* **7**, 49 (1960).
139. Mantel, N., and Bryan, W. R.: *J. Natl. Cancer Inst.* **27**, 455 (1961).
140. Mantel, N., *Clin. Pharmacol. Therap.* **4**, 104 (1963).
141. Druckrey, H.: Pharmacological approach to carcinogenesis. *In* "Carcinogenesis—Mechanisms of Action" (G. E. W. Wolstenholme and M. O'Connor, eds.), Ciba Foundation Symposium. Little, Brown, Boston, Massachusetts, 1959, p. 110.
142. Druckrey, H., and Küpfmüller, K.: *Z. Naturforsch.* **3b**, 254 (1948).
143. Druckrey, H., Schildbach, A., Schmähl, D., Preussmann, R., and Ivankovic, S.: *Arzneimittel-Forsch.* **13**, 841 (1963).
144. Schmähl, D., and Thomas, C.: *Z. Krebsforsch.* **66**, 533 (1965).
145. Laird, A. K., and Barton, A. D.: *J. Natl. Cancer Inst.* **27**, 827 (1961).
146. Fieser, L. F., Fieser, M., Hershberg, E. B., Newman, M. S., Seligman, A. M., and Shear, M. J.: *Am. J. Cancer* **29**, 260 (1937).
147. Fieser, L. F.: *Am. J. Cancer* **34**, 37 (1938).
148. Fieser, L. F.: *Am. Assoc. Advance. Sci. Conf., Washington, 1944, Rept.*, p. 108.
149. Andervont, H. B., and Shimkin, M.: *J. Natl. Cancer Inst.* **1**, 225 (1940–41).
150. Boyland, E.: *Cancer Res.* **12**, 77 (1952).
151. Eckardt, R. E.: "Industrial Carcinogens." Grune & Stratton, New York, 1959.
152. Berenblum, I.: *Cancer Res.* **35**, 188 (1939).
153. Badger, G. M.: *Brit. J. Cancer* **2**, 309 (1948).
154. Iball, J.: *Am. J. Cancer* **35**, 188 (1939).
155. Lacassagne, A., Buu-Hoi, N. P., Daudel, R., and Zajdela, F.: *Advan. Cancer Res.* **4**, 316 (1956).
156. Iversen, O. H., and Evensen, A.: *Acta Pathol. Microbiol. Scand., Suppl.* **156** (1962).
157. Iversen, O. H.: *In* "Biology and Cutaneous Cancer." *Natl. Cancer Inst. Monogr. No.* **10**, 633 (1963).
158. Lovelock, J. E., Zlatkis, A., and Becker, R. S.: *Nature* **193**, 540 (1962).
159. Allison, A., and Lightbown, J. W.: *Nature* **189**, 892 (1961).
160. Epstein, S. S.: *Acta Unio Intern. Cancrum* **19**, 599 (1963).
161. Epstein, S. S., Small, M., Koplan, J., Mantel, N., Falk, H. L., and Sawicki, E.: *Arch Environ. Health* **7**, 531 (1963).
162. Epstein, S. S., Small, M., Falk, H. L., and Mantel, N.: *Cancer Res.* **24**, 855 (1964).
163. Lewis, M. R., *Am. J. Cancer* **25**, 305 (1935).
164. Epstein, S. S., Bulon, I., Koplan, J., Small, M., and Mantel, N.: *Nature* **204**, 750 (1964).
165. Etienne, A.: Photo-Oxydes d'Acènes, Union Labile de l'Oxygène au Carbone. *In* "Traité de Chimie Organique" (V. Grignard, G. Dupont, and R. Locquin, eds.), Vol. 17, Masson, Paris, 1949, p. 1299.
166. Cornfield, J.: *J. Natl. Cancer Inst.* **11**, 1269 (1950–51).
167. Suntzeff, V., Carruthers, C., and Cowdry, E. V.: *Cancer Res.* **17**, 439 (1947).
168. Suntzeff, V., Cowdry, E. V., and Croninger, A.: *Proc. Am. Assoc. Cancer Res.* **2**, 50 (1955).

169. Neukomm, S.: *Oncologia* **10**, 107 (1957); **13**, 294 (1960).
170. Neukomm, S.: *Acta Unio Intern. Cancrum* **15**, 654 (1959).
171. Arffmann, E., and Collatz-Christensen, B.: *Acta Pathol. Microbiol. Scand.* **52**, 330 (1961).
172. Arffmann, E.: *Acta Pathol. Microbiol. Scand.* **57**, 375 (1963).
173. Guérin, M., and Cuzin, J.: *Bull. Cancer* **48**, 111 (1961).
174. Pullinger, B. D.: *J. Pathol. Bacteriol.* **50**, 463 (1940).
175. Suntzeff, V., and Carruthers, C.: *Cancer Res.* **6**, 574 (1946).
176. Schmähl, D., and Mecke, R.: *Z. Krebsforsch* **61**, 230 (1956).
177. Smith, W.: *Acta Unio Intern. Cancrum* **13**, 77 (1957).
178. Bock, F. G., and Mund, R.: *Cancer Res.* **18**, 887 (1958).
179. Argyris, T. S.: *Science* **123**, 634 (1956); *Arch. Pathol.* **61**, 31 (1956).

SOME GENERAL SOURCE BOOKS AND ARTICLES FOR SECTION 4.3

GENERAL CONSIDERATIONS, SPECIES, DOSE, SOLVENT, ROUTE, QUANTITATIVE EVALUATION

1. Hueper, W. C., and Conway, W. D.: "Chemical Carcinogenesis and Cancers." Thomas, Springfield, Illinois, 1964, 744 pp.
2. Clayson, D. B.: "Chemical Carcinogenesis." Little, Brown, Boston, Massachusetts, 1962, 467 pp.
3. Greenstein, J. P.: "Biochemistry of Cancer." Academic Press, New York, 1954, 653 pp.
4. Petrov, N. N., Editor: "Cancer—A General Guide to Research and Its Treatment." Macmillan, New York, 1962, 387 pp.
5. Hartwell, J. L.: "A Survey of Compounds Which Have Been Tested for Carcinogenic Activity." U.S. Public Health Service Publication No. 149, Washington, D.C., 1951; Shubik, P., and Hartwell, J. L.: *Ibid.*, Supplement I, 1957.
6. Dickens, F.: The influence of the solvent on the carcinogenic response. *In* "Chemical Carcinogenesis" (A. Haddow, ed.). *Brit. Med. Bull.* **4**, 348–353 (1947).
7. Bryan, G. T., and Springberg, P. D.: Role of the vehicle in the genesis of bladder carcinomas in mice by the pellet implantation technic. *Cancer Res.* **26**, 105–109 (1966).
8. Clayson, D. B., and Springle, J. A. S.: The influence of a foreign body on the induction of tumours in the bladder epithelium of the mouse. *Brit. J. Cancer* **20**, 564–568 (1966).
9. Hackmann, C.: Problems of testing preparations for carcinogenic properties in the chemical industry. *In* "Carcinogenesis—Mechanisms of Action" (G. E. W. Wolstenholme and M. O'Connor, eds.), Ciba Foundation Symposium. Little, Brown, Boston, Massachusetts, 1959, pp. 308–322.
10. Boyland, E.: The biological examination of carcinogenic substances. *In* "Causation of Cancer" (E. Boyland, ed.). *Brit. Med. Bull.* **14**, 93–98 (1958).
11. Proceedings of the European Society for the Study of Drug Toxicity, Vol. III: "Evaluation of the Potential Carcinogenic Action of a Drug," International Congress Series No. 75. Excerpta Medica Foundation, New York, 1964, 112 pp.
12. 8th Report of the Joint FAO/WHO Expert Committee on Food Additives: "Specifications for the Identity and Purity of Food Additives and Their Toxicological Evaluation: Food Colours and Some Antimicrobials and Antioxidants." World Health Org. Tech. Rept. Ser. No. 309, Geneva, 1965, 25 pp.
13. Roe, F. J. C.: The relevance of preclinical assessment of carcinogenesis. *Clin. Pharmacol. Therap.* **7**, 77–111 (1966).
14. Iversen, O. H., and Evensen, A.: "Experimental Skin Carcinogenesis in Mice," Norwegian Monographs on Medical Science. Norwegian Univ. Press, Oslo, 1962, 184 pp.

GENERAL GUIDELINES AND TECHNIQUES FOR
MICROSCOPIC STUDY

1. Galigher, A. E., and Kozloff, E. N.: "Essentials of Practical Microtechnique." Lea & Febiger, Philadelphia, Pennsylvania, 1964, 484 pp.
2. Carleton, H. M., and Drury, R. A. B.: "Histological Technique." Oxford University Press, London and New York, 1957, 343 pp.
3. Todd, C. J., Davidsohn, I., and Wells, B. B.: "Clinical Diagnosis by Laboratory Methods—A Working Manual of Clinical Pathology." Saunders, Philadelphia, Pennsylvania, 1962, 1020 pp.
4. Addison, W. H. F.: Histologic methods adapted to rat tissues. *In* "The Rat in Laboratory Investigation" (E. J. Farris and J. Q. Griffith, eds.). Hafner, New York, 1963, pp. 453–466; Strong, R. M.: The osseous system. *Ibid.* pp. 467–482.
5. Mayer, E.: "Introduction to Dynamic Morphology." Academic Press, New York, 1963, 545 pp.

Synoptic Table to Section 4
Structural Formulas of Some Chemical Carcinogens

a. Polynuclear Aromatic Hydrocarbons and Related Compounds

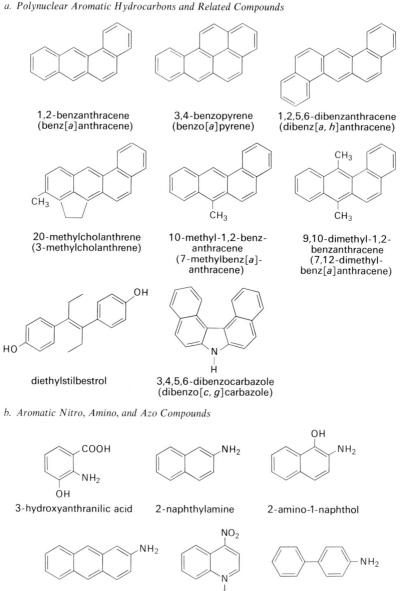

1,2-benzanthracene
(benz[*a*]anthracene)

3,4-benzopyrene
(benzo[*a*]pyrene)

1,2,5,6-dibenzanthracene
(dibenz[*a, h*]anthracene)

20-methylcholanthrene
(3-methylcholanthrene)

10-methyl-1,2-benz-
anthracene
(7-methylbenz[*a*]-
anthracene)

9,10-dimethyl-1,2-
benzanthracene
(7,12-dimethyl-
benz[*a*]anthracene)

diethylstilbestrol

3,4,5,6-dibenzocarbazole
(dibenzo[*c, g*]carbazole)

b. Aromatic Nitro, Amino, and Azo Compounds

3-hydroxyanthranilic acid

2-naphthylamine

2-amino-1-naphthol

2-anthramine

4-nitroquinoline
N-oxide

4-aminobiphenyl

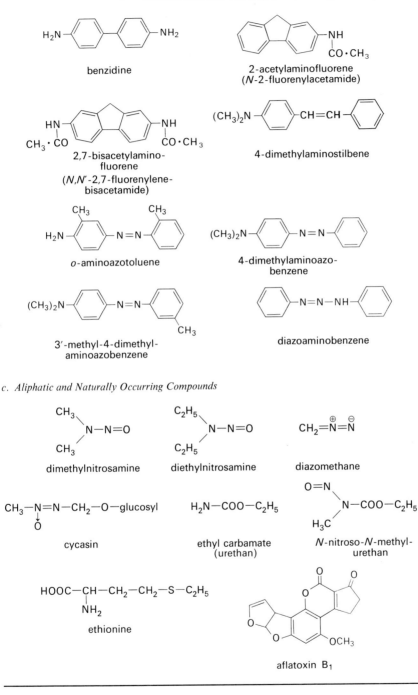

benzidine

2-acetylaminofluorene
(*N*-2-fluorenylacetamide)

2,7-bisacetylamino-
fluorene
(*N,N'*-2,7-fluorenylene-
bisacetamide)

4-dimethylaminostilbene

o-aminoazotoluene

4-dimethylaminoazo-
benzene

3'-methyl-4-dimethyl-
aminoazobenzene

diazoaminobenzene

c. Aliphatic and Naturally Occurring Compounds

dimethylnitrosamine

diethylnitrosamine

diazomethane

cycasin

ethyl carbamate
(urethan)

N-nitroso-*N*-methyl-
urethan

ethionine

aflatoxin B₁

Author Index

Numbers in parentheses are reference numbers and indicate that an author's work is referred to although his name is not cited in the text. Numbers in italic show the page on which the complete reference is listed.

A

Adamson, A. W., *298*
Addison, W. H. F., *463*
Adler, I., *222*
Aisenberg, A. C., *11*
Alam, A., *230, 295*
Albert, A., *296*
Alden, R. A., 172
Alder, K., 31, 76, 83
Allen, E., 345, *457*
Allen, M. J., 387(79), 388(79), *388,* 389, 390(79), *396,* 397, 398(79), *459*
Allison, A., 445, *461*
Amano, S., 398(107), *460*
Ambrose, E. J., *12*
Andervont, H. B., 324, *338,* 382, 392 (96), 423, 424, 432, 441, *459, 460, 461*
Antoni, F., 309(10), *315*
Andreasen, E., 318, 319, *321, 338*
Andrews, L. J., *297*
Arcos, J. C., *11, 230, 295, 324,* 375(54), 385(54), 399(110, 112), 401(110), 406(110), 422(112), 433(138), *433, 458, 460, 461*
Arcos, M., *11,* 399(112), 442(112), *460*
Arffmann, E., 449, *462*
Argus, M. F., *230, 295, 324,* 324(9), *338,* 346(14), 414(119), *457, 460*
Argyris, T. S., 450, *462*
Armstrong, H. E., 66
Aronow, L., *13*
Arrhenius, S. A., 206
Avogadro, A., 153, 204, 262
Ayres, F., *223*

B

Badger, G. M., 442(153), *461*
Bärlund, H., 244

Baeyer, A., 25, 39, 46, 49, 66, 139
Balmer, J. J., 89, 90, 144
Bandel, W., *297*
Barnes, J. M., 346(19), *457*
Barton, A. D., *438,* 439, *461*
Basu, S., *296*
Bateman, J. B., *297*
Bates, M., *6*
Bauer, K. H., *11*
Bauman, R. P., *223*
Baumann, C. A., 391(88), *459*
Beaven, G. H., *223*
Beck, S., 393(98), *460*
Becker, R. S., 445(158), *461*
Beer, A., 219
Begg, R. W., 308(7), *314*
Bell, J., 3
Bennett, C. A., *252*
Berenblum, I., 1, 310(16), *315,* 319, 320, *321,* 322(5), *338,* 345(9), 391, *405,* 442, *457, 459, 461*
Bergel, F., *11*
Bergmann, H., 310(13), *315*
Berry, J. P., 345(8), *457*
Berwick, L., 308(8), *314*
Bielschowsky, F., 346(11), 377(11), *457*
Biesele, J. J., *10*
Birks, J. B., *258, 297*
Bittar, E. E., *296*
Björksten, J., 286
Black, L. M., 312(27), *315*
Bloch, B., 3
Bloom, W., *339*
Blum, H. P., *10*
Bock, F. G., 450, *462*
Bohr, N., 88, 89, 90, 91, 94, 102, 103, 142, 144, 146, 148, 213
Boltzmann, L., 153, 247, 248
Bondi, A., *298*

Subject Index